CW00952518

A DICTIONARY OF PLANT-LORE

A DICTIONARY OF
PLANT-LORE

ROY VICKERY

OXFORD UNIVERSITY PRESS
1995

Oxford University Press, Walton Street, Oxford OX2 6DP

Oxford New York
Athens Auckland Bangkok Bombay
Calcutta Cape Town Dar es Salaam Delhi
Florence Hong Kong Istanbul Karachi
Kuala Lumpur Madras Madrid Melbourne
Mexico City Nairobi Paris Singapore
Taipei Tokyo Toronto
and associated companies in
Berlin Ibadan

Oxford is a trade mark of Oxford University Press

British Library Cataloguing in Publication Data
Data available

Library of Congress Cataloging in Publication Data
Vickery, Roy.
A dictionary of plant-lore / Roy Vickery.
p. cm.
Includes bibliographical references (p.   ) and index.
1. Plants—Folklore—Dictionaries. I. Title.
GR780.V53   1995   398.24'2'03—dc20   94-37393 CIP
ISBN 0-19-866183-5

1 3 5 7 9 10 8 6 4 2

Typeset in Monotype Bembo by
Pure Tech Corporation, Pondicherry, India
Printed in Great Britain by
Biddles Ltd
Guildford and King's Lynn

CONTENTS

FOREWORD

ALTHOUGH interest in the folklore and traditional uses of plants is undoubtedly widespread and growing, there are few reliable sources of information on this important part of Britain and Ireland's traditional culture. At various times conscientious attempts have been made to provide accurate information on different aspects of plant-lore, but all too often these attempts have been made by either botanists or folklorists who lack any appreciation of the others' discipline. Less careful efforts have been made by writers of popular books and articles, who have, on the whole, been content to rely on late nineteenth-century books, which even by the standards of their time were rarely more than adequate.

This reliance on previously published work has led to an almost total neglect of contemporary material. All too often writers on folklore have quarried for fossilized information in printed books and have made no attempt to collect fresh, living, and lively material from the true authorities—the 'folk' themselves. Most recent publications on the folklore of plants tell us more about late nineteenth-century plant-lore than about present-day beliefs and practices. Indeed, there is a widespread but mistaken belief that little remains to be collected today. Even in the field of plant-names, where one might expect ever-increasing standardization, there are still many names that remain unrecorded.

The present work attempts to remedy the lack of reliable information, and, as emphasis is placed on contemporary material, it seeks to demonstrate that at the end of the twentieth century plant-lore thrives in the British Isles.* A consistent effort during the years 1981–94 to collect information from all parts of the British Isles resulted in approximately 5600 items of information being received from about 700 informants. Whatever inevitable shortcomings there may be in this book, it has, at least, brought together a great mass of information which otherwise would never have been recorded. Obviously it has not been possible to use more than a relatively small amount of the material received, but all of it has been carefully sorted and saved, and

* Throughout this book 'British Isles' is used to include the United Kingdom, the Republic of Ireland, the Isle of Man, Guernsey, and Jersey. 'Ireland' is used to include both the Republic of Ireland and the north-eastern counties, variously known as Northern Ireland, the Six Counties, and Ulster. Both British Isles and Ireland are used in a strictly geographical sense, and are not considered to have any political connotations.

will eventually be placed in the care of the Botany Library of the Natural History Museum in London. All those who have in any way contributed to this mass of information are warmly thanked for giving so freely of their time, energy, and enthusiasm.

This book aims to provide a reliable source of information on the folklore and traditional uses—ethnobotany—of plants in the British Isles. As defined here plants include flowering plants, ferns and their allies, mosses and liverworts, algae, lichens, and fungi. Both wild and cultivated plants are included. Priority is given to beliefs and practices which were current or remembered during the period 1975–94.

The primary organization of the work is according to the standard English name of the plant involved, but there are also a number of entries on subjects such as Christmas greenery, funeral flowers, and well-dressing. Users who are unfamiliar with standard English names and know only scientific (Latin) ones should consult the index on pages 431-7. In a few cases where the name most often used by the 'folk' differs from the standard or 'book' name, priority is given to the former, although there is an entry for the standard name which provides a lead to the folk one. For example, the plant called navelwort in books is usually referred to as pennywort in common speech, therefore the main entry for this plant is under pennywort and the entry under navelwort merely directs the reader to pennywort.

Words in small capitals in the text indicate the subjects of entries elsewhere in the book.

Within each entry information is arranged as far as possible in the following sequence: general folk-beliefs ('superstitions'), use in traditional customs, use in folk medicine, other uses, and legends concerning individual representatives of the species. Not all of these categories are relevant for all entries: for some species only one category is needed and for a minority all five are relevant. Categorization can be difficult: if it is considered lucky to place a certain plant above the door on May Eve, is this a folk-belief or a custom?

Where other writers' interpretations of a belief or custom are given, this does not imply that these are accepted. They are given so that readers are made aware of how such things have been interpreted, and it is left to the readers themselves to make up their own minds as to whether or not such speculations are valid.

Medicinal and other uses are given as they were received from informants or found in publications. No attempt has been made to evaluate them, so great caution should be exercised by anyone contemplating the use of remedies and recipes mentioned. Readers tempted to try any of the remedies mentioned are advised to read and ponder over the report of box being used as a vermicide.

Every effort is made to ensure that an impression is given of the geographical range of a belief or practice, but obviously it is undesirable to list, for example, all the localities from which records of hawthorn blossom being 'unlucky' indoors have been received. Although much time and energy was expended in trying to gather material from all parts of the British Isles, the final results were inevitably patchy. The people of County Antrim were extremely generous in providing information; people in some other places were much less forthcoming.

Local or vernacular English names are listed only where they are mentioned in the text. These names have often been referred to as 'common' names, but it is apparent that they are often far from common, being restricted to one locality or one group of people, so the term 'local' is considered more accurate. Thousands of these names exist in English, and there are also many hundreds in the minority languages of the British Isles, including over 220 Guernésiais [Marquand, 1906]. Regrettably it is not possible for all of these names to be included. This vast number of local names, some of which may have been current only for a limited period of time, has led to considerable difficulty in interpreting some of the material recorded by folklorists. What, for example, was *mothan*, a herb used throughout the Highlands of Scotand for protecting milk from evil influences? Unless such plants can be identified with certainty, they are not included.

Another problem arises in the publications of botanists. Often the compilers of county floras included in their works a mass of information on the uses and folklore of various species, without stating the source of this information. It is difficult, if not impossible, to work out if they are referring to material they received from local people while recording plants or if their material is derived from a variety of printed sources. Is the information local, or is the author merely repeating something he has read, possibly derived from a non-British source?

It is hoped that information relating to the folklore and traditional uses of plants will continue to be collected and added to the material accumulated during the compilation of this dictionary, therefore readers are encouraged to send information to the author at the address given below. All information, no matter how widespread and well-known it may appear to be, will be gratefully received, for many more records are required before it is possible accurately to plot the distribution of Britain's plant-lore.

Inevitably in a compilation of this scope, some aspects appear to be insufficiently covered and some questions raised remain unanswered.

If readers are encouraged to investigate and study these areas, the work will have succeeded in fulfilling one of its major objectives. One can do no better than quote from C. T. Prime's introduction to his monograph *Lords and Ladies* [1960: xiv]:

> Despite all the help so kindly given, I have ventured into so many fields that I fear I must have fallen into some errors or missed something important. Here I must beg the indulgence of the reader, and hope that he will find some compensation in the text, and come to share an interest.

ROY VICKERY

The Natural History Museum
London SW7 5BD

August 1994

ACKNOWLEDGEMENTS

The compilation of this work has been aided by the enthusiasm, skills, and knowledge of innumerable people. There have been hundreds who supplied information on the plant-lore which they personally know, as well as people who have generously passed on scraps of information they have come across during their reading. Many of these people have been contacted as a result of appeals which editors kindly published in local newspapers.

There have been the custodians of libraries, archives, and museums who have made their rich resources available. Equally important are the organizations—universities, learned societies, national museums, and local authorities—who have provided the necessary financial support for the maintenance of these libraries, archives, and collections.

There have been clergymen and others who have generously responded to my appeals for local information. These people have been contacted through the use of a variety of directories, which have been meticulously prepared by mostly anonymous people. The value of a humble telephone directory when undertaking many kinds of research is seldom appreciated and never fully acknowledged.

There have been those who have provided editorial guidance, advice on the physical preparation of the typescript, and discussion when it seemed necessary.

Clearly the list could be extended indefinitely. A full list of helpers who are known would be prohibitively long and still omit those who are unknown, whose contributions have been equally important. All those who contributed to the inception, gestation, and completion of this work are profoundly thanked.

PLANT-LORE STUDIES IN THE BRITISH ISLES

THE earliest information we have on the folklore of plants is found in the writings of early herbalists and antiquaries. In due course scientific botany broke away from herbalism, and much later folklore emerged from what had become archaeology and local history. Occasionally a writer ventured into both fields, the prime example of such a person being John Ray (1627–1705), who not only produced the first flora of the British Isles and the first flora of a British county, but also published a collection of English proverbs.

The writings of English herbalists were to a very great extent derived from Continental, often Mediterranean sources, and contained few original observations relevant to the British flora. None the less, the 'father of English botany', William Turner (*c.*1508–68) mentioned the Holy or Glastonbury Thorn in his *New Herball* of 1562.

The Thorn was also mentioned, without enthusiasm, by John Gerard (1545–1612) in his *Herball* of 1597. In her classic study *Herbals* (1912, 2nd ed. 1938; reprinted 1986) Agnes Arber was rather dismissive of Gerard's work, claiming that he used a translation of Rembert Dodoens' *Stirpium historiae pemptades sex* (1583) without acknowledging his debt to the translator. Almost 400 years later it seems unlikely that we shall ever find out who contributed what to the *Herball*, but the work contains a useful amount of information on where various plants were found and some notes on local uses. For example, butterwort

> groweth in a field called Cragge close, and at Crosbie, Ravenswaith in Westmerland, upon Ingleborough fels, twelve miles from Lancaster . . . wives of Yorkshire do use [it] to annoint the dugs of their kine with the fat and oilous juice of the herbe butterwort, when they are bitten with any venemous worm . . . and hurt by any other means.

In the seventeenth century antiquarians started travelling the country or delving into their home areas, seeking out antiquities and stories associated with archaeological remains. John Aubrey (1626–97) observed that dwarf elder—'danes-blood'—grew abundantly at Slaughtonford in Wiltshire, formerly the site of a 'fight with the Danes', and John Taylor, in his *Wandering to see the Wonders of the West*

(1649) described the destruction of the Holy Thorn by a Roundhead who 'did cut it downe in pure devotion'.

The same century saw the publication of Ray's *Catalogus Plantarum circa Cantabrigiam nascentium* (1660), Britain's first county flora. This contains much information on the uses of the plants listed, most of it taken from a wide variety of non-British sources. However, some notes appear to be original, such as the recommendation that water found in the leaf bases of teasel plants is a cure for warts. Ray also mentions the Jew's-ear fungus found on elder, and uses the opportunity to denounce robustly the doctrine of signatures, which suggested that the ear-shaped fungus was good for the ears.

This accumulation of ethnobotanical information continued in later county floras, in which the compilers usually repeated material from other works, without making much, if any, effort to collect local information. There are, however, a few admirable exceptions, such as John Lightfoot, who in his *Flora Scotica* (1777) included a mass of information which he had collected in the Highlands and Islands, and related this to material he had come across elsewhere.

In the mid-nineteenth century a number of semi-popular works on wild plants included valuable information on plant-lore. Books like this included C.A. Johns' *Forest Trees of Britain* (2 vols, 1847 and 1849) and Anne Pratt's *Wild Flowers* (1857)—both published by the Society for Promoting Christian Knowledge—and Lady Wilkinson's *Weeds and Wild Flowers: Uses, Legends, and Literature* (1858). This tradition was continued in such books as A.R. Horwood's six-volume *New British Flora* (1921).

The 1870s and 1880s saw an unprecedented number of publications on the folklore of plants. In 1878, the year in which the Folklore Society was formed, the first part of the English Dialect Society's *Dictionary of English Plant-names*, compiled by James Britten and Robert Holland, was produced. The *Dictionary*, which was completed in further parts published in 1880 and 1886, is an underrated work, which contains much material relevant to the folklore of plants. Britten and especially Holland continued to accumulate plant-names until the end of their lives, but no supplement to the *Dictionary* was ever produced. These notes are now in the care of the Botany Library of the Natural History Museum, London.

In September 1870 Britten appealed for information for inclusion in a 'small volume on folklore connected with plants' [*Notes and Queries*, 4 ser. 6: 230]. This work was never published, but Britten produced a large number of semi-popular articles on plant folklore, often in magazines in which one would not expect to find such things.

However, from October 1884 Britten, a devout—almost fanatical —
convert to Roman Catholicism, threw his energy and enthusiasm into
the revival and organization of the Catholic Truth Society. This activity filled most of his spare time until his death forty years later,
although he continued to produce occasional articles and book
reviews about the folklore of plants.

Other works produced during the 1880s included Hilderic Friend's
Glossary of Devonshire Plant-names in 1882 and *Flowers and Flower Lore*
in 1884. Although the latter is typical of its period, being a lengthy
accumulation of poorly authenticated material, Friend had attempted
to collect information from people he met as he walked through the
countryside in the course of his duties as a Methodist minister. These
scraps of information ensure that Friend's *Flower and Flower Lore* remains of some lasting value. He promised further volumes on the
folklore of plants—notably on the plant-lore of the Far East, where he
had spent some time as a missionary—but these never materialized. As
a leading authority on earthworms, it is probable that Friend's work in
this field overwhelmed his plant-lore activities.

Also published in 1884 was Richard Folkard's *Plant Lore, Legends
and Lyrics*, which uncritically threw together a wide range of fact,
fiction, and folklore derived from a wide variety of sources. Many of
the more outlandish statements found in popular works on plant-lore
can be traced back to this volume.

A little later, in 1889, T.F. Thiselton Dyer published his *Folklore of
Plants*, one of several similar books on various aspects of folklore
that he produced. Thiselton Dyer's work was a rapid and rather
superficial survey of plant folklore which relied heavily on information published in the magazine *Notes and Queries*, but it
gained rapid respectability, as several careless reviewers confused the
clergyman T.F. Thiselton Dyer with his better-known brother,
W.T. Thiselton-Dyer, Director of the Royal Botanic Gardens, Kew.
Thus the work became attributed to the British Empire's foremost
botanist.

The late nineteenth century was also the greatest time for the compilation of dialect dictionaries, extensive surveys assembled by local
enthusiasts, encouraged and often published by the English Dialect
Society. These culminated in Joseph Wright's *English Dialect Dictionary*, first published in six volumes between 1898 and 1905, and reprinted in 1986. Wright not only incorporated material previously
included in county dictionaries, but also utilized the enthusiasm and
local expertise of a large number of 'voluntary readers', compilers of
unprinted collections, and correspondents. The dictionaries include a

vast number of plant-names, usually carefully identified, and often give explanations of why these names were used.

The Folklore Society was formed in 1878 and early volumes of its journal included a wealth of information sent in by collectors working in rural areas. The first volume of the journal contained an extensive article on the folklore of west Sussex, contributed by Charlotte Latham, a local clergyman's wife. This was followed by an article in which James Britten attempted to put Latham's plant-lore into context by citing similar beliefs and customs from other parts of the British Isles. Although much of the material included in the journal is valuable, it is seriously marred by the fact that little attempt was made to check the identities of the plants involved in various remedies and beliefs. What, for example, was 'red roger', which in 1897 was recorded as being 'used to stop bleeding at the nose' in County Down? Lengthy articles detailing the folklore of various parts of the British Isles continued to be published in the journal until around the end of the nineteenth century. Then, until about the outbreak of the Second World War, came short notes contributed by correspondents in country villages. Later articles in the journal tended to be less concerned with recently collected material and concentrated on the interpretation of previously published work.

Between 1895 and 1914 the Society also produced a series of volumes on the folklore of various counties. These did not contain newly collected material, but reflected the Society's historical bias by restricting contents to extracts from previously published books.

The war years, 1939–45, led to a re-evaluation of Great Britain's heritage of wild edible and medicinal plants, leading to the publication of Mary Thorne Quelch's *Herbs for Daily Use* (1941) and Florence Ransom's *British Herbs* (1949). This tradition continued with the production of Richard Mabey's *Food for Free* (1972; new 'all-colour' edition, 1989).

The growth of nationalism and interest in national identity resulted in conscious efforts to collect and preserve folklore in Ireland, Scotland, and Wales. As early as 1919 Michael F. Moloney published his *Irish Ethno-botany*, which 'endeavoured to indicate the wealth now lying hidden in the Gaelic nature creeds'. This publication appears to have introduced 'ethnobotany'—a term first used by J.W. Harshberger in a lecture to the Chicago University Archaeological Association in December 1895—to the British Isles. The Irish Folklore Commission was established in 1935, the Welsh Folk Museum in 1948, the School of Scottish Studies in 1951, and the Ulster Folk Museum in 1961. These organizations have devoted much time to recording material in their countries, often concentrating their efforts on collecting in minority languages—Irish, Welsh, and Gaelic. Pre-eminent among these organizations is the Department of Irish Folklore at University College, Dublin, the successor to the Irish Folklore Commission, which holds an estimated twenty tons of archives covering all parts of the country. The Department has a tradition of professional collectors working in the field, and their collections were extensively supplemented by material contributed to the Commission's Schools' Scheme of 1937–8, when children attending Ireland's 5000 primary schools were encouraged to collect local folklore. The material contributed to the Scheme contains a wealth of information on herbal remedies and other aspects of plant-lore, including a large number of riddles, a subject which tended to be neglected in other collections.

As the historically dominant nation, the English have not considered it necessary to gather their folklore and use it to establish an identity. Consequently there is no publicly funded national centre in England. While the Irish, the Welsh, and the Highland Scots are proud of their folklore and their knowledge of it, the English tend to deny any acquaintance with such matters. However, there have been some signs of activity in England. At the University of Leeds the English Dialect Survey was established in the late 1940s, leading to the initiation of the Leeds Folklife Survey in 1960 and becoming the School of Dialect and Folk Life Studies in 1964. The School flourished for twenty years, closing in 1984. The University of Sheffield's Centre for English Cultural Tradition and Language developed from the Survey of Language and Folklore which was inaugurated in 1964 and continues to teach folklore, developing strong links with the Department of Folklore, at the Memorial University, St John's, Newfoundland, and maintaining an extensive library and archive collection.

In England folklore studies have struggled along rather informally, with folklore sometimes being included in the journals of local history or archaeological societies. Most of the well-established county societies have included some folklore in their journals over the years, particularly the Devonshire Association for the Advancement of Science, Literature and the Arts, which since 1876 has included 86 reports on folklore and 94 reports on dialect in its transactions.

1955 saw the first publication of Geoffrey Grigson's *Englishman's Flora*. Although this is primarily a personal 'literary' look at British plants, the work has been essential bedside reading for people interested in plant-lore and plant-names ever since. Elegantly written and derived from wide reading and a thorough knowledge of plants and their habitats, the *Flora* exerted considerable influence, both positive and negative. Grigson alerted the reading public to the quantity of names which had been given to British plants (although he was, perhaps, ungenerous in ackowledging his debt to Britten and Holland and other nineteenth-century collectors of dialect words). On the negative side his work unintentionally gave the impression that everything that could be gathered concerning British plant-lore had been garnered. There was no further work to be done, nothing further to be said. This spurious belief, together with the more recent, but widely held, impression that ethnobotany is something which only exists—or is only interesting—when 'primitive' isolated tribal peoples are concerned, has seriously impeded further investigation.

Four years later, in 1959, Iona and Peter Opie published their *Lore and Language of Schoolchildren*. This work, like Grigson's, was considered to have brought together all that could be said on its subject and thus did not stimulate further work in its field. However, the work of the Opies, together with the publication of material gathered by Enid Porter of the Cambridge and County Folk Museum, demonstrated that the collection of British, especially English, folklore was a worthwhile persuit. The 1960s revival of interest in traditional song, music, customs, and dance, along with the availability of comparatively cheap and portable tape recorders, led to further collecting activities. Many of the collectors of this period, some of whom are still active, remained content merely to collect. They were amateurs with limited spare time and money, who prefered the excitement of collecting 'before it was too late' to organizing and publishing their material. What might be considered as the last phase of this period was the publication of a series of 'county' folklore books, under the general editorship of Venetia Newall, then Honorary Secretary of the Folklore Society. This ran to seventeen volumes published between 1973 and 1978, and involved a variety of authors ranging from well-known folklorists to folk singers and journalists, all of whom tried to supplement information derived from earlier publications with newly collected material.

In March 1982 the Folklore Society initiated a survey of plants which were believed to produce misfortune if picked or taken indoors. The survey continued until October 1984, by which time information on over seventy 'unlucky' plants had been received, vividly demonstrating the widespread knowledge and distribution of such beliefs. Many of those collected in the early 1980s—for example, the belief that the picking of cow parsley led to the death of one's mother—had not been collected before. Had these beliefs come into

being in comparatively recent times or had they escaped the collector's net in the past? The survey also revealed how much people
wanted to record and pass on the information they had.

More recently two major attempts have been made to collect plant-
lore. One of these has resulted in the production of the newsletter
Plant-lore Notes and News (1988–) and the current dictionary. The
other, supported by the environmental group Common Ground, will
lead to the publication of Richard Mabey's *Flora Britannica* in 1995.

It is interesting that these projects were initiated approximately a
century after the nineteenth-century flurry of interest in the subject,
for students of plant-lore are able to compare and contrast methods
and results in the 1880s and the 1990s.

NOTES FOR THE READER

QUOTATIONS followed by a place and date in square brackets, such as [Waltham Abbey, Essex, March 1991], are taken from material accumulated by the compiler.

Quotations from previously published works are followed by the author, date of publication, and usually page number, all in square brackets. When a publication has been reprinted frequently a chapter number, rather than a page number, is considered to be more useful and has been given. A list of published sources is provided on pages 415-29. The abbreviation *N & Q* refers to the periodical *Notes and Queries* (1849–).

Quotations taken from unpublished sources are distinguished by having 'MSS' included in the square brackets which follow them. A list of these sources is given on pages 429-30.

A number of abbreviations have been used in connection with scientific names. These are:

agg. –   a group (aggregate) of closely related species, e.g. *Rubus fruticosus* agg., the common blackberries.

cv. –   a plant of cultivated origin, derived from known species (e.g. both beetroot and mangold are cultivars of the wild beet, *Beta vulgaris*) or of uncertain parentage (e.g. banana, *Musa* cv.).

sp. –   species (singular), used when the exact specific indentification of the plant is unknown.

spp. –   species (plural), used where two or more species are referred to.

syn. –   synonym, used to indicate a Latin name which was formerly used but is now considered to be incorrect.

Readers unfamiliar with plants mentioned might find the illustrations in W. Keble Martin's *Concise British Flora in Colour* (1976), M. Blamey and C. Grey-Wilson's *Illustrated Flora of Britain and Northern Europe* (1989), and F. H. Brightman and B. E. Nicholson's *Oxford Book of Flowerless Plants* (1966) useful.

Where items are stated to be in museum collections it should not be assumed that these are necessarily on show. Few if any museums keep all of their holdings on permanent display, and it would be sensible to make an appointment to see some items which are not housed in public areas.

A

Abortifacients – plants used include HOUSELEEK, PARSLEY, PENNY-ROYAL, and TANSY.

Adder – associated plants include GREATER STITCHWORT and LORDS AND LADIES; see also SNAKE.

Adder's tongue fern (*Ophioglossum vulgatum*)

[The greatest use of adder's tongue fern] was as an ingredient in an ointment, which, under the name of adder's spear ointment, is still, or was until recently, employed in some parts of Sussex and Surrey. This ointment was used, among other purposes, as a healing application to the inflamed udders of cows. [Britten, 1881: 182]

Crushed and boiled in olive oil it is used as a dressing for open wounds. Most gypsies . . . denied knowledge of it, but I have had it given to me by three old women in widely separated districts. [Vesey-FitzGerald, 1944: 22]

Aert-bark – a Shetland name for TORMENTIL root.

African marigold (*Tagetes erecta*) and **French marigold** (*T. patula*)

A tip for TOMATO-growers: put a French marigold plant among the tomato plants in the greenhouse to keep greenfly away. [Didcot, Oxfordshire, February 1991]

African marigolds were planted along with CARROTS and ONIONS to keep away pests. [Barnstaple, Devon, July 1992]

See also COMPANION PLANTING.

Agrimony (*Agrimonia eupatoria*)

There are few of our wild plants which are in more esteem with the village herbalist than the agrimony. Every gatherer of simples knows it well, and the author has often seen the dried bundles of the plant hung up not only by the cottage fire place, but in shops, in several of the towns of France, where it is exposed for sale. [Pratt, 1857, 2: 78]

Somewhere around 1914 . . . after cutting the hay, the carter went down the rows picking out . . . agrimony, and hanging a great sheaf of it on the tail-board of his cart. On asking him what it was for, he replied 'Agrimony tay, the best physic as there is come spring- time.' [Charlbury, Oxfordshire, January 1991]

[In the village of Horseheath, Cambridgeshire] agrimony tea was supposed to be good for LUMBAGO. [Parsons MSS, 1952]

When shepherd Tidmarsh [presumably of Ashton-under-Hill, Worcestershire] was ill he asked me to collect the little yellow flowers of agrimony for him. He used this as an infusion to make a kind of tea which he said stimulated the bladder. [Archer, 1990: xiii]

Ague – prevented by QUAKING GRASS and TANSY; cured using Beaumont's Tree (an ELM) and GROUNDSEL.

Aigie berries – a Derbyshire name for fruits of HAWTHORN.

Alder (*Alnus glutinosa*). The fruits of alder are known as black knobs in the Peak District of Derbyshire, where they are much used in WELL-DRESSING. [Porteous, 1973: 3]

Known in the local dialect as aul, alder was watched by fishermen in Herefordshire, where it was said:

> When the bud of the aul is as big as a trout's eye
> Then that fish is in season in the River Wye.
>
> [Britten and Holland, 1886: 19]

Occasionally alder had medicinal uses.

A superstition exists in some parts of the county [of Worcestershire] that if pieces of the alder tree are carried in the waistcoat pocket, they will be a safeguard against RHEUMATISM. [Gomme, 1884: 134]

In the late 1950s my father-in-law, Ernest, had a bad attack of GOUT. An elderly country farmer, well-known locally for herbal cures . . . came to see him.

'What's wrong wi you Ern?' he asked. 'I don't know what's wrong, but I do know tis bloody painful' Ernest replied. 'All you want to cure that is some ripe alder cones, and boil in water till tis a rich brown colour, and then you drink a wine glass full of the juice every day for a wik, and thees'll be as right as rain, long before that.'

And so, having faith (or fear of more pain), Ernest decided to try this. Our sons went out and collected some cones which were duly boiled for a long time (about two hours, I think), and when it was cold Ernest had his first glass. No result. The next day he had another glass, but still no result. So came the third day, and doubts about the cure began to creep in, but Ernest carried on. But after dinner poor Ernest began to feel giddy and could hardly stand. Funnily enough at that time the herbalist, Mr Isaiah Bowditch, arrived. He took one look at Ernest and said 'You don't look no better Ern.' By this time Ernest was in no mood to take that type of joke, and said 'Tis all thy fault, it's that old muck you told I to take, I can't stand up now.' Isaiah said 'I think the best thing you can do is see the doctor quick.' Ernest did this, and was soon cured by conventional medicine. [Thorncombe, Dorset, April 1990]

Alder buckthorn (*Frangula alnus*)

The berries make a very powerful purgative. Once popular, this is very rarely used nowadays. A decoction of the bark is used [by gypsies] as a purgative, being mild in action. [Vesey- FitzGerald, 1944: 23]

The wood yields by distillation in close vessels a very superior charcoal for making gunpowder, for which purpose . . . it is planted in some parts of Kent and Sussex. [Bromfield, 1856: 108]

Ale-hoof – a name for GROUND IVY.

Alexanders (*Smyrnium olusatrum*)

The flower buds of alexanders are delicious in salads, and the roots may be served instead of parsnips. The leaves can be used as herbs or made into a white sauce, and the soft stems can be cooked like asparagus. [Letter from Etchingham, East Sussex, in *The Times*, 7 May 1988]

Alexanders is prolific by the sea. Some people locally use the very young shoots as a vegetable although I have no personal experience of this. [Plymouth, Devon, January 1993]

Alleluja – a name for WOOD SORREL.

All Souls' Day. London's Polish community maintains the tradition of decorating graves for All Souls' Day (2 November). By early afternoon on Saturday 1 November 1980 most of the Polish graves in Brompton Cemetery, London, had been decorated with cut flowers (usually CHRYSANTHEMUMS) and lighted candles. Even the most neglected graves had single stems of chrysanthemum flowers and a solitary candle placed on them by the decorators, most of whom were middle-aged women.

On the following afternoon a service was held at the Streatham Park Cemetery in south London. The entrance to the cemetery was crowded with cars, and most of the Polish graves had been tidied and decorated with flowers and lighted candles. The flowers most often used were chrysanthemums, but various pot plants, wreaths (mostly of RED AND WHITE FLOWERS), miniature Polish flags, and small branches of EVERGREENS were also used. A priest accompanied by a cross-bearer and servers led an informal procession of about a hundred people of all ages around the cemetery, starting at the elaborately decorated grave of a priest who had died about two years earlier and continuing around the cemetery, stopping wherever there was a concentration of

Polish graves. At each stop prayers were recited and holy water sprinkled [personal observation].

Cf. FLOWERING SUNDAY.

Almond – see NUT.

Alpine meadow-rue (*Thalictrum alpinum*)

Alpine meadow rue = redshank; produces gold and olive DYE. [Lerwick, Shetland, March 1994]

Altar lily – see ARUM LILY.

Amber – a Kent name for TUTSAN.

Amphibious bistort (*Persicaria amphibia*)

Formerly used [on the Shetland Islands] to produce a yellow DYE . . . as yallowin' girse or persicaria, and reported to us as still being used for this purpose in Fair Isle. [Scott and Palmer, 1987: 113]

Angelica (*Angelica* spp.)

They used to hang angelica over their doors in the gypsy camp near Fremington 'to ward off dark spirits'. [Barnstaple, Devon, May 1991]

[Gypsies used to smoke HOGWEED] and wild angelica too, the latter sometimes filled with dried and crushed ELM leaves. [Barnstaple, Devon, September 1992]

Annual knawel (*Scleranthus annuus*)

[Ireland:] is given in urinary complaints. Is a favourite herb with the herbalists of the present day. It is given by them in all diseases accompanied by a disordered urinary function. [Moloney, 1919: 38]

Antirrhinum (*Antirrhinum majus*), also known as snapdragon

Other plants grown on or about the roof of the house to bring good luck and guard against FIRE were [BITING] STONECROP (*Sedum acre*) around Tramore, county Waterford, and snapdragon (*Antirrhinum majus*) in county Westmeath. [Ó Danachair, 1970: 25]

Aphids (greenfly) – deterred using AFRICAN MARIGOLD.

Aphrodisiacs – plants believed to be include: BROAD BEAN, EARLY PURPLE ORCHID, LORDS AND LADIES, PENNYROYAL, SUN SPURGE, and TUBEROSE.

Appetite – stimulated using DWARF CORNEL and HOP.

Apple (*Malus domestica*). In common with other FRUIT TREES, it was believed that if an apple tree blossomed out of season misfortune or death was foretold.

Remarking an apple blossom a few days ago, month of November on one of my trees I pointed it out as a curiosity to a Dorset labourer. 'Ah ! Sir,' he said, ''tis lucky no women folk be here to see that'; and upon my asking the reason he replied 'Because they's sure to think somebody were a-going to die.' [N & Q, 4 ser. 10: 408, 1872]

[Southmolton, Devon:] We had apples and blossom on one branch of the tree one September, and were told it was a sign of death. [Chope, 1929: 125]

If an apple tree blossoms very much out of season it foretells a tragedy in the family before the year is out. [Reading, Berkshire, February 1987]

A belief recorded from Derbyshire [N & Q, 1 ser. 8: 512, 1853] and elsewhere was that if the sun shone through the branches of apple trees on Christmas Day, or Old Christmas Day, an abundant crop of apples was foretold. In Dorset this belief was expressed in the couplet:

> If wold Christmas Day be fair and bright
> Ye'd have apples to your heart's delight.
>
> [Carre, 1975: 12]

At about the same time of year apple trees were wassailed.

In certain parts of this country superstitious observances yet linger, such as drinking health to the [apple] trees on Christmas and Epiphany eves, saluting them by throwing toasted crabs or toast round them, lighting fires &c. All these ceremonies are supposed to render the trees productive for the coming season.

I once had the occasion to pass the night preceding Twelfth day at a lone farm-house on the borders of Dartmoor, in Devonshire, and was somewhat alarmed at hearing, very late at night, the repeated discharge of fire- arms in the immediate vicinity of the house. On my inquiring in the morning as to what was the cause of the unseasonable noise, I was told that the farm-men were firing into the Apple-trees in the orchard, in order that the trees might bear a good crop. [Johns, 1847: 303]

Four years later it was reported:

Amongst the scenes of jocund hospitality in this holiday season, that are handed down to us, is one which not only presents an enlivening picture, but offers proof of the superstition that still prevails in the western counties. On 'Twelfth Eve,' in Devonshire, it is customary for the farmer to leave his warm fireside, accompanied by a band of rustics, with guns, blunderbusses, etc., presenting an appearance which at other times would be somewhat alarming. Thus armed, the band proceed to an adjoining orchard, where is selected one of the most fruitful and aged of the apple-trees, grouping round which they stand and offer up their invocations in the following quaint doggerel rhyme:

> Here's to thee
> Old apple tree!

> Whence thou mays't blow
> And whence thou mays't bear
> Apples enow:
> Hats full!
> Caps full!
> Bushels, bushels, sacks full,
> And my pockets full too!
> Huzza! Huzza!

The cider jug is then passed around, and, with many a hearty shout, the party fire off their guns, charged with powder only, amidst the branches, sometimes frightening the owl from its midnight haunt. With confident hopes they return to the farm-house, and are refused admittance, in spite of all weather, till some lucky wight guesses aright the peculiar roast the maidens are preparing for their comfort. This done, all enter, and soon right merrily the jovial glass goes round—the man who gained admission receiving the honour of 'king of the evening', and till a late hour he reigns, amidst laughter, fun, and jollity. The origin of this custom is not known, but is supposed to be of great antiquity. [*Illustrated London News*, 11 January 1851]

This custom seems to have been most prevalent in Devon and Somerset. It also occurred in other apple-growing districts, but appears to have been absent from the cider-making area around Hereford. In Sussex, where the custom was known as 'howling', the earliest reference dates back to 1670, when the Rector of Horsted Keynes recorded in his diary on Boxing Day, 'Gave to the howling boys sixpence' [Simpson, 1973: 102]. At Duncton, in West Sussex, 'Spratty' Knight was the chief wassailer in the 1920s. He was 'Captain' of a team of wassailers who would assemble at the village pub and go around the local farms asking each farmer 'Do you want your trees wassailed?'

The gang, followed by numerous small children, then went to the orchard. Spratty blew through a cow's horn, which made a terrible sound. It was to frighten away any evil spirits that might be lurking around, Next one of the trees, generally the finest one, would be hit with sticks and sprinkled with ale. This was a gift to the god who looked after the fruit trees. Lastly all the company joined the wassailing song, the words of which were as follows:

> Stand fast, root, bear well, top,
> Pray, good God, send us a howling crop,
> Every twig, apples big, every bough, apples now;
> Hats full, caps full, five bushell sacks full,
> And a little heap under the stairs,
> Hulloa, boys, hulloa, and blow the horn!

And hulloa they did, to the accompaniment of the horn. This completed the wassailing, and everyone trooped out of the orchard up to the farm-house door, where they were greeted by the farmer's wife with drinks and goodies. Sometimes money was given instead of good cheer . . . and then on around the village, till they arrived at the Cricketers' Inn, which was their last port of call. [*West Sussex Gazette*, 26 December 1966]

Similarly, in Devon in the 1940s:

The sun on the apple trees on Christmas Day would mean a good crop, and at Dunkerswell up the Culm Valley, on Twelfth Night they went out from the local pub at night to shoot into the branches and sing an old song. [Tilehurst, Berkshire, February 1987]

The wassailing of apple trees seems to have survived longest at Carhampton in Somerset, where the custom continues to take place in the orchard behind the Butchers Arms Inn each January [Patten, 1974: 7]. Elsewhere wassailing has been revived as a publicity venture by cider companies. Thus in 1974 the Taunton Cider Company promoted a wassailing, complete with a Wassail Queen, at Norton Fitzwarren, in west Somerset [*Western Gazette*, 25 January 1974]. A particularly vigorous revival is the Apple Howling event which the Chanctonbury Ring Morris Men put on each year.

The practice is undoubtedly traditional to Sussex where it is known as 'Apple Howling' rather than 'Wassailing the Apple Trees', but the proceedings, as conducted by the Chanctonbury Ring Morris Men, are a compilation of traditions from various parts of the country rather than a purely Sussex tradition. We have used such sources as Christina Hole's *British Folk Customs* and records of the event at Carhampton, Somerset, to produce an hour long event which has proved a great success. As you will see in Geoffrey Palmer and Noel Lloyd's *A Year of Festivals* [1972] it is our team at Tandring, Hailsham, which is used to illustrate this traditional event! This was the first occasion that we did it, in 1967 (January 6th) . . . Chanctonbury Ring M.M. have now successfully done their apple howling for the last two years at Furner's Farm, Henfield, Sussex. We try to do it on the Eve of Epiphany, but since Friday clashes with a Folk Song Club commitment we have chosen a Thursday on both occasions. We had 300 spectators this year and in addition there were 25 morris men. Mr Whittone, the owner of the orchard, is most co-operative! The morris men are enthusiastic! [Dick Playl, past squire of Chanctonbury Ring Morris Men, January 1978]

In 1978 the programme proceeded from a 'cacophonous noise' to signal the start, through a series of traditional activities, including the placing of spiced wassail cake in a fork of the tree 'to ensure the goodwill of robins and other birds', to a 'general hullabaloo', followed by three cheers for the orchard owner, before concluding with the distribution of 'traditional spiced Wassail Cake and English cider from the barrel'. Sixteen years later, in May 1994, the bagman of the morris men reported:

> We still go Apple Howling on or very near Twelfth Night. Of late we have taken to doing it on the nearest Saturday, in the early evening as it is very popular with the children. We regularly get audiences of 100 . . . Furner's Farm is a working orchard on a commercial scale with a considerable amount of trees for this part of the country. It has packing sheds where we retire to after the ceremony to eat wassail cakes (locally made spiced buns), drink cider and to perform some dances. This is given as a thank you to all our loyal followers, and gets larger by the year, despite the weather in January which can be quite inclement at times. It also ensures that everyone has played their part in bringing a good crop for next year.

This revival took place at a time when there was a resurgence of interest in English folk music and dance. In the 1990s, following a period of interest in 'green' and New Age ideas, revivals reflect these enthusiasms.

> There seems to be no record of apple tree wassailing in Yorkshire, and my attempts at reviving the custom will undoubtedly be frowned upon by some folklorists who are of the opinion that such a revival should not be contemplated in an area where the custom has not been previously performed. My reply is that apple trees have a right to be wassailed wherever they grow . . . There is a great affinity between trees and humans, but also, unfortunately at present, great isolation. Wassailing the apple trees is one way of helping to restore harmony and thus correcting this imbalance . . .
>
> This year I finally managed to find a suitable location in the Sheffield area, although only 5 people attended . . . Plans for 1994, apart from a repeat of the 1993 wassails, include a possible second wassailing location in the Sheffield area, and a possible one near Rotherham. [Sheffield, April 1993]

Writing in 1884, Sabine Baring-Gould recorded a north Devon belief that it was usual for there to be late frosts, which severely damaged apple blossom, on the nights of 19, 20, and 21 May. This period was known as ST FRANKIN'S DAYS. The pre-Reformation Church blessed each year's new apple crop on St James's Day (25 July) [Brand, 1853: 346], while in the seventeenth century it was recorded:

> In Herefordshire, and also in Somersetshire, on Midsommer-eve, they make fires in the fields in the waies :sc—to Blesse the Apples. I have seen the same custome in Somerset, 1685, but they doe it only for custome sake. [Aubrey, 1881: 96]

In a letter written from Elton, north Herefordshire, in 1880, it was stated:

Unless the orchards are christened on St Peter's Day [29 June] the crop will not be good; and there ought to be a shower of rain when the people go through the orchards, but no one seems to know for what purpose exactly. [Leather, 1912: 104]

St Swithin's Day (15 July) was another day on which apples were christened.

In the Huntingdonshire parish wherein I passed St Swithin's Day, 1865, we had not a drop of rain. A cottager said to me, 'It's a bad job for the apples that St Swithin hadn't rained upon 'em.' 'Why so?' 'Because unless St Swithin rains upon 'em they'll never keep through winter.' [N & Q, 3 ser. 8: 146, 1865]

When I was a lad we were told not to eat apples before St Swithin's Day or they would make us ill, as they had not been christened. This was in South Notts. [N & Q, 8 ser. 10: 112, 1896]

The Christening of the Apples. This was a common expression for St Swithin's Day in the neighbourhood of Banbury in the middle of the last century. On that day apples were supposed to begin to get big and mature quickly. [N & Q, 11 ser. 10: 152, 1914]

The Apple Christening Day is still a common folk-name given to St Swithin's Day in Surrey as well as in Berkshire and Oxfordshire, as I am told by many friends. [N & Q, 11 ser. 10: 152, 1914]

But the idea of apples being blessed on St James's Day also lingered.

'On St James' Day the Apples are Christened.' This saying is found among the people in Wiltshire and in Somersetshire. Was St James considered to be the patron of orchards? and was he invoked for a blessing on the infant fruit? as, at that season, May 1, the apple trees are in bloom. [N & Q, 2 ser. 1: 386, 1856]

In 1913 a farmer living at Veryan, Cornwall, advised:

Never pick apples before St James' Day, when they get their final blessing. [Peter, 1915: 132]

Clearly there is some confusion over which St James's Day is intended: the first quotation refers to the feast of St James the Less (1 May) and the second apparently refers to the feast of St James the Greater (25 July).

Since 1989 the environmental group Common Ground has been promoting 21 October as Apple Day, in the hope it will stimulate a greater appreciation of old varieties of apple. It remains to be seen whether or not this annual event will prosper, but according to a report in *The Times* of 17 October 1992:

More than 80 apple-promoting events have been planned around the country next week, from the planting of a new orchard of Cox's Orange

Apple

Pippin, near the Slough home of its 19th-century founder . . . to cider-making demonstrations and tastings in Devon and Somerset, and a children's apple activity day at the Greenwich Borough Museum.

Particularly in Ireland, apples are widely used in HALLOWE'EN activities.

> Hallowe'en is celebrated on the night of 31st October . . . The children get a tub full of water and put it in the middle of the floor. They put an apple or a couple of apples into the tub. The children then kneel down around the tub and put their heads into the water, to try to catch an apple in their mouth. They enjoy themselves very much at this. This night is also known as 'Snap-Apple Night'. [IFCSS MSS 350: 397, Co. Cork]

> I was born in 1946 and brought up in a working class area of Manchester . . . [At Hallowe'en] occasionally during my childhood we bobbed for apples in a tin bath, or tried to eat them off strings with hands tied behind back. This happened once or twice in early childhood. Nowadays we have apple bobbing, apples on strings. [Acomb, North Yorkshire, August 1989]

In nineteenth-century Cornwall:

> The ancient custom of providing children with a large apple on Allhallow-eve is still observed, to a great extent, at St Ives. 'Allan-day' as it is called is the day of days to hundreds of children, who would deem it a great misfortune were they to go to bed on 'Allan-night' without the time honoured Allan apple to hide beneath their pillows. A quantity of large apples are thus disposed of, the sale of which is signified by the term Allan Market. [Hunt, 1881: 388]

Similarly, in the twentieth century:

> Allantide was still a popular occasion in my Newlyn childhood, and extra-large 'Allan Apples' very much in demand. The older girls put them under their pillows to dream of their sweethearts. While boys hung them on a string and took large bites! [Williams, 1987: 98]

The peeling of an apple (or occasionally an ORANGE) so that the peel remains in one long strip, which is then thrown over the shoulder to form the initial of a potential husband on the ground, is a widely reported activity, particularly at Hallowe'en.

> 'At midnight,' says a 14-year-old in Aberdeen, 'all the girls line up in front of the mirror. One by one each girl brushes her hair three times. While she is doing this the man who is to be her husband is supposed to look over her shoulder. If this happens the girl will be married within the year.' 'After they have done this' continues the young Aberdonian, 'each girl peels an apple, the peel must be thrown over her left shoulder with her right hand. This is supposed to form the initial of her husband-to-be.' [Opie, 1959: 53]

In Cornwall a more rough and ready method of DIVINATION was used:

An apple pip flicked into the air indicated the lover's home, so long as this verse was used:

> North, south, east, west,
> Tell me where my love does rest.

[Deane and Shaw, 1975: 53]

Similarly, in Lancashire:

In order to ascertain the abode of a lover, the anxious inquirer moves round in a circle, squeezing an apple pippin between finger and thumb, which, on pressure being employed, flies from the rind in the supposed direction of the lover's residence. The following doggerel is repeated during the operation:

> Pippin, pippin, paradise,
> Tell me where my true love lies;
> East, west, north or south,
> Pilling brig or Cocker-mouth.

That the reply may be corroborated, the inquirer afterwards shakes another pippin between the closed hands, and, on ascertaining the direction of the point of the pippin to the point of the compass, the assurance is supposed to be rendered doubly sure, if the charm works as desired, but not otherwise. [N & Q, 4 ser. 6: 340, 1870]

It is recorded that Dorset girls might use an apple pip to test their lovers' fidelity:

If on putting it in the fire, it bursts with the heat she is assured of his affection; but if it is consumed in silence she may know that he is false. Whilst they anxiously await the effect the following couplet is usually announced:

> If you love me, pop and fly;
> If you hate me, lay and die.

[Udal, 1922: 251]

In 1882 it was recorded that on St Thomas's Day (21 December) Guernsey girls would use an apple to obtain a glimpse of their future lovers.

On the day you must take a golden pippin, and having walked backwards to your bed, and having spoken to no one, you must then place it underneath the pillow, and St Thomas will grant to you when asleep a vision of your future consort. On placing the pippin underneath the pillow, the following charm must be repeated:

> *Le jour de St Thomas,*
> *Le plus court, et le plus bas,*
> *Dieu, fais me voir un mon dormant,*
> *Ce que j'aurai pour mon amant.*
> *Montre moi et mon épousé*
> *La maison ou j'habiterai.*

[Stevens Cox, 1971: 9]

Apple

In Lancashire in the 1980s:

> I remember twisting off apple stalks, each time the apple was turned a letter of the alphabet was said, when the stalk broke that letter was the initial of the Christian name of the one you were to marry. The broken stalk was then poked into the apple, counting letters again, when the skin broke that letter was his surname initial. [Kensington, London, November 1991]

Awd Goggie and Lazy Lawrence were NURSERY BOGIES which children were warned protected orchards and unripe fruit. In the East Riding of Yorkshire:

> There is another wicked sprite, who comes in most usefully as a protector of fruit. His name is Awd Goggie, and he specially haunts woods and orchards. It is evident, therefore, that it is wise on the children's part to keep away from the orchard at improper times, because otherwise 'Awd Goggie might get them.' [Gutch, 1911: 40]

Further south:

> Lazy Laurence was a guardian spirit of the orchard, both in Hampshire and in Somerset . . . In Hampshire, he sometimes took the form of a colt and chased orchard thieves . . . In Somerset, Lazy Laurence seems rather to afflict the thieves with what is described in one of the night spells as 'Cramps and crookeing and fault in their footing.' The Somerset proverbial saying runs:
>
> > Lazy Laurence, let me goo,
> > Don't hold me Winter and Summer too.
>
> [Briggs, 1976: 262]

The Somerset folklorist Ruth Tongue (1898–1981) recorded vague recollections of the Apple-Tree Man, which was, apparently, the oldest tree in the orchard.

> Pitminster was the place where in my childhood I was gravely and proudly conducted by a farm-child to a very old apple tree in their orchard and told mysteriously that it was 'the Apple Tree Man.' In 1958 I heard of him again on the Devon–Somerset borders. [Briggs and Tongue, 1965: 44]

The proverb 'An apple a day keeps the doctor away' seems to have been first recorded in the form 'Eat an apple on going to bed. And you'll keep the doctor from earning his bread' in 1866 [Simpson, 1982: 5]. Some west Dorset farming families seem to have taken the injunction quite literally, for apple dumplings formed a standard part of their daily evening meal, and:

> They used to keep the apples from one year so that the last of them could be made into a pie eaten at the end of sheep shearing time [in May] the following year. [Thorncombe, Dorset, autumn 1974]

Apples were used in a variety of traditional remedies.

During my childhood in a Pennine village I was sent to the greengrocer for a rotten apple—a mouldy one—as a remedy for an obstinate stye. [Letter from Streatham, London, in *Sunday Times*, 21 December 1958].

Thoroughly rotten apples were threaded onto CHILBLAINed toes to cool the burning and itching. [Lisburn, Co. Antrim, March 1986]

According to my 86-year-old aunt, an apple was placed in a room where there was SMALLPOX; as the apple went mouldy the smallpox was believed to be transferred from the patient to it. [Histon, Cambridgeshire, January 1989]

Burning apple WOOD 'will scent your room with an incense-like perfume' [letter from Five Ashes, Sussex, in *The Times*, 1 March 1929] or 'will fill your room with the gentlest of perfume' [letter from Middle Winnersh, Berkshire, in *TV Times*, 23 December 1989].

See also CRAB APPLE.

April Fools' Day – associated plants include GOOSEGRASS.

Arb-rabbit – a Devon variant of HERB ROBERT.

Arrowroot (*Maranta arundinacea*) – LORDS AND LADIES used as a substitute.

Arse-smart – a Cornish name for YELLOW BARTSIA.

Arthritis – treated using BOGBEAN, COMFREY, NETTLE, and SAGE.

Arum lily (*Zantedeschia aethiopica*). In many parts of the world the arum lily is associated with mourning and used to decorate graves. Thus it is often considered to be inappropriate for domestic flower arrangements or hospitals.

In 1946, following demobilisation from the Royal Navy, I emigrated to New Zealand. I was lucky enough to obtain an appartment in St Heliers Bay, Auckland. The rent included the garden, the maintenance of which I took on.

At the bottom, in a sort of wild corner, was an enormous spread of arum lilies. They were breathtaking in their beauty, and finding a huge vase which stood on the floor, I cut some of the lilies and arranged them to make a pleasant display.

Next day my landlady arrived to check that I had everything I wanted . . . On entering the living room, her hands flew to her mouth and she cried out: 'Oh, whatever have you done!' She turned to me, eyes blazing: 'You've brought arum lilies into the house. Don't you know you must never do that? They mean there will be a death in the house.'

I confessed my ignorance of this 'old wives tale' and said they looked so beautiful I could not resist bringing them in. She said that in New Zealand arum lilies grew like weeds and were treated as such. When she told a neighbour what I had done the other woman actually crossed herself, and, needless to say, I did not do that again! [Plymouth, Devon, June 1983]

In hospitals they used to think lilies—you know, the big ones they used to have in wedding bouquets—arum lilies—unlucky, and wouldn't allow them in the wards. When I worked in a hospital I ignored this twice, but each time, that night . . . [Lewisham, London, April 1986]

Other flowers considered inauspicious when taken indoors include LILAC, MOCK ORANGE, and RED AND WHITE FLOWERS.

The EASTER LILIES associated with 1916 Easter Rising in Ireland are arum lilies, and not the species more widely known by that name.

The republican women . . . devised, made and sold the Easter lily emblems from 1926 onwards. Representing the arum lilies traditionally used to decorate churches at Easter, they were also partly inspired by the red POPPIES commemorating British victims of the First World War. Like them, and like the SHAMROCK, they are simple, personal, natural, religiously inspired emblems. [Loftus, 1994: 86]

Since the late 1960s the Easter lily has been an important emblem of the Nationalist communities in Northern Ireland. At their Easter parades:

nearly all those attending display a single emblem. This is generally a paper Easter lily. The style in which it is worn indicates whether its owner supports the Officials or the Provisionals. When the republican movement split in 1969, the Officials choose to stick the lily to the coat lapel, while the Provisionals opted to use a pin . . . So important is this distinction that when, in the 1980s, the Provisionals were driven by increasing costs to employ sticky badges themselves, they reputedly had a drawing of a pin superimposed on the design. [Loftus, 1994: 92]

Arvi – a Shetland name for CHICKWEED.

Ascension – an East Anglian name for GROUNDSEL.

Ash (*Fraxinus excelsior*). In the nineteenth century it was believed that if ash trees failed to produce fruit—keys—disaster was foretold. In Yorkshire:

Some people every summer examined the ash tree . . . to see whether or not they had produced any seed; for the barrenness of the ash was said to be a sure sign of public calamity. It was a tradition among aged and thoughtful men, that the ash trees of England produced no seed during the year in which Charles the First was beheaded. [Jackson, 1873: 14]

In East Anglia:

The failure of the Crop of Ash-keys portends a death in the Royal Family . . . The failure in question is certainly, in some seasons, very remarkable;

many an old woman believes that, if she were the fortunate finder of a bunch, and could get introduced to the king, he would give her a great deal of money for it. [Forby, 1830: 406]

ROWAN or mountain ash, an unrelated tree which has leaves similar to those of ash, was widely considered to provide protection. Occasionally ash itself was also believed to be protective.

Rowan and ash sticks were used to drive cattle . . . believed to be 'kindly' and both trees were believed to be endowed with properties that ensured no interference from harmful influences. [Larne, Co. Antrim, October 1993]

In rural areas 'even' ash leaves—those leaves which lack a terminal leaflet and therefore have an even number of leaflets—were used in love DIVINATION. In Dorset:

The ash leaf is frequently invoked by young girls as a matrimonial oracle in the following way: The girl who wishes to divine who her future lover or husband is to be plucks an even ash leaf, and holding it in her hand, says:

'The even ash leaf in my hand,
The first I meet shall be my man.'

Then putting it into her glove, adds:

'The even ash leaf in my glove,
The first I meet shall be my love.'

And lastly, into her bosom, saying:

'The even ash leaf in my bosom,
The first I meet shall be my husband.'

Soon after which the future lover or husband will be sure to make his appearance. [Udal, 1922: 254]

According to a 52-year-old woman who described how she used ash leaves for divination during her childhood:

Start at the bottom leaflet on the left-hand side and say:

An even ash is in my hand
The first I meet will be my man.
If he don't speak and I don't speak,
This even ash I will not keep.

As each word is said, count a leaflet around the leaf until the rhyme is completed (this probably entails going round the leaf several times). When the rhyme is finished, continue by reciting the alphabet until the bottom right-hand leaflet is reached. The letter given to this leaflet gives the initial of your boyfriend. Two or three leaves may be used so that you get a greater range of letters. [Thorncombe, Dorset, June 1976]

In many parts of northern Britain ash was known as esh. In north Lincolnshire:

there is a widespread opinion that if a man takes a newly-cut 'esh-plant' not thicker than his thumb, he may lawfully beat his wife with it. [Britten and Holland, 1886: 170]

Burning the ashen faggot—a faggot made from young ash saplings—was a widespread Christmastide custom in Devon and Somerset during the nineteenth and early twentieth centuries. According to a late nineteenth-century writer, it was:

an ancient ceremony transmitted to us from the Scandinavians who at their feast of Juul were accustomed to kindle huge bonfires in honour of Thor. The faggot is composed of ashen sticks, hooped round with bands of the same tree, nine in number. When placed on the fire, fun and jollity commence—master and servant are now all at equal footing. Sports begin—jumping in sacks, diving in the water for APPLES, and many other innocent games engage the attention of the rustics. Every time the bands crack by reason of the heat of the fire, all present are supposed to drink liberally of cider or egg-hot, a mixture of cider, eggs, etc. The reason why ash is selected in preference to any other timber is that tradition assigns it as the wood with which Our Lady kindled a fire in order to wash her new-born Son. [Poole, 1877: 6]

Ashen faggots are still burnt in a few West Country pubs, and miniature faggots are occasionally prepared for burning on domestic hearths.

On the evening of January 5th ('old' Christmas Eve) at Curry Rivel, a Somerset village situated on the southern edge of Kings Sedgemoor, the wassailers go 'visiting' around the parish with their wassail song and the ashen faggot is ceremoniously burned at the King William IV public house. The faggot is made from young ash saplings and bound with bonds ('fonds,' 'fronds,' 'thongs,' or 'bonds') of withies (osiers); bramble has been used occasionally in the past. The number of bonds is variable but since the bursting of any one during the burning is a signal to 'drink up,' decency and country logic demands a 'reasonable few'. Either five or six are normally used. At the appropriate moment the faggot is placed on the fire, traditionally by the oldest customer—one villager can recall the faggot being brought in a wheelbarrow as was 'right and proper' —and as each bond bursts there is much cheering and a general clamour for drink. The landlord, Mr John Cousins, prepares a bowl of hot punch for the occasion to augment the barrel of beer usually provided by the house Brewery. Until quite recently cider was consumed in large quantities; the 'brew' of cider and perry donated by the (Langs) Hambridge Brewery in 1957 is particularly remembered. [Willey, 1983: 40]

In the first half of the nineteenth century:

Some towns in Somerset held 'Ashen Faggot Balls'. The one in Taunton on January 2nd, 1826 was 'most respectably attended by the principal families of the town and neighbourhood'. It was still held twenty years later, but by then the event was losing its appeal. [Legg, 1986: 54]

In some parts of southern England ash twigs were carried by children on ASH WEDNESDAY.

> In villages around Alton in Hampshire, and as far away as East Meon, near Petersfield, at Crowborough in Sussex, and doubtless in other places, children pick a black-budded twig of ash and put it in their pocket on this day. A child who does not remember to bring a piece of ash to school on Ash Wednesday can expect to have his feet trodden on by every child who possesses a twig, unless, that is, he or she is lucky enough to escape until midday. [Opie, 1959: 240]

> I was born and lived as a child in Crowborough . . . On Ash Wednesday it was always the custom to take a piece of the [ash] tree around with you. The piece had to have a black bud, without it it was void. If you were unable to produce the piece when asked the rest of the children could stamp on your toes. I remember one day whan I was playing about with it in school and was told to take it to the front and leave it in the waste-paper basket—and all the way back to the seat had to dodge the stamps! Ever prudent I had another piece for play time! This all stopped at 12 mid-day. [Pershore, Worcester shire, October 1991]

> [At Heston, Middlesex, in the 1930s] on Ash Wednesday we all took a twig of ash tree to school and produced it when challenged or risked a kick—and we had to get rid of it at 12 noon. We even risked the wrath of the teacher by rushing to an open window to throw out our twigs as soon as the mid-day dinner bell rang. [St Ervan, Cornwall, February 1992]

A widespread cure for HERNIA involved passing the patient through a split ash sapling, preferably one which had grown naturally from seed and had not previously been damaged by man. The tree was then tightly bound up and as it grew together so the patient would be healed. A full description provided in 1878 by the wife of a Sussex clergyman demonstrates how this cure, which required communal co-operation, was considered to be quite normal:

> A child so afflicted must be passed nine times every morning on nine successive days at sunrise through a cleft in a sapling ash tree, which has been so far given up by the owner of it to the parents of the child as that there is an understanding that it shall not be cut down during the life of the infant that is passed through it. The sapling must be sound of heart, and the cleft must be made with an axe. The child, on being carried to the tree, must be attended by nine persons, each of whom must pass it through the cleft from west to east. On the ninth morning the solemn ceremony is concluded by binding the tree tightly with a cord, and it is supposed that as the cleft closes the health of the child will improve. In the neighbourhood of Petworth some cleft ashes may be seen, through which children have very recently been passed. I may add that only a few weeks since, a person who lately purchased an ash-tree standing in this parish,

intended to cut it down, was told by the father of the child who had some time before passed through it, that the infirmity would be sure to return upon his son if it were felled. Whereupon the good man said, he knew such would be the case; and therefore he would not fell it for the world. [Latham, 1878: 40]

Similarly:

A remarkable instance of the extraordinary superstition which still prevails in the rural districts of Somerset has lately come to light at Athelney. It appears that a child was recently born in the neighbourhood with a physical ailment, and the neighbours persuaded the parents to resort to a very novel method of charming away the complaint. A sapling ash was split down the centre, and wedges were inserted so as to afford an opening sufficient for the child's body to pass through without touching either side of the tree. This having been done, the child was undressed, and, with its face held heavenward, it was drawn through the sapling in strict accordance with the superstition. Afterwards the child was dressed and simultaneously the tree was bound up. The belief of those who took part in this strange ceremony is that if the tree grows the child will grow out of its bodily ills. The affair took place at the rising of the sun on a recent Sunday morning, in the presence of the child's parents, several of the neighbours, and the parish police-constable. [*Bath and Wells Diocesan Magazine*, 1886: 178]

An example of an ash thus used can be seen in the Somerset Rural Life Museum at Glastonbury. A similar practice could be used to overcome IMPOTENCE.

In Wales the similar ritual was to split a young ash or HAZEL stem and hold it just fastened at the top. This made a symbolic vulva into which the impotent male introduced his recalcitrant organ. Binding up the tree again enabled it to heal, during which the impotence faded. [Richards, 1979: 13]

In Cheshire a cure for WARTS

was to steal a piece of bacon and push it under a piece of ash-bark. Excrescences would then appear on the tree; as they grew, the warts would vanish. [Hole, 1937: 12]

In Wiltshire sufferers seeking a cure from NEURALGIA were advised:

Cut off a piece of each finger and toe nail and a piece off your hair. Get up on the next Sunday morning before sunrise and with a gimlet bore a hole in the first maiden ash you come across and put the nails and hair in; then plug the hole up. [Whitlock, 1976: 167]

In many areas 'shrew-ashes' were used to cure lameness in cattle and other illnesses. In a letter dated 8 January 1776, Gilbert White of Selborne, Hampshire, wrote:

A shrew-ash is an ash whose twigs or branches, when gently applied to the limbs of cattle, will immediately relieve the pains which a beast suffers

from the running of a shrew-mouse over the part affected . . . Against
this accident, to which they were continually liable, our provident fore-
fathers always kept a shrew-ash at hand, which, once medicated, would
maintain its virtue for ever. A shew-ash was made thus:- Into the body of
the tree a deep hole was bored with an auger, and a poor devoted shrew-
mouse was thrust in alive, and plugged in, no doubt, with several quaint
incantations long since forgotten. [White, 1822, 1: 344]

In the nineteenth century a particularly well-known shrew-ash grew
in Richmond Park, Surrey. According to the park-keepers' tradition
'good Queen Bess had lurked under its shade to shoot deer as they
were driven past' [Ffennell, 1898: 333]. This tree was closely observed
by Sir Richard Owen (1804–92), first director of the Natural History
Museum in London, who lived near the tree, at Sheen Lodge, from
1852.

Either the year he came to live in the park or the year after . . . he first
encountered a young mother with a sick child accompanied by 'an old
dame', 'a shrew-mother', or, as he generally called her a 'witch-mother'.
They were going straight for the tree; but when they saw him, they
turned off in quite another direction till they supposed he was out of sight.
He, however, struck by their sudden avoidance of him, watched them
from a distance, saw them return to the tree, where they remained some
little time, as if busily engaged with it; then they went away. He was too
far off to hear anything said, but heard the sounds of voices in unison on
other occasions. He heard afterwards from the keeper of Sheen Gate . . .
that mothers with 'bewitched' infants, or with young children afflicted
with WHOOPING COUGH, decline, and other ailments, often came, sometimes from long distances, to this tree. It was necessary that they should
arrive before sunrise . . . Many children were said to be cured at the tree.
The greatest secrecy was always observed when visiting. This was respected by Sir Richard Owen, who, whenever he saw a group advanc-
ing towards it, moved away, and was always anxious that they should
not be disturbed. He could not tell me in what year he last saw a group
approach the tree to seek its aid. He could only say he had seen them
often, and thought they continued to come for many years. [Ffennell,
1898: 334]

During a recent survey [of Richmond Park] the site of the old shrew ash
was identified. This proved to be . . . the spot where an ancient ash still
stood in 1987. A sucker from its roots was still alive, although the tree itself
was passé. The storm of autumn brought the trunk down. A railing has
now been erected around the remains, which are to be left in the ground,
and a young ash is to be planted alongside the stump. Presumably it will
eventually replace the old tree, but it means that the site at least will remain identifiable. [Kew, Surrey, February 1994]

Other uses included curing EARACHE, RINGWORM, and SNAKE BITES.

Ash Wednesday

The sap of a young ash sapling was used to cure earache. A sapling was cut and put into a fire so that when the stick started to burn the sap came out the end and was caught on a spoon. This could be put on cotton wool and put into the ear. [Daingean, Co. Offaly, January 1985]

Ringworm was more common in my childhood . . . a remedy resorted to was to burn ash twigs in a tin box or similar container and allow the smoke from the smouldering twigs to envelop the affected part—usually arms, neck or face. [Larne, Co. Antrim, October 1993]

Ash leaves are used to combat viper bites. When an animal has been bitten farmers boil ash leaves and give the animal the resulting liquid and place the boiled leaves as a poultice on the bite. Works on people too! [Dorchester, Dorset, February 1992]

Ash sticks were used as weapons.

The Joyces are tinkers . . . they are wary and row among themselves. They do have some fierce fights in which the women join in. When they have each others heads well cut with ash plants they settle down and are as friendly as ever. [IFCSS MSS 750: 242, Co. Longford]

Stories relating to Ireland's past tell of fair-day brawls where ash plants were used and blood flowed freely. [Ballymote, Co. Sligo, May 1994]

For weather rhymes concerning oak and ash, see OAK.

Ash Wednesday – associated plants include ASH.

Aspen (*Populus tremula*)

The Highlanders entertain a superstitious notion, that our Saviour's cross was made of this tree, and for that reason suppose that the leaves of it can never rest. [Lightfoot, 1777: 617]

The people of Uist [Hebrides] say '*gu bheil an crithionn crion air a chroiseadh tri turais*'—that the hateful aspen is banned three times. The aspen is banned the first time because it haughtily held up its head while all the other trees of the forest bowed their heads lowly down as the King of all created things was being led to Calvary. And the aspen is banned the second time because it was chosen by the enemies of Christ for the cross upon which to crucify the Saviour of mankind. And the aspen is banned the third time—here the reciter's memory failed him. Hence the ever-tremulous, ever-quivering, ever-quaking notion of the guilty hateful aspen even in the stillest air.

Clods and stones and other missiles, as well as curses, are hurled at the aspen by the people. The reciter, a man of much natural intelligence, said that he always took off his bonnet and cursed the hateful aspen tree in all sincerity whenever he saw it. No crofter in Uist would use aspen about his plough or about his harrows, or about his farming implements of any kind. Nor would a fisherman use aspen about his boat or about his creels or about any fishing-gear whatsoever. [Carmichael, 1928: 104]

Cf. WHITE BEAM and WHITE POPLAR.

Asthma – treated using BEETROOT, EYEBRIGHT, MULLEIN, NETTLE, ROWAN, and THORN-APPLE.

Astrological botany. Popular books on the folklore of plants often contain statements which associate various plants with different planets.

> Astrologically under the sign of Saturn, black nightshade [*Solanum nigrum*] is the birthday flower for 23 January, and in the LANGUAGE OF FLOWERS means 'Your thoughts are dark.' [Addison, 1985: 194]

Such statements derive from systems expounded by seventeenth-century philosophers and herbalists, who believed that every plant and every illness was governed by a constellation or planet. A disease caused by one planet could be cured by the use of a herb belonging to an opposing planet. Alternatively, illness could be cured by sympathy —by the use of herbs belonging to the planet which was responsible for the disease.

> Every Planet cures his own diseases, as the Sun and Moon by their Herbs cure the Eys, Saturn the Spleen, Jupiter the Liver, Mars the Gall and diseases of the Choller, and Venus disease in the Instruments of generation.

Conversely, the blessed thistle, a herb of Mars, cured the French pox (syphilis) 'by antipathy to Venus who governs it', while sanicle (*Sanicula europaea*), a herb of Venus, was recommended as a cure for wounds and 'other mischiefs Mars inflicteth upon the body of Man'.

The best remembered of these astrological botanists is Nicholas Culpeper (1616–54). After having set himself up in practice as an astrologer physician in Spitalfields, Culpeper published his *Physicall Directory* in 1649. This work, he proclaimed, superseded all previous publications, which, in his opinion, were as 'full of non-sense and contradictions as an Egg is full of Meat'. The *Physicall Directory*, a pleasant little octavo volume, was followed in 1652 by his *English Physician*, a work which proved so popular that forty-five editions of it were produced before the end of the eigtheenth century. A Welsh edition, translated by D.T. Jones of Llanllyfni, was produced in 1816/17 [Jones, 1980: 59], and the book has continued to be in print in various forms for over three hundred years. Although Culpeper's work is now invariably referred to as his 'Herbal', the word herbal did not appear in its title until over a century after its original publication, when Ebenezer Sibley published an illustrated edition entitled *Culpeper's English Physician, and Complete Herbal* in 1789.

Today astrological botany is often derided, but those who do so fail to realize that the idea that plants were 'under the dominion' of planets was not isolated from other beliefs prevalent during the period in which it evolved. During the seventeenth century there was a widespread belief that astrology, which was avidly studied by many leading intellectuals, held the key to the understanding of the universe [see Thomas, 1971, especially chapters 10–12].

Atheists' tombs. In 1913 three tombs in Hertfordshire which had trees—in one case a FIG tree, and in the other two SYCAMORE trees— growing from them, were recorded as being the tombs of atheists, who declared their disbelief in certain aspects of Christian faith, and stated that, in the unlikely event of the Christian teaching being correct, trees would grow from their tombs.

Aubergine (*Solanum melongena*). Late in March 1990 it was reported that the word Allah, written in Arabic, had been found inside aubergines in Muslim households in the English Midlands.

> The curious phenomenon of God's name appearing in Arabic inside aubergines has spread from Nottingham to Leicester, where three cases have been reported by devout Muslims in the past week. As many as 5,000 pilgrims from all over the Midlands are reported to have visited the remarkable vegetables.
>
> Tasleem Moulvi, of Kingnewton Street, Leicester, told the *Independent* yesterday that her mother found two significant aubergines on Friday night when she sliced them open after visiting another one, exposed in Bakewell Street. One, sliced twice, shows the Arabic characters for Allah, repeated three times; the other, she said, appeared to contain a verse from the Koran, though this has not yet been deciphered. [*Independent*, 28 March 1990]

> Thousands of Muslims are travelling to a terrace house in the backstreets of Leicester to see what is claimed to be a miraculous aubergine.
>
> Farida Kassam asks visitors to take off their shoes as a mark of respect for the sliced vegetable, exhibited in a bowl of white vinegar in her front room. Beside it is a plate bearing the Arabic inscription Yah-Allah, meaning Allah is everywhere. Mrs Kassam, aged 30, proudly points out that the unusual seed pattern inside the aubergine appears to match the Arabic writing. The discovery has fulfilled the faithful and confounded the curious, who have flocked to inspect the evidence. A magnifying glass has been thoughtfully provided . . . Mrs Kassam said: 'It is a miracle. This has happened to an ordinary family, that is why I am very proud of it. Allah never forgets anybody. We will preserve the aubergine as long as we can and then bury it in holy ground.' [*Guardian*, 28 March 1990]

No further reports of such aubergines have appeared since 14 April 1990, when it was reported in the *Nairobi Nation* that:

A family in Nairobi got an Easter and Ramadan surprise when they cut open an aubergine and found the word Allah in Arabic. A week earlier, a member of the family studying in Britain had had a similar experience. [*Fortean Times* 55: 5, 1990]

Aul – a Herefordshire variant of ALDER.

Aul man's bell – a north-east Scotland name for HAREBELL.

Autumn gentian (*Gentianella amarella*)—known on the Shetland Islands as deadman's mittens, the 'half-open buds like livid finger-nails protruding through the green' [Tait, 1947: 81].

B

Babies – children were told that babies originated in GOOSEBERRY bushes or PARSLEY beds.

Baby's breath – see GYPSOPHILA.

Bacon – a name for young shoots of DOG ROSE.

Bad man's baccy – a Northumberland name for COW PARSLEY.

Bad man's oatmeal – a Northumberland name for UMBELLIFERS.

Badman-whotmeal – a Humberside name for HEMLOCK.

Baldness – cured using ONION and ST JOHN'S WORT.

Balm (*Melissa officinalis*), also known as LEMON BALM.

> Grown in gardens on account of its medicinal virtues. A tea made by pouring boiling water on the leaves is esteemed an excellent restorative. [Marquand, 1906: 45]

> Grown in gardens [in the Forest of Dean], dried and made into tea—for stomach problems/colic. [Cinderford, Gloucestershire, November 1993]

Banana (*Musa* cv.)

> Very popularly a banana is asked to decide whether a boy is being faithful. When the question has been asked, the lower tip of the fruit is cut off with a sharp knife, and the answer found in the centre of the flesh, either a Y meaning 'Yes' or a dark blob meaning 'No.' [Opie, 1959: 336]

This means could also be used to predict the outcome of many other activities, or solve any problem which required a simple yes or no answer [Barnes, London, October 1979].

Banwort – a name commonly used for DAISY in seventeenth-century Cumberland.

Barberry (*Berberis vulgaris*)

> In many parts of Cornwall the Barberry is called 'JAUNDICE tree'. On the 'DOCTRINE OF SIGNATURES', an infusion of the yellow under-bark of this shrub is supposed to be a perfect cure for jaundice, and I have known it to be frequently planted in gardens and shrubberies for this purpose. [Davey, 1909: 17]

> The berberis is a well-known shrub . . . if a branch of this shrub is plucked and the bark peeled off the stems, the inner part of the stems and the

branch, which may be broken into smaller pieces, is then boiled in milk, and the drink is said to cure jaundice. [IFCSS MSS 593: 116, Co. Clare]

Barley (*Hordeum vulgare*) should be sown when BLACKTHORN or WHITLOW GRASS is in flower or when ELM trees come into leaf.

'When the blackthorn is white, sow barley both day and night.' This came either from south Wiltshire or from mid-Hants. I learnt it working on a farm in 1942–44. [Salisbury, Wiltshire, February 1989]

Alternatively, the 'temperature of the land for sowing barley in spring is right if the soil is warm to one's bare bottom' [letter from Wickhambrook, Suffolk, in *Farmers' Weekly*, 10 January 1964].

Barley has the unusual distinction of having a traditional song devoted to it, or, perhaps more correctly, to whisky distilled from it. An elaborate version of the song 'John Barleycorn' was printed early in the seventeenth century, and the song has remained in the oral tradition ever since [Vaughan Williams and Lloyd, 1968: 116]. The song starts with the sowing of barley seed, and tells of its subsequent growth:

> He laid there till midsummer time of the year
> Till the weather was pleasant and warm
> And there Sir John how he grew a beard
> And he soon became a man.

Then came harvesting and the the conversion of the grain into whisky:

> You can put Sir John in a nut brown jug
> And he'll make the merriest man.
> He'll make a maid dance around this room,
> Stark naked as she was born,
> He'll make a parson pawn his books
> With a little John Barleycorn.

> [Lomax and Kennedy, 1961]

Barren ground. A number of local legends relate how plants will not grow on certain patches of ground owing to evil deeds having taken place there. A letter dated 17 July 1778 records the legend of 'the Brothers' Steps' in London:

They are situated in a field about half a mile from Montague House, in a North direction; and the prevailing tradition concerning them is, that two brothers quarrelled about a worthless woman, and . . . decided it by duel. The print of their feet is near three inches in depth, and remains totally barren . . . Their number I did not reckon, but suppose they may be about ninety. A bank on which the first fell, who was mortally wounded and died on the spot, retains the form of his agonising posture by the curse of barrenness, while grass grows around it. A friend of mine showed me these steps in the year 1769, when he could trace them back by old people to the year 1686; but it was generally supposed to have happened in the early part of the reign of Charles II. There are people now living who well remember their being ploughed up, and barley sown, to deface them; but all was labour in vain; for the prints returned in a short time to their original form. [*Gentleman's Magazine,* 74: 1194, 1804]

[The patch on which the wounded brother fell] and the bank on which the woman sat are now gone, but it is said that the Brothers' Steps themselves can still be seen in the south-west corner of Tavistock Square Gardens, near the tree planted in 1953 in honour of Mahatma Gandhi. I am happy to report that there are bare patches there which could be taken for footprints. [Westwood, 1985: 127]

On Dragon's Hill, near the famous white horse at Uffington, Berkshire:

St George is said to have slain the Dragon . . . where the Dragon's blood was spilt, grass has never grown. [Bergamar, n.d.: 7]

Although shrubby vegetation flourishes, trees will not grow in Ashdown Forest, Sussex:

All attempts to restock it with trees have failed; this dates from the time when the first cannons were cast, because the trees were used for charcoal for iron smelting and whereas they were quite willing to help make tools and other objects of a peaceful nature, they refused to let themselves be used for making weapons. My mother was born in the house of Ralph Hogge, the founder of the first cannon in 1492.

It seems strange that trees have never grown extensively on the uplands again since the founding ceased in the seventeenth century, although they have on the lower reaches of the Weald. It also seems strange that there are quite extensive fires on (we never say 'in') the Forest around Easter each year. These fires are often deliberately started by gypsies who prefer the Forest to remain open land. [Hythe, Kent, June 1973 and November 1987]

In Ulster bare patches persist on the grave of a rioter shot in 1845, the bare earth in this case presumably bearing testimony to innocence rather than to his crime.

A young man, John Boyle, was shot dead in a riot in Armagh on 12 July 1845. His grave is much visited and has always been an object of wonder. There are a number of bare round depressions on the grave, about four inches in diameter, on which grass never grows. Traditionally people say that these are the signs of the wounds he received (although he received one wound). The grave has been re-dug a number of times, as recently as last year when the whole graveyard was cleared and re-sown. Still these patches appeared. [Armagh, September 1985]

Baskets – made from DOCK, MARRAM GRASS, and WILLOW.

Bastard-killer – a Somerset name for JUNIPER.

Bath asparagus – see SPIKED STAR OF BETHLEHEM.

Bath of Venus – a seventeenth-century name for TEASEL.

Battle of Flowers. On Jersey an annual Battle of Flowers is held on the second Thursday in August. The first of these events was held to celebrate the coronation of King Edward VII in 1902. In its current form the 'battle' consists of a procession of about thirty elaborately decorated floats. During the Battle's early years the floats were decorated with flowers, mainly HYDRANGEAS, but in recent years there has been an increasing tendency for paper to be used. Thus in 1987 it was reported:

> Mr Graeme Rabet, Association Chairman, said that there is now almost an equal number of paper and fully floral entries in the parade. 'The standard of the paper floats is extremely high, and we regard the part they play in the parade as a vital one,' he said.

In earlier times it was customary for participants to throw flowers at each other, hence the name 'battle'. Immediately after the judging of floats had finished on 12 August 1909:

> On the 'commence fire' being sounded by buglers, the real fun commenced. We speak of the Battle of Flowers the whole year round, but the actual battle is only a ten-minute 'turn'. Still, people come from the north, the south, the east and the west to see it. They lose their individuality too!
>
> Staid old men become again as romping children, the stern official throws off his robe of dignity and austerity, and even the cleric forgets for a moment that he has a distinguishing collar that gives him away. If one threw a bunch of flowers at a fellow on an ordinary day we should most probably be summoned for assault, but with the Battle of Flowers everything is different.
>
> So it was yesterday; the aristocracy pelted the democracy, and vice versa. Alas for the erstwhile decorated cars! They were soon shorn of their grandeur and the roadway was ankle-deep in blooms. Alas for the poor flowers!

However, violent hooliganism in 1960 brought such practices to an end, leaving a rather decorous, but extremely popular, parade of floats [Lake, n.d.]. A museum at St Ouen is devoted to the Battle, and displays

> only a fraction of the entries made by Miss F. Bechelet during the last 36 years in the Jersey Battle of Flowers. All her floats have the distinction of being made entirely of wild flowers grown in the west of the island . . . Miss Bechelet has won the highest awards in classes in which she has competed. [Museum leaflet, January 1990]

Cf. FLOWER PARADE.

Bay (*Laurus nobilis*)

In the New Forest the bay tree was planted not only for the flavour of its leaves, but for the protection it afforded against all things evil. It had the power to fend off the Devil or WITCHES, as well as to safeguard one from THUNDER, lightning and forest fires. [Boase, 1976: 118]

When my brother and sister-in-law moved to a house in south Devon . . . 30 years ago, they were told that the bay trees which grew at the entrance would protect the house, but my sister-in-law said they didn't, because she always said the house had a ghost. [Oxford, January 1991]

Cf. MYRTLE.

[In Hartland, Devon] on Valentine's Eve take five bay leaves, and pin them to your pillow—one at each corner and one in the middle. Then lying down, say the following seven times, and count seven, seven times over at each interval.

> Sweet guardian angels, let me have
> What I most earnestly do crave—
> A Valentine endued with love,
> Who will both true and constant prove.

If you carefully observe this ceremonial, your future husband will appear to you in a dream. [Chope, 1938: 359]

Bean

I have heard it said that every seventh year the bean turns in the pod. The normal attachment of the bean to the pod is reversed at the seventh year and then reverts to normal attachment the following season. My father believes this to be true and gives the following account of the learning of this fact. 'In the year 1919, my brother George and myself were carting stone to a road-building site at Westwoodside. Old Edmund Cooper came up to us and said "Do you know that this year is the year when beans hang t'other road in 't pod?" We had never heard of it, so he said "Come down this lane to a field of beans and I'll show you what I mean." We were shown that the beans were indeed hanging the wrong way in their pod.' My father claims that he has checked this phenomenon in later years and has found it to be quite true. [SLF MSS, West Butterwick, Humberside, 14 September 1970]

See also BROAD BEAN and RUNNER BEAN.

Bear's foot – a name for HELLEBORE.

Beech (*Fagus sylvatica*). Although beech trees are large, attractive, and long-lived, they appear to have attracted very little folklore.

The disruptions on the bark of the smooth beech, where old growth has ceased, is thought in areas of Dorset to represent the 'evil eye', and the sinister beech grove at dusk is an unlucky place in which to be found alone. [Palmer, 1973: 79]

As children in Notts in the 1920s we gathered beech nuts and threaded them to make necklaces. [Oban, Argyllshire, October 1990]

[During my childhood over sixty years ago, at Wimborne St Giles, Dorset] we ate beech nuts in small quantities, but as there was a grove of sweet CHESTNUTS in a field we preferred these. [Sidmouth, Devon, October 1991]

We ate SORREL, beech leaves, briar tops. [Farnborough, Kent, January 1993]

On the way home from school [Crondall, Hampshire, 1920s] she and her friends gathered wild STRAWBERRIES, ELDERberries, beech leaves, sorrel grass and BRAMBLE to eat along the way. [Fleet, Hampshire, March 1993]

Bee-sookies – a Shetland name for LOUSEWORT.

Bee trap – an Inverness name for LARGE and/or HEDGE BINDWEED.

Beetroot (*Beta vulgaris* cv.)

[I was born in Jamaica; I came to Bristol in 1960.] Beetroot and CARROT juice is very good to drink. It prevents DIARRHOEA. [Francis, 1988: 95]

Beetroot wine was very popular against ASTHMA, CHILBLAINS, EARACHE and, some say, SNAKE BITES. I knew a gypsy named Penfold who told me his people kept beetroot by them for snake bites, and adders of course are common hereabouts. He said the gypsies planted theirs at night. In fact, though travellers, I was surprised to learn they would have a variety of 'stewpot' vegetables growing just inside wood edges in their 'territory' . . . as well as helping themselves en route. [Barnstaple, Devon, May 1991]

Bellies-and-bums, fingers-and-thumbs – an Essex name for BIRD'S–FOOT TREFOIL.

Bent – a Shetland name for MARRAM GRASS.

Bent grass (*Agrostis* spp.)

As a child, evacuated to Elgin, Scotland, during World War II, I used to chew a grass which the local children called bread and cheese. I have since identified this as the common bent, *Agrostis tenuis* Sibth. [syn. *A. capillaris* L.]. In fact, a local mound was named after it, 'Bread-and-Cheese Hill'. Chewing it now, it doesn't taste a bit like bread and cheese. [Stevenage, Hertfordshire, January 1993]

Bermuda buttercup (*Oxalis pes-caprae*)

[On the Isles of Scilly] stems of Bermuda buttercup are eaten by children for their sour taste. [Woodnewton, Northamptonshire, June 1992]

The local children call them sour-saps—chewing the sharp tasting stems of the flowers. [St Mary's, Isles of Scilly, September 1992]

Cf. WOOD SORREL.

Betony (*Stachys officinalis*). Despite having the scientific name *Stachys officinalis*—officinal or medicinal stachys—there is little evidence for betony being much used in British and Irish folk medicine. The few records of such use that exist come mainly from gypsies.

[Derbyshire gypsies:] betony . . . infusion of leaves remedies stomach troubles; ointment made from juice of fresh leaves and unsalted lard removes poison from STINGS and bites. [Thomson, 1925: 160].

Bilberry (*Vaccinium myrtillus*), also known as blueberry and whortleberry. Although the fruits of the bilberry are only small, where the plant is abundant they were sometimes gathered on a commercial scale. Thus on Exmoor during the early years of the twentieth century, as soon as the berries were ripe:

The head teacher would consult the rector, and school would be broken up then and there for five or six weeks.

Children, sometimes accompanied by their mothers, would set off for the moor early in the morning with a basket and sandwiches to last all day . . .

A large medicine bottle of cold tea was also carried, and this was secured to the handkerchief by a string . . .

After picking had started it was a point of honour not to have our dinner until a certain quantity of whorts had been picked or as we said, 'we had to earn our dinner first.'

A mark would sometimes be made with a squashed berry on the side of the basket, or sometimes a turned-down withy in the basket would be used, to indicate when it was considered that enough had been gathered . . .

When several of the same family went, the younger members would pick into a cup or pint mug, and (when full) empty it into mother's or elder brother's or sister's basket . . .

The first place where the whorts ripened was on Grabbist. Not a favourite place as the berries grew between gorse, and fingers and legs were very sore at the end of the day, so we were always glad when the whorts were ripe on Dunkery.

Annicombe was also one of the first, and we always enjoyed getting there, where the whorts were much bigger and there was also the attraction of the stream in which we could paddle in the dinner break.

Dunkery Hill Gate, Bincombe, and the slopes under Dunkery Beacon were all visited in turn.

Sometimes when these places failed we used to walk through Cloutsham to Stoke Ridge, which took nearly two hours.

The whorts were sold to Mr Tom Webber and his sister, who had a horse and open cart in which small barrels were carried . . . The price was 4d a quart at the beginning of the season, dropping to 3d or 2½d as they became more plentiful . . . Money earned was used to buy clothes for the winter . . . We were allowed to keep what money we earned on the last day of whorting, so we were usually very energetic on that day. [Court, 1967: 42]

Similarly, in Ireland:

In the woods that lie on the slopes of the Galtee mountain there are always a good supply of whorts.

Every summer people go out into the wood picking these whorts, this has been done for about 200 years. They start picking on 29 June and continue to the end of August. Pickers, consisting sometimes of the whole family, leave early in the morning for the wood, and after picking for some hours one of their number will light a fire and prepare some tea, which they all sit down and enjoy about mid-day.

Sometimes the fruit is plentiful and pickers have no difficulty in filling their cans, but very often they are not so fortunate.

They often sing songs to lighten their work which is not always pleasant as in warm days flies are a torment and the pickers have their heads covered with a handkerchief soaked in Jeyes Fluid to hunt them away.

Some people pick from three to seven gallons in the day and get from nine pence to one shilling per gallon.

The worts are sent across to England where they are used to make DYE or to mix with the cheaper kinds of jam.

Buyers meet the pickers every evening to buy their day's picking. [IFCSS MSS 575: 382, Co. Tipperary]

In Ireland the gathering of bilberries was associated with the ancient festival of Lughnasa, which celebrated the beginning of the harvest early in August each year.

One of the customs connected with the festival is the picking of bilberries. There are many places in Ireland where all other features of the survival have disappeared but the festive outings to pick bilberries are still continued. [MacNeill, 1962: 20]

While walking in April near Llanthony on the English/Welsh border, John Hillaby [1983: 96] came across a shepherd:

He had been up to the tops looking at the leaf . . . [which] is blueberry and sheep, he told me, love blueberry. As soon as it begins to sprout in the spring, the custom is to drive the flocks up into the hills from the valley foldings, for the shepherds know the animals will be comfortable there and less likely to stray down again.

Bilberries do not appear to have been much used in folk medicine in the British Isles.

The berries have an astringent quality. In Arran and the Western isles they are given in diarrhaeas and dysenteries with good effect. [Lightfoot, 1777: 201]

My late parents came from Poland after the Second World War and my mother occasionally used certain plants as herbal remedies . . . Fruits of the bilberry were preserved in sugar in glass jars and a few teaspoons of the concentrated juice diluted with water and warmed as a most effective cure for DIARRHOEA. [Bromley, Kent, April 1991]

Billy buttons – a Cornish name for BURDOCK.

Bindweed (*Convolvulus arvensis*)

In the 1950s in Invergowrie, Perthshire, bindweed was known as 'young man's death.' If you pick bindweed your boyfriend will die— seems to be associated with the rapid fading of the flower. [Stevenage, Hertfordshire, May 1982]

I was brought up in Shropshire . . . Thunder Flowers we always called bindweed (convolvulus) because if we picked these it would be sure to THUNDER before the day was out. [Bessacar, South Yorkshire, April 1984]

These beliefs are probably brought about to discourage children from gathering bindweed flowers and thereby causing damage to crops; cf. POPPY. For the children's game of making the fairy dance see POPPY. See also LARGE BINDWEED and SEA BINDWEED.

Birch (*Betula pendula*)

A custom, dating from time immemorial, is that of using the branches and sprigs of the birch tree for decorating churches for WHIT SUNDAY. [Wright, 1936: 157]

Whitsuntide . . . is not with us [in Shropshire] the holiday time that it is in many counties. The only local custom peculiar to the season . . . is that of decking the churches on Whit Sunday with birch branches stuck into holes in the tops of pews. Hordley Church was thus adorned up to the year 1857; at St Mary's, Shrewsbury, the custom was kept up until about the year 1865; at St Chad's it was continued up to 1855, and probably later. [Burne, 1883: 350]

The tradition of using birch branches at Pentecost [Whitsun] is still maintained at St John the Baptist Church, Frome. We are allowed the top of young silver birch trees in the woods of Longleat each year and we fix the resultant five or six foot branches to the pillars which separate the nave from the north and south aisles.

We believe that the significance of the branches is twofold: being young growths, they represent the renewal of life; and the stirring of the leaves resulting from the moving air currents in the church respresent the sound of the 'rushing mighty wind' as the Holy Spirit descended on the Apostles.

We have however nothing but tradition by word of mouth to support this interpretation nor can we say when the custom began, except to say we know that it was already in operation by 1836, since we have amongst our church records a contract by which the verger undertook to obtain HOLLY to decorate the church at EASTER and birch branches at Whitsun. [Frome, Somerset, March 1994]

Bird cherry (*Prunus padus*)

[In north-east Scotland] the wood of the 'hackberry' or bird cherry (*Prunus padus*) is not used as a staff or for any other purpose, as it is looked on as the WITCH's tree. [Gregor, 1889: 41]

Bird-eyes or bird's eye – names for SPEEDWELL, especially GER-MANDER SPEEDWELL.

Bird-lime – prepared from HOLLY bark.

Bird's-foot trefoil (*Lotus corniculatus*)

No Blame. In the south of Ireland children gather this plant to take with them to school in the belief that the possession of it will save them from punishment; and it is said they will go miles out of their way to obtain it. [Britten and Holland MSS]

Although there is little folklore associated with bird's-foot trefoil, the plant has attracted a remarkably large number of local names. Names collected in the 1990s include: bellies-and-bums, fingers-and-thumbs (Hadleigh, Essex), cockies and hennies (Burghead, Morayshire), eggs and bacon (widespread), fingers and thumbs (Lytchett Matravers, Dorset), fisherman's baskets (Radnorshire), granny's toenails (Ashford, Kent), horse yakkels [yakkels = molar teeth] (Lerwick, Shetland), pigtoes (Ashford, Kent), shoes and stockings (west Gwent), and tom thumbs (Portland, Dorset).

Biscuities – a Morayshire name for the fruits of MALLOW.

Bistort (*Persicaria bistorta*; syn. *Polygonum bistorta*)

When I used to work in Cumbria, everyone used to make Easter Ledges—there were various recipes, but they always contained *Polygonum bistorta*— and eat them during the spring. They were supposed to purify the BLOOD. [Girton, Cambridge, September 1985]

Easter ledges—or Herb Pudding or Yarby Pudden—depending on which part of Cumbria one is in— seems to have been made early in the year when there were few vegetables, and eaten with 'Tatty Pot' which is mainly onions, potatoes, and as much mutton as one had.

3 good handfuls of Easter Ledges
3 good handfuls of NETTLES

Bistort

1 good handful of CABBAGE or broccoli or DANDELION leaves with a few
RASPBERRY, BLACKCURRANT and/or GOOSEBERRY leaves
1 ONION
1 large cup BARLEY—previously soaked overnight in water. Salt and pepper, or sometimes PARSLEY

Method: Wash greens, and chop with onion. Put in a muslin bag and boil
for one and a half hours. Empty bag into a bowl and beat in three eggs,
bacon dripping, and about 2 oz of butter. Reheat in oven. In Cumberland they used oats instead of barley and after it had been boiled put it on
top of hard-boiled eggs. [Clappersgate, Cumbria, October 1985]

When we were children we lived on the Cumberland coast, and when
spring came we had to gather Easter Ledges about half a mile away; we
were a big family so we had to get a lot. Nettles, SOUR DOCKING and dandelion were washed and cut up, barley was washed; and into the bag went
the greens, next barley, until it was used up. The herb pudding in bag was
put into a pan of boiling water, with a plate at the bottom of the pan to
keep it from sticking, and boiled for one and a half hours. We had it every
Sunday until it went to seed—a pink flower on the top of the stem. [Win-
dermere, Cumbria, November 1988]

In parts of Yorkshire bistort is known as passion dock, from the custom of eating pudding made from it during Passiontide, the last two
weeks in Lent.

Everyone has their own idea about what should go into dock pudding,
but the basic method is to wash and chop the dock leaves, boil them with
onions and then add oatmeal to thicken it up . . .

Full of iron and vitamins, it used to be eaten to 'clear the blood' in
springtime like other spring greens, but the tradition has adapted to the
times. Nearly everyone said they made enough to freeze, and this was
often then served as a special treat for breakfast on Christmas Day . . .

The tradition of collecting and eating passion docks . . . has remained
strong in the Calder Valley for generations, but it was only in 1971 that
the first World Championship Dock Pudding Contest was held as a pre-
lude to the Calder Valley Festival of the Arts. This took place in Hebden
Bridge and there were hundreds of entries. The *Halifax Courier*, the local
newspaper, provided a trophy and there were other prizes for the winner
and runners-up. Since that date the number of entrants decreased dramatically and it has not been held every year. It appears to be gaining
popularity again; there were thirteen entrants in 1988, competing for
prizes of £25, £15, £10 and, of course, the silver cup to be held for
twelve months. [Smith, 1989: 11]

In Warcop, Cumbria, bistort was used as a VERMICIDE:

The moon must be full when the bistort is picked to cure worms. [Short,
1983: 124]

See also AMPHIBIOUS BISTORT.

34

Biting stonecrop (*Sedum acre*)

Stonecrop is seen on many thatched and other cottages and farmsteads in Wales. It was originally placed there as a protection against thunderbolts, LIGHTNING and WITCHES. [Trevelyan, 1909: 95]

Plants grown on or about the roof of the house to bring good luck and guard against fire were stonecrop (*Sedum acre*) around Tramore, County Waterford, and snapdragon (ANTIRRHINUM *majus*) in County Westmeath. [Ó Danachair, 1970: 25]

The stems are by children stripped of their leaves and scraped across each other fiddle-fashion to produce a squeaking noise . . . The name is only known among old people now, as very few know what 'Crowdy-kit' means; but an old woman at Ipplepen, well-versed in herbs (eighty-eight years of age and still *yark*), gave me both the name and how it was to be explained. Her family used to be very musical, and she could remember hearing the fiddle called crowdy. [Friend, 1882: 18]

Cf. WATER FIGWORT.

Bitten-off root – a former name for DEVIL'S BIT SCABIOUS.

Bittersweet (*Solanum dulcamara*), also known as woody nightshade.

TEETHING troubles: make a necklace of dried nightshade berries, let baby wear it, and it will prevent CONVULSIONS. [Taylor MSS, Sprowston, Norfolk]

[In the Cotwolds] the berries of bittersweet . . . were used [to cure CHILBLAINS], well rubbed in; they were preserved in bottles for winter use. [Bloom, 1930: 25]

Bitter vetch (*Lathyrus linifolius*)

[On Colonsay] the tuberous roots [of bitter vetch] were dug up and eaten raw, or tied in bundles and hung up to the kitchen roof to dry, and afterwards roasted. Used for flavouring whisky. [McNeill, 1910: 114]

Blackberry – see BRAMBLE.

Black bryony (*Tamus communis*)

The berries, when steeped in gin, [are a] popular remedy for CHILBLAINS in this island [of Wight], where the power they possess, in common with the root, of removing superficial discolorations of the surface from BRUISES, SUNBURNS, &c., is equally well known and applied in practice.

My friend Lady Erskine informs me that the black bryony is called in Wales 'Serpent's Meat', and that an idea is there prevalent that those reptiles are always lurking near the spots where the plant grows. [Bromfield, 1856: 507]

Black currant (*Ribes nigrum*). Even before its vitamin C content was discovered the black currant was used to prevent or cure COLDS.

> Old remedies for a cold . . . black currant tea, that is hot water and black currant jam. [Llanuwchyllnn, Gwynedd, April 1991]

> My [Cornish] great grandmother died at 86 years old in 1932, her know-ledge of vitamins would be nil, obviously, but in winter she always kept a jug of hot water with big dollops of black currant jam in it on top of the 'slab' (Cornish name for kitchen range) and we always as children had to drink a cup of black currant tea 'to protect our lungs and keep away colds' daily. [Calpe, Alicante, Spain, December 1991]

Blackheads – cured using BRAMBLE.

Black knobs – a Peak District name for ALDER fruits.

Blackman flower – a name for SELF-HEAL.

Black medic (*Medicago lupulina*) – occasionally considered to be SHAMROCK:

> The plant that I grew from seed, sent home on a St Patrick's Day—some-time about 1915—was *Medicago lupulina*. [Ballycastle, Co. Antrim, January 1991]

Black poplar (*Populus nigra*). At Aston-on-Clun, Shropshire, a black poplar tree, said to be over 250 years old, is decorated with flags on 'Arbor Day'—29 May—each year. These flags remain in position until the following year, when they are replaced by new ones [Shuel, 1985: 39].

> The custom of dressing a tree with flags survives from an ancient era when it was done in worship of Bridget, goddess of fertility. Later sanctified as St Bridget or St Bride, the goddess had a tree for a shrine, on which tribal emblems and prayer flags were hung. A Bride's Tree still survives at Aston-on-Clun, but it is unclear whether the name derives from Bridget or the following:
> On 29 May 1786 John Marston, the squire of Aston-on-Clun, married Mary Carter by special licence at Sibdon Carwood parish church. As the wedding couple were returning home in their carriage, exuberant vil-lagers stopped it at the parish boundary, dragged it to the Bride's Tree, and the couple were presented with boughs as symbols of good luck.
> Mary was so enchanted with the dressing of the Bride's Tree that she saw to it that the custom would continue. [Sykes, 1977: 71]

Since 1977 an annual fête to raise money to pay for the flags has been held on a Sunday near to Arbor Day. The fête 'is rapidly becoming a more substantial event than the one it is intended to finance' [Shuel, 1985: 40]. 29 May is also OAK Apple Day, so it is probable that Arbor

Day is in some way derived from celebrations to mark the restoration of the monarchy in 1660.

At one time pieces of the Bride's or Arbor Tree were given to couples on their wedding day. According to a local man interviewed for a television programme shown in November 1991:

> The parish used to present couples in the village with a cutting from this tree, as a sort of good luck thing, and they stopped doing that because all the women got pregnant within the year . . . They didn't necessarily want that to happen so quickly in a relationship so the vicar stopped doing it . . . people used to write to the parish asking for a cutting from this tree because they couldn't have children themselves, in the 1950s or 60s there was a kind of outbreak of people wanting a cutting from this magic tree, because they heard that all the village maidens were having babies very easily. [Milner MSS, 1991–2]

Presumably he was referring to the situation in 1960, when it was reported:

> There is unlikely to be a pageant this year at the annual dressing of the ancient Arbor Tree . . .
>
> This has been decided by the Parish Council, which is anxious to avoid what it feels has been 'garbled publicity' about the event in the past. The tree will continue to be decorated with flags on Arbor Day, May 29.
>
> In recent years a pageant, in which schoolchildren have taken part, has been organized as part of the celebrations. It is said that the custom goes back to the ancient fertility rites. Matters came to a head after last year's ceremony when the Rector, the Revd T.S.D. Barrett, who is also chairman of the Parish Council, received letters from women in Italy and the United States who thought the tree might be able to help them have children.
>
> Mr Barrett said yesterday: 'We want to bring it down to its proper level. A small local affair for this dressing of flags would be nice, but we do not want all this nonsense about fertility rites.' [*Birmingham Post*, 12 April 1960]

Black spleenwort (*Asplenium adiantum-nigrum*)

[Guernsey:] a strong decoction of this plant, to which is added plenty of brown sugar, or sometimes dried FIGS, is considered a sovereign remedy for COUGHS. [Marquand, 1906: 38]

Blackthorn (*Prunus spinosa*), also known as sloe. In common with HAWTHORN, blackthorn blossom is often banned from the house.

I remember that in April 1948 when I was in the maternity home at Bishop Auckland, Co. Durham, my husband brought a spray of blackthorn into the ward for my enjoyment, to the great consternation of the nursing staff. Although the word 'death' was not actually mentioned, I think the term 'bad luck' was only used as a substitute out of consideration for any patients who were within earshot. One nurse certainly mistook it for hawthorn, and could not be convinced that it was a different plant—it is possible that others also misidentified it, but my recollection is that both plants were highly suspect, and the blackthorn was thrown out. [Wolsingham, County Durham, May 1982]

[I was born in Hardwicke, near Gloucester, and my memories stem from there.] It was considered to be bad luck to pick blackthorn and on no account was it to be taken into the house. A scratch from the thorns could cause BLOOD POISONING. This was thought to be because Christ's CROWN OF THORNS was made from it. [Newcastle-under-Lyme, Staffordshire, March 1983]

I once put some blackthorn in the church as a decoration, but they were all mad with me and made me take it out. They thought it was hawthorn. [Angarrack, Cornwall, February 1989]

The flowering of the blackthorn is said to coincide with a cold spell of weather.

A period of weather, which happens commonly whilst the sloe is blossoming, is called by the country people here [Isle of Wight] the 'blackthorn winter'. [Bromfield, 1856: 141]

The weather here is very dull and really cold with a north-east wind, but the blackthorn is out, so I suppose it's the blackthorn winter. [Thorncombe, Dorset, April 1974]

As a youth my late father worked on the land, as did his father. A keen gardener [he made sure] . . . nothing of a tender nature was planted out until after the blackthorn winter. [St Osyth, Essex, February 1989]

However, the period when the blackthorn flowered was considered to be the ideal time for sowing BARLEY. In north-east England and south-east Scotland:

When the slae tree is white as a sheet
Sow your barley, wither it be dry or wet.
[Johnston, 1853: 57]

Further south, in Gloucestershire:

When the blackthorn blossom's white
Sow your barley day and night.
[Phelps, 1977: 175]

In Sandwich, Kent, each incoming mayor of the town is presented with a blackthorn stick. The Customal of Sandwich, written by Adam Champneys, the town clerk in 1301, and now in the Kent County Archives at Maidstone, states:

When the mayor of the preceding year and the jurats and commonalty are assembled in the church, and the sergeant has brought his horn, the mayor takes his stick and the horn from the sergeant, and the keys of the chest from the two jurats the keepers, and puts them near him.

Almost four centuries later:

When the mayor goes in form to the court-hall or to church, he is preceded by the common wardman and the two sergeants-at-mace, in liveries, each bearing on his shoulder a mace of silver gilt; and he carries himself in his hand a black knotty stick, as a badge of his office. [Boys, 1792: 403]

Two centuries later:

Tradition has it . . . that this blackthorn wand is carried to safeguard the holder against evil spells cast by witches and, by its very presence, repels any evil witch who may wish to cast a spell. Today (and certainly for the past hundred years) the Town Segeant is responsible for selecting an appropriate wand from the local hedgerows and for drying same and preparing it for presentation to each new mayor on the occasion of his taking office, in return for which duty he is presented by the mayor with a crown (five-shilling piece). Each mayor retains his wand after his year of office, and a new one is prepared for the new mayor. [Sandwich, Kent, March 1994]

Three such sticks are in the collections of the Sandwich Guildhall Museum.

In nineteenth-century Ireland blackthorn sticks (shillelaghs) were favoured as weapons in faction fights [Gilmore and Oalcz, 1993: 10]. Today miniature versions of such sticks are widely sold as tourists' souvenirs. [Personal observation, Dublin and Belfast, May 1994].

Sometimes little sloe bushes grew in a group in the corner of a field, and one of them might be cut down and used to clean the chimney by pulling the bush up and down. Long pieces in the hedgerow were cut and made into blackthorn walking sticks; some people do them still, as they are bought by tourists; long ago old men used them as walking sticks. [Lenamore, Co. Longford, April 1991]

The fruits of blackthorn—sloes—are gathered to make sloe gin.

The sloes are called bullums in these parts. Sloe gin is widely made here, at home, and commercially for 200 years. Most people roughly follow this method: Take a large spirit bottle. Fill it with sloes whose skins have been well pricked. Add half a pound of white sugar. Top up bottle with gin; Plymouth gin is best of course! Screw on the cap. Shake the bottle to dissolve the sugar. Shake again once or twice a week for 2–3 months. Rack off and bottle, if you can resist drinking it. Sloe gin made in autumn will be ready for Christmas. [Plymouth, Devon, May 1986]

In County Carlow dried blackthorn leaves, known as Irish tea, were used as a substitute for TOBACCO [IFC MSS, 462: 305, 1937–8].

Bladder wrack (*Fucus vesiculosus*)—gathered for manuring POTATOES in Ireland; see SEAWEED.

[On the Channel Islands] this seaweed was placed in a jar, and soaked in rum for three months. The resulting mixture was used . . . as an embrocation for children with muscular weakness or RICKETS. [Bonnard, 1993: 11]

Used [by gypsies] in hot water and sometimes in whisky as an embrocation. Very good for RHEUMATISM. [Vesey-FitzGerald, 1944: 23]

A tang-bowe made an excellent water pistol. A tang-bowe is a sizeable bladder of seaweed which was removed from the parent plant, then the end bitten or cut off. It was pressed flat to expel the air inside, then immersed in water until filled to capacity, and used very effectively as a water pistol or 'skeetie' when squeezed. [Lerwick, Shetland, March 1994]

Bleeding – stopped using GREATER MEXICAN STONECROP, KIDNEY VETCH, PUFF-BALL, and YARROW.

Blind-ball – a County Meath name for PUFF-BALL.

Blind eyes – a Yorkshire name for POPPY.

Blind flower – a County Durham name for GERMANDER SPEEDWELL.

Blindness – caused by GERMANDER SPEEDWELL and POPPY.

Blistered seaweed – an Irish name for BLADDER WRACK.

Blood – plants used to 'purify' blood include BISTORT, DOCK, and NETTLE; plants with leaves which are said to be spotted or stained with blood include EARLY PURPLE ORCHID, REDSHANK, and TUTSAN; plants said to grow where blood has been spilt include DWARF ELDER, FOX-GLOVE, LILY OF THE VALLEY, PASQUE FLOWER, POPPY, and WINTER ACONITE; see also BARREN GROUND.

Blood poisoning – caused by BLACKTHORN; treated using MALLOW.

Bluebell (*Hyacinthoides non-scripta*)
[In Hartland, Devon] it is unlucky to bring bluebells into the house. [Chope, 1933: 122]

HAWTHORN blossom and bluebells: both of these were never allowed into the living room and the rest of the house, except they were allowed in the wash house (scullery). [Stoke-on-Trent, Staffordshire, March 1983]

As a child [in Yorkshire] I used to pick masses of bluebells, but my mother would never let me bring them into the house . . . I tried to dismiss this kind of thing as superstitious nonsense, but found it most disturbing when my small son brought me a bunch of bluebells on May Day last year and insisted that we had them inside. [Stetchworth, Cambridgeshire, December 1991]

In County Offaly GERMANDER SPEEDWELL was known as bluebell. See also GRAPE HYACINTH.

Bog asphodel (*Narthecium ossifragum*)

It is believed that if [bog asphodel is] eaten by sheep it would give them stiffness in their bones. [IFCSS MSS 589: 62, Co. Clare]

I lived for seven years in the Lake District. The fell farmers particularly feared bog asphodel in respect of their sheep, as it was a plant which 'softened their bones'. I must say I came across very many dead sheep on my fell walks, tangled in thorns, etc., but I have been told that the belief that they could have been weakened first by bog asphodel is sheer superstition. [Worthing, West Sussex, September 1982]

The specific epithet *ossifragum* was given to bog asphodel by Linnaeus in his *Species Plantarum* (1753) and is derived from the Latin *os* (bone) and *frangere* (to break). The belief that bog asphodel weakens sheep's bones is rather more than superstition for it has been shown that it is poisonous to both sheep [Stabursvik, 1959] and cattle.

Fifteen cows among a herd of 50 suckler cows and calves rapidly lost body condition and became dull and anorexic after grazing pasture containing bog asphodel . . . during the summer of 1989. The affected cows had evidence of kidney damage characterised by elevated plasma urea and creatinine concentrations. Eleven cows died and diffuse renal tubular necrosis was present in three cows which were examined post mortem. Similar renal lesions were reproduced experimentally by feeding bog asphodel to a healthy calf. [Malone et al., 1992: 100]

Cf. BUTTERWORT and SUNDEW.

Bogbean (*Menyanthes trifoliata*)

Bogbean (leaves boiled) juice is good for kidneys. [IFCSS MSS 313: 213, Co. Cork]

Bogbean was very valuable for RHEUMATISM and skin diseases. [IFCSS 1121: 354, Co. Donegal].

Granda told me bogbean was boiled as a medicine for CONSTIPATION. [Omagh, Co. Tyrone, March 1986]

I worked on a mixed farm of some 90 acres, on the outskirts of the town of Morriston, in the Swansea Valley . . . In 1949 . . . I had to go down to the wet boggy land below the farmhouse to collect bogbean. It was boiled to make a herbal tea. The farmer and his sister-in-law both drank the bogbean tea, which they swore gave relief to inflamed finger joints, etc. They both suffered with either ARTHRITIS or a similar condition. [St Fagans, South Glamorgan, February 1991]

[In Llanfaircaereinion, Montgomeryshire, in 1991, bogbean] leaves were dried and a decoction drunk as a tonic. [Llandrindod Wells, Powys, September 1991]

Bogbean—gulsa girse—once used in the treatment of JAUNDICE. The Shetland name for jaundice is 'gulsa' from the Old Norn *gukusótt*, meaning yellow sickness. The plant makes a green DYE. [Lerwick, Shetland, March 1994]

Bog cotton – a name for COTTON GRASS.

Bog myrtle (*Myrica gale*), also known as gale.

The poor inhabitants [of north Wales] are not inattentive to its virtues; they term it Bwrle, or the emetic plant, and use it for this purpose. An infusion of the leaves as tea, and an external application of them to the abdomen, are considered as a certain and efficacious VERMIFUGE . . . It furnishes a yellow DYE for woollen cloth; and by its powerful odour is fatal to MOTHS and bugs. [Evans, 1800: 149]

'Gale' beer brewed from a plant growing on the moor above Ampleforth, in Yorkshire, is made and sold by Mrs Sigsworth of the 'Black Horse,' the best public house in that long village. It bears a high local celebrity for its regenerative powers. [*N & Q*, 3 ser. 4: 311, 1863]

In Isla and Jura the inhabitants garnish their dishes with it, and lay it between their linen and other garments, to give a fine scent, and drive away moths. [Lightfoot, 1777: 614]

[Islay:] bog myrtle gathered and hung up in kitchen to keep flies away. [SSS MSS SA1969/28/A12]

Sprigs of bog myrtle were frequently placed among bed-clothes by the Northumbrian housewife as a cure for fleas. [Dixon, 1890: 111]

Therefore it was given the local name of 'flea wood'.

[On the Hebrides] an infusion of the leafy tops [of bog myrtle] was given to children as a remedy for worms. [McNeill, 1910: 167]

[Barra:] bog myrtle was hung, dried, and infused among tea, and given to children suffering from gastric or skin conditions. [SSS MSS SA1970/164/A2]

Bog onion – a name for ROYAL FERN.

Boils – cured using BRAMBLE, DAISY, DOCK, ELDER, and ORANGE LILY.

Boojuns – an Inverness name for HAWTHORN fruit.

Boortree, bourtree – names for ELDER.

Box (*Buxus sempervirens*). It is sometimes considered unlucky to take box twigs indoors.

Have you heard about box? It's meant to be unlucky to bring it indoors: 'bring box into the house, take a box out.' [Thorncombe, Dorset, April 1985]

[Well into my sixties now, I was born in Mitcham, Surrey; my grandma] threw up her apron in alarm if box or HAWTHORN neared the front door and she would not have LILAC indoors or in the garden. [Paston, Cambridgeshire, November 1993]

In 1868 a reporter sent to cover the aftermath of a colliery disaster at Hindley Green, near Wigan, wrote:

I find an old Lancashire custom observed in the case of this funeral. By the bedside of the dead man, the relatives, as they took their last look at the corpse, have formed a tray or plate, upon which lay a heap of sprigs of box. Each relative has taken one of these sprigs, and will carry it to the grave, many of them droppping it upon the coffin. Ordinarily the tray contains sprigs of ROSEMARY or THYME; but these poor Hindley people not being able to obtain those more poetical plants, have, rather than give up the custom, contented themselves with stripping several trees of boxwood, hence it is that the mourners carry the bright green sprigs which I have seen. [*Daily Telegraph*, 1 *December* 1868; quoted in *N & Q*, 4 ser. 6: 496, 1870]

In some churches box is used on PALM SUNDAY. The French Catholic Church of Notre Dame de France in Soho, London, blesses box as 'palm' on this day [personal observation, 8 April 1979]. At the Polish Catholic Church of Christ the King, in Balham, south London, bunches of box, SALLOW, and DAFFODILS are sold by young people in the church's forecourt on Palm Sunday. These are bought by members of the congregation, and at the conclusion of the service the priest walks down the aisle and back sprinkling holy water on the bunches of 'palm' [personal observation, 27 March 1983].

There are occasional records of box being used as a VERMICIDE.

In the early 1930s my father, who was a ploughman, discovered that one of his horses had worms. His employer told him to treat it with the following remedy. Bake some box leaves in a tray in the oven until dry and crisp, rub to dust, then mix with the horse's feed of oats and chaff, and feed last thing at night. My father pointed out that the box was poisonous; the boss said that was the idea, the worms would feed off the box and die. Reluctantly my father carried the orders out. It is debatable whether the worms died or not, but one thing is for sure, the horse did. When my father went to the stables in the morning, there it was stretched out dead. [Pimperne, Dorset, January 1992]

Boy's-bacca – a Devon name for HOGWEED and a Sussex name for TRAVELLER'S JOY.

Bracken (*Pteridium aquilinum*), often known simply as fern.

> Our [West Sussex] custom of cutting the common brake or fern just above the root to ascertain the initial letters of a future wife's or husband's name. [Latham, 1878: 31]

> My mind went back over some 70 years to a childish game we used to play [in Scotland] called 'Holy Bracken'. Selecting a fat, juicy specimen. I used my pocket knife to sever it close to the ground and . . . there was: a perfect example of the most famous initials in the world—JC . . . It is considered very lucky to find a good example. [*Sunday Express*, 17 June 1979]

> When I was a boy they used to say that if you split a bracken stem you would see a picture of King Charles hiding in his oak tree. I often wondered what would have been seen by those who split bracken stems before King Charles had hid in his oak tree. [Paddington, London, May 1989]

> I remember being shown how if you make a horizontal cut through the stem (not root) of a fern an oak tree will appear. [Bath, Avon, January 1991]

The fact that bracken, like other ferns, lacked flowers and seeds gave rise to many odd folk beliefs. In 1660 John Ray wrote:

> Many superstitious practices are associated with the gathering of the female fern [i.e. bracken] which some affirm ought to be on the day of solstice, others on St John's Day. [Ewen and Prime, 1975: 64]

Presumably Ray was refering to the fern 'seed' which developed on this night and had the property of making those who collected it invisible.

In the seventeenth century it was believed that the burning of bracken—either in the preparation of potash, or for its control—would lead to rain. In a letter to the High Sherriff of Staffordshire on 1 August 1636, the Lord Chamberlain wrote:

> His Majesty taking notice of an opinion entertained in Staffordshire that the burning of Ferne doth draw down rain, and being desirous that the country and himself may enjoy fair weather as long as he remains in those parts, His Majesty hath commanded me to write unto you, to cause all burning of Ferne to bee forborne, until his Majesty be passed the country. Wherein not doubting but in consideration of their own interest, as well as that of his Majesty, will invite the country to a ready observance of his Majesty's command. [Rymer, 1976: 172]

The few records which exist of bracken being used in folk medicine come from gypsies: 'decoction of sliced roots taken in wine expels WORMS' [Thompson, 1925: 161] and 'commonly used as a cure for CONSTIPATION' [Vesey-FitzGerald, 1944: 23].

In the past bracken had many uses, including the preparation of potash (which was used in the manufacture of glass and soap), as a fuel, as thatch, as bedding for cattle, as compost, and, in some parts of the world, as a food [Rymer, 1976].

> In several places in the north the inhabitants mow it green, and burning it to ashes, make those ashes up into balls, with a little water, which they dry in the sun, and make use of them to wash their linen with instead of soap. [Lightfoot, 1777: 658]

> In this district, long, long ago the old people made their own soap. First of all they gathered faded ferns from the mountain side. Then they burned the ferns to ashes. Then they moistened the ashes with a drop of clean water and baked into cakes. After a while they took this up and they shaped it into rings. When this stiffened they bored a hole through it. Then they put a small portion of wire through this hole and they left it up to dry. When it was dry they took it down and used it as soap. This soap was made not later than half a century ago. This soap was used for all household purposes. [IFCSS MSS 200: 300, Co. Leitrim]

> In Glen Elg, in Inverness-shire, and other places we observed that the people thatch'd their houses with the stalks of this fern . . . sometimes they used the whole plant for the same purpose, but that does not make so durable a covering. [Lightfoot, 1777: 659]

Today bracken is considered to be a serious pest.

> Ferns grow in arable land and spread rapidly and impoverish the soil. This weed can be banished by being mown twice each year, first in June and later in September. A continual repetition of this for a few years banishes the fern. [IFCSS MSS 593: 115, Co. Clare]

Bramble or **blackberry** (*Rubus fruticosus*, agg.). Throughout much of Britain there was a widespread belief that blackberries should not be eaten after a certain date.

> [In the Lake District] the belief that when blackberries have been frosted they become Devil's Fruit and are no longer fit for human consumption is still held locally. [Rowling, 1976: 101]

> Blackberries should not be eaten after Michaelmas Day (29 September) as they have the DEVIL in them after that. This has much truth in it in that a fungus attacks the plants about then, I believe. Personally I don't eat them after that day because I imagine they are probably unpalatable! They are usually wet and nasty anyway. [Stoke Bishop, Avon, December 1982]

> According to my grandmother and mother ('rural Somerset'): never pick blackberries after Michaelmas because the devil peeps over the hedge-rows and blasts them. [Norton Fitzwarren, Somerset, July 1983]

> Blackberries should not be picked after November 1st (some people say October 1st) so that the Devil may have his share. [Ashreigney, Devon, July 1983]

It was reckoned to be unlucky to pick blackberries after Michaelmas Day (old Michaelmas Day, October 11th), as, on that day, the Devil spits on them. [East Tuddenham, Norfolk, October 1984]

A Worcestershire correspondent, in *Country Life* of 19 October 1972, stated that the disfigurement caused to bramble leaves by the activity of leaf-miner grubs was known as 'devil's marks'. In some parts of England witches were responsible for ruining late blackberries, while in Ireland the bogey Pooka (also known as *puca* and Phooka) spoiled late fruits.

According to my mother, born Buxton, Derbyshire, 1901, blackberries should not be picked after September 30th, because then 'the witch got into them.' [Bath, Avon, January 1988]

[In the Midlands] never pick blackberry after 31 October. The witches pee on them! [Sampford Brett, Somerset, October 1993]

The Pooka is out on HALLOWE'EN. It is supposed to crawl on blackberries and after that no one will eat a blackberry. [IFCSS MSS 800: 113, County Offaly]

It was said that blackberries shouldn't be eaten after Hallowe'en (31st October) as the Pooka (a kind of naughty fairy) spits, or does worse, depending on who is telling the story. [Lenamore, County Longford, April 1991]

It appears that in Sussex in the mid-nineteenth century, the picking of blackberries was prohibited only on 11 October.

[A farmer's wife living near Arundel] is in the habit of making every year a large quantity of blackberry jam, and, finding that less fruit than she required had been brought to her this autumn, she said to the charwoman, her assistant, 'I wish you would send out some of your children to gather me three or four pints more.' 'Ma'am!' exclaimed the woman, 'don't you know this is the 11th of October?' 'Yes,' was the answer. 'Bless me ma'am!' the response, 'and you ask me to let my children go out blackberrying!' Why, I thought everybody knew that the Devil went round on the 10th of October and spat on all the blackberries, and that if any person were to eat one on the eleventh they or someone belonging to them would die or fall into great trouble before the year was out. No, nothing should persuade me to let any child of mine go blackberrying on the 11th of October' [Latham, 1878: 14]

Conversely, in Herefordshire:

An old gardener at Dadnor, near Ross, used to say that blackberries were not good to eat, 'the trail of the serpent is over them,' he said. My informant added that blackberries were not eaten in the district until comparatively recent times. [Leather, 1912: 21]

In Hampshire, a spell of fine weather 'generally experienced' at the end of September and early October when blackberries were ripening was known as the 'Blackberry Summer' [Britten and Holland, 1886: 46]. Elsewhere it was believed that the period when blackberries were ripe was inauspicious. In Devon:

Cats are never very well at blackberry time. Reported by Mrs M.C.S. Cruwys, as told by a man from Cruwys Morchard.

Horses, also unwell at this time; a widespread belief, reported by Miss K.E.F. Bate of Chudleigh Knighton.

Chicken also included in this category in many parts. No doubt the observation refers to the slight physiological change many animals undergo in preparation for the winter. [Brown, 1953: 217]

Jack Hurley relates that, when attending the funeral of a young man who had committed suicide at Watchet, a woman said to him: 'Ah, you know what they say, the blackberries be about;' inferring, he assumed, that the fall of the year symbolised the waning of man's powers, his life's autumn, and that depression, sometimes leading to suicide could be expected. [Patten, 1974: 15]

Kittens born in September are known as Blackberry Kittens and are usually small and weak and difficult to rear. They are also very mischievous and naughty—more so than those born in other seasons. [Oxford, August 1987]

However, in west Dorset 'blackberry chickens' were 'always the best'.

We couldn't afford to support a hundred and eighty fowls through the winter . . . so I got old Gappy from the village to come up one day . . . we put fifty of the oldest hens in wooden crates, and he took them off . . . A few days later, an ageing hen who had stolen a nest walked out of the bushes with eleven tiny chicks tottering behind her . . . 'They'm blackberry chickens' cried old Daisy delightedly when she saw them, 'always the best, born late—but I never knowed 'em born so late as this in the year!' [Eastwood, n.d.: 80]

Brambles were sometimes planted, or placed, on graves.

Brambles were planted round graves to keep the dead from walking. [Whalton, Northumberland, October 1984]

The Old Man of Braughing [Hertfordshire] can rest in peace. For once more the villagers have completed the traditional ceremony of sweeping Fleece Lane and putting brambles on the old man's grave.

The old man 'died' at a ripe old age and the bearers were carrying his coffin down Fleece Lane to the churchyard when they stumbled on some stones and the coffin fell and broke open. The Old Man sat up and soon afterwards was married again. When he died eventually he left cash for Fleece Lane to be swept clean of stones each year and for brambles to be placed on his grave to keep the sheep off it. [*Evening Standard,* 8 October 1957]

Brambles are able to spread rapidly across poorly tended land by the production of long arching shoots—stolons—which root and form new plants where their tips touch the ground.

> If a person go under a briar that has both ends growing in the ground and give themselves up to the devil, it is supposed that person will have great luck in card-playing. [IFC MSS 782: 257, Co. Kerry, 1941]

> If you go under a briar that has taken root at both ends it is said that you will be very lucky playing cards. Others say that going under such a briar gives one exceptional strength and vigorous health. [IFCSS MSS 450: 163, Co. Kerry]

> [In Wales] children troubled with RICKETS were put to crawl or creep under blackberry brambles three times a week, and the same remedy was used for infants slow to walk. [Trevelyan, 1909: 320]

> [In Herefordshire a] woman cured her grandson of WHOOPING COUGH by holding him up to inhale the breath of a piebald horse. The boy's sister had the cough very badly, but when she got it there was no piebald horse . . . so they passed her under a bramble-bush rooted at both ends, for nine mornings. She got better . . . The bramble-bush was supposed to be quite effectual in a recent case at Weobley, but the child was passed under nine times on one morning only, and an offering of bread and butter was placed beneath the bramble arch. 'She left her cough there with the bread and butter,' said my informant. [Leather, 1912: 82]

> A widespread cure for whooping cough was to creep under a bramble or briar that has formed an arch by rooting itself at the tip . . . This cure was still in use in 1937 at Wolvesnewton in Monmouthshire. One suspects that a pun on 'whoop' and 'hoop' may have contributed to the popularity of the charm. [Simpson, 1976: 108]

> [In Staffordshire a cure for whooping cough] was to find a briar on a bramble bush that was growing into the gound at both ends, and pass the child under and over it nine times on three mornings before sunrise, while repeating:
>
> > Under the briar, and over the briar,
> > I wish to leave the chin cough here.
> >
> > [Raven, 1978: 51]

> [In Somerset] HERNIA could be cured by passing the patient under a black-berry bramble which re-rooted a distance from the original root. [K. Palmer, 1976: 114]

> [In Dorset] to creep under a bramble three mornings following against the sun, just as it rises, is said to afford a complete cure for BOILS. [Udal, 1922: 255]

> In Zennor [Cornwall] a certain cure for BLACKHEADS was to crawl nine times around a bramble bush. [Deane and Shaw, 1975: 135].

In East Anglia 'a species of bramble with a bigger berry than most others . . . is given the name of MULBERRY' [Evans, 1969: 13]. Thus it might be possible that the children's singing game, 'Here we go round the mulberry bush,' may have evolved from cures involving brambles.

In addition to eating blackberries, children ate young stalks of brambles.

On the way home from school [in the village of Crondall in the 1920s] she and her friends . . . broke off the young growing shoots of the suckers [of brambles] peeled off the skin and ate the rest. It was sweet and juicy. [Fleet, Hampshire, March 1993]

I was born near Shrewsbury in Shropshire in 1928 . . . as a child I ate each year at the appropriate season . . . the peeled stems of new bramble shoots. [Porlock, Somerset, October 1993]

Bread and butter – a Somerset name for SILVERWEED.

Bread and cheese – a name for BENT GRASS, HAWTHORN, SILVER-WEED, and WOOD SORREL.

Bread and cheese plant – a Dorset name for WOOD SORREL.

Break your mother's heart – a name for COW PARSLEY.

Broad bean (*Vicia faba*). In Huntingdonshire it was recommended that broad beans should be planted on 14 February:

> On St Valentine's Day
> Beans should be in clay.
> [N & Q, 4 ser. 1: 361, 1868]

In Wiltshire the first two days in March were preferred:

> Sow PEAS and beans on David and Chad
> Whether the weather be good or bad.
> [Wiltshire, 1975: 113]

In was widely thought that it was necessary to plant four bean seeds for every plant which eventually grew.

> One for rook,
> One for crow,
> One to rot,
> One to grow.
> [Wicken, Cambridgeshire, March 1993]

The scent of broad bean flowers was often considered to be an APHRODISIAC.

[In Oxfordshire, c.1920] there ent no lustier scent than a beanfield in bloom. [Stewart, 1987: 98]

[In Suffolk between the two World Wars it was believed that] peas and beans inflame lust . . . Ducks' eggs were supposed to have the same randy effect.

But best of all traditional aphrodisiacs was the scent of the bean flower, for this not only stimulates passion in the man, but extreme willingness in the girl. The frustrated lover was always told 'take har into a bin field boy, and if there's a thorn bush or bit of barbed wire, back har up agin it and she'll keep a' comen farrad to ye.' [Barrett, 1967: 97]

I remember when working on a farm near Thetford beans were sown on the field beside our row of houses. It was a common chant to me for weeks as they grew and flowered giving off their delicious scent that 'It wouldn't be long before the missus was calving.' It had no effect on me I must say. The chant came from the two young owners who were Suffolk bred people. [West Stow, Suffolk, January 1991]

The white fluffy inside of broad bean pods is widely used as a cure for WARTS.

To cure warts—break open a broad bean pod—eat the beans and then rub the warts with the inside of the skin. Finally bury the skin, by the time it has rotted your warts will have disappeared. This is more effective when done by moonlight. [Ryde, Isle of Wight, November 1988]

My mother used the inside of a broad bean pod—the soft fluffy side, to get rid of warts which we children frequently developed on our hands and feet. This was back in the 1940s/50s.

I had forgotten about the cure until, a few years ago, I developed a large and painful wart on my heel, which I proceeded to treat with all sorts of commercial compounds, to no avail. Then I remembered the broad bean pods. Fortunately it was the right season. I rubbed the wart two or three times a day with a pod, and within less than a week it had disappeared. [Chard, Somerset, February 1991]

However, it must be admitted that this cure is not always successful.

I was once advised to try using broad beans to cure warts myself, and did, but in vain! As the method I was told involved rubbing only once and then burying the pod, this is hardly surprising. [Worthing, West Sussex, September 1991]

More rarely recorded remedies include:

Carry a few horse beans [a variety of broad bean] in waistcoat pocket—a sure cure for THIRST. [Taylor MSS, Lincolnshire]

Remedy for WHOOPING COUGH: carry the babe through a field of beans in blossom, walking up and down the rows to let the child inhale the powerful scent. [Taylor MSS, Sproughton, Suffolk]

In west Dorset:

John W came down last night. He said he had a COUGH, and if you caught a cough in March you never lose it until the broad beans are in flower. [Thorncombe, Dorset, April 1982]

See also BEAN.

Bronchitis – cured using COLTSFOOT, MULLEIN, NETTLE, and YARROW.

Broom (*Cytisus scoparius*)

[In Sussex] a good old gentleman of my acquaintance . . . strictly forbade green brooms being used in his house during the month of May, and, as a reason for this prohibition, used to quote the adage:

> If you sweep the house with broom in May,
> You'll sweep the head of that house away.

and this superstitious association between broom and death in the month of May is extended to its blossom. A poor girl, who was lingering in the last stage of consumption, but whose countenance had always lighted up with pleasure at the sight of flowers, appeared one morning so exceedingly restless and unhappy, after a fresh nosegay of gay spring flowers had been laid on her bed, that I asked her if the scent of them was disagreeable to her. 'Oh! no,' she exclaimed, 'they are very nice indeed to smell; but yet I should be very glad if you would throw away that piece of yellow broom; for they do say that death comes with it if it is brought into the house in blossom during the month of May.' [Latham, 1878: 52]

Hilda [born in Reading, *c*.1900] remembers her mother telling her: 'Don't bring any broom home and don't bring any may [HAWTHORN].' She said:

> If you bring broom into the house in May
> It will sweep the family away.
>
> [Edinburgh, March 1984]

Broom was used as a remedy for JAUNDICE and RHEUMATISM.

[Norfolk:] An infusion of broom (flowers, stalks, and root), boiled and strained, is given in small doses as a cure for jaundice. [*Folk-lore*, 36: 257, 1925]

A herbalist, practising in Tunstall, Staffordshire, about 50 years ago, used to collect sprigs of broom from the local countryside, which he then cut up into short pieces, placed in packets and sold as a cure for rheumatism, instructing the customer to make a tea from the sprigs by pouring boiling water over them. [Steele MSS, 1978: 38]

Broom is usually considered to be the PLANTA GENISTA from which the Plantagents derived their name.

Bruises – treated using BLACK BRYONY, BUTTERCUP, COMFREY, HORSE CHESTNUT, ONION, ROYAL FERN, SOAPWORT, SOLOMON'S SEAL, WOOD, and YELLOW HORNED POPPY.

Bruseroot – a name for YELLOW HORNED POPPY.

Buck's horn plantain (*Plantago coronopus*); formerly known in East Anglia as star of the earth, or earth star.

> [*c.*1683] Star of ye Earth grows on Newmarket heath and is of extraordinary and admirable virtue in the curing of bitings of mad dogs either in Beast or Man being infus'd in wine with treacle and one or two more simples.

> Near Elden [Suffolk] they call it Earth Star and give ye whole plant bruised and rowled up in Butter or in Milk and water to Sheep bitten by mad-dog. The cure performed 2 or 3 times taking. [Newton MSS]

> [A well remembered cure for HYDROPHOBIA] was the buck's horn plantain. This formerly grew in abundance . . . in South Glamorgan . . . the root and leaves were made into a decoction, sweetened with honey, and administered to the patient. [Trevelyan, 1909: 313]

Bull-faces, bull-fronts, bull-toppings – see TUFTED HAIR GRASS.

Bullums – a Devon name for BLACKTHORN fruit.

Bulrush (*Typha latifolia*)

> Bulrush—near River Itchen, Winchester, Hants, in Irish household, about 1967/8. Child brought bulrushes into house and same day scalded herself with kettle of boiling water. An aunt who was visiting (southern Irish origin) immediately broke the bulrushes into pieces and threw them out of the house saying they were the cause of the accident. [Five Ashes, East Sussex, April 1983]

> I've been informed that bulrushes and peacocks' feathers are supposed to be bad luck if taken inside the house. [Leek, Staffordshire, August 1983]

Bulrushes – a Wiltshire name for MARSH MARIGOLD.

Bum-pipes – a Banffshire name for DANDELION.

Burdock (*Arctium* spp.)

> [In Cornwall] 'Piskies' or 'Pixies' a race of fairies or 'small people', are said to amuse themselves at night by riding colts furiously around the fields and plaiting their manes, or tangling them with the 'Billy Buttons' [i.e. burrs] of the burdock. [Davey, 1909: 261]

> As children in Essex we threw the burrs of burdock on to the backs of unsuspecting friends—if they stuck they had a sweetheart; if they fell off after a short while their affection was not reciprocated. I lived in the then countryside of the Chigwell/Hainault area, but my children played the same game 20 years later at Witham, Essex. [Yafforth, North Yorkshire, January 1990]

Cf. GOOSEGRASS.

Burdock burrs form an essential part of the costume used in one of Britain's most enigmatic traditional customs. Each year on the second Friday in August—the day before the Ferry Fair at South Queensferry, Lothian—'the Burry Man perambulates the town visiting the houses and receiving cheerful greeting and gifts of money from the householders' [Hole, 1976: 39].

In 1971 the Burry Man was the local grave-digger, John Hart, who in fact has been performing the ceremony for many years. In the evenings during the preceding week he collects the burrs from a nearby disused quarry, and with them makes up forty-two patches of square brown paper in one of the rooms of the town hall. On the Thursday evening, he 'plants' his bowler hat, covered with crochet, with seventy ROSES and one dahlia, the traditional number of flowers. The following morning at 7 a.m. in the town hall, with the help of his assistants, he puts on a pair of long combinations over his working clothes, and a traditional pair of black boots. Over his face he wears a balaclava back to front, in which holes are cut for eyes, nose and mouth. His helpers then fasten a Union Jack around him and fold on the patches of burrs. Also they make up the staves that he carries, which are wrapped with Union Jacks and then decorated with garden flowers. At 10 a.m. he prepares to leave the town hall but not before one final decoration is added— four roses on his front and four on his back. [Sykes, 1977: 144]

Thus dressed, the Burry Man calls on the provost before proceeding to walk the town boundaries, stopping at all the public houses, until the evening, when he returns to the town hall, where the collected money is divided between him and his helpers. Nothing is known about the origin of this custom, which does not appear to have been recorded before the mid-nineteenth century. According to one popular book on folk customs:

There are two theories suggesting an explanation of this strange custom. The first is that the Burry Man is a manifestation of the Spirit of Vegetation in another guise, similar to the 'Little Leaf Man' of Central Europe and 'JACK-IN-THE-GREEN' of England. The other theory is that he is a survival of the scapegoat of antiquity. Like the scapegoat, the Burry Man was probably believed to carry away all evil influences from the community and would be driven from the village. [Anon., 1967: 92]

Another theory is 'that it commemorates the landing at South Queensferry of Queen Margaret, the saintly wife of King Malcolm Canmore, from whom the town derives its name' [Hole, 1976: 40].

Gypsies utilized burdock to prevent or cure RHEUMATISM:

Infusion of leaves or flowers, or better still of crushed seeds, relieves and will cure rheumatism . . . Some gypsies carry the seeds in a little bag slung round the neck as a preventative of rheumatism. [Vesey-FitzGerald, 1944: 23]

Burnet rose (*Rosa pimpinellifolia*)
On the small islands of the Steep and Flat Holmes, Sully and Barry, in the Bristol Channel, the blossoming of the burnet rose out of its proper season was regarded as an omen of shipwreck and disaster. [Trevelyan, 1909: 99]

Burns – treated using CARRAGEEN, wild CELERY, ELM, HART'S TONGUE FERN, HOUSELEEK, IVY, LAUREL, LICHENS, PENNYWORT, PRIMROSE, and ST JOHN'S WORT.

Burra, burri-stikkels – Shetland names for HEATH RUSH.

Butcher's broom (*Ruscus aculeatus*)
Butchers are said to make use of it in some parts of England for driving away, and perchance impaling on its sharp spines, the flies that settle on their meat and chopping-blocks. The more gentle of the craft with us [on the Isle of Wight] are content to deck their mighty Christmas sirloins with the berry-bearing twigs, and it contributes at that festive season, with other evergreens, to the decoration of our churches and dwellings. [Bromfield, 1856: 509]

[In 1966 I noted down from my great-aunt, born in 1881:] a cure for DROPSY was butcher's broom boiled and put on the affected part in poultice form. [Belfast, February 1991]

Butterbur (*Petasites hybridus*)
A number of victims of the plague were buried in Veryan churchyard [Cornwall], on their graves nothing but plaguewort—butterbur—will grow. [St Ervan, Cornwall, February 1992]

As children we considered butterbur and convolvulus (or field BIND-WEED) as absolute poison and no one would have dared to pick them. When the leaves of the butterbur appeared we knew them as rat leaves and could safely play amongst them. [Blackburn, Lancashire, April 1994]

I remember as a child having a . . . cream being made from butterbur and applied to spots and SORES. [Cotherstone, Co. Durham, April 1994]

Buttercup (*Ranunculus* spp., especially *R. repens*). 'Rustics in the Midland Counties' knew the common meadow buttercup by the name of crazy:
'Throw those nasty flowers away' said a countrywoman to some children who had gathered their handfuls of buttercups, 'for the smell of them will make you crazy.' [*N & Q*, 5 ser. 5: 364, 1876]

The belief that buttercups can cause insanity appears to have been forgotten, but the name is still remembered.

A gardener, who was with two generations of my family for 40 years, called *Ranunculus repens* 'crazies'. [Minchinhampton, Gloucestershire, January 1991]

Widespread among twentieth-century children is the idea that butter-cups can be used to see if one likes butter.

I was born in Lichfield in 1943 . . . You can tell if someone likes butter by holding a buttercup under the chin and seeing if a yellow reflection appears. [Stratton, Dorset, September 1983]

Buttercups held under the chin to see if one is as good as gold or likes butter. [Langtoft, Humberside, July 1985]

My mother, who is 86, remembers from her childhood in Higham Ferrers, Northants, that . . . a buttercup held under a person's chin indicated that he or she liked butter if it reflected on their skin. [Waltham Abbey, Essex, March 1991]

Occasionally it was thought that buttercups were responsible for giving butter a rich golden colour.

If you see the buttercup weed plentiful on a pasture field it is supposed to be rich as it enriches the milk of the cows and improves the colour of the butter made from such milk. [IFCSS MSS 375: 93, Co. Cork]

Butter was a luxury which for many people, who had to make do with dripping or margarine, was unobtainable. Thus butter can symbolize wealth.

[On returning from a christening at Shottery, Warwickshire, in the 1930s] Else held a buttercup under his chin. 'E's goin to be rich!' she said. [Hewins, 1985: 69]

Buttercups appear to have been widely used in folk medicine.

[In Cornwall the creeping buttercup was] sometimes known as 'Kennel Herb' or 'Kenning Herb' from its use in making an ointment for the cure of 'Kennels' or 'Kennings', the local name for ulcers of the eye. [Davey, 1909: 10]

For all skin troubles: BRUISES, SORES, insect bites, roughness of skin, etc. $\frac{1}{2}$ lb pure vaseline into a pan with as many buttercup flowers not stems as can be pressed into it. Allow to simmer (not boil) for $\frac{3}{4}$ hr. While still hot strain through muslin into small pots. Ready for use when cold. [Thorncombe, Dorset, April 1986]

Crowfoot or buttercup if applied and held in position with a bandage would cause rheumatic joints to blister and was said to cure this complaint. [Cong, Co. Mayo, January 1992]

See also CELERY-LEAVED BUTTERCUP.

Butterflies – killed using LAUREL.

Butterwort (*Pinguicula vulgaris*). On Colonsay, in the Inner Hebrides, butterwort:

> Together with WHIN and JUNIPER, was believed to act as a charm against WITCHcraft. Cows that ate it were said to be safe from elfish arrows and supernatural ailments that were supposed to make much havoc in olden times. It was believed that a healthy, nice-looking baby was sometimes coveted and, when the opportunity occurred, even carried off by the FAIRIES and a languishing, old-fashioned creature left in its place. Some women, as the story goes, who were watching a new-born infant in a house in Machrins to make sure that the child would not be changed, heard two fairies coming to the window, and the following conversation take place. 'We will take it,' said one. 'We will not, we cannot,' said the other; 'its mother partook of the butter of the cow that ate the butterwort.' [McNeill, 1910: 105]

Elsewhere butterwort was associated with early Christian missionaries.

> I do recall one piece of lore first mentioned to me by an aunt on the Island of Soay (Skye), but later traced to the island story-teller, one John MacRae, whose nephew, a retired windjammer sailor and fisherman passed on to me many of the local tales John had told him (*circa*) 1840s. . . . this item referred to a little heath flower that grew among the peat heather of Soay—I'm ashamed to admit I do not know its name. The saying went that where the flower grew was where St Moalrudha touched the ground with his staff. I suppose that was meant to signify the extent of St Moalrudha's travels, which were, indeed, very wide.
>
> Professor Charlesworth, the well-known Northern Ireland geologist, once told me that when he was young in Antrim the flower was known as ST PATRICK's spit, or St Patrick's staff, attached to which was the story that while crossing a wide bog St Patrick lost his STAFF and unable to find a tree came upon one of these plants whose stem had grown so long and strong that he was able to use it as a staff. The flower on the head (which is shaped with a curve like a staff) never faded and afterwards wherever the staff touched the ground the flower sprang up. The flower is very small on a single straight stem; the most noticeable feature being the leaves in a star shape and very flat, touching the ground. [Salisbury, Wiltshire, November 1985]

In common with other plants, such as BOG ASPHODEL and SUNDEW, which grow in the same habitat, butterwort was believed to cause ill health in sheep and cattle. This belief gave rise to such names as rot-grass and sheep-rot in northern Britain [Grigson, 1987: 312].

Butterwort was widely used as a substitute for RENNET in cheesemaking. In Lanarkshire it was known as earning grass:

> [Earning is a North Country word for cheese rennet] and to earn means to curdle milk. The plant is so called because it has this property. [Britten and Holland, 1886: 163]

C

Cabbage (*Brassica oleracea* var. *capitata*). Throughout Ireland cabbages have been used for love DIVINATION at HALLOWE'EN.

On Hallow Eve Night the boys and girls go to somebody's cabbage-garden, and each one pulls up the first head of cabbage he meets. By this he can tell the future. If there is a bit of clay on it he will get a rich wife. If it is a long straight stalk she will be tall. If it is a short stalk she will be small. If it is crooked then so will she be. The owners of cabbage-gardens have often to sit up all that night, watching the garden or all the cabbages would be destroyed. [IFCSS MSS 812: 155, Co. Offaly]

[In County Down] the girls were blindfolded and went out in pairs, hand in hand, to the garden or field and told to pull the first cabbage they found. Its size and shape—whether it was big or small, straight or crooked—would indicate the shape and stature of their future spouse. If much earth adhered to the root they would have plenty of money; if there was only a little they would be poor. The taste of the 'custoc', i.e. the heart, would tell them his temper and disposition, according to whether it was sweet or bitter. Finally the 'runts' or stems were hung above the door; each was given a number and the name of a boyfriend, for an example Barney might be the name given to the third runt. If Barney was the third person to enter the house on the night, this was considered to be a good omen. [Pollock, 1960: 62]

In England the verse:

> My love is like a cabbage
> Often cut in two,
> The leaves I give to others
> The heart I give to you

is often written on Valentine cards or in schoolgirls' autograph books. On the Shetland Islands:

Cabbage plants, complete with roots, were thrown through open doors and down chimneys at Hallowe'en. This was usually accepted in good spirits, although some house-proud women may have regarded it in a different light. [Lerwick, Shetland, March 1994]

Various traditional practices were used to ensure that cabbage plants thrived.

One always planted cabbages on the new MOON or the next day and we would plant SAGE or THYME in the rows to keep away pests. [Barnstaple, Devon, May 1991]

A slice of RHUBARB placed in the bottom of a 'dibbed' hole will prevent club root in brassicas. (It does!) [Horsted Keynes, West Sussex, February 1991]

Cabbage was also used in folk medicine.

Fever: heat cabbage leaves and place them on the soles of the feet. [IFCSS MSS 880: 331, Co. Wexford]

[Gypsies] bind a cabbage leaf round the leg for swellings . . . an elderly woman I know had a swollen knee and tied a cabbage leaf round it and she said afterwards that it helped. That was only last year. [UCL EFS MSS M3, Hauxton, Cambridge, October 1963]

[In the Cavan-Leitrim area] varicose ULCERS, and ulcers in general, sometimes treated with a plaster of fresh cow dung. Another, more usual method was to treat the ulcer with fresh, green cabbage leaves. [Logan, 1965: 52]

Cabbage = kell—a kell bled (cabbage leaf) which is heated and placed on a septic wound is very effective in drawing out pus or a foreign body, e.g. splinter. [Lerwick, Shetland, March 1994]

As a boy I wandered the countryside with a poacher just after World War II. My old friend always drank cabbage water after a HANGOVER, as a cure that is. If he had a bad HEADACHE, say from colds or flu, he would pick cabbage leaves and chew them, as quite a few locals did also. [Barnstaple, Devon, May 1991]

A riddle frequently contributed to the Irish Folklore Commission's 1937–8 Schools' Folklore Scheme ran:

Patch upon patch without any stitches; riddle me that and I'll buy you a pair of breeches.
A cabbage.
[IFCSS 500: 90, Co. Limerick]

In the nineteenth century wild (or sea) cabbage was occasionally gathered for food.

Though very bitter in their uncooked state, they [the leaves] may, by repeated washings, be rendered fit for food, and they are often boiled and eaten at sea-coast towns. At Dover they are gathered by boys from the cliffs, and carried about for sale. [Pratt, 1857, 1: 21]

During the nineteenth century and the early part of the twentieth a giant cabbage, the stems of which were reputed to reach up to 20 feet in length, was widely cultivated on Jersey. The leaves of these plants were pulled off and fed to cows. When the growing points were about to run to flower they were cut off and either used for human consumption or fed to cattle, leaving the woody stalks, which were unsuitable for food, and were used mainly for making walking sticks.

A leading manufacturer of these sticks was Henry Charles Gee, who
sold them at his shop in St Helier from the 1870s until 1928. During
the late Victorian period Mr Gee sold some five or six hundred sticks
a year, but by the late 1930s, when his daughter was continuing the
business, only about 150 were sold each year. In the sixth (*c*.1907) edition of Ward Lock's guide to the Channel Islands it was reported that
'the craving by visitors for these [cabbage] sticks is humorously known
as the Jersey fever. Nearly all holiday-makers sucumb.' Until at least as
late as 1969 it was still possible to see small clumps of the giant cabbage
growing on Jersey [Parker and Stevens Cox, 1974].

Cactus

Between 1964 and 1966 three instances have been recorded, two in Cambridge and one in Grantchester, of the belief that it is unlucky to bring any
species of cactus into the house. One of the informants said that not only
would she never have one of these plants, but that she would never give
one to anybody else, 'they're so unlucky.' [Porter, 1969: 43]

[In Cornwall] as the spikes of a cactus grew so did one's troubles. [Deane
and Shaw, 1975: 135]

Cacti are considered unlucky inside the house in Hungary. An aunt emigrated to England from Hungary and started a collection of cacti. Her sister
came to visit her and was horrified to see the cacti. My aunt assured her
that it was only a Hungarian superstition that cacti were unlucky. A few
weeks after her visit to England her sister died. My aunt threw out all her
plants when she heard the bad news, and she never allows one in the
house now. [Golders Green, London, May 1882]

Being adapted to climatic conditions where water is rarely available,
cultivated cacti often suffer from overwatering.

You should stop watering cacti in September, when there is an R in the
month. Don't water them when there are Rs in the month; I did this to
mine and they flowered really well this year. It's a useful general rule of
thumb. [Barons Court, London, August 1985]

On Christmas morning they always water the cactus as a sign of good luck.
[SLF MSS, Sheffield, January 1970]

Calvary clover (*Medicago intertexta*)

The restoration of St Bartholomew the Great Church, West Smithfield,
London, has been promoted to the extent of £120 by the sale during Lent
for the last few years of the pods of a kind of trefoil called Calvary clover
at the price of sixpence each pod. It is in many ways an interesting plant;
the leaves have a blotch at the base of each leaflet, bearing quite a striking resemblance to a spot of fresh blood, which gradually dies away as
the plant grows. The pod is spirally wound into a ball, bearing numerous

interlacing thorns on its margin, and, when unwound, which is easily done, is remarkably like a crown of plaited thorns. It seems to be the custom to sow the seeds on GOOD FRIDAY. [N & Q, 8 ser. 12: 26, 1897]

A certain garden clover has red spots on its leaves, which are said to have been caused by drops of Christ's blood when He hung on the cross on Mount Calvary. The dried seed-pod when bent into circular form resembles a miniature crown of thorns, and, of course, the trifoliated leaf is emblematic of the Trinity. [Chope, 1931: 124]

Campion (*Silene* spp.)

Red and white campions were always known to me as pudding bags, after their shape, similar to the boiled puddings in cloths eaten by the country families. The suet dumplings or puddings were the daily diet for farm labourers; also the pudding known as the Bedfordshire clanger, which consisted of a suet dough roll covering meat one end and jam the other, divided by a section of the dough. [Felmersham, Bedfordshire, March 1993]

See also RED CAMPION and SEA CAMPION.

Cancer – treated using VIOLET and YEW.

Cannabis – see HEMP.

Caper spurge (*Euphorbia lathyris*)

Some people swear by it as a mole deterrent but it has never been effective in our garden . . . It was *herbe d'chorchi* to a Jerseyman because a plant in the garden provided protection against WITCHES. [Le Sueur, 1984: 91]

Carl doddies – a Scottish name for RIBWORT PLANTAIN; also, as curly doddie, 'a general name for all Shetland orchises' [Tait, 1947: 74].

Carling Sunday – a north-country name for PASSION SUNDAY, on which PEAS are traditionally eaten.

Carnation (*Dianthus caryophyllus*) – associated with MOTHER'S DAY (see MOTHERING SUNDAY) in the USA.

Carrageen (*Chondrus crispus*), also known as Irish moss.

The housewives of the Hebrides still use carrageen for making a delicious milk jelly which has a pleasant tang of the sea in its flavour. [Newton, 1951: 106]

Carrageen moss is used for BURNS. [IFCSS 213: 93, Co. Leitrim]

The statement that carrageen gets its name from Carragheen, a small coastal town near Waterford in Ireland, has frequently been repeated, but it has been shown to be false. No such town exists [Mitchell and Guiry, 1983].

Carrot (*Daucus carota*). In the Hebrides:

On this day [MICHAELMAS] wild carrots are presented by the girls in a house to male visitors. An old woman named Campbell describes how 'All week before St Michael's Day we gathered wild carrots, and each hid our store on the machair. On St Michael's Day we took them up, and we girls had a great day cooking and eating them and dancing and singing. The boys had their own fun. They used to try and find and steal our carrots. We had always to give some to the first person we met after pulling them up, and also to the first person we met coming into the house when we got home.' [Goodrich-Freer, 1902: 45]

According to a Jamaican woman settled in Bristol:

BEETROOT and carrot juice is very good to drink. It prevents DIARRHOEA. [Francis, 1988: 95]

Catarrh – cured using EYEBRIGHT and ST JOHN'S WORT.

Cedar (*Cedrus libani*)

One of the oldest, if not the oldest Cedars of Lebanon in England is that standing in Bretby Park, Derbyshire . . . planted in February, 1676 . . . This tall Cedar has lost many limbs, and is now scantily provided. The stump of every lost limb has been carefully sealed with lead, and each remaining branch is supported by chains.

There is a legend that a limb of this tree falls at the death of a member of the family . . . The family history is a mournful one. The last Earl died a young man and childless on returning home after a visit. His sister was the wife of Lord Carnarvon, and her death will be remembered. The fall of these recent limbs has left the old tree a wreck—a lofty and noble trunk, almost naked, except a few remaining branches on the top, supported by artificial means. [Evershed, 1877: 40]

A cedar at Bretby, Derbyshire, has its main branches chained and braced to prevent the collapse of any part of the tree. At one time this tree belonged to the Caernarvon [sic] family, and prophesied the death of a member of that family should a major branch fall. The last fall of a limb is said to have taken place on the death of Lord Caernarvon after his discovery of the tomb of Tutankhamun. [Wilks, 1972: 133]

See PROPHETIC TREES.

Celandine (*Ranunculus ficaria*), also known as pilewort.

The time for sowing in this district was when the flower *Llygad Elrill* or celandine appeared, which was the beginning of April. [Llanuwchyllln, Gwynedd, April 1991]

In his *Names of Herbes* (1548), William Turner referred to the celandine as fygwurt—'fig' being a former name for PILES. More recently celandine has been known as pilewort, for its root tubers resemble piles, and therefore according to the DOCTRINE OF SIGNATURES, celandine was used to treat piles.

[Guernsey:] a remedy for piles is made by boiling fresh lard and straining it through the flowers of this plant [Marquand, 1906: 45]

[On Colonsay, celandine] roots are still used as a cure for piles, CORNS, etc. [McNeill, 1910: 96]

Pilewort . . . the common country remedy for piles, hence the popular name. The usual gypsy remedy for the same complaint. (I have been assured by more than one gypsy that, by merely carrying a sprig or two in one's pocket, a complete cure may be effected.) Besides being used as an ointment, an infusion taken four times a day will effect a cure. [Vesey-FitzGerald, 1944: 27]

Skin cleanser: drop a handful of celandine leaves into a pint of boiling water, strain and allow to cool. Apply the liquid to the face with lint, to tighten the skin, close pores, and remove wrinkles. [Driffield, Humberside, July 1985]

Celery (*Apium graveolens*)

If you have RHEUMATISM boil celery seed and drink it. [IFCSS MSS 919: 10, Co. Wicklow]

I recently met an old friend of my father, who, on hearing from me that father was having some urinary trouble, told me to tell him to eat plenty of boiled celery, saying 'finest thing there is for watter [sic] trouble.' [SLF MSS, West Butterwick, Humberside, March 1970]

An ointment good for all sores: the green leaves of celery cooked in home dried lard (to make sure there is no salt in it), strained, and put into pots for general use. [Taylor MSS, Norwich, Norfolk]

Wild celery has also been found effective in the healing of BURNS. An Exeter gentleman witnessed the following cure just after the end of the First World War: his sister, who was about 15 at the time, was very badly burnt at the back of her head and shoulders, and the local doctor felt powerless to help. An old herbalist living nearby heard about the accident and claimed to be able to heal the child: he gathered wild celery and boiled it in water, and then used the liquor to bathe the burns. He subsequently applied the wild celery as a plaster. The treatment proved to be effective, and is said to be equally useful for healing infected breasts. [Lafonte, 1984: 83]

Celery-leaved buttercup (*Ranunculus sceleratus*)

The whole plant has a most acrimonious quality; if bruised and laid upon any part of the body it will in a few hours raise a blister. Strolling beggars have been known sometimes purposely to make sores with it, in order the more readily to move compassion. [Lightfoot, 1777: 291]

The whole plant is very corrosive, and beggars use it to ulcerate their feet, which they expose in that state to excite compassion. [McNeill, 1910: 95]

Centaury (*Centaurium* spp.)

[Known as gentian in Scotland,] on the shores of the Moray Firth, where an infusion is drunk as a tonic. [Britten and Holland, 1886: 202]

As a boy on holiday in Towyn, Merioneth [in *c.*1915] I watched an old lady gathering a large bunch of centaury on the sand dunes, and was informed that it was to make 'tonic'. [Charlbury, Oxfordshire, February 1991]

Common centaury (*Centaurium erythraea*) . . . was used as a 'nerve calmer' by drinking an infusion of leaves and flowers. [St Mary's, Isles of Scilly, September 1992]

Chamomile (*Chamaemelum nobile*)

Chamomile root is a cure for TOOTHACHE. It should be put down on the aching tooth. [IFCSS MSS 1128: 26, Co. Cork]

Dried chamomile flowers, stewed, added to the last rinse for blondes, made a nice shine; also drunk for NEURALGIA. [Quinton, West Midlands, 19 April 1993]

Change-of-the-weather – a Somerset name for SCARLET PIMPERNEL.

Charcoal – made from ALDER BUCKTHORN.

Charles II, King – hid in an OAK tree at Boscobel, Shropshire.

Charlock (*Sinapis arvensis*), known in Irish as *praiseach* or prushia. Although charlock is now considered to be a harmful weed, it was formerly used as a food, during times when other foods were scarce. In 1757 the Revd Philip Skelton

went out into the country [of County Donegal] to discover the real state of his poor . . . he was then a witness to many scenes of sorrow . . . in one cabin he found the people eating boiled prushia by itself for their breakfast, and tasted this sorry food which seemed nauseous to him. Next morning he gave orders to have prushia gathered and boiled for his own breakfast, that he might live on the same sort of food with the poor. He ate this for one or two days; but at last his stomach turning against it, he set off immediately for Ballyshannon to buy oatmeal for them. [Burdy, 1792: 122]

Early in the nineteenth century, in County Kilkenny, it was observed that in the spring poor people were often reduced to eating 'charlock, *Sinapis arvensis* and a few other weeds' [Tighe, 1802: 483]. In the twentieth century it was remembered that during famine times:

they would walk for miles gathering stuff called presha [praiseach]. This would bloom in the summer with a yellow blossom and the people would gather burdens and boil it. [IFCSS MSS 1112: 19, Co. Donegal]

These records imply that the foliage of charlock was used for food in Ireland. In Scotland the seeds were eaten in times of scarcity. Thus in 1884 it was recorded:

> for about three month of the year, when grain supplies had run out . . . any bread eaten was made from the seed of wild mustard or charlock, and was called 'reuthie' bread—'reuth' being the local Orkney name for such seeds. [Drury, 1984: 49]

Perhaps it is noteworthy that recent writers on wild plants which can be used as food make little mention of charlock. Richard Mabey in his *Food for Free* (1972) does not give an entry for charlock, but mentions under chickweed that it can be added 'for bulk' to early spring salads.

Cheese rennet – a widespread name for LADY'S BEDSTRAW.

Cheeses – a widespread name for the fruit of MALLOW.

Chequers – a Kent and Sussex name for the fruit of WILD SERVICE TREE.

Cherry (*Prunus* spp.).

> My mother always found that an infusion of cherry stalks was the perfect cure for inflammation of the bladder. Between the wars I remember being sent out to purchase some from a London chemist. [Letter from London, W1, in *Country Life*, 30 December 1971]

The cherry features in one of England's traditional carols. This tells how Joseph, traditionally much older than his bride, finds her to be pregnant. While walking through an orchard of cherries, Mary asks Joseph to pluck her a cherry, but Joseph, 'with words most reviled' replied 'Let he pluck thee a cherry that brought thee with child.' Christ, speaking from his mother's womb, asks the cherry trees to lower their branches so that his mother can gather their fruit. The trees obey him, and Joseph repents [Keyte and Parrott, 1992: 440].

The Japanese cherry (*Prunus serrulata*)—the common showy flowering cherry of suburban gardens—has become a symbol for the remembrance of the many thousands who died a result of the dropping of atomic bombs on Hiroshima and Nagasaki in 1945. The anniversaries of these bombings (6 and 9 August) are occasionally marked by the planting of cherry trees or gathering around such trees planted in previous years [personal observation, Streatham, London, 5 August 1984].

See also BIRD CHERRY and WILD CHERRY; for counting rhymes using cherry stones see FRUIT STONES.

Cherry laurel – see LAUREL.

Chestnut (*Castanea sativa*)

The powdered nuts are good for PILES. Some gypsies wear the nuts in a little bag round their necks as preventative of piles. The bag must never be made of silk. [Vesey-FitzGerald, 1944: 23]

[In Sussex during the war] one lady asked them (them being my cousin and her charges, the schoolchildren) to collect sweet chestnut leaves, as she made a COUGH mixture from them. [Melksham, Wiltshire, April 1990]

See also HORSE CHESTNUT.

Chickweed (*Stellaria media*)

Arvi (common chickweed) is said to grow wherever the soil is good quality. [Lerwick, Shetland, March 1994]

Traditional remedies which use chickweed include:

[In north-east England] this weed is a popular remedy, applied fresh, to allay the swelling caused by the STING of a bee. [Johnston, 1853: 43]

[In the Orkneys] The leaves when bruised are applied as poultices in cases of inflammation. [Spence, 1914: 100]

A painful arm or leg: chickenweed boiled and the juice rubbed on the place in the arm or leg where the pain is. [IFCSS MSS 790: 161, Co. Dublin]

Chickweed can be made into an ointment for CHILBLAINS, RASHES, RHEU-MATISM and stiff joints. Wash ½ lb chickweed and simmer with $\frac{1}{2}$ lb lard for two hours, strain through muslin and put in jars. [Boat-of-Garten, Inverness-shire, November 1991]

Recent writers on wild plants which can be used as food recommend chickweed.

Chickweed must, after BINDWEED, be the gardener's most hated weed. Yet it is one of the most deliciously tender of all wild vegetables. [Mabey, 1972: 92]

Chicory (*Cichorium intybus*). Gypsies used a decoction of chicory root as a cure for JAUNDICE [Vesey-FitzGerald, 1944: 23].

Chilblains – cured using APPLE, BEETROOT, BITTERSWEET, BLACK BRYONY, CHICKWEED, HOLLY, ONION, and POTATO.

Childbirth – eased using SEA BEANS.

Children's pastimes. In addition to the traditional games which are played with plants, such as making DAISY chains or playing with flowerheads of RIBWORT PLANTAIN, children also use plant materials in more spontaneous pastimes.

I think most of this must have been done at primary school age . . .
Today's children with sophisticated toys and computer games would be
baffled by these activities, and no doubt today's parents would think some
of them fairly destructive, but we seemed to spend a lot of time out of
doors while such toys as we had remained indoors. On the edge of a small
town [Winchester] even quite modest houses had quite large gardens and
we were free to roam the streets and found such pastimes as we could.
Calystegia [LARGE BINDWEED]: you stretched your mouth round the bell
of the flower and blew and it collapsed. Don't know why this was done,
but quite satisfying.
Narrow-leaved [i.e. RIBWORT] PLANTAINS were used as missiles. The stem
was looped over the base of the flowerhead and the stem just behind the
loop pulled sharply so the head would fly off. Important to choose stems
in just the right condition.
Hardheads (KNAPWEED buds) also used as missiles, but just thrown.
HAZEL used for bows and arrows.
Eschscholzia [Californian poppy] 'hats' taken off—the calyx comes off up-
wards in one piece.
Sunflower [*Helianthus annuus*] stems used for pea-shooters. [Lee, London,
April 1993]

Flowers and plants have always played a part in children's games and pastimes, and many flowerheads have been demolished to become necessary
items in a little girl's pretend house. DAISY petals could be rice or coconut,
and SORREL seeds packed tightly in a glass jar with a little water added
looked very much like jam, while the heads of PINEAPPLE WEED made
dainty cup-cakes for a doll's tea-party.
   Probably the plant which contributed most to the pretend house was
the DOCK. The seeds, varying in plumpness, could become several things,
e.g. sugar, pulses, grains, or even rough salt, but the stalks were almost
always rhubarb. Dock leaves were very versatile too, but perhaps topped
the list as kippers, followed fast by other fillets of fish and bacon rashers.
Other more artful creations involved flowers, like daisy chains and floral
necklaces, or collections of pressed flowers, some of which were framed
as pictures.
   Flowers are used mainly in girls' games, but boys can put them to use as
well, in a more war-like fashion. Any hard centre can be ammunition for
a catapult. [Lerwick, Shetland, March 1994]

Chimney-sweeps, chimneysweepers– names for WOOD RUSH.

Chinese New Year celebrations – associated plants include PEACH
and TANGERINE.

Chives (*Allium schoenoprasum*)
   Years ago when my son—then about four years of age—was having a
violent fit of WHOOPING COUGH an old lady stopped and asked if I had any

chives in my garden. She told me to make some bread and butter sandwiches, filling them with chopped chives, and make him eat some after
each fit of coughing, and he would be well in four days.

I did as bid and my son was well as she said. [Uphill, Avon, January 1993]

Christmas – associated plants include HOLLY, IVY, and MISTLETOE.

Christmas Eve – HOLY THORN supposedly blossoms; plants used for
love DIVINATION on this day include HEMP.

Christmas greenery. Evergreens, such as HOLLY, IVY, and MISTLE-
TOE, have long played a significant role in Christmas celebrations. According to some writers, the use of such greenery at this time of year
is a survival of extreme antiquity.

> Long before the Christian era began, evergreens, which flourish when
> everything else in nature is withered and dead, were regarded as symbols
> of undying life, and used in magical rites to ensure the return of vegeta-
> tion. The sacred buildings of Europe and Western Asia were decked with
> them for the Winter Solstice rituals. In ancient Rome, houses were
> adorned with laurels and BAY at the Kalends of January, and green gar-
> lands were worn and given as presents during the week-long celebrations
> of Saturnalia in December. [Hole, 1976: 50]

However, it is equally, if not more likely that, rather than being the
survival of ancient practice, the bringing of evergreens indoors at
Christmas is something which has developed simply because evergreens were readily available to bring a little extra colour to dwelling-
houses at the festive time. In theory, if not in practice, Christmas
greenery should not be brought indoors before Christmas Eve, and
most of it should be taken down before Twelfth Night (6 January) or,
more rarely, New Year's Day.

> A: 'CHRISTMAS TREES should not be brought indoors before Christmas
> Eve.'
> B: 'Holly must be taken down before Twelfth Night.'
> A: 'Yes, but it's lucky to leave a bit up.'
> [Cambridge, November 1985]

> It was most important that the greenery of Christmas decorations was out
> of the house by Twelfth Night and ivy and the Christmas tree was not
> burnt. [St Davids, Dyfed, October 1991]

> The holly and ivy that decorates the houses at Christmas is taken down
> after Twelfth Day and stored up until Pancake Night and burned under
> the pancakes when they are baking. [IFCSS MSS 775: 122, Co. Kildare]

> [Bradford, 1961; Castleford, 1962:] Evergreens must be removed before
> New Year's Day, except for a piece of holly, which must be burned under
> the pancakes on SHROVE TUESDAY. [McKelvie MSS, 1963: 176]

Christmas tree. Although the Christmas tree is an important part of Christmas festivities in many homes, shopping centres, and civic buildings, its history in the British Isles is not lengthy. The idea of the Christmas tree is attributed to Martin Luther (1483–1546):

> After wandering one Christmas Eve under the clear winter sky lit by a thousand stars, he set up for his children a tree with countless candles, an image of the starry heaven whence Christ came down. [Miles, 1912: 265]

However, the first known record of a Christmas tree such as we would recognize today is dated 1605, when it was recorded:

> At Christmas they set up fir trees in the parlours at Strasburg and hang thereon roses cut out of many-coloured paper, apples, wafers, gold-foil, sweets, etc. [Miles, 1912: 265]

Christmas trees do not appear to have reached the British Isles until the first half of the nineteenth century, when they arrived via three routes: Hessian soldiers serving in the army of King George III, German members of the Court, and German merchants who had settled in various English cities [Hole, 1976: 53]. In 1800 Queen Charlotte celebrated

> Christmas evening with a German fashion. A fir tree, about as high again as any of us, lighted all over with small tapers, several little wax dolls among the branches in different places, and strings of almonds and raisins alternately tied from one to the other, with skipping ropes for the boys, and each bigger girl had muslin for a frock, a muslin handkerchief, and a pretty necklace and earrings besides. As soon as all the things were delivered out by the Queen and Princesses, the candles on the tree were put out, and the children set to work to help themselves, which they did very heartily. [Combermere and Knollys, 1866: 419]

However, the Christmas tree did not become widely known until 1841, when Queen Victoria and Prince Albert had a tree at Windsor Castle, which was widely reported and illustrated in the press. Thereafter Christmas trees became fashionable, although until as late as 1912 [Miles: 264] they were described as being only 'a luxury for the well-to-do'.

Christmas trees were set up in the private houses of the wealthy and cottagers and their children might be invited in to marvel at the splendidly decorated tree. Later, particularly after the availability of electric lights, trees were also set up outside, so that today even the most hard-pressed public authority places a lighted tree in its major shopping thoroughfares. The first of these public trees of which there is any record was set up in Pasadena, California, in 1909 [Hole, 1976: 54]. In Britain the best-known of these trees is the one set up in Trafalgar Square, London, each year. Since 1947 this tree has been donated by the citizens of Oslo to the citizens of London, in appreciation of Britain's help to Norway during the Second World War.

Although HOLLY was (or, perhaps, still is) occasionally used as a Christmas tree, it is far more usual for various species of conifer to be used, with the Norway spruce being most popular. In *The Times* of 12 December 1992 it was reported that:

> More than five million are expected to be sold in Britain over the Christmas season, with prices ranging from about £2 a foot for a Norway Spruce to about £4 a foot for a Nordmann fir.

In addition to these a large number of artificial trees are bought each year. In the early 1990s concern about the environment led to a vogue for recycling Christmas trees. Recycling schemes were arranged either by environmental groups, such as Friends of the Earth [personal observation, Glastonbury, Somerset, January 1992], or local authorities.

> Recycle your Christmas tree.
> The Royal Borough of Kensington and Chelsea in conjunction with their parks contractor, Serco Ltd, are offering residents the chance of recycling their Christmas trees.
> Members of the public can take their Christmas trees to the Serco nursery in Holland Park between the 4th and 15th of January 1993 . . . the trees will be shredded and chipped and the material used for mulching shrub beds within the park. [Notice in the borough public libraries, January 1993]

Alternatively, in 1992 people in Hampstead were given the opportunity to send their trees back for replanting.

> The environmentally friendly Christmas tree business is the brainwave of two brothers, François and Rufus Hartwell.
> Trees supplied by a friend and by the Forestry Commission are delivered before Christmas to house-holders in London. On Twelfth Night the customers dump them on their doorsteps and the Hartwell brothers pick them up and take them back to Wales to be replanted . . .
> Customers are given a leaflet explaining how to look after the tree.

During the first year of the scheme thirty householders bought Christmas trees, costing between £30 and £75—about 50 per cent more than the price of a conventional throw-away tree—encouraging the brothers to expand their business to cover the whole of London in 1994 [*The Times*, 14 December 1993].

Chrysanthemum (*Dendranthema* cv.). In some parts of Europe the chrysanthemum is a favourite funeral flower and is associated with ALL SOULS' DAY. Consequently it is sometimes considered to be an unlucky flower to have indoors.

Cineraria

My hairdresser is an Italian, but she's married an Englishman and lived here for many years, so she's picked up the English ways. But her mother from Italy, who was staying here, was very upset when the hairdresser was given some chrysanthemums. 'They all wish you dead, they wish you dead' she said. In Italy chrysanthemums are used at funerals and are therefore associated with the dead, so if they are given to anyone it's sort of saying: 'I wish you were dead.' The hairdresser said it was only an Italian superstition, and she didn't mind. She's been over here so long, and was so young when she married and came here that she doesn't mind. [Streatham, London, April 1983]

Cineraria (*Pericallis hybrida*)

Cineraria—sometimes called 'da devil's flooer' and unlucky to keep in the house. [Lerwick, Shetland, March 1994]

Clan badges. Although it has often been claimed that the wearing of various plants as symbols of different Scottish clans is of ancient origin, it appears that such practices date mainly from 1822, when a great many rather spurious Scottish ceremonies were invented or revived in celebration of King George IV's visit to Edinburgh.

In the early days of our own history we find the rudest symbols were sufficient to answer the purpose of distinguishing one man, or band of men, from another. The Scottish clans were generally particularised by the pattern or colours of their tartan plaid.

But this was found to be insufficient without the aid of floral emblems, and they therefore adopted the plan of ornamenting their bonnets or helmets with a sprig or branch of a plant as a symbolical badge of their various bodies. This ancient custom was again revived when his majesty visited his northern capital in the year 1822. His loyal Scottish subjects on that joyful event, paid their respects to their sovereign, at the palace of Holyrood House, each wearing the heraldic emblem of his clan. [Phillips, 1825: 13]

Although there is widespread agreement about which plant 'belonged' to most clans, in other cases there is some confusion. The following list is an edited version of that given in Henry Phillips' *Floral Emblems* (1825):

Buchanan	BIRCH	Forbes	BROOM
Cameron	OAK	Frazer	YEW
Campbell	BOG MYRTLE	Gordon	IVY
Chisholm	ALDER	Graham	SPURGE LAUREL
Colquhoun	HAZEL	Grant	CRANBERRY
Cumming	SALLOW	Gunn	roseroot
Drummond	HOLLY	Lamont	CRAB APPLE
Farquharson	FOXGLOVE	MacAllister	HEATHER
Ferguson	POPLAR	MacDonald	HAREBELL

MacDonnell	LING	MacRae	fir clubmoss
MacFarlane	cloudberry	Menzies	ASH
MacGregor	SCOTS PINE	Munroe	eagle feathers
MacIntosh	BOX	Murray	JUNIPER
MacKay	club rush	Ogilvie	HAWTHORN
Mackenzie	deergrass	Oliphant	SYCAMORE
MacKinnon	ST JOHN'S WORT	Robertson	BRACKEN
MacLachlan	ROWAN	Rose	DOG ROSE
MacLean	CROWBERRY	Ross	bearberry
MacLeod	cowberry	Sinclair	CLOVER
MacNab	'ROSE bush berries'	Stewart	THISTLE
MacNeill	BLADDER WRACK	Sutherland	smaller cat's-tail grass
MacPherson	variegated BOX		
MacQuarrie	BLACKTHORN		

Clary (*Salvia verbenaca*)

Clary, or wild sage, is locally [in the Cotswolds] supposed to be a legacy of the ROMAN occupation of Britain. The soldiers dropped the seed as they marched across the country. In proof of this, country people will point to the fact that it frequently flourishes along the old Roman roads. [Briggs, 1974: 119]

Cleavers – see GOOSEGRASS.

Clover (*Trifolium* spp.). Clovers which produce leaves with four instead of the usual three leaflets have long been considered to be 'lucky'.

He that fyndeth the trayfle [trefoil] with foure leues, and kepe it in reuerence knowe for also true as the gospell yt he shall be ryche all his life. [*Gospelles of Dystaues*, part 2: xv, 1507]

If a man walking in the fields, find any four-leaued grasse, he shall in a small while after finde some good thing. [Melton, 1620: 46]

[In Wales] it was considered lucky, and a token of marriage to find the four-leaved variety. Worn upon the person, or placed under the pillow, it induced cheerfulness of mind and made people light hearted. It is given and accepted as an emblem of good luck. [Trevelyan, 1909: 95]

In my childhood, Hilda [born in Reading, Berkshire, about the turn of the century] always used to tell me 'Always wish when you see a four-leafed clover.' [Edinburgh, March 1984]

A four-leafed clover should bring one luck if one should find one. [Maynooth, Co. Kildare, February 1991]

[In Horseheath, Cambridgeshire] a girl who put a four-leafed clover in her shoe did so in the knowledge that she would marry the first man she met. [Parsons MSS, 1952]

Four-leafed clovers also enabled one to see fairies and break the powers of enchantment. According to Michael Aislabie Denham, in an article published in the 1840s:

> In South Northumberland a great deterrent as well as revealer of fairies, and a preventative of their influence, was the 'four-neuked clover' (a quadrifoil) although a 'five-neuked' specimen (a cinquefoil) is reckoned equally efficacious. This I learned from the people. Mr Chatto furnishes an instance. 'Many years ago, a girl who lived near Netherwitton, returning home from milking with a pail upon her head, saw many fairies gambolling in the fields, but which were invisible to her companions, though pointed out to them by her. On reaching home and telling what she had seen, the circumstance of her power of vision being greater than that of her companions was canvassed in the family, and the cause at length discovered in her weise [a circular pad of grass placed under a pail when carried on the head], which was found to be of four-leaved clover—persons having about them a bunch, or even a single blade, of four-leaved clover being supposed to possess the power of seeing fairies, even though the elves should wish to be invisible; of perceiving in their proper character evil spirits which assumed the form of men, and detecting the arts of those who practised magic, necromancy and witchcraft.' [Hardy, 1895: 142]

In his collection of Cornish folklore, first published in 1865, Robert Hunt gives a rather similar tale.

> A farmer lived in Bosfrancan in St Burrien, who had a very fine red-and-white cow called Daisey. The cow was always fat with her dewlaps and udder sweeping the grass. Daisey held her milk from calf to calf; had an udder like a bucket, yet she would never yield more than a gallon or so of milk, when one might plainly see that she still had at least two gallons more in her udder . . .
>
> One midsummer's day in the evening, the maid was later than usual milking . . . Daisey was the last cow milked, and the bucket was so full she could scarcely lift it to her head. Before rising from the milking-stool, the maid plucked up a handful of grass and clover to put in the head of her hat, that she might carry the bucket the steadier. She had no sooner placed the hat on her head, than she saw hundreds and thousands of Small People swarming in all directions about the cow, and dipping their hands into the milk, taking it out on the clover blossoms and sucking them . . .
>
> Her mistress came out into the garden between the field and the house, and called to know what was keeping the maid so long. When the maid told what she had seen, her mistress said that she couldn't believe her unless she had found a four-leaved grass. Then the maid thought of the handful of grass in the head of her hat. In looking it over by the candle-light, she found a bunch of three-leaved grass, and one stem with four leaves. [Hunt, 1881: 107]

Many years since, there lived as housekeeper with a celebrated squire . . . one Nancy Tregier . . . Nancy left Pendeen one Saturday afternoon to walk to Penzance, for the purpose of buying a pair of shoes. There was an old woman, Jenny Trayer, living in Pendeen Cove—who had the reputation of being a witch . . . Nancy first called on the old woman to inquire if she wished to have anything brought home from Penzance. Tom, the husband of Nancy's friend, did no work . . . When Nancy went into Jenny's cottage, Tom was there, and right busy was she preparing some ointment, and touching her husband's eyes with it: this Jenny tried to hide in the mouth of the oven at the side of the chimney. Tom got up and said he must be off, and left the two women together. After a few idle compliments, Jenny said that Nancy must have something to drink before she started for Penzance, and she went to the spence for the bottles. Nancy, ever curious, seized the moment, dipped her finger into the pot of green ointment, and, thinking it was good for the eyes, she just touched her right eye with it before Jenny returned . . .

Penzance Market was in those days entirely in the street . . . Nancy walked about doing a little business and a great deal of gossiping; when amongst the standings in Market-Jew Street, whom should Nancy see but Tom Trayer, picking off the standings, shoes, stockings, hanks of yarn, and pewter spoons—indeed some of all the sorts of things which were for sale. Nancy walked up to him, and, taking him by the arm, said, 'Tom ar'then't ashamed to be here carrying on such a game? However thee canst have the impudence, I can't think, to be picking the things from the standings and putting them in thy pocket in broad daylight, and the people all around thee.' Tom looked very much surprised when Nancy spoke to him. At last he said, 'Is that you, Nancy?—which eye can you see me upon?' Nancy shut her left eye, this made no difference; then she shut her right eye, and there was Tom as before. She winked, and winked, and was surprised, you may be sure, to find that she could not see Tom with either eye. 'Now, Nancy,' said Tom, 'right or left.' 'Well,' said Nancy ''tis strange; but there is something wrong with my left eye.'

'Oh, then, you see me with the right, do you?'

Then Tom put his finger on her right eye, and from that moment she was blind on that side . . .

Jenny's ointment is said to have been made with a four-leaved clover, gathered at a certain time of the moon. This rendered Fairyland visible, and made men invisible. [Hunt, 1881: 109]

In Ireland:

There was a great fair being held in Dingle one day long ago . . . there was a showman there, and the trick that he had was a cock walking down the street ahead of him, drawing a big, heavy beam tied to his leg. At least all the people thought that it was a beam, and everyone was running after him . . . the crowd was getting bigger all the time . . .

There came up the street a small old man carrying a load of rushes on his back. He wondered what all the people were looking at. All that he could see was a wisp of straw being dragged along by a cock. He thought that everyone had gone mad, and he asked them why they were following the cock like that.

Some of them answered him, 'Don't you see the great wonder?' they said. 'That great beam of wood being dragged after him by that cock . . .'

'All that he's pulling is a wisp of straw,' replied the old man.

The showman overheard him saying this. Over to him he went, and he asked him how much he wanted for the load of rushes . . . The old man named a figure . . . the showman gave it to him. He would have given him twice as much. As soon as the showman took the load of rushes off the old man's back, the man followed after the crowd, but all that he could see was the cock pulling a heavy beam tied to his leg. He followed him all over Dingle.

What happened was that the old man had a four-leaved shamrock, unknown to himself, tied up in the load of rushes. That's what made what he saw different from what the people saw, and that's why the showman paid him three times of the value for the rushes. [O'Sullivan, 1966: 225; tale recorded at Dunquin, Co. Kerry, 1936]

Versions of this story, of which fifty-seven variants have been recorded from Ireland [MacNicholas et al., 1990: 84], are known throughout Europe from Scandinavia to Romania, and have been traced back to the thirteenth century [McNicholas, 1992: 210].

In Irish tradition four-leafed clover is said to be found only where a mare drops her first foal [O'Sullivan, 1966: 280].

[In Co. Wexford it is believed that] if a mare foals her first foal in open air a four-leafed shamrock is supposed to grow on the spot if the mare herself was a first foal. [Clark, 1882: 83]

According to the summary of part of a recording made on the Hebridean island of Barra in 1976:

When foal born, it sneezes before trying to get to its feet so as to dislodge *dubhliath* [looks like cormorant or rabbit's liver, about the size of a crown coin] from its nostril. [The informant] kept one to prove its existence to young people. If it is kept for seven years, a four-leafed clover will grow from it. A person searching for four-leafed clover will not find one. [SSS MSS SA1976.196.A7]

Although the finding of four-leafed clover is generally considered to be lucky:

Another thing in Ireland that several people count unlucky is the four-leaf clover. I remember one year I couldn't put a foot down but I picked up a four-leaf clover. Then one Sunday in church I had the clovers in my prayer book and a lady sitting near me whispered 'Get rid of those quickly—they bring bad luck' and speaking for myself I couldn't think that I had any good luck while I had them. [Ballaghadereen, Co. Roscommon, October 1984]

Since the Irish consider species of clover to be SHAMROCK, the three leaflets of which represent the Holy Trinity, perhaps it is not surprising that some people at least should feel uneasy with a four-leafed clover.

Although it was once necessary either to be very lucky or to search very carefully to find a four-leafed clover, plants which produce leaves with four leaflets are now grown commercially.

Looking over his many millions of four-leaf clovers is Charles T. Daniels, who grows nothing else on his Florida farm. His success obviously owes more to judgement than luck, although his stock probably originates from a single four-leaf plant, a chance mutation from the usual three-leaf variety. Mr Daniels encases his plants in plastic and sells them as a series of good luck novelties exported all over the world. [*Observer Magazine,* 4 August 1974]

We have discovered that there are clover farms in the U.S.A. that specialize in producing four-leaved clovers. One of these clover farms covers 1.5 acres, with two large glasshouses and innumerable clover plants. A secret ingredient (biogenetically treated) is added to the feed to produce many four-leaved clovers on the plants.

About 10,000 leaves are harvested daily and each is enclosed in plastic and sold as 'Good Luck' charms. Plants produced on the farm are not for sale, only the leaves, and the secret ingredient is jealously guarded. [Wenis, 1990: 24]

However, it is possible to obtain four-leafed clover plants, although it appears that these are usually species of *Oxalis* rather than true clovers.

I was given a plant of four-leaved clover (a pretty little rock plant with variegated leaves) and told to plant it in my garden. Should it not flourish I would have bad luck, but luckily for me it thrived. I have now moved to another house and have left the plant behind. I am told I have to be given a root myself! All this knowledge comes from the original donor who was a life-long farmer!! [Marston Montgomery, Derbyshire, March 1983]

Last April, when I was visiting a rare breeds farm in Kent, I bought a 'grow your own and keep good luck in your house' kit for growing 'the magic 4 leaf lucky clover'. When I got home I followed the instructions given, and waited for my four-leafed clover to grow. Nothing happened, so I wrote to the firm in Surrey which produced the kit and asked for a replacement. In reply I received a standard xeroxed letter of regret, signed by 'Tracy, Customer Services'—who presumably was very used to dealing with such complaints—and a replacement kit. This kit was somewhat more professionally produced than the original kit and was stated to have been 'made in Holland'. However, once again, nothing grew. In both cases the bulb from which the clover was supposed to sprout appeared to be of a species of *Oxalis* rather than anything to do with any clover, and the illustration on the Dutch kit appeared to represent an *Oxalis* rather than a clover. [Streatham, London, May 1991]

There are occasional records of clover leaves which have only two leaflets being considered magical:

> The following charm is used in the county of Cambridge by young men and women who are desirous of knowing the name of their future husbands or wives. The 'clover of two' means a piece of clover with only two leaves on it.
>
>> A clover, a clover of two,
>> Put it in your right shoe
>> The first young man (woman) you meet
>> In field, street, or lane,
>> You'll have him (her) or one of his (her) name.
>
> [*N & Q*, 1 ser. 10: 321, 1854]

See also CALVARY CLOVER, RED CLOVER, SHAMROCK, and WHITE CLOVER.

Clown's all-heal – a seventeenth-century name for MARSH WOUND-WORT.

Cockies and hennies – a Morayshire name for BIRD'S-FOOT TREFOIL.

Coconut (*Cocos nucifera*)

> Several months ago when passing a small newsagent's shop in Mitcham Lane, Streatham, I saw a group of Indians cracking a coconut on the doorstep. When the coconut was opened they all appeared delighted, and grinned widely whilst shaking hands. Yesterday I asked one of them about this. Apparently throughout India the custom of cracking a coconut on the steps of a new business is considered to be very lucky. [Streatham, London, December 1989]

Coconuts are considered to be particularly suitable as *prasad*—offerings—at Holi bonfires. At the Holi fire held on Streatham Common, south London, in the evening of 26 March 1994:

> Polythene bags containing foods, and many coconuts, were thrown on to the fire. On being questioned about the significance of the coconuts, participants said: 'Coconuts are considered to be a good offering at all [Hindu] festivals, even weddings, because we think they are a sort of holy fruit, and the water inside them is so pure.'
>
> 'Coconuts are given as *prasad*—that's an offering—because they are so fruitful and so useful, because you can use all parts of them—they are a sort of fertility symbol as well—so we use them at all of our festivals, including marriages.'
>
> Although the posters advertising the event stated that coconuts must not be removed from the fire, many, if not most, of the nuts were removed by men using long-handled scoops. The smouldering nuts were 'taken

home and eaten', or 'taken home and placed beside the temple'. Some nuts were cracked open and eaten on the site. [Personal observation]

A writer on Indian plant-lore has speculated:

As often happens with customs the world over, the meaning behind a ritual is lost but the symbol retained. So it is with the offering of the co-conut fruit. Long, long ago, human sacrifice used to take place to propi-tiate the deity, particularly at the temple of Bhadra-Kali. But as time passed and people got enlightened, human sacrifice gave place to animal sacrifice and ultimately to the symbolic offering of a coconut which, with its round and fibrous outer covering, the epicarp, resembles a human head and the two dark spots on it represent the two human eyes. This is the closest resemblance of any member of the vegetable kingdom to a human head. For this reason it is offered as a symbolic human sacrifice. [Gupta, 1971: 35]

Cf. KOLANUT.

Coffee substitutes – include YELLOW IRIS.

Colds – see COUGHS.

Coltsfoot (*Tussilago farfara*)

The leaves have long been used medicinally as an infusion for COUGHS, and the practice of smoking them like tobacco is still very widespread. [Pratt, 1857, 2: 59]

For BRONCHITIS—simmer a handful of coltsfoot leaves in a quart of water and allow to cool. Take a small dose every two hours until relief is ob-tained. The mixture can be sweetened with honey and also used as a gargle. [Langtoft, Humberside, July 1985]

Coltsfoot tea—very good for coughs. [Portland, Dorset, March 1991]

[On Colonsay coltsfoot leaves] were smoked as a substitute for TOBACCO. [McNeill, 1910: 137]

Columbine (*Aquilegia vulgaris*)

The juice of columbine is used as a cure for swellings and the leaves are also made into poultices for this purpose. [IFCSS 1075: 139, Co. Donegal]

Comfrey (*Symphytum* spp.). Comfrey is one of a few herbs grown in gardens for its medicinal properties.

The only local plant-name I knew in Lancashire was HEARTSEASE; it's comfrey—the plant they grow in back gardens for herbal cures. [Tooting, London, August 1987].

Comfrey leaves spread on ARTHRITIS will soothe the pain and take any inflammation out. [Omagh, Co. Tyrone, October 1986]

77

Comfrey is used for sprains. The root is pulped and applied to [the] sprain for eight hours. [IFCSS MSS 500: 75, Co. Limerick]

Comfrey was collected by a fellow student of mine as a boy in the 1940's and taken to the local white witch at Beer, Devon—I think she gave him six pence a large bag.

A friend of ours had her sprained ankle treated with a comfrey poultice in the Hebrides a few years ago—and it worked a treat! [Girton, Cambridge, June 1986]

My cousin had an ULCER on her leg from her ankle to knee. Ointment from the doctor did her no good. Someone told her to bathe the leg with comfrey—boiling the leaves—bathe two or three times a day. In just over a week it had gone down to [the size of] a postage stamp. [Windermere, Cumbria, November 1988]

I learned from a Lancashire miner that comfrey was widely used for BRUISES and SPRAINS (boiling the leaves to get a solution). [Oban, Argyll, October 1990]

Always grow comfrey—root and leaves have all kinds of medicinal uses. [Stockport, Greater Manchester, April 1991]

Comfrey is also valued as a food and a herbal remedy for domesticated animals.

Comfrey is a very useful herb the leaves of which make splendid pig feeding and its roots have many useful purposes such as making plasters for broken limbs of poultry. [IFCSS MSS 515: 148, Co. Limerick]

When working in the woods some weeks back I met a man whose dog walked with a slight limp. On asking him what caused it, he said that his vet had informed him it was arthritis. He then told me that the limp was nothing now to how it had been before he was given an 'old country recipe' for the treatment of it. He is utterly convinced that this recipe is responsible for the well-being, and even for the life, of his dog. He thought that she would have to be put down until he used it.

2 tablespoons dried comfrey leaves
1 tablespoon cider vinegar
1 dessert spoon honey
1 pint water.

Bring comfrey and water to boil, simmer for one hour. Strain, add vinegar and honey to the remaining liquid.

Dose—one wine glass full—20 ml—every day.

He told me that it keeps some time so he makes rather large batches at a time and bottles it. You have to be careful and release the caps regularly as he has known it to ferment. [West Stow, Suffolk, October 1991]

There are occasional records of comfrey being used as a food.

Throughout the county of Louth, as at Baltray on the mouth of the River Boyne, comfrey was used as a spinach like vegetable. [Synnott, 1979: 37]

Companion planting. Frequently recommended in books on organic, pesticide-free gardening is the idea of planting 'companion plants' which encourage each other's health and productivity, or deter pests from each other.

In north Devon, one always planted CABBAGES on the New Moon or the next day, and we would plant SAGE or THYME in the rows to keep away pests. [AFRICAN] MARIGOLDS were planted along with CARROTS and ONIONS for the same reasons. (We had very pretty allotment gardens!) [Barnstaple, Devon, May 1991]

For an extensive list of companion plants see Philbrick and Gregg, 1991.

Conker – see HORSE CHESTNUT.

Conquerors – a Cheshire name for HORSE CHESTNUT seeds.

Constipation – cured using BOGBEAN, BRACKEN, and GROUNDSEL; in guinea pigs and rabbits treated using BLACKBERRY and STRAWBERRY leaves. See also PURGATIVES.

Consumption – see TUBERCULOSIS.

Contraception – plants used to prevent conception include NETTLE.

Convulsions – prevented using PEONY; cured using BITTERSWEET, TEAPLANT, and TRAVELLER'S JOY.

Convolvulus – see BINDWEED and LARGE BINDWEED.

Coriander (*Coriandrum sativum*)

[From a Sikh gardener, 1991:] plant the seed directly on the ground, and break open with your bare feet, and stamp it in the ground. This works. [Leamington Spa, Warwickshire, January 1993]

Cork oak (*Quercus suber*). Fragments of bark from a 'wishing cork tree' growing in south Devon are commercially available. An account given in a Christmas card which contained a piece of the cork, received in 1988, read:

For the past 350 years a fine old cork tree has flourished in the village of Combe-in-Teignhead and surrounded itself with a strange power to bring good luck to those observing certain rituals dating back to the time of the Great Plague of London in 1665. At that time, people came from all parts of the country to walk around the tree three times and as they walked to make a wish. Some came for better health, some for better fortune, and others for a wife or husband as the case may be. It was said that few were disappointed . . . Even to this day, people from all over the world write for a piece [of its cork].

Corks were widely believed to prevent CRAMP.

> Methods of combating cramp recorded in Cambridgeshire include keeping cork under the pillow to prevent night attacks; keeping several corks strung together at the foot of the bed; carrying corks in the pocket; standing on a cork bath mat. [Porter, 1969: 78]

> A bag of bottle corks were put into the bed at night to prevent getting cramp—a family cure, always used. [Felmersham, Bedfordshire, April 1993]

Corn (BARLEY, OAT, or WHEAT)

> Get a joint of a stalk of corn and get a joint for each WART. Put the joints in a parcel, keep one and throw it over your head. Then bless yourself and the warts will die. [IFCSS MSS 1075: 111, Co. Donegal]

Corn cleavers (*Galium tricornutum*). The fruits of corn cleavers were formerly known as pin burs in Bedfordshire, where

> lacemakers in the Podington area used to collect its fruits to cover the heads of pins to protect their fingers. [Dony, 1953: 359]

Corn cockle (*Agrostemma githago*). Formerly a widespread weed, the corn cockle is now very rare. In Herefordshire an Easter Day activity was corn-showing, the purpose of which seems to have been to rid the corn fields of corn-cockle seedlings.

> At Easter the rustics have a custom called corn-showing. Parties are made to pick out cockle from the wheat. Before they set out they take with them cake and cider, and, says my informant, a yard of toasted cheese. The first person who picks the first cockle from the wheat has the first kiss of the maid and the first slice of the cake. [Fosbroke, 1821: 73]

The corn cockle is occasionally said to be the TARES of the New Testament parable.

Corn dolly. Throughout the corn-growing areas of the British Isles, and indeed, many other parts of Europe, it was usual for the last small patch of corn to be cut with some form of ceremony, and for it to be twisted or plaited into an ornamental shape. In Wales:

> When the corn harvest was reaped one tuft was left uncut in the centre of the last field reaped. When all the reapers had gathered together, each with his sickle, the head-servant would kneel before the tuft, divide it into three parts and plait the parts skilfully together in the same way that he would plait a mare's tail securing the plaited tuft a few inches above ground level. The reapers, six, eight or more, would then stand at a dis-

tance of at least ten yards from the plaited tuft and, in turn, would hurl their sickles at it, the sickles travelling horizontally just above ground level. The intention was, of course, to cut off the plaited tuft. If this were not accomplished by one of the reapers, the head-servant would then himself cut the tuft. [Peate, 1971: 177]

Competitions in which all the harvesters threw their sickles at the last sheaf were widespread in Ireland [Gailey, 1972: 7], and until the enormous changes in rural life brought about by, or coinciding with, the First World War, similar scenes could be observed in parts of England. In isolated areas of Scotland related practices continued for at least another two decades. Naomi Mitchison [1973: 252] described an odd experience which took place in 1937, while she was helping with the harvest on the island of Vallay, off North Uist. Without realizing it she gathered up and bound the last sheaf:

> The two old men came up to me and I became aware that something was happening though I did not see what . . . The two of them put a straw twist round my waist, knotting it as though I too had a sheaf. They spoke slowly and seriously in Gaelic and I do not know what they said but at the end one of them spoke in English saying to me: 'go back to the house and keep the binding and you will get your wish.' It seems to me now that I was clearly the *cailleach*, the old woman (or maiden), the sacrifice. At the time I felt rather shaken and I did not as a matter of fact get my wish. Perhaps I took the binding off too soon.

The throwing of sickles as described by Peate seems to have been the most widespread method of cutting the final patch of corn. However, in some areas it was usual for a specific person to cut the final sheaf. In the Highlands of Scotland [Ross, 1976: 1943] and in parts of Ireland [Danaher, 1972: 191] the youngest person in the harvest field was usually chosen. In other parts of Ireland the field's owner cut the final sheaf [Danaher, 1972: 191], and on the Isle of Man it was ceremoniously cut by one of the young women reapers [Killip, 1975: 174]. In County Carlow each of the unmarried girls would have a stroke with a reaping hook, and the one who succeeded in cutting down the last of the corn would marry within a year. However, in some parts of Ireland it was believed that whoever cut or bound the last sheaf would die unmarried [Danaher, 1972: 191].

Farmers on Rousay in the Orkneys, who had to contend with some of the most difficult corn-growing conditions in the British Isles, would leave a small corner of the last field to be reaped uncut; the untouched corn was said to be left for the birds [Marwick, 1975: 69].

Names given to the final sheaf, or the ornament made from it, varied. In the Orkneys a *bikko* (bitch) was made from the last corn to be reaped, and was, at one time, placed in a prominent position in the stackyard, or on one of the farm buildings [Marwick, 1975: 69]. In England the names used included baby, dolly—the name now commonly used for a wide range of traditional and non-traditional corn ornaments—or maiden, while in Wales the names *caseg fedi* (harvest mare) and *caseg be fedi* (end of harvest mare) were widespread. Other names included *y wrach* (the hag) in Welsh-speaking parts of Pembrokeshire, neighbouring parts of Cardiganshire and west Carmarthenshire, and parts of Caernarvonshire, and 'the neck' in English-speaking south Pembrokeshire [Peate, 1971: 177] and parts of England [Deane and Shaw, 1975: 183; Whitlock, 1977: 150]. The name *cailleach* (old woman or hag) was used in most parts of Ireland [Danaher, 1972: 191] and in Gaelic-speaking parts of Scotland, while *carlin* (old woman) was found in some other parts of Scotland [Peate, 1971: 183].

It is noteworthy that the names given to corn ornaments or the last sheaf of the harvest in the British Isles are almost invariably feminine. In other parts of Europe this use of female names seems to have been less general, and although such names as the corn cow do exist, the final sheaf might have been spoken of as one of a variety of beasts, including bull, cat, goat, steer, pig, and wolf [Peate, 1971: 183]. In his *Golden Bough* James Frazer [1922, chapters 45–50] devoted a great deal of attention to what he termed 'the Corn Mother' and her representation as a human female or an animal. These ideas he traced back to the Greek gods of Antiquity. Frazer's theories were extremely influential and widely accepted for the best part of fifty years, stimulating many less erudite followers.

> Once upon a time there lived in the Isle of Man a gracious lady named Luan. She was always treated with the greatest respect for she was a Goddess. No crops would grow without her aid, for she was herself the Spirit of the corn. When the crops were gathered it was essential to keep her spirit alive through the winter, so that the corn would grow again next year. As the harvest was being cut the Goddess retreated to the centre of the uncut and still living corn. Here the reapers formed a ring and none wishing to be identified with the act of severing her from the soil they threw their sickles at the last of the standing corn. The last sheaf cut contained the Spirit of the Goddess herself, and its name is *mheillea*. It was, therefore treasured with the greatest care. [Davies, 1949: 9]

However, today such speculations tend to be rejected by serious folklorists.

After the ornament had been cut there were several customs which were commonly practised. In Cornwall, north Devon, and some other areas it was usual to Cry the Neck. The reaper who cut the last tuft of corn would hold it aloft shouting 'I have it! I have it! I have it!' to which the others would shout 'What have 'ee? What have 'ee? What have 'ee?' and he would reply 'A neck! A neck! A neck!' Then there would be cheers for the farmer, followed by cider and cake for the men [Deane and Shaw, 1975: 183]. According to a correspondent writing in 1826 about north Devon in Hone's *Every-Day Book*:

I have once or twice heard upwards of twenty men cry it, and sometimes joined by an equal number of female voices. About three years back, on some high grounds, where our people were harvesting, I heard six or seven 'necks' cried in one night, although I knew that some of them were four miles off. [Hone, n.d.: 586]

By the 1920s the custom had almost died out in Cornwall, and was believed to have been continued by only two farmers living in the Gweek area. However, late in the summer of 1928 the custom was revived by the St Ives Old Cornwall Society on a farm belonging to Mr Hugh Dunstan, near the church at Towednack [Jewell, n.d.]. In more recent years crying the neck has been revived by other Old Cornwall Societies, so that in the mid-1970s the event was held annually by the Societies of St Just, Madron, Penzance, Helston, and Mullion. The ceremonies are usually followed by a short church service at which either a lesson is read or the Lord's Prayer is recited in the Cornish language. At Madron the service is held in the parish church and the Methodist chapel in alternate years. Refreshments, which can vary from tea and biscuits or pasties to elaborate harvest suppers, are provided after the service [Launceston, Cornwall, November 1976].

Such emasculated events bear little resemblance to the boisterous and unruly activities formerly practised elsewhere. In the Scottish Highlands and some other areas it was usual for a young man to seize the ornament, or *cailleach*, rush to a neighbouring farm which was still reaping, and throw it in front of the reapers. He would then retreat at even greater speed, for if he was caught his punishment would be rough; his beard and hair might be shaved off, or he might be stripped, beaten and sent home naked [Ross, 1976: 144]. It was considered to be a very bad omen for any farmer to receive a *cailleach*. As in some other parts of the British Isles, in Ireland it was believed that a hag or witch could turn herself into a hare and steal cows' milk, so the *cailleach* (hag) was driven from farm to farm until she reached the last field in the parish to be reaped. The owner of this field would be forced to support the *cailleach* until the following year [Danaher, 1972: 191]. Similarly, in the western Highlands and the Hebrides the last sheaf was known as the *gobhar bhacach* (lame goat) and bloody battles might occur when a crofter threw his sheaf into the field of a more tardy neighbour. The last person to finish his harvesting was considered extremely unfortunate, for it was believed that:

> Loss of cattle, loss on account of death and accident
> Will befall the luckless one of the *gobhar bhacach*.
>
> [Ross, 1976: 144]

In Wales it was usual for the cutter of the mare to take it into the farmhouse living-room to show all the corn had been reaped. The process was often enlivened by the servant girls who, being forewarned, would assemble and try to drench the carrier with water or any other available liquid. If a dry mare was placed safely on the living-room table its bearer was rewarded with a place of honour at the harvest feast. If unsuccessful he was placed at the foot of the table or forced to pay a forfeit [Peate, 1971: 178].

Throughout Wales it was generally considered lucky for the mare to remain dry, and, in some areas, a mare which had been soaked by the servant girls was not allowed into the house. In Ireland the bearer of the last sheaf, who was usually the person who had cut it, was subjected to a variety of pranks, the most widespread of which was the throwing of water at him and his burden. In County Leitrim it was thought that this would prevent drought for the next twelve months, and in County Clare holy water was sprinkled over the sheaf and its bearer [Danaher, 1972: 191].

At the end of the 1940s a corn ornament was displayed in the parish church at Martinhoe in north Devon. According to the church guide book:

> It (the nek) is plaited from the first cut: three plaits which represent earth, air and water. And they (the reapers) form a circle with the man with the nek in the centre, and after bowing three times and crying 'The nek—I've got 'im' he had to break through the ring, and all the folks around bear water in jugs, etc. which they try to throw on the nek. If he gets to the farm or the church with nek dry, it denotes a good harvest; if wetted a poor one. [Brown, 1951: 76]

This ornament appears to be unusual in that it was made at the start of the harvest rather than at the end.

Although most of the end of harvest activities have completely died out, one of the reminders of pre-mechanized harvesting is the revival of corn ornament making. Skilful men and women plait elaborate designs, most of which are based on traditional patterns. Their accounts of their ornaments or dollies are usually derived from Frazer's *Golden Bough*, so the ornament is usually said to be an ancient symbol of fertility or a representation of 'Mother Earth'. The coloured ribbons, without which no modern dolly would be complete, are said to represent various aspects of the cornfield. Red and blue, the colours most frequently used, are said to represent the POPPIES and CORNFLOWERS which formerly infested the field. Yellow ribbons are said to symbolize the ripe grain, and green is said to represent the young growing corn [Peter Oakley, corn-dolly maker, October 1970].

Taken as a whole such ideas are inaccurate, but the makers are, understandably, more interested in intricate and graceful designs than in tracing the dolly's origins. Some makers have been fortunate to find elderly people who remember traditional designs and are are able to pass them on to a new generation. Others have sought out dollies in local museums and have copied them, while the majority have taken their designs from books and pamphlets on the subject [Lambeth, 1969 and 1977; Sandford and Davis, 1964].

When the craft was first revived makers experienced difficulty in obtaining suitable long, hollow straw, but, with an increase in interest, several growers have begun to cultivate old-fashioned varieties of corn solely for the use of corn-dolly makers. It is also possible to obtain specially made elongated drinking-straws, which can be used when the craft is being taught in schools or to Women's Institutes and similar organizations.

Corn dollies can be purchased in craft shops throughout the country, and they are also found decorating 'olde worlde' country pubs. The elaborate designs are worthy of admiration and have, no doubt, undergone great transformation since the days when corn ornaments were hurriedly produced at the harvest's end or plaited to help pass time when inclement weather prevented field work. The names given to modern dollies usually describe the ornament's shape and the county from which it is said to have originated. Thus a popular book on corn dollies [Lambeth, 1977] depicts such items as the Herefordshire fan, Suffolk horsehoe, Cambridgeshire umbrella, and Northamptonshire horns. The commercialization of corn-dolly making has led to a belief that the possession of a dolly will ensure peace and plenty in the home [New Malden, Surrey, September 1978].

It has been suggested that the practical purpose of a corn dolly was to preserve seed corn for sowing the following spring. However, while the final patch of corn to be cut might be comparatively weed-free and therefore suitable for preservation as seed, and although in some parts of the British Isles it was usual to sow grain from the corn dolly [Gailey, 1972: 22], there seems to be no British evidence to suggest that the grain from corn ornaments, or the final sheaf, was ever sown to any significant extent.

What eventually happened to the corn dolly varied throughout the British Isles. Usually it was hung in the farmhouse kitchen until it was replaced by a new one at the end of the following year's harvest [Danaher, 1972: 198; Leather, 1912: 104; Peate, 1971: 178]. The country kitchen or hearth, which is a favourite exhibit in local history and folk museums, often displays such a dolly. On some farms each dolly remained in place until it eventually disintegrated, so that dollies from many years' harvests might accumulate [Danaher, 1972: 198; Peate, 1971: 178].

In Scotland the *cailleach* was fed to horses at the start of ploughing [Ross, 1976: 143] or harvesting [Mitchinson, 1973: 253]. Similarly, in Ireland it was sometimes fed to horses to increase their strength or to poultry to ensure a good supply of eggs. In County Donegal some people made their ST BRIGID's crosses from the straw of the last sheaf [Danaher, 1972: 198]. Elsewhere in Ireland the last sheaf was believed to possess curative powers and was given to sick animals or fed to calving cows [Danaher, 1972: 198; Gailey, 1972: 22]. When burnt to ashes its grain was used to make an ointment for treating skin ailments. In County Laois the grain was thrown to the poultry and the first cock to reach it was selected for killing on the eve of St Martin's Day, when it was usual to shed blood by slaughtering a domestic animal. 'Burying the sheaf' was a sinister ritual which was sometimes attempted in north Leinster. A last sheaf was stolen and given the name of an intended victim. After it had been 'killed' by being stabbed or struck, it was buried; as it decayed in the soil, so would the victim sicken and die. His or her life would be spared only if the sheaf was found, dug up, and burnt [Danaher, 1972: 198].

Cornflower (*Centaurea cyanus*)

The blue cornflower . . . is the traditional flower of Harrow School and is frequently worn by Old Harrovians at 'special events' such as Ascot, as well as part of everyday dress. Indeed it has almost become a badge of recognition and this ordinary little flower inspires great affection amongst Old Boys. The cornflower is much in evidence during the annual Eton versus Harrow cricket match . . . Many of my friends go to great lengths to obtain a flower for the match, some try growing their own. [Letter from Llandrindod Wells, Powys, in *This England,* Spring 1988]

I don't know when the cornflower was chosen for wearing at Harrow; I assume it was in the nineteenth century. It is mainly worn at the Eton and Harrow Match. Eton and Harrow have predominantly blue uniforms, and the cornflower was chosen to contrast with the Eton blue. Cornflowers mainly appear outside the School only for the Eton and Harrow Match, but they do play a significant part in decorations in the school when they're in bloom. [Harrow School, January 1994]

When my sons attended Alleyn's School in Dulwich, South London, scholars, staff and visitors wore a cornflower on Founder's Day. This was to commemorate Edward Alleyn, as the cornflower was his favourite flower. [Letter from Ontario, Canada, in *This England,* Summer 1988]

The cornflower is worn on Founder's Day (the Saturday nearest 21 June being the anniversary of the day in 1619 when James I granted Letters Patent for the Foundation of God's Gift to be created) by all members of Alleyn's School and Dulwich College. On the following Saturday James Allen's Girls' School has its Founder's Day and cornflowers are then worn by them.

The cornflower . . . is depicted in the reredos over the altar in the Foundation Chapel in Dulwich Village. The scene is the stable in Bethlehem with some additions—one of the wise men is Edward Alleyn but there are two extra 'visitors' to the Christ child, two boys in the original school uniform. One holds a model of the Chapel, the other a bunch of cornflowers . . .

Records show that the cornflower tradition within the Alleyn Foundation started (probably) in June 1620 and has been carried on ever since. Thousands of the flowers are used by us every June. Three huge wreaths, each $2\frac{1}{2}$ feet across, are laid by the three schools on the Founder's Grave and over 6000 pupils are wearing them in Dulwich over that weekend (i.e. staff, pupils, former pupils and parents). I understand that it is impossible to buy cornflowers elsewhere in London then. [Herne Hill, London, January 1994]

[The cornflower] was in memory of the French soldiers who died in two World Wars and was on sale with the red POPPY for Armistice Day. Quite a number of people used to wear them side by side. I don't know if it was all over the country but they were on sale in London. [Letter from Cheltenham, Gloucestershire, in *This England*, Spring 1988]

Corn marigold (*Chrysanthemum segetum*).

A persistent weed, known in County Carlow as Mogue Tobin from a farmer who was driven out of his farm when unable to grow anything else. [Booth, 1980: 110]

On Colonsay, in the Inner Hebrides, corn marigold 'was used to soothe throbbing pains' [McNeill, 1910: 136].

Corns – treated using CELANDINE, GREATER PLANTAIN, HOUSELEEK, IVY, and PENNYWORT.

Corn-showing – an Easter custom in Herefordshire, the purpose of which was to remove CORN COCKLE from the corn fields.

Corn spurrey

Corn spurrey (*Spergula arvensis*)

A profusion of meldi (corn spurrey) is a sign that more manure needs to be applied [to the soil]. [Lerwick, Shetland, March 1994]

Corn thistle – a former name for CREEPING THISTLE.

Corpus Christi. Since the thirteenth century the Roman Catholic Church has commemorated the institution of the Eucharist at the Feast of Corpus Christi, observed on the Thursday after Trinity Sunday. After solemn Mass, Christ's Body (Corpus Christi) is carried in procession as a public witness to the belief in the true presence of Christ in the Eucharist.

> In the ancient world it was the custom to strew flowers in the path of important persons as a sign of respect. This custom was adopted by the Church in honour of the Blessed Sacrament, carried in procession in the festival of Corpus Christi. In some places in Europe this practice was extended so that whole streets were carpeted with flowers. Even today, in some towns in Italy, a carpet of flowers is laid the entire route of the procession, in intricate patterns and pictures depicting scenes from the gospels. [The Revd Anthony Whale, Cathedral of Our Lady and St Philip Howard, Arundel, West Sussex, March 1990]

In Britain the most well-known of these floral carpets is that prepared each year at the Roman Catholic Cathedral in Arundel, West Sussex.

> The tradition of the carpet of flowers was taken from the village of Sutri outside Rome and introduced to Arundel by the 15th Duke of Norfolk in 1877. It seems not to have been carried on during the First World War, but was revived in 1919 and has continued ever since; the whole work being undertaken by parishioners. [Anon., n.d.: 23]

In recent years the carpet, which is six feet wide and runs the length of the aisle (97 feet) is laid on the Tuesday before the feast day, is on display to the public all day on Wednesday and until 5.30 p.m. on the Thursday, when the service of Mass is held. A different design is used each year, but the plants employed are usually the same: mainly CHRYSANTHEMUMS to give large splashes of bright colours, CARNATIONS to provide more intricate highlights, and Lawson's CYPRESS which provides a sombre background [personal observation, 1980, and Mrs Stella Smart, chief 'flower lady', March 1978 and August 1980].

At least two Anglo-Catholic churches in London prepare Corpus Christi carpets for the Sunday after the feast day. At All Saints Church, Notting Hill, a carpet similar to the Arundel one has been prepared every year since either just before or just after the Second World War.

> The designs have varied, though today we use one that was drawn by one of our West Indian parishioners. The design is drawn in chalk onto the

88

floor of the aisle. The present design is in three parts—there is a cross, a host and chalice, and a dove. A collection is made in the weeks preceding, and, depending on when Corpus Christi falls in the year, flowers are bought—as the feast is variable the flowers are usually akin to the season. Most of the flowers are stripped of their petals and these petals are what make up the design. It doesn't last long. Usually it is made the day before and by the next evening you can usually see the signs that it is beginning to go. The carpet's primary function is to be the carpet for the beginning of the Blessed Sacrament procession and it is not walked upon until that stage at the end of Mass (after which it is destroyed by those who walk upon it in the procession). The carpet is an overall parish job, done by the parishioners over an afternoon, with much labour. [The Revd Jeremy Fairhead, All Saints, September 1987]

A rather different kind of carpet is prepared at St Mary's, Bourne Street, Belgravia, where

Our Corpus Christi procession goes back beyond living memory [but not, presumably, before 1874, when St Mary's was built] and does not march over a carpet of flowers, as is the custom in many places. ROSE petals are scattered by little girls in front of the procession of the Host, but the carpet on the floor is of leaves and herbs. The herbs are sweet smelling, but most of them are straight kitchen herbs and then occasionally the odd spot of verbena or scented geranium gets included. I do not know of any particular significance of the plants used, but I can assure you that the smell of the church is like something in an especially aromatic wood. [Fr John Gilling, St Mary's, October 1987]

Cosmic plant – see KARMIC PLANT.

Cotten sedges – a name for COTTON GRASS.

Cotton grass (*Eriophorum* spp.)

Bog cotton, or cotten sedges—lukki-minnie's oo—very unlucky to pick and bring indoors. [Lerwick, Shetland, March 1994]

Cotton thistle (*Onopordum acanthium*) is often considered to be the Scottish THISTLE; also associated with Mary Queen of Scots, who was executed at Fotheringhay, Northamptonshire, in 1587:

On returning through the village an old dame enquired if we had been gathering Queen Mary's Thistle, alluding to *Onopordum*, which tradition says was brought to Fotheringhay . . . by Mary's attendants. [*Pharmaceutical Journal*, 12 June 1875: 997]

Couch grass (*Elytrigia repens*). Gypsies considered a decoction of couch grass in cold water to be useful for reducing temperature and treating gall-stones [Vesey-FitzGerald, 1944: 24].

Cough flannel – a Devon name for MULLEIN.

Coughs and **colds** – treated using BLACK CURRANT, BLACK SPLEEN-WORT, CHESTNUT, COLTSFOOT, ELDER, EYEBRIGHT, wych ELM, GROUND IVY, HOREHOUND, HORSERADISH, MOUSE-EAR HAWKWEED, MULLEIN, ONION, RANSOMS, RHUBARB, RUE, SELF-HEAL, SWEDE, TURNIP, and YAR-ROW; a March cough will not go until BROAD BEANS flower.

Cow parsley (*Anthriscus sylvestris*). Many of the local names recorded for cow parsley in the nineteenth century indicate that it was considered to be inauspicious. These names include: badman-oatmeal, de'ils meal, de'il or devil's oatmeal, devil's parsley, and naughty man's oatmeal [Britten and Holland, 1886: 567].

More recently:

> Don't bring cow parsley into the house, because the SNAKES will follow it. [St Bride's-Super-Ely, South Glamorgan, October 1982]

However, most widespread of the current folklore associated with cow parsley is the belief that picking and bringing indoors its flowers will lead to the death of one's mother.

> As a child in Yorkshire, we would never pick the tallish very small white flowers which grew by the wayside. They were very pretty, tall, graceful plants, and many times I was tempted to pick them, but was told not to as it was called Stepmother's Blessing or MOTHER DIE. Needless to say, as I was very fond of my mother, I did not wish to acquire a stepmother, which was what would happen, I was informed, if I picked them. Needless to say, this wild plant flourishes very well and did so when I was very young. [Market Drayton, Shropshire, March 1983]

> My childhood was spent in the Chigwell, Ongar and Upminster areas of Essex. My mother called cow parsley 'kill your mother quick,' and would never allow it in the house—or she would die. 'Queen Anne's Lace' [another name for the plant] is generally understood to refer to its lace-like appearance, but also to her (Queen Anne's) tragic child losses. [Witham, Essex, May 1983]

> You know the wild cow parsley, which grows beside the road, we were not allowed to pick it. We called it break your mother's heart. [Wimbledon, London, November 1983]

It seems probable that these beliefs result from, or at least are reinforced by, the flowers' tendency to drop small petals and create a mess when taken indoors. Interestingly, the name mother-die is not recorded for cow parsley in nineteenth-century dictionaries of plant-names. Britten and Holland [1886: 342] list Mother Dee, but only as a name for RED CAMPION. However, a name which might have had similar connotations was used for cow parsley late in the nineteenth century.

My mother born in 1899 in Croydon, though both her parents were from Suffolk, always said that her Suffolk relatives whom she went to visit called cow parsley break-your-mother's heart. She also said this was what her own mother called it. [Ottery St Mary, Devon, March 1993]

Further evidence for cow parsley being considered inauspicious is provided by other names given to the plant.

As a child in the Ipswich district, I always called cow parsley Dead Man's Flesh—I assume because so much of it grows in grave-yards. I didn't know of any other name for the plant until much later. [Stowmarket, Suffolk, September 1985]

Cow parsley was known as bad man's baccy. [Corbridge, Northumberland, January 1993]

An old man . . . who died a few years ago aged 80, called cow parsley shit-parsley. [Wicken, Cambridgeshire, March 1993]

Cow parsley = devil's porridge. [Dublin, May 1993]

There appears to be a vague tradition which associates cow parsley with ST MARY THE VIRGIN. A name given to the plant in Dorset was My Lady's lace, while Lady's lace has been recorded from both Somerset [Grigson, 1987: 209] and Ireland.

[In Ireland] they used to call cow parsley Lady's lace, and I remember a maid we had saying 'Lady's lace looks lovely on the altar.' May was the month of Our Lady, and I remember that as children we used to make a May altar in the house. [East Bergholt, Suffolk, February 1993]

In central west Scotland cow parsley is known as dog's flourish—'as a local in her seventies said, "well, it grows on the verges where the dogs have been!"' [Helensburgh, Dunbartonshire, February 1991].

In the Forest of Dean:

Pig weed was cow parsley. All Foresters kept at least one cottage pig and bunches of cow parsley were often fed to it, together with new BRACKEN tops, BLACKBERRY tips, etc., as a change of diet from kitchen scraps. But you mustn't feed this to a little pig or you would 'stitch 'un'. In other words it would grow too quickly for its skin. [Cinderford, Gloucestershire, November 1993]

Cowslip (*Primula veris*). Formerly there was a widespread belief that both cowslips and PRIMROSES would produce red flowers if planted upside down.

A curious belief [in Cheshire] about cowslips was that if they were planted upside down they would come up red. [Hole, 1937: 48]

Also formerly widespread, but now existing only as a childhood memory of the middle-aged and elderly, was a method of love DIVINATION which used 'tissty-tossties', fragrant balls of cowslip flowers.

Cowslip

[In Herefordshire:] Make a ball of cowslip blossom, and toss it, using the same words [Rich man, poor man, beggar man, farmer; tinker, tailor, plough-boy, thief] over and over, till at the right one the ball falls to the ground. Or the ball is tossed to:

> Tisty-tosty, tell me true,
> Who shall I be married to?

Then the names of actual or possible lovers are recited, until the ball falls. [Leather, 1912: 63]

On Whit Sunday you would go out, pick bunches of cowslips, and bring them back home. You'd have two chairs and tie a piece of string, about 12 inches long between them (like when you're making a cord). Then you would pick off the flower heads and hang them on the string with about half the flowers on either side—the more flower heads the better. Twist the string and tie the ends together to form a ball.

Toss the ball backwards and forwards continually saying:

> Tissty-tossty tell me true,
> Who am I going to be married to?
> Tinker, tailor, soldier, sailor,
> Rich man, poor man, beggarman, thief.

You would eventually marry a man with the same occupation as the one named when the last flower fell out. [Thorncombe, Dorset, June 1976]

Welsh children used a similar method to find out how many years they would live.

Cowslips are still used as a pretty test by children . . . who make the blossoms into flower-balls. These they toss up and catch with the right hand only, while repeating:

> Pistey, postey, four-and-forty,
> How many years shall I live?
> One, two, three, four

and so on, until the ball falls at the fatal number. [Trevelyan, 1909: 97]

In the Severn Vale in the late 1920s or early 1930s:

[On my grandmother's farm in Arlingham] the meadows were full of cowslips. My aunt took us children into the fields where we would sit and watch her make 'cowslip balls'. I was probably 3–4 years old at the time and I cannot remember how she made them, but each ball was approximately 4 inches across and all flowers! We tossed them in the air and she would recite:

> Tisty Tosty cowslip ball
> Tell me where you're going to fall?
> Dursley, Uley, Coaley, Cam,
> Frampton, Fretherne, Arlingham?

. . . all the places mentioned are in the Severn Vale. [Harbertonford, Devon, October 1992]

Elsewhere cowslip balls were made simply as toys, or as attractive objects.

> A dodge ball is made from cowslips. A piece of twine about a foot long is got. The shanks are taken off the cowslips and the petals divided as evenly as possible and placed on the string head downwards. When the twine is almost full the ends are drawn together and tied thus forming a ball. Children have great sport dodging with their hands in the air seeing how long they are able to keep doing so. [IFCSS MSS 825: 123, Co. Laois]

> As a child [c.50 years ago] I made cowslip—paigle—balls . . . place the ball in a saucer of water. [Wicken, Cambridgeshire, March 1993]

At Lambley, in Nottinghamshire, Cowslip Sunday was celebrated:

> A few weeks ago I visited Lambley church . . . I was impressed by the beautifully embroidered altar-frontal, decorated with acorns, vine leaves and cowslips . . . The rector explained to me . . . the cowslips commemorate the village's Cowslip Sunday. Formerly the children gathered bunches on or for the first Sunday in May when the village street was lined with stalls. Coachloads of visitors came from Nottingham to buy the cowslips. Fortunately, prior to 1970, this custom was discontinued. [Newark, Nottinghamshire, March 1992]

Cowslips were valued by country wine-makers.

> Cowslip wine is good for JAUNDICE. [Portland, Dorset, April 1991]

> Remedies which my mother used: cowslip wine (home-made) when we had MEASLES. [Quinton, West Midlands, April 1993]

Children often sucked cowslip flowers.

> [During my childhood, in Kingham, Oxfordshire:] nectar sucked from cowslip flowers. [Farmoor, Oxfordshire, July 1993]

> I am nearly 75 . . . [as children we] pulled the flowers out of cowslips to suck out the sweet drops of nectar. [Shipston-on-Stour, Warwickshire, September 1993]

Crab apple (*Malus sylvestris*)

> At this season [Michaelmas] village maidens in the west of England go up and down the hedges gathering crab-apples, which they carry home, putting them into a loft, and forming with them the initals of their supposed suitors' names. The initials which are found on examination to be most perfect on Old Michaelmas Day, are considered to represent the strongest attachments, and the best for the choice of future husbands. [Brand, 1853: 56]

A widespread saying concerning crab apples (or, perhaps, rather sour cultivated fruits) is applied to girls who after having many eligible boy-friends eventually choose a husband who is considered to be inferior.

> As a child on the Dorset/Devon/Somerset borders during the early 1960s, I heard it said of one of my aunts that she 'had searched the orchard through and through, until she found the crab'. [Streatham, London, May 1991]

On the eastern edge of Dartmoor a spinster who married late in life was said to have 'searched the orchard for the sweetest apple and picked the grab [crab] in the end' [Dunsford, 1978: 209]. Similar expressions were used in Kent, where they were applied to philanderers of both sexes [Shepherdswell, Kent, October 1979].

Crack willow (*Salix fragilis*)

Two Sussex men who were felling a crack willow tree on Bookham Common gave the tree the name 'Widow's Willow' as it is liable to shed its branches without warning and injure anyone who attempts to cut it down. [Great Bookham, Surrey, October 1979]

Cramp – prevented using a shrew ASH, CORK, and POTATO; stomach cramp cured using CREEPING THISTLE and HORSERADISH.

Cramp-thistle – a Warwickshire name for galled CREEPING THISTLE.

Cranberry (*Vaccinium oxycoccos*)

At Longtown, on the borders of Cumberland, they are made so considerable an article of commerce, that at the season when they are ripe, no less than 20 or 30 pounds worth are sold by the poor people each market day for five or six weeks together, which are afterwards dispers'd over different parts of the kingdom, for making the wellknown cranberry-tarts. [Lightfoot, 1777: 203]

Crazies or **crazy** – names for BUTTERCUP.

Creeping buttercup – see BUTTERCUP.

Creeping cinquefoil (*Potentilla reptans*)

A decoction of *Potentilla reptans* roots is given to Manx cats with DIARRHOEA (they are very prone to this). [Malew, Isle of Man, 1965; Manx Folklife Survey]

Creeping thistle (*Cirsium arvense*), formerly also known as corn thistle.

[A Warwickshire cure for] CRAMP: the swollen stems of the cramp-thistle, i.e. the gall not infrequent on the flowering shoots of soldiers (the corn thistle). [Bloom, 1920: 245]

See also THISTLE.

Crested dog's-tail (*Cynosurus cristatus*)

[In Yorkshire] during summer the children are fond of making 'trees' or 'dollies' out of dogtail grass (*Cynosurus cristatus*). Gathering a handful, they twist other individual heads of grass round the stalks of the former, binding bunches of more heads at intervals down the stems, so that they stick out from the sides in a fancied resemblance to branches of trees. In Lincolnshire, the men used to amuse themselves by making similar devices on Sunday afternoons. Beyond passing the time, it did not appear to be done for any definite purpose, though 'the tree' was often presented to the lady-love when completed. [Fowler, 1909: 296]

My mother, last summer, showed me how to make what she called 'Trees'. They are probably distant relatives of the CORN-DOLLIES. They can only be made from one particular grass, the Crested Dog's Tail grass (*Cynosurus cristatus*). One begins with three strands of the grass (including the inflorescence) and winds the inflorescence of another strand around the three stalks . . .

After the inflorescence has been wound round the stalk is passed once round the others and knotted by passing the free end through the loop thus formed. The stalk is then bent down with the first three and another inflorescence is wound around them. By this means they increase in girth as they get longer. My mother then explained that they could be joined in groups to form the trees. However she was rather vague as to the precise form of the trees . . .

I discovered another local woman (local to Haslemere in Surrey where my mother lives) who also remembers making less complicated things she called Rats Tails which were made up in the same way but were unbranched. [Conquer, 1970: 145]

[Shortlane End School, near Truro, 1934–1938:] dog's-tail grass—pick the flowering heads and make a bunch like a corn dolly. [St Day, Cornwall, January 1994]

Crop circles. In the late 1970s a number of flattened circle formations started appearing in fields of growing corn [Delgado and Andrews, 1989]. These circles attracted some attention, especially as they appeared to be most prevalent in areas of Hampshire and Wiltshire which were rich in prehistoric remains or had, during the 1960s and 1970s, been associated with alleged UFO activity. Although these comparatively simple formations attracted some esoteric explanations, others prefered to attribute them to the action of wind or birds. Others tried to relate the crop circles of the 1980s to some of the folklore associated with FAIRY RINGS in earlier centuries [Rickard, 1990: 62].

Throughout the 1980s an increasing number of circles were observed each year. Towards the end of the decade, and particularly in the early 1990s, elaborate patterns—pictograms—also began to appear in crops [Delgado, 1992]. Some of these patterns (and some of the earlier circles) were undoubtedly hoaxes, but others remained unexplained. It is clear, however, that these pictograms could not have been formed by normally behaving winds, birds, or animals. Various explanations were put forward, but no consensus of opinion appears to have been reached [Noyes, 1990]. Some people claim that the pictograms occur on ley lines and similar points of power. Others suggest that they 'represent . . . certain cosmic principles of the Ancient Wisdom which were implanted in the matrix of human consciousness millennia ago' and are created by intelligent non-human beings who 'are desperately worried at the worsening ecological state of the planet and are trying to communicate not only to express this, but to suggest ways of collaboration which will improve matters' [Green, 1990].

However, since the autumn of 1991, when a number of people—including two Southampton men in their sixties—admitted to creating circles and pictograms, interest in the subject appears to have waned [Schnabel, 1993].

Crotal (*Parmelia* spp.) – see LICHENS.

Crowberry (*Empetrum nigrum*)

> The highlanders frequently eat the berries, but they are not very desirable fruit. Boil'd in allum-water they will DYE yarn a black fuscous colour. [Lightfoot, 1777: 613]

Crow garlic (*Allium vineale*), also known as crow onion and wild onion.

> [A Warwickshire cure for WHOOPING COUGH:] take bulbs of the crow onion and grate them, place in a sock of flannel, and let the child wear it in its boots. [Bloom, 1920: 246]

Crowdy-kit – a Devon name for WATER FIGWORT.

Crowdy-kit-o'-the-wall – a Devon name for BITING STONECROP.

Crown imperial (*Fritillaria imperialis*).

> The Crown Imperial Lily has water in it always, because it weeps for refusing to bow down when Our Lord passed by. [Hole MSS]

The crown imperial was particularly sought after for inclusion in MAY GARLANDS.

> On May Day the children went round the village [Long Crendon, Buckinghamshire] with garlands of flowers, sometimes tied to sticks in the shape of a half loop, sometimes tied round a straight stick, with a crown imperial lily stuck on the top. In those days, most gardens had a group of those lilies. The little girls wore their Sunday best and made the rounds of the larger farm houses collecting pennies. [Donald, 1973: 31]

Crown of thorns – made from BLACKTHORN and HAWTHORN.

Cuckoo flower (*Cardamine pratense*), also known as lady's smock.

My mother was not superstitious, and loved the cuckoo flowers, and we picked masses for her. Neighbours, though, would not have them in their house, as they brought 'bad luck'. [Brize Norton, Oxfordshire, August 1992]

Although cuckoo flowers are usually omitted from modern [MAY] GARLANDS with as much care as in the past, the rule is not observed everywhere. In Oxford, the cross-shaped garlands carried about the streets on May-morning by little bands of children almost always contain a profusion of these forbidden flowers, and no one seems to be aware that they are supposed to be unlucky. [Hole, 1976: 131]

[Children were warned against] the Cuckoo Flower or Lady's Smock, known in Horseheath [Cambridgeshire] as 'Headaches' because its scent was supposed to bring on HEADACHE. [Parsons MSS, 1952]

Cuckoo flowers = lady's smock. Never taken indoors by my grandmother—'They bring sickness.' [Taunton, Somerset, April 1994]

Other flowers which are considered to be unlucky include COW PARSLEY and HAWTHORN.

In Derbyshire Lucy Locket signifies the cuckoo flower. When the children gather it they say:

Lucy Locket lost her pocket in a shower of rain,
Milner fun'it, Miller grum it in a peck of grain.
[*Journal of American Folklore*, 8: 83, 1895]

Cuckoo pint – see LORDS AND LADIES.

Cuckoo's bread and cheese – a Radnorshire name for WOOD SORREL.

Cucumber (*Cucumis sativus*). A Guernsey rhyme advised that cucumbers should not be sown too early.

Seume tes coucaombres en mars, tu n'éras pas d'faire de pouque nic sac,
Seume les en avril, tu n'éras aen p'tit,
Mé, j'les seum'rai en mai, et j'en erai pus-s-que té.

Sow your cucumbers in March, you will need neither bag nor sack,
Sow them in April, and you will have few.
But I will sow mine in May, and I will pick more than you.
[De Garis, 1975: 122]

Cudbear (*Ochrolechia tartarea*) – see LICHENS.

Curly doddie – see CARL DODDIES.

Cutfinger – an Oxfordshire name for PERIWINKLE.

Cut-flower – a Sussex name for VALERIAN.

Cuts – healed using DOCK, FOXGLOVE, GREATER MEXICAN STONECROP, GREATER PLANTAIN, GROUNDSEL, HORSERADISH, JERSEY LILY, LICHENS, LILY OF THE VALLEY, MADONNA LILY, MALLOW, ONION, ORANGE LILY, ST JOHN'S WORT, VALERIAN, and WATER FIGWORT.

Cyclamen (*Cyclamen* spp.). In many herbals the cyclamen was recommended to ease childbirth.

> The Root hung about a Woman's Neck in Labour occasions a speedy Delivery. It is very dangerous for Women with Child to make use of it, or to step over it. [K'Eogh, 1735: 115]

Cypress (*Chamaecyparis* spp., especially *C. lawsoniana*, and × *Cupressocyparis leylandii*).

> [In the 1920s] to plant two small cypress trees in one's garden would mean peace and prosperity to the household. [Colwyn Bay, Clwyd, June 1992]

Further evidence for the beneficial influence of cypress could be found in County Mayo where, when POTATOES were planted, 'a piece of cypress is stuck in the ridge . . . and on harvesting a branch of the same is burned' [Salaman, 1949: 117].

Cypress is used for making CORPUS CHRISTI floral carpets, and in Ireland, particularly in urban areas [personal observation, Dublin, May 1993 and 1994], may be used as palm on PALM SUNDAY (see under YEW).

D

Daffodil (*Narcissus* spp., especially *N. pseudonarcissus*). In common with PRIMROSES, daffodils were sometimes banned from the house by POULTRY-KEEPERS.

[In Herefordshire] if daffodils be brought in when hens are sitting, they say there will be no chickens. [Leather, 1912: 17]

[In Hartland, Devon] the number of goslings hatched and reared is governed by the number of wild daffodils in the first bunch of the season brought into the house. [Chope, 1932: 154]

Unlucky to take daffodils into the house before the goslings are hatched. [Isle of Man, spring 1982; Manx Folklife Survey]

The occurence of wild daffodils is sometimes said to indicate the former site of a religious foundation.

[At Frittlestoke, near Torrington, Devon, it was recorded in 1797 that] the people of the village call these plants Gregories, a name that struck us on account of its coinciding with the appellation of the order to which the neighbouring monastery belonged (the Canons of St Gregory). [Britten and Holland, 1886: 541]

In both Hampshire and the Isle of Wight it was generally said that wild daffodils indicated the site of a monastery. St Urian's Copse, a short distance from Brading on the Island, is well known for its primroses and daffodils. There is a tradition that daffodils grow in profusion on only one side of a track running through the copse because a religious house once stood there. [Boase, 1976: 115]

The only sizeable population of wild daffodils in the London area is found at Abbey Wood, a locality whose name commemorates Lesney Abbey. [Members of the South London Botanical Institute, March 1979]

At Fovant, in Wiltshire, daffodils were used to commemorate soldiers who died in 1918.

During the World War, 1914–1918, there was a large camp of Australian soldiers at Fovant, Wilts. Many died during the flu epidemic of 1918, they were buried in a nearby churchyard. Since that date to the present time local schoolchildren on a certain day each year lay a single daffodil on each grave. [Pimperne, Dorset, January 1992]

This practice seems to have died out many years ago, as in June 1994 neither the rector of Fovant nor the headteacher of the village school could gather any recollections of it. However, Australian soldiers were unflatteringly associated with daffodils during the Second World War. *The Times* of 12 January 1993 reported that:

> Australian war veterans have angrily rejected newly released War Office papers blaming the cowardice of Australian soldiers for the fall of Singapore in 1942. 'The Australians were known as daffodils, beautiful to look at but yellow all through,' says one of the documents.

Both the daffodil and the LEEK are national symbols of Wales.

> The daffodil is associated with St David because it is traditionally said to bloom first on his day. It is an easier emblem to wear than the older leek, and every schoolchild in Wales sports one, real or artificial, on March 1st. [Hole, 1950: 45]

Since 1990 National Daffodil Day has been promoted by Marie Curie Cancer Care.

> Saturday is National Daffodil Day. Millions of the spring blooms will be given away around the U.K. in exchange for a donation to the Marie Curie Cancer Care. It is hoped to raise more than £20,000.
>
> The daffodil has been adopted by Marie Curie as a symbol of new hope and life, as a reminder of the many positive developments in cancer care, treatment and research. [*Balham and Tooting Guardian,* 5 April 1990]

At about the same time the Irish Cancer Society similarly adopted the daffodil as a symbol.

On the Isles of Scilly:

> Prince Charles is paid one daffodil annually as rent for the untenanted lands of Scilly—paid by local Environmental Trust. [St Mary's, Isles of Scilly, September 1992].

Dainties – a Banffshire name for DANDELION.

Daisy (*Bellis perennis*). In many parts of the country daisies were considered to be harbingers of spring.

> 'It ain't spring,' said an old cottager to me 'until you can plant your foot upon twelve daisies.' [*N & Q,* 2 ser. 3: 343, 1857]

> Spring had arrived when you could put your foot on seven, or, in some places, nine daisies—the number could vary even between neighbours. [Wicken, Cambridgeshire, April 1993]

Daisies were often used in love DIVINATION.

> In Wales the daisy is generally selected by the doubting maiden who is wishful to test the fidelity of her lover. Gathering a daisy, she commences plucking the petals off, saying with each one, 'Does he love me?—much—a little—devotedly—not at all,' and the last petal decides the question. [Trevelyan, 1909: 97]

> Pluck daisy petals—'He loves me, he loves me not.' [Llanuwchyllln, Gwynedd, April 1991]

The making of daisy chains, usually by slitting the stem of a daisy and inserting a second daisy through the slit, is a well-known and widespread childhood occupation.

> As children . . . we used to make endless daisy chains to wear round our necks and in our hair. [Hyson Green, Nottingham, October 1985]

> Daisy chains were made by children to hang round their necks. The end of each stalk was split a little way with the finger nail to make an opening big enough to poke the next daisy's head through and so on until the chain was long enough to go round one's neck. [Worcester, October 1991]

More rarely, chains are made by threading daisy flowers onto a RUSH.

> A daisy chain is made by getting a rush and if the end of the rush is brittle you should break it off. Then you would pick the daisies and nip off the stem close to the cup and press the pointed end of the rush through the flower. One by one the daisies are put on, until the rush is almost full. The rush is then curved round, the pointed end is pressed into the thick end and the chain is made. [IFCSS MSS 500: 447, Co. Limerick]

Rather unconvincingly,

> it is sometimes said that the habit of dressing children in daisy chains and coronals comes from a desire to protect them against being carried off by the fairies. Daisies are a sun symbol and therefore protective magic. [Briggs, 1976: 87]

In the south-west of Ireland in 1943:

> An old New Year custom in the form of 'Penny for Daisy' was carried out as usual by children on New Year's Day and large numbers of children collected the first flower of 1943 and received pennies for them. [*Munster Express*, 8 January 1943]

Daisies were associated with, and worn by schoolgirls on, Empire Day.

> Another recollection [of schooldays in the early 1920s] was of Empire Day, 24 May—lessons were excused and all sang patriotic songs—with the Town Mayor and Mayoress and governors come; all the girls wore daisy chains. [Bridport, Dorset, February 1985]

> We too held a special ceremony on Empire Day, and having been told that the lawn daisy grew in every country of the Empire, there was much striving to have a few to pin to your gym slip. Lawns were a bit scarce so my friends and I made our way to the nearby Olympia, at the site of which was a semi-private road which had a narrow strip of grass backed by iron railings, great was our joy on seeing it liberally sprinkled with daisies and great were our efforts to get our arms far enough through the railings to pick some. We always managed it! [Letter from Stratford-upon-Avon, Warwickshire, in *This England*, Winter 1988]

Dame's violet

[In south London in the 1920s], 'D'you remember the way we used to go around the big houses before Empire Day, asking if we could pick their daisies?'

Remember? . . . I saw the two of us stepping on the tiled paths towards great doors . . . I heard small voices asking, 'Please, can we pick your daisies?'

Daisy lawns at the top of Earlsfield were white as milk for Empire Day and many of the rich people who lived among them were glad to have them picked green. We took them to school to celebrate the Empire. The word had gone out: 'Gather daisies. The daisy is a symbol of our greatness.'

Indeed it was. The golden centre was us—Great Britain; the petals were the colonies, absolutely inseparable and dependent on us. [Chamberlain, 1990: 164]

In the seventeenth century the daisy was valued for the treatment of broken bones.

The small Daisie is of greater Reputation than the other [the ox-eye daisy], because it helpeth Bones to knit again. It is therefore called by our people in the North of England Banwort, by which name I knew it forty years ago at Keibergh in the Parish of Kirk-oswald, and County of Cumbria, where I drew my first Breath, May the last 1676. [Threlkeld, 1726: 23]

In the twentieth century:

[On Colonsay daisies were] one of the principal ingredients used in the preparation of healing ointments. [McNeill, 1910: 134]

[My south Dorset friend] gave me a cure for BOILS. 'Find a place where you can cover seven or nine daisies with your foot. Then pick and eat them.' [Rawlence, 1914: 84]

Dame's violet (Hesperis matronalis)

In Mitcham, Surrey (1928–1939) we said that it was lucky to have some dame's violet in the garden—near the back gate and the back door—we called it sweet rocket. [Paston, Cambridgeshire, November 1993]

Dandelion (Taraxacum officinale, agg.). The idea that the picking of dandelion flowers leads to bed-wetting is widespread and well-known even in urban areas.

When I was a child in Brixton (1950s) we believed that if you picked dandelion flowers you would wet your bed. [St Albans, Hertfordshire, November 1979]

Dandelions: not to be picked. Very unlucky. Children in Fife (1930s) called them 'pee-the-beds' and anyone who picked them was mocked. [Apples, Switzerland, February 1983]

An Irish lady told me that if you gathered dandelions, and brought them indoors, you would wet your bed that night! [Capel Hendre, Dyfed, September 1983]

Another day, when I was nearly seven years old, I had gathered a bunch of dandelions—this time grandmother told me that I risked wetting the bed if I had anything to do with these. [Bow Street, Dyfed, March 1984]

[I was born in 1949] as a child every other child I knew lived in horror of picking a dandelion—it was widely accepted as a fact this would lead to bed-wetting. [Belfast, February 1991]

This belief has given rise to many local names including: pee-beds [Clappersgate, Cumbria, October 1985], pee-in-bed [Accrington, Lancashire, March 1982], pee-the-bed [Belfast, February 1991], pee-the-beds [Parkstone, Dorset, June 1991], piss-i-beds [Langtoft, Humberside, March 1985], pissimire [Langtoft, Humberside, March 1985], piss-in-the-beds [Dainean, Co. Offaly, January 1985], pisterbed [Lenamore, Co. Longford, April 1991], pittly beds [Corbridge, Northumberland, January 1993], wet-the-bed [Stockport, Greater Manchester, March 1984], and wet-the-beds [Streatham, London, May 1983]

On the continent of Europe such names as the Dutch *pisse-bed* and the French *pissenlit* [Grigson, 1987: 393] reveal that similar names and beliefs are not restricted to the British Isles.

Children also use dandelion 'clocks'—ripe dandelion seedheads— to tell the time, or, more rarely, predict the future.

When dandelions lost their yellow petals and grew that fluffy material, children used to pluck them and by blowing it they imagined they could tell the time. Each blow was counted as an hour, starting at one o'clock. Whenever all the fluffy material was gone, that counted as the time of the day. [Daingean, Co. Offaly, January 1985]

As children in Notts in the 1920s . . . we blew dandelion clocks to tell the time. [Oban, Argyll, October 1990]

We used to blow dandelion seeds and count—'This year, next year, sometime, never' (to get married). [Llanuwchylln, Gwynedd, April 1991]

Learnt from my mother's knee, so to speak . . . dandelion seed heads when perfect were used to find out whether someone loved you or not by blowing short breaths at the plant and with each breath reciting 'He loves me, he loves me not,' until all the seeds had blown away and the last blow decided the result! [Worcester, October 1991].

Occasionally the seeds of dandelions are, like autumn leaves, considered to be lucky if caught.

The floating seeds of dandelions and similar plants are called 'fairies' by young children, and it is thought to be lucky to catch one. [South Kensington, London, November 1979]

Dandelion

As a child, evacuated to Elgin, Scotland, during World War II . . . Another 'taboo' plant was the common dandelion, it was supposed to make you wet the bed! . . . And yet, like all children, we didn't think anything of picking off the seed heads, which was supposed to tell you the time, according to how many times you blew on it to release all the little 'parachutes'. We believed the flying seeds were fairies, and blowing them released them from capture! If you should catch a passing fairy, you would make a wish before releasing it, then let it fly away on the wind. [Stevenage, Hertfordshire, January 1993]

Particularly in Ireland, dandelions were used in the treatment of a wide range of illnesses.

The juice that comes from the danelion [sic] is a cure for every disease. [IFCSS MSS 550: 274, Co. Tipperary]

Dandelion: Boil the leaves and the water in which they are boiled may be drunk. It is said to be a cure for anything. The leaves can also be eaten raw. Mr Sheehan has used it for his stomach. [IFCSS MSS 313: 310a, Co. Cork].

Dandelion tea from the leaves [was] a general tonic. [St Osyth, Essex, February 1989]

Roots of dandelion boiled, and strained, and drunk is good for consumptives. [IFCSS MSS 200: 73, Co. Leitrim]

KIDNEY TROUBLES: the leaf of dandelion is chewed in the mouth and the juice is swallowed. Mrs Griffin told me that this treatment cured Nora O'Callaghan . . . of the complaint about thirty years ago. [IFCSS MSS 450: 162, Co. Kerry]

Dandelion wine is good for INDIGESTION and kidney troubles. [Portland, Dorset, April 1991]

People used to go out . . . and gather dandelion. They brought them in and boiled them, the juice of the dandelions were a good cure for weak HEARTS. [IFCSS 589: 205, Co. Clare]

[The dandelion] was a great cure for the JAUNDICE, to boil it along with buttermilk and when it is boiled take out the weed and drink the mixture. [IFCSS MSS 717: 217, Co. Meath]

Dandelion Tea: First they put a knife under it and lifted it from the roots. They saved it in the sun until it got quite hard. Then they boiled the kettle and poured the boiling water on it, strained it, and then put it into bottles. Then they drank it, and it was very good for the NERVES. [IFCSS MSS notebooks 442c, Co. Kerry]

Herbal remedies for WARTS: squeeze the white milky juice of the dandelion onto the wart and allow to dry. Repeat the application as often as possible. The wart will blacken and eventually drop off. [Langtoft, Humberside, July 1985]

Dandelion milk was used by my mother to cure WARTS on the fingers. [Histon, Cambridgeshire, January 1989]

Local plant names from an elderly friend in Porthnockie . . . bum-pipes—dandelions, which were, like DOCK leaves, used to soothe stings. [Edinburgh, December 1991]

To cure a sting of a NETTLE: look around and if there is a dandelion beside it you would rub the juice of it to it, it will cure the sting. [IFCSS MSS 50: 295, Co. Galway]

POULTRY-KEEPERS valued dandelions as food for turkeys.

Dandelion is very good for turkeys. It makes them strong and healthy. [IFCSS MSS 500: 238, Co. Limerick]

We used dandelion leaves a lot in feeding young turkeys which were very delicate and hard to rear. The leaves were chopped up and mixed with scrambled or hard-boiled eggs. [Piltown, Co. Tipperary, April 1991]

Rightly or wrongly, children considered dandelion leaves to be ideal food for pet rabbits.

Local plant names from an elderly friend in Porthnockie . . . dainties or denties—both flower and leaves of dandelion, the leaves being picked to feed pet rabbits. [Edinburgh, December 1991]

Dandelion flowers are used in the making of a favourite homemade wine.

You should pick dandelion flowers for your dandelion wine on ST GEORGE'S DAY. [Wimbledon, London, November 1983]

In wine-making circles, traditionally, dandelion wine is made on 23 April. [Atkins, 1986: 37]

Dane's blood – a name for DWARF ELDER and PASQUE FLOWER.

Danewort – see DWARF ELDER.

Darnel (*Lolium temulentum*) – believed to be the TARES of the New Testament parable.

Dashel – a Cornish variant of THISTLE.

Dead man's bells – a Morayshire name for SEA CAMPION.

Dead man's flesh – a Suffolk name for COW PARSLEY.

Deadman's mittens – a Shetland name for AUTUMN GENTIAN.

Death. In Devon and Cornwall during the nineteenth century it was customary to deck pot plants with black crepe when death occurred in a household.

[In Cornwall] following death . . . plants would be put in mourning and swathed in black crepe; otherwise they too would drop their heads and die. [Deane and Shaw, 1975: 135]

In her *Walks about St Hilary* (1879), Charlotte Pascoe recorded:

I saw with my own eyes a little black flag attached to our church-woman's bits of mignonette, which she assured me had begun to quail since her poor grandson was burnt to death, but had revived after she had put on it a piece of mourning.

Not only had the woman's mignonette suffered, but plants belonging to her daughter, who lived in Penzance, had begun to droop after the accident, and had revived only after a piece of black cloth had been tied to each one [Radford, 1961: 268].

See also FUNERAL FLOWERS.

Denties – a Banffshire name for DANDELION.

Devil – associated plants include BRAMBLE, COW PARSLEY, FOXGLOVE, PARSLEY, PARSNIP, and SELFHEAL.

Devil's bit scabious (*Succisa pratensis*; syn. *Scabiosa succisa*)

The scabious . . . was once called forebitten more or bitten-off root. In order to account for this strange appearance in the root it was asserted that it had been bitten off by someone, and surely no one but the devil could perform that, underground. So the tale started that he did it out of malice, for he saw that the herb was good for all manner of diseases, and he begrudges man the use of such a valuable medicine. The plant now bears the name of devil's bit in England; in German it is similarly known as *teufels abbiss* . . . [Alternatively] with this root the devil practised such power, that the Mother of God, out of compassion, took from him the means to do so with it any more. In the great vexation he felt at being thus deprived of his power, he bit off the root, which has never grown again. [Friend, 1884: 50]

In Gloucestershire the name [fire-leaves] is given to the leaves of Plantains, more especially *Plantago media*; and we have heard it in Herefordshire used for the *Scabiosa succisa* (Devil's bit), which is very prevalent on the flats of the Wye. Both are named fire-leaves on the same principle, for we have seen a farmer in Gloucestershire with a Plantain leaf and he of Herefordshire with a Scabious leaf, select specimens, and violently twist them to ascertain if any water could be squeezed out of them. If so, this moisture is said to induce fermentation in newly carried hay sufficient to fire the rick. Both are mischievous in pasture, because such thick-leaved plants take longer to dry than the Grasses. [*Gardeners' Chronicle*, 11 August 1870: 738]

Cf. FIRE GRASS and HOT WEED.

Devil's flooer – a Shetland name for CINERARIA.

Devil's ha'pence – a Kent name for HONESTY.

Devil's hatties – a Morayshire name for SEA CAMPION.

Devil's tobacco – a Staffordshire name for HOGWEED.

Diabetes – treated using REFLEXED STONECROP, PEANUT, and PELLI-TORY OF THE WALL.

Diarrhoea – prevented using BEETROOT and CARROT; cured using BILBERRY, HEDGE VERONICA, MULBERRY, OAK, RASPBERRY, SHEPHERD'S PURSE, TORMENTIL, and WOOD AVENS; in Manx cats cured using CREEP-ING CINQUEFOIL.

Diphtheria – caused by PRIVET.

Disco grass – a Radnor name for PURPLE MOOR GRASS.

Divination – plants and plant materials used in love divination in-clude: APPLE, ASH, BAY, BRACKEN, CABBAGE, COWSLIP, CRAB APPLE, FLAX, FRUIT STONES, GOOSEGRASS, HEMP, IVY, KNAPWEED, LAUREL, ORANGE, ORPINE, OXEYE DAISY, PEA, RIBWORT PLANTAIN, RYE GRASS, TURNIP, and YARROW. See also DOWSERS.

Dock (*Rumex* spp.). Dock leaves are a commonly used cure for nettle stings.

> Up to the age of 11 I attended the local primary school . . . on 29 May all the children had to wear a piece of OAK leaf, preferably with an oak apple on it (thereby known as Oak Apple Day). Punishment for not wearing a piece of oak leaf was being stung by a nettle of which there were many to perform this task. Whoever was stung rubbed the place with a dock leaf, whilst saying the phrase 'Dock leaf, dock leaf, you go in; Sting nettle, sting nettle, you come out.' [Dobwalls, Cornwall, January 1985]

> If one got a sting of a nettle and one rubbed a dock leaf it would cure it, and we did this as children and it seemed to bring relief. I am going back to the 1950s and 1960s, as I was born in 1951. [Maynooth, Co. Kildare, February 1991]

> The dock leaf or 'docken' . . . was a cure for a nettle sting, saying 'Docken, docken, cure nettle,' but this was not much good. The real cure was where a new leaf was growing down at the ground, there was a drop of liquid in it, this liquid rubbed on the sting cured it. [Lenamore, Co. Longford, April 1991]

Cf. HORSERADISH.

Dock

According to William Coles in his *Art of Simpling*, published in 1656:

The seeds of docke tyed to the left arme of a woman doe help Barrennesse.

More recently in County Donegal:

No woman may fear to be barren who carries a bag filled with docken seeds under her left oxter. [St Clair, 1971: 58]

Docks could be used to treat a variety of ailments.

Men working in the ironstone quarries near Deddington [Oxfordshire] often get a peculiar SORE on their arms, and this they treat by cutting a dock-root across and rubbing the sore with the fresh cut surface . . .

To purify BLOOD an infusion made by pouring boiling water on to young dock-roots or COLTSFOOT leaves is sometimes recommended. [C., 1951: 13]

A cure for BOILS: Take as many dock roots as you can find and boil them in water until you get a thick gooey liquid, which the patient should drink. [Thorncombe, Dorset, September 1977]

For RHEUMATISM: Gather dock leaves, carefully dry them and bind them around the affected joint. (Said to be a complete cure). [Thorncombe, Dorset, April 1986]

When I was a child (I am now 91) we lived on the Isle of Man, we were quite hard up and couldn't afford doctors' bills. My father was mowing grass one day and the scythe slipped and cut him very badly on the leg, he daren't stay home from work, so with my mother's help, doctored himself; every day after school I collected large dock leaves, which mother crushed with a rolling pin, then applied leaves straight on to the CUT which in time healed and caused no further trouble. [Tiverton, Devon, February 1991]

As children in the 1920s dock leaves were picked to ease nettle stings and SUNBURN . . . we would wrap these around arms and legs. [Colwyn Bay, Clwyd, June 1992].

My father was a builder and in going to work in hot weather, he always used to place a dock leaf in each boot (veins uppermost). These were taken out on returning home. My father used to say this was good for perspiring feet . . . he never had bad feet, and he used to walk great distances. [SLF MSS, Stannington, South Yorkshire, September 1970]

Non-medicinal uses included:

Farm workers put a dock leaf in their tobacco pouches to keep contents moist. [Pimperne, Dorset, January 1992]

I know someone who uses dock leaves to keep his tobacco moist—he's Jamaican. [South Kensington, London, February 1994]

If the old horse-men found a dock root when they were ploughing they would pick it up and feed it to their horses . . . to bring up the 'hammer marks' [dapple marks] on their coats. [Rodmell, East Sussex, December 1992]

Docken—the seeds stripped off and lightly boiled were widely used as an addition to normal poultry feeding, and the stalks were used to make BASKETS. The stalks had to absorb salt to keep them pliable, and this was done either by immersion in the sea for some hours, or by sprinkling with salt. [Lerwick, Shetland, March 1994]

Doctrine of Signatures. A theory elaborated in the sixteenth and seventeenth centuries, which observed that plants had characters or 'signatures' which provided guidance to the diseases which they were capable of curing. It is difficult to ascertain the extent to which the Doctrine was accepted by the educated classes, from whom it might have been passed on to the mostly illiterate poor. It is probable that the Doctrine has received more than its fair share of notice in popular twentieth-century publications.

An admirable summary of the Doctrine's history is provided by Agnes Arber in her study *Herbals* (1938). The first writer to propound the theory was Theophrastus Bombast von Hohenheim (1493–1541), better known by his Latinized name of Paracelsus. Hohenheim, who had a meagre knowledge of plants, experienced a varied career which culminated in a short-lasting appointment as a professor at Basle. His ideas were enthusiastically taken up and expanded by Giambattista Porta in his *Phytognomonica*, first published in Naples in 1588. Porta's work included the suggestion that long-lived plants would lengthen man's life, whereas the eating of short-lived plants would shorten the eater's life.

In Britain the Doctrine was wholeheartedly commended in the publications of William Coles. In chapter 17 of his *Art of Simpling* (1656), Coles declared that although sin and Satan had plunged mankind into an ocean of infirmities, God in his mercy had made herbs for the use of man, and had 'given them particular signatures whereby man may read even in legible Characters, the use of them'. However, not even Coles could find signatures on all plants. In chapter 18 he attempted to deal with this problem, and explained that although God had provided guidance by imprinting signatures on some herbs, as man had not been created to be 'like an idle loyterer or Truant' other herbs had been left unmarked so that man might discover their virtues by his own ingenuity. A year later Coles published his larger work, entitled *Adam in Eden*. This included such observations as:

> The milky juyce which Issueth forth from the wounded stalks and Leaves [of lettuce] is a sufficient signature, that this Herb, if it be eaten boyled or raw, maketh plenty of milke in Nurses. [Coles, 1657: 186]

> A Decoction of the long Mosse that hangs upon Trees, in a manner like hair, is very profitable to be used in the falling off of hair, and this it doth by Signature. [Coles, 1657: 31]

At the time Coles was writing it was not usual to distinguish between mosses and lichens, and it seems that Coles' 'long Mosse' was in fact a 'beard lichen' of the genus *Usnea*. A shampoo which contains usnic acid, derived from *Usnea* spp. and other lichens, is currently available from health-food shops [personal observation, Streatham, London, September 1993].

The Doctrine was repudiated before the end of the sixteenth century by writers such as Dodoens (1517–85), but continued to be mentioned in works published in the eighteenth century. More recently popular writers on folklore have included the Doctrine of Signatures, but it is difficult to work out if it ever strayed far from the published works to become a genuine folk belief.

Although the Doctrine of Signatures did not necessarily conflict with the beliefs held by astrological botanists, Coles thought it necessary to expose the fallacies he found in the writings of the leading astrologer-herbalist, Nicholas Culpeper. He did this by calling as evidence the opening verses of the Bible. God created plants on the third day and the heavenly bodies on the fourth, so these later creations could not be expected to influence the earlier ones [see Lownes, 1940].

Dodder (*Cuscuta epithymum*)

> *Herbe d'émeute* . . . so named from its powerful properties, which are utilised by Guernsey farmers on particular occasions in the treatment of horned cattle. A handful of the fresh plant is placed on a CABBAGE leaf, which is then rolled up and given to a cow to eat. [Marquand, 1906: 41]

Doddering dickies – a Yorkshire name for QUAKING GRASS.

Dog daisy – a name for OX-EYE DAISY.

Dog oak – a Northamptonshire name for FIELD MAPLE.

Dog rose (*Rosa canina*)

> 'A school prank in east Hertfordshire, 1945–50 . . . the most awful itching material was made from rose hips—the hairs on the seeds being put down someone's neck—a bath and complete change of clothing being the only cure.'

> 'I can confirm being a sufferer of rose hip hairs down the back of my collar at school (*c*.1936–39), Sutton, Surrey. It was a regular autumn practice!'

Also known in County Durham; Blackpool, Lancashire in the 1950s, and Dorset in the 1970s. [Members of the Botanical Society of the British Isles meeting in London, November 1991]

During and for some years after the Second World War, children in the north-east of England and elsewhere used to collect rose hips which were used in the manufacture of rose-hip syrup.

Children in Northumberland and parts of north Durham gathered rose hips and sold them; for several years I and several friends did this each autumn.

The man who started the practice was a friend of my family. He was Mr Norman Pattison and he worked for the firm of Scott and Turner, the makers of Andrews Liver Salts, at their factory in Gallowgate, Newcastle-upon-Tyne.

In his early years with the firm he was a delivery driver, and when the company first began to make Delrosa, before the Second World War, he gathered wild rose hips for them. Then his wife joined in, and more of his friends and relatives. Mrs Pattison was a former teacher of girls' P.E. at Jarrow Grammar School, and was a close friend of my aunt, also a teacher. So when I started at that school as a pupil in 1941, Mrs Pattison had enlisted the help of at least two of her former colleagues on the staff, who organized groups of pupils (almost every one of us girls) to go out in late September and October, on Saturdays (I don't recall Sundays) and gather the hips from the hedgerows. Two teachers—the Geography and Botany mistresses—combined the hip gathering with field studies of their own subjects, and we enjoyed these outings, apart from the scratches!

Our rose hips were weighed and Scott and Turner paid us 3d a pound for them; I know we received a letter from them telling us how much we were contributing to the war effort by enabling more rose hip syrup to be made—a valuable source of vitamin C, which would maintain our health during wartime.

I went on these expeditions until 1948, when I left school for college. [Heworth, Tyne and Wear, December 1985]

I'm 48 and I have lived within a mile of my present address all my life.

For several years, up to the time I left school aged 15, myself and other of my fellow scholars who felt so inclined, gathered hips in our spare time. We then took them to school where they were weighed by a particular teacher (a Miss Temperley) and we were paid 3d (old money) for every pound collected. The accumulation of hips collected was made up in sacks, which were at intervals collected by a company, I think its name was Scott Turner of Gallowgate in Newcastle-upon-Tyne, who made the hips into rose hip syrup.

I was quite a keen collector and having a bicycle I often ventured alone and further afield to places rich in hips and unknown to my school pals.

This resulted, in my final year at school, in my gathering about 23 stone of hips. I ended up being the highest collector that year, which earned me the princely sum of over £4, and as the Company gave me a bonus of a free bottle of syrup for every fifty pounds gathered, also six free bottles of syrup plus a badge (long gone) proclaiming me top collector. [Wideopen, Tyne and Wear, November 1985]

I picked rose hips during the last war. The collection was just one of the many things organized by my school—Gaynes, Upminster—and was one of many things we were expected to do for the war effort—from writing ration books to collecting razor blades! We were definitely not paid for any war effort activities.

We used the term 'Hipseyhaws' to cover rose hips and HAWTHORN haws—never two separate words. [Yafforth, North Yorkshire, January 1990]

The firm of Scott and Turner has now been taken over by Winthrop Laboratories, who continue to make rose-hip syrup.

We currently obtain our rose hips through a U.K. agent, who obtains supplies on the international market, and these are supplied de-seeded, halved and dried. The most common source at the present time is Chile. [The Senior Packaging Buyer, Winthrop Laboratories, January 1986]

The hips and young shoots of dog roses were eaten by children.

[I am an Invernessian:] rose hips were edible, once one removed the rather furry growth around the seeds, which was inclined to stick in the throat. The skins however were soft and very sweet. They were called muckies. [Solihull, West Midlands, March 1991]

We ate SORREL, beech leaves and briar tops. [Farnborough, Kent, January 1993]

My cousin, now aged 78, remembers chewing new wood from the base of wild roses when they first began to shoot and called this bacon. [Corbridge, Northumberland, February 1993]

The moss gall, or robin's pincushion, which frequently occurs on wild rose bushes, was formerly much used to prevent a variety of illnesses.

Hang round the patient's neck the excrescence often found upon the briar-rose, and called here in Sussex by the name of Robin Redbreast's Cushion; it is the finest thing known for WHOOPING COUGH. [Latham, 1878: 38]

[In Shropshire] the wild-rose gall is . . . considered good for TOOTHACHE. 'If you light on a briar-boss *accidental* w'en yo' an' the tuthache, an' wear it in yore boasom, it'll cure it.' [Burne, 1883: 194]

[In Wiltshire, canker rose] the mossy gall on the dog rose, formed by *Cynips rosae* [now known as *Diplolepis rosae*]; often carried in the pocket as a charm against RHEUMATISM. [Dartnell and Goddard, 1894: 23]

In Wales they say if this [a moss gall] is placed under the pillow of a person who cannot SLEEP, it will perfectly restore him. But it was necessary to remove it at a given time, or, according to the old story, he would never awake. [Trevelyan, 1909: 98]

Isle of Axholme . . . A green 'tossel' from a wild rose briar gathered and hung up in the house will prevent whooping cough. [Rudkin, 1936: 28]

Briar-ball: an excrescence from the briar, placed by [Northamptonshire] boys in their coat cuffs, as a charm to prevent flogging. [Baker, 1854: 78]

Dog's dick – a Warwickshire name for fruiting LORDS AND LADIES.

Dog's flourish – a central west Scotland name for COW PARSLEY.

Dog's mercury (*Mercurialis perennis*)
It is called on the Isle of Sky *Lus-glen-Bracadale*, and I was informed that it is there sometimes taken by way of infusion to bring on salivation. [Lightfoot, 1777: 621]

Dool tree – see JOUG TREE.

Dropsy – cured using BROOM, BUTCHER'S BROOM, FOXGLOVE, and PELLITORY OF THE WALL.

Dowsers – plants used by include HAZEL and TAMARISK.

Drunkenness – alleviated using SALAD BURNET.

Duckweed (*Lemna minor*). The NURSERY BOGEY Jenny Greenteeth was associated with duckweed-covered pools in the Liverpool area and other parts of north-west England, where she may still be used to frighten children away from dangerous places. According to some people Jenny (or Jinny, as she is more usually known outside books) Greenteeth is simply a name for duckweed.

At this day in all east Lancashire the older inhabitants call the green moss which covers the surface of stagnant ponds 'Jenny Greenteeth'. Further, I have often been told by my mother and nurse that if I didn't keep my teeth clean I should some day be dragged into one of these pools by Jenny Greenteeth, and I have met many elderly people who have had the same threat applied to them. [N & Q, 10 ser. 1: 365, 1904]

I was brought up in the Upton/Cronton area of the west side of Widnes in Lancashire (now Cheshire), about twelve miles inland from Liverpool. It was, and still is, largely a farming area, and many of the fields contain pits—never ponds—which, I believe, are old marl pits. Some of them have quite steep sides. Jinny was well known to me and my contemporaries and was simply the green weed, duckweed, which covered the surface of stagnant water. Children who strayed too close to the edge of these pits would be warned to watch out for Jinny Greenteeth, but it was the weed itself which was believed to hold children under the water. There was never any suggestion that there was a witch of any kind there. [Woolton, Merseyside, December 1980]

As a child in Cheshire I heard the name Jenny Greenteeth given to the bright green water plant that lies on the surface of stagnant ponds (the minute leaves are rather like tiny teeth) and imagined that if one fell into the pond, the green scum-like plant would close over one's head, thus Jenny (or Jinny) Greenteeth had 'got you'. [Great Meols, Cheshire, November 1980]

According to other people the growth of duckweed on a pool's surface is a certain indication that Jenny lurked in its depths.

As a child, about 50 years ago in the Liverpool area, I was frightened by Jenny Greenteeth, a sort of fairy, who would drag people down into deep pools. Jenny was particularly associated with pools covered with duckweed. [Kensington, London, November 1979]

[I am now 34] I remember, as a very small child, being told by my mother to stay away from ponds as Ginny Greenteeth lived in them. However, I only recall Ginny living in ponds which were covered in a green weed of the type which has tiny leaves, and covers the entire surface of the pond.

The theory was that Ginny enticed little children into the ponds by making them look like grass and safe to walk on. As soon as the child stepped onto the green it, of course, parted, and the child fell through into Ginny's clutches and was drowned. The green weed then closed over, hiding all traces of the child ever being there. This last point was the one which really terrified me and kept me well away from ponds, and, indeed, my own children have also been told about Ginny, although ponds aren't as numerous these days.

As far as I know Ginny had no known form, due to the fact that she never appeared above the surface of the pond. [Irby, Merseyside, November 1980]

However, according to a 68-year-old woman, the Jenny Greenteeth which was believed to inhabit two pools beside Moss Pitts Lane in Fazakerley, 'had pale green skin, green teeth, very long green locks of hair, long green fingers with long nails, and she was very thin with a pointed chin and very big eyes' [Bebington, Merseyside, November 1980].

Occasionally Jenny could be found well away from watery places. In the 1930s Liverpool children would rush past the old St James's Cemetery, which was reputedly her home, and in the 1940s children living in south Cheshire were told that Jenny would seize them if they ventured too near railway lines [Vickery, 1983: 249].

Dug's lug – a Shetland name for YELLOW IRIS.

Dulse (*Rhodymenia palmata*)

Seaweed—dulse—is quite a sought after delicacy near Ballycastle. One can see men wading at low tide among the rocks in spring to gather it. We used to nibble bits raw, but more traditionally it is dried—and may be sold in shops or (very traditionally) at the Lammas Fair at the very end of August in Ballycastle. [Ballycastle, Co. Antrim, January 1991]

Dwarf cornel (*Cornus suecica*)

The berries have a sweet waterish taste, and are supposed by the highlanders to create a great appetite, whence the Erse name [*Lus-a-chraois*, plant-of-gluttony]. [Lightfoot, 1777: 12]

Dwarf elder (*Sambucus ebulus*), also known as danewort, or Dane's blood, from the widespread belief that it grew where Danes had been slaughtered. Thus in the seventeenth century John Aubrey wrote:

Danes-blood (*ebulus*) about Slaughtonford [Wiltshire] in plenty. There was heretofore a great fight with the Danes, which made the inhabitants give it that name. [Aubrey, 1847: 50]

This belief was also known in Scandinavia, for on 29 May 1741 Carl Linnaeus examined what was thought to be a mysterious plant growing in Smaland:

On a field grew almost nothing but hound's tongue [*Cynoglossum officinale*] and the plant which is called *Mannablod* [Man's blood].

   This *mannablod* or *manna-wort* [man's herb] is a plant which is much talked about in Sweden . . . for it was said that it grows in no other place in the world but here at Kalmar Castle, where it once grew up from the BLOOD of Swedes and Danes, killed in warfare on this field. We were much taken aback when we realised that the plant was nothing but the common *Ebulus* or *Sambucus herbacea* . . . which grows wild in the greater part of Germany, around Vaxjo and in gardens. [Asberg and Stearn, 1973: 40]

An alternative reason for dwarf elder being associated with Danes was given in John Parkinson's *Theatrum Botanicum* [1640: 210]:

It is supposed it tooke the name Danewort from the strong purging quality it hath, many times bringing them that use it into a fluxe, which then we say they are troubled with the Danes.

On the Isle of Wight:

The plant is, I understand, sought after by farriers and horse-doctors as a stimulant and to improve the coats of horses, which may account for its present scarcity in some localities, as between Chine cottage and Rose cliff, where a countryman informed me he had formerly seen it in abundance. [Bromfield, 1856: 231]

Cf. WHITE BRYONY. In Ireland:

About Williamstown and Mullincross in mid Louth . . . dwarf elder (*Sambucus ebulus*), there called she-elder, was used to make a preparation for the treatment of ULCERS on cows' udders and teats. [Synnott, 1979: 37]

Dyer's broom – a name for DYER'S GREENWEED.

Dyer's greenweed (*Genista tinctoria*)
A plant which is known to have abounded in the neighbourhood of Kendal [Cumbria] many years ago, though it be now nearly uprooted, called by Linnaeus *Genista tinctoria*, and commonly called 'Dyer's Broom', was brought in large quantities to Kendal, from the neighbouring commons and marshes, and sold to the dyers. The plant, after being dried, was boiled for the colouring matter it contained, which was a beautiful yellow. The cloth was first boiled in alum water, for the mordant, and then immersed in the yellow dye. It was then dried, and submerged in a blue liquor extracted from woad [to produce the famous Kendal green]. [Nicholson, 1861: 238]

Dyes – plants used include ALPINE MEADOW-RUE, AMPHIBIOUS BISTORT, BILBERRY, BOGBEAN, BOG MYRTLE, CROWBERRY, DYER'S GREENWEED, FUCHSIA, GORSE, HAZEL, HEATHER, IRISH SPURGE, LADY'S BEDSTRAW, LICHENS, LUPIN, OAK apples, ONION, PINEAPPLE WEED, POPPY, WALNUT, WHITE WATERLILY, and YELLOW IRIS; for further information see Grierson, 1986.

E

Earache – caused by POPPY; treated using ASH, BEETROOT, ONION, and WILLOW.

Earaches – a Nottinghamshire name for POPPY.

Early purple orchid (*Orchis mascula*).

> One species of orchis, which in Cheshire is called Gethsemane, is said to have been growing at the foot of the cross, and to have received some drops of blood on its leaves: hence the dark stains by which they have ever since been marked. [*Quarterly Review*, July 1863: 231]

> I was told by Mrs D (a devout Catholic) of Chillington, Ilminster, in the 1950s that the red spots on the leaves of orchids are where the BLOOD dropped from Christ when he was on the Cross. [Radstock, Avon, March 1982]

> I was born in a village called Hardwicke, near Gloucester, and my memories all stem from my life there. 'Tom Thumb', or early purple orchids, were a bit suspect in the house. They were connected with death. [Newcastle-under-Lyme, Staffordshire, March 1983]

The root system of the early purple orchid typically consists of two swollen tubers, which somewhat resemble testicles. Thus the plant is associated with love-making and procreation.

> The decoction of the roots drank in Goats-milk mightily provokes Venery, and helps Conception, and strengthens the Genital parts. [K'Eogh, 1735: 49]

> [North-east Scotland:] To gain love there were various methods. The roots of the orchis were dug up. (The old root is exhausted, and when cast into water, floats—this is hatred. The new root is heavy, and sinks when thrown into water—this is love, because nothing sinks deeper than love.) The root—love—was dried, ground, and secretly administered as a potion. Strong love was the result. [Gregor, 1874: 106]

> In Co. Wicklow the early purple orchis is called Mogra-myra, and is supposed to be most efficient as a love-potion. [Kinahan, 1881: 117]

> The orchid vies with the MANDRAKE as an APHRODISIAC—excessive ardour can be cooled with STRAWBERRY leaf tea. [Larne, Co. Antrim, January 1992]

According to many commentators, the LONG PURPLES mentioned in Shakespeare's *Hamlet* were early purple orchids, but see discussion under LORDS AND LADIES.

Earning grass

Earning grass – a Lanarkshire name for BUTTERWORT.

Earth star – an East Anglian name for BUCK'S HORN PLANTAIN.

Easter eggs – dyed using GORSE and ONION; for a more extensive list of egg-dyes see Newall, 1971: 380.

Easter Eve – graves decorated with flowers; see FLOWERING SUNDAY.

Easter ledges – a Cumbrian name for BISTORT.

Easter lily (*Lilium longiflorum*)

At Easter churches—or at least our church—are decorated with lilies—ARUM LILIES, and mostly nowadays *Lilium longiflorum*—bought in memory of the dead. [Purley, Surrey, April 1983]

The Easter lily associated with the 1916 Rising in Ireland is the ARUM LILY.

Eczema – treated using GOOD KING HENRY and IVY.

Eelgrass (*Zostera marina*), also known as marlie on the Shetland Islands.

The late W.H. Roberston told us that the marlie used to be so abundant towards the head of Weisdale Voe that a channel sometimes needed to be cut to allow the passage of small boats . . . The autumn gales would drive masses of eelgrass on to the beaches from where it was harvested for bedding cattle and for stuffing mattresses; for the latter purpose it had to very carefully dried. In the Weisdale area these practices continued into the early 1920s. In Orkney it was formerly used as a manure for fields and as a THATCH. [Scott and Palmer, 1987: 339]

Collected and dried as a stuffing for mattresses as it was believed to be proof against FLEAS. [Lerwick, Shetland, March 1994]

Eelworm – deterred using PHACELIA.

Egg and cheese – a Sussex name for WOOD SORREL.

Eggs and bacon – a widespread name for BIRD'S FOOT TREFOIL.

Egyptian plant – see KARMIC PLANT.

Elder (*Sambucus nigra*), also known as boor or bour tree. Elder is one of the most enigmatic plants in British folk tradition. On one hand it is feared and associated with WITCHES and on the other it is valued for its protective qualities, as a fly repellent, and for its use in many herbal remedies.

The whole plant hath a narcotic smell; it is not well to sleep under its shade. [Withering, 1776: 186]

[In Leitrim, Waterford and the south of Ireland] the elder or 'bore' tree is believed to have been the tree from which Judas Iscariot hanged himself. The proof of which is the fact that its leaves have an 'ugly smell', and, moreover, that its fruit has since degenerated from its original size and excellent flavour, and become worthless both as to size and taste. [Anon., 1916: 425]

It was said at Beckley that if you burn elder wood you will become bewitched. You never cut it down. In Wootton they say that the elder is a witch tree. You should not mend a wattle hedge with it, as it will give the witches power. If you cut it, it will bleed. [Oxfordshire Women's Institute groups, 1950s]

Unlucky to burn Tramman [elder], it is the FAIRIES' tree. [Lezayre, Isle of Man, c.1975; Manx Folklife Survey]

Normally in the Isle of Man elder is the fairies' tree which it is unlucky to cut down, or burn when fallen. I was told in 1992 by a forestry worker of his pleasure that a large elder had blown over into the field adjoining his garden and thus relieved him of the need to find someone willing to remove it. [Union Mills, Isle of Man, October 1993]

Elder flowers—it is alright to pick the flowers for wine or culinary use, but the tree is a friend of witches and the wood should never come into the house. [Ashreigney, Devon, July 1983]

Elder—unlucky to bring either flowers or wood into a house: (a) because it is the witches' tree, (b) because it was believed that Judas Iscariot hanged himself from an elder tree, (c) because if you fall asleep under elder flowers the scent will poison you or you will never wake up. [Driffield, Humberside, March 1985]

Collecting firewood from the hedges surrounding the cottage and returning happily laden, but being accused of bringing bits of elder into the house—it was considered unlucky to use these to light a fire. [Bow Street, Dyfed, October 1984]

The only unlucky plant which I have heard of is the elder tree, which the old people looked upon as unlucky. As I have heard the old people say, it was unhealthy to have an elder tree growing near the house as it was often noted the inhabitants seemed more prone to TUBERCULOSIS or 'Consumption' as it was known in Ireland in the old days.

However, as TB was rampant all over the country at that time, I don't know if the belief would have any significance. My own people however would not cut down an elder bush or burn it no matter how old or rotten it was. Nor allow an elder stick in the house, and it would be an unforgivable act to strike a child or even an animal with one. [Kill Village, Co. Kildare, October 1984]

The family name dies out on the property where the elder grows in the kitchen garden. [Skibbereen, Co. Cork, January 1993]

Do you know the Rollright Stones in Oxfordshire? You can't count them; you never get the same number twice. In the next field there is a big stone called King Arthur, and there are various stones called after his Knights around. There are some elder bushes nearby. We used to go there as children on our bicycles and try to count the stones. We were told that if we picked a flower or a berry from these elderberry bushes we would be turned into stone. We used to dare each other to pick a berry or a flower, but no one ever did. [Mitcham, Surrey, May 1986]

However, in the early part of the nineteenth century:

On Midsummer Eve, when the 'eldern' tree was in blossom, it was a custom for people to come up to the King Stone and stand in a circle. Then the 'eldern' was cut, as it bled 'the King moved his head.' [Evans, 1895: 20]

Sometimes it was thought that wood, berries, or flowers could be safely taken from an elder only if the tree's permission had been sought first.

Hearing one day that a baby in a cottage close to my own was ill, I went across to see what was the matter. Baby appeared right enough, and I said so; but its mother promptly explained. 'It were all along of my maister's thick 'ed; it were in this how: t'rocker cummed off t'cradle, an' he hedn't no more gumption than to mak' a new 'un out on illerwood without axing the Old Lady's leave, an' in coorse she didn't like that, and she came and pinched t'wean that outrageous he were a'most black i' t' face; but I bashed 'un off, an putten an' esh 'un on, an' t'wean is as gallus as owt agin.'

This was something quite new to me, and the clue seemed worth following up. So going home I went straight down to my backyard, where old Johnny Holmes was cutting up firewood—'chopping kindling,' as he would have said. Watching the opportunity, I put a knot of elder-wood in the way and said, 'You are not feared of chopping that are you?' 'Nay,' he replied at once, 'I bain't feared of choppin' him, he bain't wick (alive); but if her were wick I dussn't, not without axin' the Old Gal's leave, not if it were ever so' . . . (The words to be used are): 'Oh, them's slape enuff.' You just says, 'Owd Gal, give me of thy wood, and Oi will give some of moine, when I graws inter a tree.' [Heanley, 1901: 55]

If you chop an elder tree or fell it, you should bow three times and say:

Old Woman, Old Woman,
Give me some of your wood
And when I am dead
I'll give you some of mine.

[Whitwick, Leicestershire, August 1983]

[Staffordshire, 1930s:] my mother said it was the thing if one wanted blossoms or fruit from an elder tree to say 'Please Mother Elder may I have . . .' [Ponsanooth, Cornwall, November 1993]

In addition to records of elder being inauspicious, there are many records of it being a beneficial, protective tree.

[In Northumberland] an old man told me that his aunt used to keep a piece of bour tree, or elder, constantly in her kist (chest) to prevent her clothes from malign influence. [Hardy, 1895: 325]

In south Wales it was deemed very dangerous to build any premises on or near the spot where an eldertree stood.

In the past an elder planted before the door of a cow-shed or stable protected the cows and horses from witchcraft and sorcery. [Trevelyan, 1909: 103]

[In Scotland elder was] often planted near old crofts and cottages as protection from witches. [Webster, 1978: 342]

[In Guernsey elder] had to be planted as near as possible to the back door, the most used entrance, since it was a sacred tree and a good protection against witchcraft. [McClintock, 1987: 33]

[In Ireland] it is considered lucky to have an elderberry bush grow near your house, especially if it is 'self-set'. [Bracknell, Berkshire, August 1984]

Mother used elder leaves to make a pattern on the floor-bricks. Painting around them with red paint. Making the cross with elder leaves.
This was an old custom, going back to her grandmother's time, so the custom had to be continued despite the time-consuming nature of the work. [Bow Street, Dyfed, March 1984]

Elder: this was called Boortree . . . The leaves were boiled and the water used to dose pigs. For this purpose, and because it was supposed to be a protection against LIGHTNING, there was a tree of it at every house. It can still be seen growing in places where there are no houses now, but where houses were years ago. [Lenamore, Co. Longford, April 1991]

Family folklore passed on to me includes . . . one should plant a ROWAN and elder tree and never cut them down, in order to keep witches away. [Parkstone, Dorset, June 1991]

I can remember as a child elder growing around the wooden bottom-of-the-garden 'lavvy' at my uncle's farm near Brentwood, Essex, and many other similar loos with elder adjacent. I was told that the elder would live 'almost for ever', as if one root died off another would spring from a fallen branch or twig. They were treated with 'respect' as they kept away bad magic—no one used the word 'witches'—but the inference was there. [Yafforth, North Yorkshire, January 1990]

More usually elder trees were planted around toilets and other buildings to deter FLIES.

Elder bushes are invariably to be seen outside the dairy windows on the north side of old-fashioned farmhouses in the Midlands. This was done because elder-leaves are supposed to be very objectionable to flies, wasps and other insects, the tree thus provided both shade and protection. For the same reason a switch of elder with leaves on is used when taking or driving a swarm of bees. [N & Q, 11 ser. 12: 489, 1915]

When inspecting a slaughter house [in Cornwall] a summer or two ago, I commented on the absence of flies, and was told that this was due to a large elder bush growing some feet away and that branches of elder in any building would keep flies away. [Peter, 1915: 123]

An elderberry tree was always grown near the house—I think it was to keep flies away. [Didcot, Oxfordshire, February 1991]

According to some friends of mine elderberry bushes were planted by water butts and outside privies so that the smell would keep the flies away. [Horseheath, Cambridgeshire, April 1991]

As a youth my late father worked on the land . . .Often handling horses it was common practice to tie bunches of elder leaves to the harness to ward off flies. [St Osyth, Essex, February 1989]

My wife, who comes from Northumberland, tells me that her mother used to make up a concoction with elder flower when she was a child. All the family washed their faces in it to keep virulent Northumbrian midges at bay. She remembers it smelling not too pleasant, and tended to keep other children away as well, so she would take the first opportunity to wash it off! [Hexham, Northumberland, June 1988]

About twelve years ago in Girton, Cambridge, a small swarm of bees (apparently known as a 'cast') settled on a plum tree in our garden, about six feet up. A neighbour, Mr C. G. Puck (now 84 years old), a retired shepherd and lifelong beekeeper, came to collect the bees. He removed the queen bee from the swarm and placed her under a small open wooden box inverted on the ground under the tree. He then asked for a sprig of elder and laid this about nine inches above the swarm, saying that the smell of it was disliked by bees, and by the early evening all the bees had moved into the box . . . He had learned of the use of elder in this fashion from his beekeeper father, in his native village of Thriplow, south Cambridgeshire. [Girton, Cambridge, May 1988]

On the Isle of Man:

Each old cottage has a 'trammon', or elderberry tree, outside the door. This is used by the 'Phynodderree' to swing in. He is a kind of faun who can bring much luck, and even helps materially in outside work. [Daily News, 27 January 1926]

[Fairies] liked most of all to swing and play in the elder trees, and these were always thought of as fairy trees in the Isle of Man. There wasn't a house or farm that didn't have its 'tramman' tree planted by the door or in the garden 'for the fairies'. Many of them are still to be seen; the single tree will soon have grown into a thicket, hiding the old ruined house, but a sure sign that a house once stood there . . . When the wind was blowing the branches, it was then that the fairies were believed to be riding the tramman trees, but it was said that they would desert a house or a farm where the trees had been cut down. This must have happened only very rarely: no-one would cut a branch of the tramman, let alone the tree itself, but if it was done the fairies grieved. [Killip, 1975: 35]

Regardless of whether elder is considered to be malevolent or protective, most of the folk beliefs associated with the tree appear to be concerned with its protection and preservation. Two quotations from herbalists writing in the 1940s demonstrate the value of the elder tree.

[According to my gypsy friend] the healingest tree that on earth do grow be the elder, them sez, and take it all round I should say 'twas. [Quelch, 1941: 78]

[Elder has] the unusual distinction of being useful in every part. [Ransom, 1949: 55]

Thus it is possible that the various folk beliefs associated with elder were due, at least in part, to efforts to protect a valuable resource.

The period when elder flowered was sometimes considered to be a time when the weather was poor. In the Basingstoke area of Hampshire this time was known as the elderbloom winter [Maida Hill, London, December 1982], while in Cheshire:

Weather prophets say that if the weather breaks while the elder-flowers are coming out, it will be soaking wet (in Cheshire parlance, drabbly) until they fade. [Hole, 1937: 49]

Francis Bacon (1561–1626) recorded: 'They say' WARTS can be removed by rubbing them 'with a Green Elder Sticke and then burying the Sticke to rot in Mucke' [Bacon, 1631: 258]. Similarly:

A 15-year-old girl, writing in 1954, says that her grandfather told her to pick a small twig of elderberry, touch her warts with it, chant the words,

Wart, wart, on my knee,
Please go, one, two, three.

and put it 'down the toilet'. [Opie, 1959: 315]

Elder is, perhaps, the wild plant most widely used in folk medicine.

Queen of all Forest [of Dean] remedies was 'ellum blow tea' . . . The flowers were gathered in the spring and hung up to dry in closed paper bags . . . in the kitchen . . . You dared not sneeze in the winter or down came the bag, a good handful was put in a jug, covered with boiling water, covered with a tea towel, and left to infuse. One had to force this evil-smelling brew down one's throat willy-nilly. I loathed it, and to this day can recall that smell of cats which emanated from it. Poultices of the mixture were used for SPRAINS, aches, etc., in joints, also for boils and 'gathered' fingers—whitlows and so on. It seemed to be a universal panacea; the only use it didn't have was for constipation . . . Elder berries were favoured too; they were boiled up with sugar, the resulting syrup strained, bottled, and used in winter for coughs and colds . . . There is not a Forester alive over the age of 70 who does not know ellum blow tea. [Cinderford, Gloucestershire, November 1993]

Elder berries when fried with mutton fat are used for BOILS and ULCERS. [IFCSS MSS 414: 43, Co. Clare]

Elder root when boiled and the water drank supposed to cure RHEUMATISM. [IFCSS MSS 700: 35, Co. Meath]

An infusion of elder flowers in boiling water will alleviate PILES. [Horsted Keynes, West Sussex, February 1991]

A green ointment could be made from the leaves, based on mutton fat, and the creamy white flowers made Elderflower Water for the complexion. The flowers, dried in the sun and stored in a paper bag make a good remedy to break a hard COUGH and bring up phlegm. I always pick and dry some when they are in bloom, put the full of your fingers (one hand) in a mug, pour boiling water over and let it infuse for ten minutes. A little milk or fruit juice can be added. [Lenamore, Co. Longford, April 1991]

For flus and FEVERS
40 oz whiskey bottle.
Pick, clean, weigh, one pound ripe elder berries.
Delete the strings (most strings anyway) using a fork, and put berries into empty bottle.
Add ¼ lb sugar.
Top up with a bottle (or most of a bottle) of whiskey.
Seal well. Store for 3 months and strain.
Use strongest spirit.
Dose. Strong glass of this 'Elderfire'—add hot water (as hot as possible) and drink. Take 2 or 3 spoons of honey with drink. Repeat each night (or more frequently)—usually two nights is sufficient to clear the flu/fever—results guaranteed. [Killarney, Co. Kerry, September 1991]

[My mother, who was 94 when she died in 1987] used to collect elderflower in the spring, and dried it. In the winter if we had colds or flu, the elderflower was put in a jug covered with boiling water and put on the hob to stew. At night we were given this (strained) with sugar and a few drops of peppermint oil added. We were given a teacup full of this at night, and in the morning we had to drink half a cupful of this cold mixture.

It was supposed to sweat out the fever. She used to tell me how she pulled me through PNEUMONIA by poulticing with hot flannel and sips of elderflower tea, day and night. [Hill, Worcestershire, October 1991]

When my three children were small and we had wintery weather (and it can be *very* cold up here at the foot of the Cairngorms), I made elder-flower wine, and when it was time for them coming from school I had three cups, bowl of sugar, bottle of elderflower wine and the kettle boiling, and I gave them a tody; they never had colds or flu. [Boat-of-Garten, Inverness-shire, November 1991]

Elder flowers and berries are widely collected by makers of home-made wines. The flowers can also be used in cooking [Ó'Ceirin, 1980: 91], and the fruits have been recommended as a substitute for currants [Ransom, 1949: 55]. Elder leaves have been used as a TOBACCO substitute.

Myself, my brother and a friend always smoked elder leaves when money was not available for tailor-made cigarettes. We spent much time in the woodland of Thetford Chase, where on our regular walks we would break down, but not completely snap off, small sprigs of the elder. We found that if we severed the supply of sap completely the leaves on the sprig would dry out resulting in a hot strong smoke. We found that if the leaves remained just slightly damp they were a quite pleasant smoke. It was obviously trial and error, sometimes they remained too wet to burn properly. We would stuff the leaves very lightly into the stems of various umbel-lifers . . . We actually prefered these cigarettes to the tailor-made, but they were not available during winter. [West Stow, Suffolk, November 1992]

Elder wood is characterized by its pith, which can be easily removed.

[On Colonsay] boys aspiring to be pipers made chanters of the young branches [of elder], which are full of pith and easily bored. [McNeill, 1910: 130].

Haw-blowers are made by scooping the pith out of an elder branch. Haws are blown through these. [IFCSS MSS 700: 338, Co. Meath]

The people of the parish were able to make toy guns. They got an elder stick about one and a half feet long and scraped out the inside. Then they got a stick about the same length and made it fit into the hole and then the gun was made. [IFCSS MSS 867: 132, Co. Kilkenny]

At the beginning of the century children in parts of Devon used to make 'pop-guns' out of elder: they would force a hole through the pith, and then fashion a ram-rod out of HAZEL wood. Chewed paper would be rammed down the hollowed elder sticks, and pressed out with considerable force. Great sport ensued. [Lafonte, 1984: 35]

There was another use for the Boor tree in olden times. A suitable length was cut and seasoned, then the white pith in the centre was scraped out, lead was then melted and poured in. When set, this made a good weapon for protection on a journey or out walking at night . . . My aunt who was born in 1894 remembered one man who had such a stick. [Lenamore, Co. Longford, April 1991]

[In Horsefield, Cambridgeshire] for winter feeding one beekeeper used to make little troughs out of elder wood; he cut pieces about the thickness of a finger and five or six inches long, tapered off one end and removed the pith, and used them for replenishing the bees' honey by inserting this end in the exit hole. [Parsons MSS, 1952]

Elecampane (*Inula helenium*)

Elecampane was used by my grandmother, a late Victorian lady, for all kinds of ailments. [Ryde, Isle of Wight, November 1988]

This statement is supported by the frequent mention of elecampane, or corruptions of the word, in the doctor's speech in traditional mummers' plays. In a version of the play remembered by Thomas Hardy in 1920, when the Hardy Players were preparing a dramatized version of *The Return of the Native*, the doctor exclaims:

Yea, more; this little bottle of alicampane
Will raise dead men to walk again.

[Stevens Cox, 1970: 450]

More specifically, in Glamorgan elecampane was used in the treatment of HYDROPHOBIA.

There lived about sixty years ago an old woman in . . . Bridgend who cultivated elecampane in her garden. She was noted for curing hydrophobia in cattle, and farmers in the surrounding district came to her for the remedy. She made a decoction of it mixed with milk and a quantity of fowl's feathers. The other ingredients were kept as a profound secret, which she took to the grave. [Trevelyan, 1909: 314]

Elm (*Ulmus* spp.) The elm tree was formerly so common in Warwickshire that it was known as Warwickshire weed [Grigson, 1987: 241], and according to a rural versifier its leaves provided guidance for the sowing of certain crops:

When the elmen leaf is as big as a mouse's ear,
Then to sow BARLEY never fear;
When the elmen leaf is as big as an ox's eye,
Then says I, 'Hie, boys, Hie!'
When elm leaves are as big as a shilling,
Plant KIDNEY BEANS, if to plant 'em you're willing;
When elm leaves are as big as a penny,
You must plant kidney beans if you want to have any.

[R. Palmer, 1976: 62]

On Guernsey:

> *Quànd tu veit la fieille d l'orme,*
> *Prends ta pouque et seme ton orge.*
> When you see the elm in leaf,
> Take your seed-bag and sow your barley.

> [De Garis, 1975: 121]

In the nineteenth century an elm tree in Bedfordshire was resorted to as a cure for ague.

> A friend who had lived at Silsoe, Beds., between 1880 and 1890 told me the following.
>
> On the right of the road leading from Silsoe to Maulden, and about mid-way between the two villages, is a green lane known as Beaumont's Tree Lane. Beaumont's Tree was an elm standing at the entrance to the lane that had grown from a stake stuck through the body of Beaumont, a murderer, buried at this spot. Until thirty or forty years before (i.e. before 1880–90) people in the district suffering from AGUE would nail strands of their hair or toe nail clippings to the tree, to effect a cure. He has himself seen such nails in the tree. [*Folk-lore*, 56: 307, 1945]

Other remedies which used elm include:

> Many villagers [in the Upper Thames area], in cases of COLD or sore throat, strip off the inner bark of the young wands [of wych elm, *Ulmus glabra*] and chew it raw, or boil it and drink the liquor. This, when cold, settles into a brown jelly that is not unpleasant to the taste. I have often taken it as a boy, preparing it according to the directions given me by my old grandmother. [Williams, 1922: 275]

> The bark of elm tree boiled and put on a BURN cures it. [IFCSS MSS 190: 115, Co. Leitrim]

> A cure for yellow JAUNDICE is to boil the bark of an elm tree in new milk and leave it boiling for two hours. Then take it up and give the milk to the person that would have the yellow jaundice. [IFCSS MSS 850: 56, Co. Kilkenny]

> [Gypsies smoked wild ANGELICA] sometimes filled dried and crushed with elm leaves. [Barnstaple, Devon, September 1992]

Emetics – plants used include BOG MYRTLE and DODDER.

Empire Day (24 May) – associated with DAISY.

English stonecrop (*Sedum anglicum*)

> [In Gaelic Scotland] white or pink stonecrop (*Sedum anglicum*) was considered to be a delicacy and was given the name *Biadh an t-Sionnaidh*, the prince's or lord's food. [Bennett, 1991: 57]

Esh – a variant of ASH.

Everlasting pea (*Lathyrus latifolius*)

About 20 years ago I found some narrow-leaved everlasting pea, *Lathyrus sylvestris*, on the local railway embankment. I planted the seed along the roadside on my farm and now I have a mile of them. People come from miles just to see them when in flower during the first week in August. Some local people call them Pharaoh's Peas. The story is that a person from the nearby village of Weebly went to Egypt and brought home some seeds which were said to come from a royal tomb in a pyramid. [Rushton, Northamptonshire, July 1985; site visited August 1992, and plant identified as the broad-leaved everlasting pea, *L. latifolius*]

As neither species of everlasting pea has ever been recorded from Egypt or any neighbouring countries, it appears that this legend has no factual basis.

Everlasting sin or sin – Shropshire names for SLENDER SPEEDWELL.

Eyebright (*Euphrasia* spp.)

It has been reputed good for sore EYES, but the gentlemen of the faculty have declared it does more harm than good in applications of that kind, there having been instances of persons rendered almost blind by the use of it. The highlanders do however still retain the practice of it, by making an infusion of it in milk and annointing the patient's eyes with a feather dipped in it. [Lightfoot, 1777: 323]

Infusion of leaves taken internally cures COUGHS, applied in a lotion strengthens the eyes and heals sore ones . . . I have met gypsies who smoked it mixed with COLTSFOOT—and it is an ingredient of most herbal TOBACCOS—maintaining that it cured ASTHMA and CATARRH. Is widely used by gypsies for eye troubles. [Vesey-FitzGerald, 1944: 24]

Eye complaints – treated using BUTTERCUP, EYEBRIGHT, GREATER CELANDINE, GROUND IVY, HEMLOCK, MALLOW, RASPBERRY, SCARLET PIMPERNEL, TEASEL, and TREE MALLOW.

F

Fairies – associated with CLOVER, ELDER, FOXGLOVE, GUERNSEY LILY, and RED CAMPION, protection from them provided by BUTTERWORT, HAWTHORN, and PRIMROSE; also a name for floating seeds of DANDELION and similar plants.

Fairies' petticoat – a Cheshire name for FOXGLOVE.

Fairy-cap – an Irish name for FOXGLOVE.

Fairy flax (*Linum catharticum*). As its scientific name implies, fairy flax was formerly used as a PURGATIVE. This use continued on the Hebridean island of Colonsay until early in the twentieth century [McNeill, 1910: 108].

Fairy foxglove (*Erinus alpinus*). A native of mainland Europe, the fairy foxglove is cultivated in Britain as a rock-garden plant, and naturalized in some areas.

> Fairy foxglove is a small purple flower which grows intermittently on stone walls in north-east England. Local tradition says that it only grows where ROMAN soldiers have trod, and certainly it is to be found in the village of Wall (which is, of course, located near Hadrian's Wall in Northumberland). [Hexham, Northumberland, June 1990]

Fairy ring – a circle of dark green grass formed by the growth of fungi, or a ring of toadstools. John Aubrey recalled:

> In the year 1633–4, soon after I had entered into my grammar school at the Latin School at Yatton Keynel [Wiltshire], our curate, Mr Hart was annoyd one night by these elves or fayries comming over the downes, it being near darke, and approaching one of the faery dances as the common people call them in these parts, viz., the greene circles made by those sprites on the grasse, he all at once saw an unnumerable quantitie of pygmies or very small people dancing rounde and rounde, and singing and making all maner of small odd noyses. So being very greatly amaz'd, and yet not being able, as he says, to run away from them, being as he supposes kepte there in a kinde of enchantment . . . he fell downe scarcely knowing what he did; whereupon these little creatures pinch'd him all over . . . but at length they left him, and when the sun rose he found himself exactly in the midst of one of these faery dances. [Ramsbottom, 1953: 114]

Later writers abandoned any belief that the rings resulted from the activities of fairies, and until late in the eighteenth century suggested that they resulted from lightning strikes [Ramsbottom, 1953: 116–18]. However, in the second edition of his *Systematic Arrangement of British Plants*, William Withering [1792: 336] put forward the idea that fairy rings were formed as a result of fungal growth. In a discussion on *Agaricus oreades* (now known as *Marasmius oreades*, the fairy-ring champignon), he declared 'I am satisfied that the bare and brown, or highly verdant circles, in pasture fields, called Fairy Rings, are caused by the growth of this Agaric.' Withering's explanation that fairy rings are caused by fungal growth is now accepted by scientists, but the old beliefs still linger.

> In the meadows, there is sometimes seen in the middle of them a circle or ring of rich grass. This is the fairies circle and it is not lucky to run or walk around it, but a person may walk through it, but not around it, as that is the fairies' path. [IFC MSS 36: 236, Co. Laois, *c.*1930]

> [Hampshire:] rings of toadstools in the grass, or darker rings of grass, mark spots where the fairies dance at night. It is unlucky to step within the ring. [Heather, 1941: 117]

However, there are records of fairy rings being considered 'lucky':

> Fairy rings—circles of rank grass where toadstools grow—potential source of good luck/wish. [Leamington Spa, Warwick shire, January 1993]

Cf. CROP CIRCLES.

Fairy thimble – a name for FOXGLOVE.

Fairy thorn – see LONE BUSH.

Fat goose – a name for GOOD KING HENRY.

Fat hen (*Chenopodium album*). Although it is now considered to be a troublesome weed, fat hen was formerly valued as a food.

> The leaves were boiled, pounded, buttered and eaten like spinach. [McNeill, 1910: 161]

> There used to be what I thought was a weed growing in quantities in this area, but I have heard it said that in days gone by, when green vegetables were scarce, this weed—fat hen, as it was called—was used as a vegetable. [Maulden, Bedfordshire, April 1993]

Fathers' Day. Unlike MOTHERING SUNDAY, which has traditional roots, Fathers' Day—the third Sunday in June—started in the early 1970s as the purely commercial invention of greeting-card manufacturers and similar companies. By 1977 Fathers' Day had already begun to provide florists with an opportunity to increase their takings, with some graves in the London Road Cemetery, Mitcham, Surrey, being decorated with Fathers' Day wreaths.

In the church of St Peter and St Paul, Kirton in Holland, Lincoln-shire, there is a corner which has a list of parishioners who have died in recent years, below which is a shelf on which vases of cut flowers are placed in remembrance of those listed. Many of the vases of flowers placed on the shelf in late June 1990 had cards attached with such sentiments as 'Remembering you always, but especially on Fathers' Day' written on them.

Feast Sunday

At Histon [Cambridgeshire] the first Sunday in July is Feast Sunday; the family comes to dinner and the first bait of vegetables is eaten. PEAS, CAR-ROTS and POTATOES are planted on GOOD FRIDAY, regardless of the weather, and the first of these vegetables is always eaten on Feast Sunday, even if they were ready before. People, including my 26-year-old son, still keep these traditions up. Feast Sunday dates back to at least 1894, and used to be about the only time when girls who were in service were allowed home to visit their families. [Histon, Cambridgeshire, January 1989]

Similar practices were widespread.

[My family originated from the village of Whitwick, near Coalville, in Leicestershire.] Set early potatoes on Good Friday, they were then ready for boiling for Whitwick Wake . . . this coincided with the Church an-niversary—St John the Baptist Church. [Hornchurch, Essex, August 1992]

Fennel (*Foeniculum vulgare*)

Sprigs of fennel are placed in horses' harnesses to keep FLIES away. It is also used in a sauce eaten with the locally caught and popular mackerel. [St Saviour, Jersey, May 1993].

Fern – see BRACKEN

Fever – prevented using TOADFLAX; treated using ELDER.

Feverfew (*Tanacetum parthenium*)

Feverfew boiled and strained is used to allay pain. [Taylor MSS, Attle-borough, Norfolk]

Fever-plant – a Yorkshire name for YARROW.

Fevertory – a Wiltshire variant of FUMITORY.

Fiddle-wood – a name for WATER FIGWORT.

Field gentian (*Gentianella campestris*)

Field gentian = sôta (meaning sweet as in nature/character)—helps diges-tive disorders. Is also known as ridin' girse and was fed to cows that were reluctant to come into season—perhaps an aphrodisiac. [Lerwick, Shet-land, March 1994]

Field maple (*Acer campestre*). In Devon in the late nineteenth century field maple was frequently known as OAK and worn as such on Oak Apple Day.

> I have been astonished to find how constantly the Maple is called Oak. On Whit-Monday, which this year was Oak-apple Day as well (May 29th), I took an early walk into Bradley Woods. Here I met a number of children decorated with Maple, and asked them what it was for. 'It's Oak-apple Day sir; and if you ain't got a piece of *oak-apple* they'll pinch you, or sting you.' 'Will they?' I replied, 'then I must get a piece.' 'Here's a piece, sir,' said a bright lad. It was a sprig of Maple, as was all the rest they had. I said, 'This is not Oak, is it?' to which they all replied, 'It's *oak-apple*, sir.' I could give illustrations from conversations with grown people showing the same error. [Friend, 1882: 41]

In Nottinghamshire maple was distinguished from oak, but might be worn as a substitute for oak on Oak Apple Day:

> Some who are unable to procure it [oak], endeavour to avoid the penalty [of being stung with NETTLES] by wearing dog oak (maple), but the punishment is always more severe on the discovery of the imposition. [E., 1884: 382]

Field scabious (*Knautia arvensis*)

> [Derbyshire gypsies:] infusion of leaves strengthens lungs, and will cure pleurisy. [Thompson, 1925: 163].

Fig (*Ficus carica*). A fig tree which grows from the south wall of St Newlyn East church in Cornwall is said to have sprouted from a STAFF carried by St Newlina, an obscure virgin martyr.

> The tradition in the village here, recorded by one of my predecessors in the 1930s, is that St Newlina, a Christian princess, planted her staff in the ground and said that this should be the site of a church. The wall of the church from which the fig tree grows is, however, 14th century and I have heard that fig trees were not introduced into this country until the sixteenth century . . . From time to time the tree has to be pruned, but by a remarkable number of coincidents some of those who have done so have met with misfortune and death. [The Revd Peter Denny, St Newlyn East, January 1978]

A postcard on sale in the late 1970s depicts the tree, and gives the verse:

> In ancient days Newlina came,
> The Saint who gave this place its name.
> Her staff she planted and she prayed,
> 'Let here a Church to God be made.'
> This fig tree is her staff folks say;
> Destroy it not in any way,

Upon it lies a dreadful curse,
Who plucks a leaf will need a hearse.

However, according to a report in the *Sunday Express* of 1 June 1958:

Four Cornishmen have defied a 'curse of death' and lived. Warning of the 'curse' is printed beside a fig tree which grows out of the wall of the ancient parish church of St Newlyn East, near Newquay.

It says death will follow within the year if any man so much as plucks one leaf from the tree.

Twelve months ago four men of the village pruned the tree. One of them . . . said yesterday: 'When I was aked if I would prune the tree I said "Certainly. I'm not superstitious." But soon afterwards, when I went to fell some trees one fell on me putting me off work for three months.'

Does he believe in the 'curse' now? 'Not a bit. I think it was invented to make a good yarn.'

Edgar Thurston in his *British and Foreign Trees in Cornwall* (1930) makes no mention of the legend of St Newlina, even though he mentions and gives a photograph of the fig tree. Since Thurston's work reveals an interest in folklore which leads to the inclusion of material irrelevant to trees and shrubs, the omission of the legend is perhaps significant: was it missed by Thurston, or was it invented rather than collected by the parish's incumbent a few years later?

In 1913 a description was given of three 'ATHEISTS' TOMBS' in Hertfordshire. One of these was an altar tomb (no longer in existence) on the south side of Watford church, which bore no inscription, but had a well-developed fig tree growing from it. According to legend, a lady or a well-known local farmer lay buried therein, and she or he asked for a fig to be placed in her or his hand; if it was true that there was another world beyond the grave, the fig would produce a tree [*N & Q*, 11 ser. 8: 425, 1913].

Do you know the Watford fig tree? It grows in the churchyard there. The story is that years ago there was an unbeliever who the local vicar kept on trying to convert. When the unbeliever died he said that a fig tree would grow from his grave if there was a god. I don't know if the tree is still there, I haven't been to Watford for a long time. [Lewisham, London, April 1986]

In some parts of England PALM SUNDAY was known as Fig Sunday.

My family, on all sides, and for generations back, come from a village in north Bucks, called North Marston, where I spent much of my childhood, girlhood and later. In this area it was customary to eat figs on Palm Sunday, always called 'Fig Sunday.' See Mark, chapter 11, verse 13.

With so many newcomers in the area I doubt if the custom is still remembered . . . I still eat figs on Fig Sunday. [Bow, London, April 1990]

Figwurt

In the Lake District:

> Fig Sue is a GOOD FRIDAY drink—I don't know why only Good Friday. It is: Stew 4 oz figs in 1 pint water until tender. Rub through sieve, add one tablespoon sugar and a pinch of ground ginger. Warm 2 pints of ale, and add puree, bring to boil and serve. [Clappersgate, Cumbria, October 1985]

Figwurt (fygwurt) – a sixteenth-century name for CELANDINE.

Fingers and thumbs – a Dorset name for BIRD'S-FOOT TREFOIL.

Fire – plants giving protection against it include ANTIRRHINUM, BITING STONECROP, and HOUSELEEK.

Fire grass – a name for RIBWORT PLANTAIN; cf. FIRE-LEAVES and HOT WEED.

Fire-leaves – a Herefordshire name for DEVIL'S BIT SCABIOUS and a Gloucestershire name for HOARY PLANTAIN.

Fisherman's baskets – a Radnorshire name for BIRD'S-FOOT TREFOIL.

Fishing – plants which provide guidance on when fishing should start include ALDER and FOXGLOVE.

Fits – caused by MEADOWSWEET.

Flax (*Linum usitatissimum*), also known as lint.

> [Northeast Scotland:] When the shades of evening were falling [on Hallowe'en], the maiden had to steal out quietly with a handful of lint-seed, and walk across the ridges of a field, sowing the seed, and repeating the words:
>
> > Lint-seed I saw ye,
> > Lint-seed I saw ye,
> > Lat him it's to be my lad
> > Come aifter and pu' me.
>
> On looking over the left shoulder she saw the apparition of him who was to be her mate crossing the ridges, as it were, in the act of pulling flax. [Gregor, 1874: 103]

Cf. the similar method of DIVINATION using HEMP.

Fleas – associated with MEADOW FOXTAIL GRASS and WALL BARLEY; deterred using BOG MYRTLE and EEL GRASS.

Flea wood – a Northumberland name for BOG MYRTLE.

Flies – deterred using ELDER, FENNEL, MINT, and TANSY.

Floss – a Shetland name for both compact and round-fruited RUSH.

Flower communion

Eastern European Unitarians have, for the last 70 years or so, celebrated a 'flower communion', now used widely in western Europe and North America as well. In this ceremony, all attending bring cut flowers of any sort, which are gathered together in large containers at the front of the chapel at the beginning of the service. At the close of the service people file forward and take a flower, different from the one they brought, and take it home to place on their table or mantel . . . as a symbol of the larger community of the congregation of which they are a part.

Our own congregation [in Hampstead] has a variety of this we also do once a year. Our flower arrangers make displays which are solely leaf backgrounds. Near the start of the service everyone files forward, receives a flower, and places it wherever they wish in the displays. Thus the congregation creates its own focal point in that service, while symbolically celebrating, in the vast variety of flowers purposely used, the beauty created by welcoming differences, and viewing them as a strength and not a threat. [Hampstead, London, October 1993]

Flowering currant (*Ribes sanguineum*)

My wife will not have the red flowering currant in the house; many years ago her mother said it would bring bad luck to the house (no other explanation). [Shavington, Cheshire, March 1983]

Flowering Sunday. In parts of Wales Palm Sunday is known as *Sul y Blodau*, or Flowering Sunday, and formerly it was a widespread custom to decorate graves with flowers on this day. Although the name *Sul y Blodau* occurs as early as the fifteenth century in Welsh literature, the restricting of the day to Palm Sunday appears to date from the latter half of the nineteenth century [Owen, 1978: 80]. Late in the nineteenth century the custom became popular in urban parts of south Wales, where in 1896 a writer decribed how thousands of people would visit the cemetery in Cardiff, 'the roads thereto presenting an appearance like unto a fair' [*Bye-gones*, 9 September 1986]. The custom, although now less important, survives to the present time, and in many parts of Wales graves continue to receive special attention, usually by having bunches of DAFFODILS placed on them [St Fagans, South Glamorgan, April 1983].

In Radnorshire graves were decorated on Easter Saturday. On 16 April 1870 Francis Kilvert recorded in his diary:

When I started for Cefn y Blaen only two or three people were in the churchyard with flowers. But now the customary beautiful Easter Eve Idyll had fairly begun and people kept arriving from all parts with flowers to dress the graves. Children were coming from the town and from neighbouring villages with baskets of flowers and knives to cut holes in the turf. The roads were lively with people coming and going and the churchyard a busy scene with women and children and a few men moving about among the tombstones and kneeling down beside the green mounds flowering the graves . . . More and more people kept coming into the churchyard as they finished their day's work. [Plomer, 1977: 30]

In parts of Ireland similar practices took place on local feast days.

Dressing the graves is a custom which is practised in every parish with a few exceptions in south and mid Louth. Each parish and each churchyard or graveyard has its own patron day. On that day or the Sunday following Mass is said for the dead in the parish church. The graves are beautifully dressed with whatever flowers are in season.

A cross of flowers 2½ or 3 ft high stands at the head of the grave.

The grave itself is covered with moss or evergreen and outlined with BOXWOOD or palm [YEW] neatly clipped. Wreaths of flowers in blending colours—red and white, pink and white, purple and white, etc. are placed in the enclosure. People from all around come to pray for their dead and incidentally to criticise the dressing. [IFCSS MSS 675: 93, Co. Louth]

Cf. ALL SOULS' DAY.

Flower Parade. Since 1959 the annual Flower Parade, held at Spalding, Lincolnshire, on the first Saturday in May, has been a popular tourist attraction. The Parade consists of about twenty floats elaborately decorated with TULIPS and other cut flowers.Commercial bulb growing started in the Spalding area in about 1890, when tulips were grown as cut flowers, and by the 1920s the fields were attracting a steady stream of tourists. In 1935, when the silver jubilee of the reign of King George V and Queen Mary coincided with tulip time, the bulb growers planted their fields with an emphasis on red, white, and 'blue' tulips, an act which brought much publicity and resulting traffic chaos to the town. The following year an official Tulip Time Committee was set up to sort out the traffic problems and assume overall responsibility for Tulip Time.

As the years went on the number of bulbs grown for cut flowers gradually decreased, and more and more growers grew tulips for their dry bulbs. Tulips grown for bulbs usually have their flowers removed to encourage the rapid development of new bulbs. There were fewer fields of flowering tulips for visitors to see, but vast quantities of detached tulip flowers. Thus in 1959 the Spalding branch of the National Farmers Union organized the first Flower Parade which from its start attracted large numbers of visitors.

The initial form and steel skeleton of each float is skilfully constructed by a local blacksmith, Geoff Dodd, into the outline shape of the subject.

Until 1985 the steelwork was then covered with a special straw matting to form a base to receive the flowers. Polyethylene foam has now replaced the use of straw matting. The final stage is reached twenty-four hours before the actual Parade when hundreds of volunteers work into the night weaving delicate patterns in flowers. Each tulip head is deftly secured to the base with a wire pin until the whole float is literally covered with tulips. A single float, which may be as much as fifty feet in length, may be decorated by as many as half a million tulips, supplemented by numerous individual flower arrangements created by the local Flower Lovers' Club. Other colourful spring flowers and materials are also used to complement the float's design. The result is one of indescribable beauty and it is not surprising that even visitors returning year after year still gasp with astonishment at the wonder of it all. [Simpson, 1987]

When spring is late DAFFODILS may have to be substituted for tulips [*The Times*, 28 April 1986]; when spring is early:

Thousands of tulips that have bloomed too early are being picked and put in cold storage to preserve them for the annual flower parade at Spalding, Lincolnshire, on May 4. [*The Times*, 25 April 1991]

Cf. BATTLE OF FLOWERS.

Flowers. In the 1920s children living in the poorer parts of London would happily pick up and devour any food which they found lying on the pavement: 'Waste not, want not, pick it up and eat it.' But a dropped flower was different, for 'if one of the younger children went to touch it, the rest of us dragged him back gasping "pick up a flower, pick up fever." ' [Gamble, 1979: 94]. Similarly:

It was unlucky to pick up flowers which have been dropped on the ground (brings sickness into the house!). [Aberdovey, Gwynedd, July 1983]

Such beliefs probably date from the time when the urban poor only bought or had flowers when a corpse was in the house awaiting burial, so it was not surprising that the juvenile mind should associate flowers with sickness and death. Less common is a total prohibition of flowers indoors.

A farmer's wife from Inkberrow [Worcestershire] (*c*.1887), visiting my mother at Aloechurch, was given, was given a bunch of roses from our garden. But before going back to the house she contrived to drop them quietly one by one. This was noticed by my brother, who knew the reason—it brings bad luck to the chickens if flowers are taken inside the house. [Partridge, 1917: 311]

My mother, born in 1903, and grandmother, would not have any blossom of any description in the house, believing it would bring bad luck to the family. [Macclesfield, Cheshire, April 1982]

Flower Service

Occasionally this ban is restricted to wild flowers.

> Flowers unlucky indoors: lilac, *all* wild flowers. [Caernarvon, Gwynedd, March 1993]

> I was born in Lincolnshire 68 years ago . . . we picked bunches of wild flowers whenever we went out, though we were never allowed to bring them indoors. They had to be put into a jam jar and left on an outside windowsill. My mother would never have wild flowers indoors, she said it was unlucky, though what she was most adamant about was May blossom (HAWTHORN). [Wheatley, Oxfordshire, June 1993]

On the stage:

> There is this theatre superstition that you should not have live flowers on the stage. I've been told, but I don't think I believe it, that if fresh flowers fell there is a danger that the performers might slip. [Paddington, London, July 1990]

In some areas flowers were among the things which should not be handled by menstruating women.

> When I was a girl in the Basingstoke area of Hampshire, my mother told me I must never touch flowers during my period, or they would wilt and die! [Maida Hill, London, December 1982]

See also FUNERAL FLOWERS, RED FLOWERS, and RED AND WHITE FLOWERS.

Flower Service. For many years until the 1970s a Flower Service was held at the parish church of St Mary's, Bridport, Dorset. According to a report in the *Bridport News* in May 1905 [quoted in Udal, 1922: 42], this service dated back to at least 1788, when Sunday Schools were first held in the town. However, it seems that the Flower Services of later years were very dependent on rail transport, so it would seem that the Service in its twentieth-century form evolved some time in the mid to late nineteenth century.

> May Sunday was kept as Sunday School Festival Day—an event which was looked forward to, as most of the girls had new dresses and hats for the occasion—usually white—they must have worn layers of warm clothing underneath if it was as cold as recent Mays. Saturday was picking day when hordes of people took the train to Powerstock, the first stop, where the fields were covered with PRIMROSES, COWSLIPS, BLUEBELLS, wild hyacinth, etc.—but cowslips were the best that travelled and retained their lovely smell. All the children brought them to church, after parading around the town to show off their bunches, which had labels with their names and addresses on them. Some 200 plus children and parents and relations filled the church during the service. The Rector then received the flowers at the chancel steps, on trays, which were then packed in cartons—sometimes twelve or more—and taken to the station to catch the

3.30 to Paddington, where they were collected and delivered the same evening to the elderly, sick and under-privileged people.

Most of the recipients sent letters of thanks to children by the following Sunday, when letters were read at school. Eventually there was too much traffic on the Main Road, so the procession was shortened. Then unfortunately British Rail closed our branch line, so we had to send the flowers by road to Dorchester station (some 15 miles) to arrive in London the next morning to be collected by the ladies of St Stephen's, Westminster, for their old people's club. Some of the letters received then spoke of the flowers being the first wild flowers the recipients had seen. One lady who was 80 years old spoke of being in Dorset when she was a girl. It was quite apparent that the flowers brought a little joy and a touch of the country to the city, but it was ended in the 1970s due to people complaining about the picking of flowers. [Mr F.T. Record, Sunday School Teacher at St Mary's, February 1985]

Fool's parsley (*Aethusa cynapium*)

Fifty-one years ago, I picked some wild flowers for my mother who was ill and my grandmother was caring for us; as I approached the house my old gran said 'Don't bring those MOTHER DIE into the house they are bad luck,' so sadly they went into the bin. (My mother passed away a few weeks after.) [Shavington, Cheshire, March 1983]

Cf. COW PARSLEY.

Forebitten more – a former name for DEVIL'S BIT SCABIOUS.

Forsythia (*Forsythia* spp.)

In the 1950s in Wiltshire, my grandmother would not allow MIMOSA indoors because it was unlucky; she also wouldn't allow forsythia indoors, but mimosa was the one she went really mad about. [Winchmore Hill, London, May 1984]

Foxglove (*Digitalis purpurea*), also known as fairy thimble in Ireland.
It is generally accepted that the name foxglove is a corruption of folk's [i.e. fairies'] glove. According to James Britten:

The name Foxglove has, in all probability, nothing to do with Reynard, but is rather connected with the fairies or little folk. This derivation is fully borne out by other of its names; e.g. the North Country name, 'Witches' Thimbles'; the Irish name 'Fairy-cap'; the Welsh, 'Maneg Ellylln' (Fairies' Glove); the Cheshire, 'Fairies Petticoat'; and the East Anglian 'Fairy-thimble'. [*Science Gossip*, 1 February 1870: 43]

However, a belief collected from County Leitrim implies that foxgloves, rather than being fairy plants, are dangerous to fairies.

If you have a cross or peevish child, or one that from being in good health becomes sickly, and you have reason to believe it is a fairy child, the following plan may be tried in order to ascertain whether this is the case.

Take lusmore (foxglove) and squeeze the juice out. Give the child three drops on the tongue, and three in each ear. Then place it at the door of the house on a shovel (on which it should be held by some one), and swing it out of the door on the shovel three times, saying: 'If you're a fairy away with you!' If it is a fairy child, it will die; but if not, it will surely begin to mend. [Duncan, 1896: 163]

There are occasional records of foxgloves being considered to be either 'unlucky' or an omen of war.

[Around Tutbury, Staffordshire, in the 1950s] picking foxgloves was unlucky and they were absolutely forbidden inside a house as this gave WITCHES/the DEVIL access to the house. [Stevenage, Hertfordshire, May 1982]

The summer of 1914 was a record one for foxgloves, regarding which an old [Staffordshire] man remarked, 'I don't like them, missus; they mean war. Them foxgloves is soldiers.' [Hodson, 1917: 452]

Children inflate foxglove flowers and pop them.

[In Cornwall foxglove is known as pop dock:] Dock from its large coarse leaves; pop, from the habit of children to inflate and burst the flower. [Britten and Holland, 1886: 153]

[Gloucestershire, Forest of Dean, 1920s:] amusing ourselves lazily popping 'snompers'. We picked spikes of beautiful pink foxgloves . . . then took off each flower, trapping the air with thumb and forefinger, and pushed the ends together till they'd explode with a pleasant little pop. [Foley, 1974: 18]

Similarly, in the same area:

[From my grandparents, b. 1856 and 1860:] Snomper, or snowper (rhyme with cow) = foxglove. A favourite admonition to a noisy child: 'Shut thee chops; thee bist like a bumble bee in a snowper.' A favourite occupation in summer was to trap a bee in a foxglove bell to hear it buzz angrily! [Cinderford, Gloucestershire, November 1993]

On Guernsey the foxglove was known as *claquet*, 'derived from the children's amusement of popping or bursting (*claquer*) the flowers on the palm of the hand,' and its flowering provided guidance as to when mackerel-fishing should start:

> *Quand tu vé epani l'claquet*
> *Met tes leines dans ten baté*
> *En t'en vâs au macré.*

(When you see the foxglove blossoming, put your fishing-tackle into your boat, and go off for mackerel). [Marquand, 1906: 39]

At Hartland in north Devon foxgloves are associated with the osbcure St Nectan, to whom the parish church is dedicated. According to what appears to be a comparatively recent tradition, St Nectan and his sister arrived in Cornwall from Wales, and made their way towards

Hartland. At Stoke they were attacked by robbers, and the Saint was decapitated. However, their journey was not delayed, for the Saint picked up his head and continued. Wherever a drop of BLOOD fell from his wound a foxglove sprang up [Dunsford, 1981: 176]. Today a Foxglove Procession is observed 'with great gusto' before the morning Sung Eucharist on the Sunday nearest the patronal feast, 17 June. Although parish magazines survive from 1909, the Procession is not mentioned until 1927, when the then incumbent arranged a procession after 3 p.m. Evensong on St Nectan's Day [The Revd Louis Coulson, Vicar of Hartland, January 1982].

In folk medicine:

> Foxglove leaves were placed in children's shoes and worn thus for a year, as a cure for scarlet fever—in Shropshire. [Haynes, Bedfordshire, August 1984]

> The *lus mor*—or soft leaves in the heart of the plant out of which the fairy thimbles grow—is good for healing a CUT. The little hard hard thread on the back of the leaf should be pulled out and the leaf heated at the fire and applied to the cut. [IFCSS MSS 1128: 26, Co. Cork]

The foxglove provides the major British example of how traditional remedies might prove worthy of investigation. In 1775 William Withering was asked for an opinion on a traditional Shropshire remedy for DROPSY. Of the twenty or so herbs the remedy contained, Withering quickly concluded that the important active ingredient was foxglove leaves. Thus, as patients for whom all other remedies had failed became available, he began to experiment by administering differing dosages of foxglove leaves in a variety of forms. After ten years he published his results, listing 163 of his own patients and a number treated by other physicians, and, although foxglove leaves had originally been used to stimulate the production of urine, he was also able to report that they had 'a power over the motion of the heart to a degree not yet observed in any other medicine' [Withering, 1822: 103]. Several of his contemporaries also considered foxglove leaves to be useful in the treatment of TUBERCULOSIS, but this was never proved, and it is as a drug for the treatment of heart ailments that an extract of foxglove—now usually the Mediterranean woolly foxglove (*Digitalis lanata*)—continues to be used.

Francismass – see ST FRANKIN'S DAYS.

Frawcup – a Thames valley name for FRITILLARY.

Freckles – removed using FUMITORY, SILVERWEED, and SUNDEW.

Friendship bush – a Hampshire name for ROSEMARY.

Fritillary (*Fritillaria meleagris*)

Frawcup Sunday was a Sunday in early May. Children in the Thames villages, such as Haddenham, Cuddington, Dinton, Ford, Marsh, the Kimbles and in other parts, dressed in their prettiest attire and garlanded with May flowers, brought posies of the delightful little fritillary, locally known as frawcups, to the cottage doors. Older members of our village communities still recall with fervent nostalgia memories of this lovely event to herald the advent of warm summer sunshine and the promise of abundance of nature's gifts. [Weston Turville, Buckinghamshire, June 1987].

Fruit

Make a wish when you have the first of the season. [Edgware, Middlesex, March 1977]

People used to make a wish when they had the first fruit or vegetable. They always used to do that. [Great Bedwyn, Wiltshire, January 1991]

Fruit stones

Memories of children's folklore from *c.*1935–45: Cherry stone counting rhyme:- 'This year, next year, sometime, never.' When counting and reciting this, one must *not* let anyone else know what is the wished-for event about which one is consulting the oracle. [Worthing, West Sussex, January 1989]

Fruit trees. It was believed that when fruit trees blossomed out of season misfortune was foretold.

> A blossom on the tree when the APPLES are ripe
> Is a sure termination of somebody's life.
>
> [*N & Q*, 9 ser. 12: 133, 1903].

In the Basingstoke district of Hampshire it was believed that war was foretold when fruit trees blossomed at unusual times. [Maida Hill, London, March 1978]

My grandmother told me, when I was very young, that it was unlucky to take into the house, or indeed pick, a flower that was 'blooming out of season.' Quite often an odd sprig of cherry or plum will blossom in December or January because 'the devil has touched it' and he wants to bring his influence into the house. [Towcester, Northamptonshire, August 1982]

A fruit tree which does not bear has nails (iron) knocked into it. This may be an offering to the tree. [Taylor MSS, Mattishall, Norfolk]

Fuchsia (*Fuchsia* spp.)

The blossom of the fuchsia when boiled DYES dark red. [IFCSS MSS 1112: 453, Co. Donegal]

[I was told in *c.*1950] *Fuchsia* spp.—not to be taken into a house—as unlucky. [Bromborough, Merseyside, November 1990]

Honeysuckle = the fuchsia (grown as a hedge, common name in Co. Antrim and Co. Down at present time—the nectar is sucked by children. [Holywood, Co. Down, December 1991]

Fumitory (*Fumaria* spp.). A cosmetic for removing FRECKLES was distilled from fumitory, formerly known in Wiltshire as fevertory:

> If you wish to be pure and holy
> Wash your face with fevertory.
> [Dartnell and Goddard, 1894: 55]

In the Orkneys:

> The juice of this was given to children as a cure for WORMS; also to foals, but in much larger doses, of course. [Spence, 1914: 101]

Funeral flowers. It appears that plant materials have been associated with mourning ceremonies since early in the history of mankind. As on other ceremonial occasions, flowers and evergreens were often the only source of colour readily at hand. Although archaeological excavations have revealed something of the mourning practices of early man, and written records exist of great funerals in the past, it is inevitable that comparatively little is known of the funeral practices of the common people.

In addition to providing colour, many of the plant materials associated with mourning were also important in that their odour masked the smell of decaying flesh. In earlier centuries many people had a great fear of being prematurely buried. Possibly the simplest method to ascertain that a corpse was truly dead was to keep it until signs of decay were unmistakably apparent. Thus a dead body was often kept unburied for up to a week to ensure that life was extinct.

> My Welsh relatives . . . rarely had flowers in the house, except at funerals to overcome the aroma of the non-refrigerated deceased, no doubt. [Gronant, Clwyd, April 1994]

In chapter 16 of her novel *Wuthering Heights*, first published in 1847, Emily Brontë, under her pseudonym of Ellis Bell, a clergyman's daughter, provided a brief account of the mourning practices of the Yorkshire gentry early in the nineteenth century. The body of the elder Catherine Linton, who died in the early hours of Monday morning, was placed in an open coffin, strewn with flowers and scented leaves, and left in the drawing-room of her home until her funeral on Friday.

About a century later, on 4 January 1914, a promising young boxer died in South Shields, County Durham. Towards the end of her life his widow recalled the time immediately following his death:

> That was the finish now. Exceptin' old Mrs Hancock from the market. She brought me a sandwich and a pot of tea up. The only thing to heat with in the room was the fire, so I couldn't even boil a kettle. I daresn't light it in case it would turn poor Johnny. I had already poured two bottles of whiskey down his throat, but he was still turnin' . . . Durin' the days Johnny lay in that room waitin' to be buried, hardly a soul came near the place. He was dead . . . I hardly knew what I was doin' or what day it was as I waited with im for the hours to tick away. I slept in a chair because the bed had been taken down to make room for the flowers and wreaths which arrived by the score. [Robinson, 1975: 75]

Paricularly explicit on the use of flowers to mask the smell of decay is a verse of the folk song *The Unfortunate Rake*, which was probably written in the mid-eighteenth century and continues to be popular in the repertoires of many British and American singers, under such titles as *The Young Sailor Cut Down* and *The Streets of Laredo*. In a typical version of the song:

> Get six of my comrades to carry my coffin,
> Six girls of the city to bear me on,
> And each of them carry a bunch of red ROSES,
> So that they don't smell me as they walk along.
>
> [Lloyd, 1967: 220]

It is noteworthy that in communities, such as those of Orthodox Jews, where burial takes place very soon after death, flowers are rarely associated with mourning.

In nineteenth-century north Shropshire wallflowers, roses, and other blossoms were arranged in the coffins of the poor [Burne, 1833: 299]. In Monmouthshire RUE, hyssop, or wormwood, all considered to be symbolic of repentance, were sometimes placed in coffins [Wherry, 1905: 66]. Early in the twentieth century every herb which grew in the garden, with the exception of THYME, was used to line coffins in some Oxfordshire villages [Parker, 1923: 325].

The evergreens and flowers, which were formerly placed in coffins or used to line the grave, are now usually made into wreaths or bouquets and placed on top of the coffin and, later, the newly filled grave. The floral tributes which are widely used today came into use during the second half of the nineteenth century. Hilderic Friend [1884: 8], a Methodist minister, noted with approval:

> The pretty custom of sending wreaths for the coffins of deceased friends is . . . growing, and it is certainly a delicate, expressive, and touching

method of paying tribute to their memory. The Queen and Royal Family have set us an example again and again in this matter, and it is an example which we have not been slow to imitate.

Charlotte Burne [1883: 299] noted that wreaths were not commonly used in Shropshire until the early 1870s. However, by the end of the nineteenth century the art of making floral tributes had reached its apex, and florists were adept at making such elaborate designs as pearly gates, hearts, broken columns, books, and empty chairs, in addition to the more usual range of wreaths and posies. Even the poor had elaborate and costly flowers at their funerals. In his survey of poverty in London, Charles Booth recorded how a pious Roman Catholic woman and her two daughters occupied a first-floor room in one of the poorest streets. When one of the daughters died their neighbours showed their respect by covering the coffin and almost filling the room with costly wreaths and great quantities of flowers. According to Booth, fish sellers, cats'-meat dealers, and costermongers were most addicted to showy funerals [Fried and Elman, 1969: 63 and 247].

The flowers at the funeral of Queen Victoria, in February 1901, were estimated to have cost £80,000, and produced a display of unparalleled extravagance:

> The Queen Regent of Spain sent a wreath seven feet high; the business firms of Queen Victoria Street presented a Royal Standard five feet by nine composed entirely of VIOLETS, geraniums and MIMOSA. Australia's large wreath was of finest orchids, while the King's Scholars of Westminster offered a wreath of pink and white flowers measuring twelve feet. [*Graphic*, supplementary funeral number, 9 February 1901]

> LILIES OF THE VALLEY, the Queen's favourite flower, were featured in many wreaths, including that sent by the mayor and inhabitants of Brighton, which was 15 feet in circumference and composed of some thousands of white and purple orchids, lilies of the valley, white roses and ARUM LILIES. [*The Times*, 5 February 1901]

Contrasting with such extravagant displays were the funerals of the rural poor. According to an Oxfordshire farm labourer remembering funerals in the early years of the twentieth century:

> There warn't no money for wreaths; the coffin were often bare or, at times, strewn with a few wild flowers from the verge. [Stewart, 1987: 12]

In Glen Gairn, Aberdeenshire, at about the same time, when anyone died the minister's wife

> made a wreath of flowers from the garden to place on the coffin whenever she had the opportunity, arranging the LILIES and other flowers in their season, round a circle of wire, with moss and greenery as a base. For a baby's funeral she made a little posy of SNOWDROPS, COWSLIPS, or VIOLETS

on a background of IVY leaves. Her simple tribute was often the only one. [Fraser. 1973: 164]

With the great increase in the use of cremation during the second half of the twentieth century, many people now prefer the money formerly spent on flowers to be donated to a favourite charity. Of the 24 death announcements in the *Shropshire Star* of 4 February 1993: fourteen requested family flowers only and suggested donations to various charities, four requested no flowers but donations to charities, two mentioned flowers or donations, one mentioned 'flowers suitable for hospital or donations', and the remaining three did not mention flowers.

However, elaborate floral tributes can still be seen at the funerals of some conservative communities. A gypsy woman, buried at Castor-on-Sea, Norfolk, in May 1965, had her coffin surmounted by two wreaths of flowers in the shape of bow-topped caravans drawn by horses. A few months later, in Flintshire, the coffin of a gypsy woman was bedecked with a large number of floral tributes in the shapes of a dog, a bird-cage, a box of matches and cigarettes, a chair, a cushion, a cooking-tripod, a boar's head, and a horse collar [Sanderson, 1969: 185]. About twelve years later the *Balham and Tooting News* of 8 April 1977 gave an account of a respected gypsy leader. The funeral procession was headed by a hearse pulled by two black-plumed horses, and followed by a long line of cars and lorries. The flowers were carried on flat-back trucks, with many of the wreaths being in the shape of horses and dogs.

Fairground showmen, another group of travelling people, also produce elaborate floral decorations at their burials, and the tributes sent to funerals are listed at great length in their weekly magazine, the *World's Fair* [Dallas, 1971: 51]. Obviously it is often impracticable for showmen to attend funerals in person, so elaborate wreaths are sent instead.

Massive displays of flowers are also produced following disasters in which many people are killed. In 1966, when 144 people were killed in Aberfan, Mid Glamorgan, as the result of part of a coal tip sliding down upon a mining village:

Above the two 80ft trenches that served as graves lay a 100ft tall cross made from hundreds of wreaths from all over the world—one came from South African miners.

There was a wreath made in the shape of Pantglas school, which was destroyed by the avalanche of coal waste, white and pink carnations formed the walls and laurel leaves the roof. [*The Times*, 28 October 1966]

Similarly, in 1989, following the Hillsborough football stadium disaster in which ninety-five soccer fans were killed, the home ground of one of the clubs involved was transformed:

> Day by day they have poured in to Anfield—the proud ground that is the home of Liverpool Football Club.
> And with their flowers gradually covering the pitch they have turned Anfield into a shrine. [*Daily Mirror*, 21 April 1989]

One group of people who do not use flowers in their funeral rituals or for decorating graves are Orthodox Jews. They associate flowers with joy, so that wreaths would be out of place at a time of mourning. There is an increasing tendency for Jews who worship in progressive or reformed synagogues to follow gentile traditions, so that flowers may be used to decorate graves or even at the funeral itself. The Orthodox disapprove of this tendency, which they feel is leading to a gradual blurring of the distinction between Judaism and Christianity [Ilford, Essex, July 1977]. The cemeteries of Orthodox Jews are characterized by a lack of flowers on graves, and tightly packed memorials give the impression of a wilderness almost devoid of vegetation.

After a Christian burial the various floral tributes are left on top of the grave, and eventually removed by the cemetery's caretaker when they have died and decayed. Later, bunches of flowers or pot plants are often placed on the grave, or it may be planted out as a small garden. It is apparent that many people derive great solace from such activities. At crematoria gardens of remembrance are common and it is possible to have a standard rose bush, or, more rarely, some other small shrub, planted in memory of a loved one. Often these closely planted and uniformly labelled rose bushes are treated in much the same way as a gravestone, and cut flowers are frequently placed at the base of them in much the same way as flowers are used to decorate graves [personal observation, South London Crematorium, June 1993, and West London Crematorium, August 1981].

At the anniversary of a death and at festive times, such as CHRISTMAS, Easter, MOTHERING SUNDAY, FATHERS' DAY, FLOWERING SUNDAY, and (for Poles) ALL SOULS' DAY, dead relatives are particularly remembered, and their graves receive special attention. At Christmas time in the 1970s most florists sold rather crude wreaths for decorating graves. HOLLY with wired-on plastic berries was a much used component of such wreaths, and other commonly used materials included showy white or mauve plastic flowers, somewhat reminiscent of water lilies, miniature plastic arum lilies, and red plastic poinsettias [personal observation, Tooting, London, December 1975]. Wreaths continue to be produced at Christmas, but they are now more usually used to decorate front doors; in the 1990s cut flowers appear to be favoured for decorating graves at Christmas [personal observation, Mitcham, Surrey and West Norwood, London, December 1993].

For the famous the tending of memorials may, of course, exceed the few decades which the graves of the more humble are likely to receive. It has been claimed that since her death late in the sixteenth century a fresh red flower has been kept on the memorial to Lady Anne Lee, in St Mary's church at Aylesbury, Buckinghamshire [Gascoigne, 1969: 12]. However, it appears that decorating the monument with a red flower or, in winter, red berries, started in comparatively recent times, having been inspired in part by the memorial's inscription:

> Good fre'd sticke not to strew with crims'o flowers
> This marble stone wherin her cindres rest
> For svre her ghost lyes with the heave'ly powers
> And gverdon hathe of virtvovs life possest.

In his *History of Aylesbury* [1855: 33], Robert Gibbs provided a full description of the memorial, but made no mention of red flowers decorating it, and a souvenir booklet produced in 1979 to celebrate the re-opening of the church after extensive renovations stated:

> for over a century her request has been honoured and some one has always been found to place a red flower or red berries on the tomb. [Viney, 1979]

Each year the equestrian statue of King Charles I, in Whitehall, London, is decorated with wreaths and posies in commemoration of the King's execution in 1649 [Brentnall, 1975: 176]. King Charles was canonized by the Church of England in the 1660s, and although most of the flowers displayed at the base of the statue are but modest offerings, the sentiments expressed on the accompanying cards reveal that those who placed them there sincerely believe the King to be worthy of his titles of Saint and Martyr [personal observation, 28 January 1973].

Another seventeenth-century notable still commemorated is the diarist Samuel Pepys, who was buried in St Olave's church, Hart Street, in the City of London, in 1703. On or near 26 May, the anniversary of Pepys' death, a commemoration service is held. During this the Lord Mayor or another dignitary of London places a LAUREL wreath in front of the diarist's memorial [Brentnall, 1975: 177].

On 21 October, the anniversary of the Battle of Trafalgar, a laurel wreath is placed on the spot where Lord Nelson died on the quarter deck of his flagship the *Victory*, now in dry dock in Portsmouth [Boase, 1976: 175].

Occasionally the graves (or supposed graves) of virtually unknown people attract attention. The best known of these is a small mound, known as the Boy's Grave, situated at the Chippenham-Moulton crossroads, about three miles from Newmarket in Suffolk. Several similar and intertwined local legends provide accounts of the Grave. One legend relates how a shepherd boy who lost one of his sheep, which later returned unharmed, was accused of stealing it, with the result that he committed suicide. A second legend tells how a gypsy lad who fell asleep and allowed his flock to stray was so afraid of returning to his family that he hanged himself. Alternatively, the gypsies hanged the lad in punishment for his carelessness. The Grave is said to be always well tended by roadmen and gypsies who leave bunches of flowers on it [Porter, 1974: 40; *English Dance and Song*, 27: 13, 1964].

In the 1970s and particularly the 1980s it became common to place flowers at the scenes of road accidents, and other places where people met with violent deaths.

> The early stages of popular consecration can be observed near Enfield on the A10 Cambridge road out of London, at the site of a fatal road accident some years ago. A horse chestnut tree, one of a long roadside line, is regularly garlanded and festooned with flowers, originally just by the mother of the dead youth. Other people have started adding small offerings, but presumably now 'for luck', like a wishing well. And at Barnes Common, in south London, the sycamore tree which caused the death in a car crash of the pop musician Marc Bolan in 1973 is still regularly bedecked with flowers, fan-letters and a variety of other memorabilia, fifteen years after his death. [Milner, 1992: 138]

> The heartbroken family of two teenage friends killed in a car crash in Ealing has transformed the tragic spot where they died into a blaze of colour.
>
> Best friends, Wayne Dunne, 19, and his friend Stephen Wesley Shakespeare, 18, were killed when their car hit a tree on Gunnersbury Avenue, Acton, last Monday.
>
> This week, their families have turned the tree into a memorial for the pair by bedecking it with flowers and messages. [*Ealing Guardian*, 10 January 1990]

Furze – see GORSE.

Fuzz – a Dorset variant of FURZE.

G

Gaa-girse – a Shetland name for STONEWORT.

Gale – a name for BOG MYRTLE.

Galingale (*Cyperus longus*)

Galingale, known as *han* in Jersey-Norman-French, was used in the past in place of HEMP for cords and ropes. It was used to make tethers for cows and halters for horses as well as matting for floors. A number of local place names indicate the fact that *han* grew there, i.e. Handois and Les Hanniethe. [St Saviour, Jersey, May 1993]

Gall-stones – treated using COUCH GRASS.

Garland Sunday. In County Leitrim:

On the last Sunday in July each year, called Garland Sunday, the young people still make garlands of flowers and place them around certain wells. One of these, Tober-a-dony, is in the parish of Kiltoghert, and besides the wells there is a cavern-like fissure in the side of the mountain . . . which is similarly treated. [Duncan, 1893: 182]

Also celebrated in other parts of Ireland, Garland (or Garlick) Sunday, which is said to be a survival of the ancient Celtic festival of Lughnasa, was in many areas thought to be the day on which the first of the new season's POTATOES should be eaten.

Garlic (*Allium sativum*). In recent vampire literature and films garlic is considered to be protective against vampire attacks and evil in general.

New York: Sotheby's is auctioning a 'vampire killing kit', with garlic powder, bible, wooden stake, moulds for silver bullets and a crucifix concealing a pistol. Most of the items, in a 19th-century mahogany case, are probably only 15 years old. [*The Times*, 10 January 1994]

Recently I heard a colleague comment about another who he disliked that when he knew they were working together he felt the need to come wearing a string of garlic cloves and a crucifix between his shoulder blades to prevent back-stabbing. He was making it clear that he disliked the person in question, but it seemed a very sophisticated way of doing so.

However, about ten years ago, a wealthy incomer to the Isle of Man sacked his gardener, also a come-over, under doubtful circumstances. In response his gateposts were wreathed in wild garlic (*Allium ursinum*) by the wronged party. He got the message and was very upset by it. [Douglas, Isle of Man, April 1992]

Particularly in Ireland, where it was commonly cultivated until about the time of the First World War [McBride, 1991: 83], garlic was valued in herbal remedies.

Garlic when boiled and applied to RINGWORM cures it. [IFCSS MSS 98: 154, Co. Mayo]

Yellow JAUNDICE: get two bulbs of garlic and chop them up small and boil them with a small quantity of water. Make sure no dirt enters the mixture while cooking. When the mixture is brown remove it from the saucepan and place it in a clean bowl to cool a little. Give it to the patient and allow him to drink it as hot as possible. The patient is cured after taking this mixture once. I was cured myself with this cure. [IFCSS MSS 790: 36, Co. Dublin]

Previous to the First World War garlic was used as a general cure. Slices of garlic placed in the shoes, against the soles of the feet, was a cure for whooping cough. [Larne, Co. Antrim, January 1992].

It was often believed that garlic planted on GOOD FRIDAY was particularly potent.

Garlic that has been planted on Good Friday when boiled in sweet milk and given as a drench will cure any disease in people, cattle, or fowl. [IFCSS MSS 990: 71, Co. Cavan]

If garlic is planted on Good Friday the person who plants it will not contract fever during the year. [IFCSS MSS 232: 29, Co. Roscommon]

In England, fewer remedies which use garlic have been recorded, but the plant is widely recommended by herbalists.

A cure for WHOOPING COUGH, practised in Cambridge not that long ago, was to put garlic in the sufferer's socks. [Girton, Cambridge, October 1985]

Research shows that garlic can protect against some forms of heart disease by reducing blood cholesterol levels, and the health food industry has sniffed a new way of making a fortune. The market in garlic supplements in Britain has doubled in the past three years and is now worth about £10 million annually. Every day, about half a million people in the UK swallow the virtually odourless tablets. [*The Times*, 6 March 1991]

Garlick Sunday – see GARLAND SUNDAY.

Geese and gullies – a Shropshire name for SALLOW flowers.

Gentian – the common name for species of *Gentiana* and *Gentianella*; also given to CENTAURY.

Geranium (*Pelargonium* spp.)

It is a widespread practice still to water pot plants with cold tea [which] encourages growth, especially with geraniums. One of my great aunts used to say 'Geraniums don't like to get their toes wet.' A reminder not to over-water. She always kept a scented geranium on the kitchen windowsill to clear the air of cooking smells. [Corbridge, Northumberland, March 1993]

Germander speedwell (*Veronica chamaedrys*)

Blind flower—*Veronica chamaedrys*; Durham (Hartlepool) where it is said by children that if you look steadily at it for an hour you will become blind. [Britten and Holland, 1886: 50]

Cf. POPPY.

In the Munster province of Ireland germander speedwell was known as jump-up-and-kiss-me:

the name and its meaning seem to be so wellknown that if a piece of the flower be worn, the wearer is greeted with shrieks of laughter. [Britten and Holland MSS]

In Ireland germander speedwell was widely used as a cure for JAUNDICE.

Jaundice: get a weed which is called the blue bell (germander speedwell). I have never heard it called anything else. You boil this weed in milk and then you give it to the person who is affected to drink. [IFCSS MSS 290: 159, Co. Offaly]

Speed-well-blue—a herb which grows in the locality is believed to be a cure for the jaundice. [IFCSS MSS 440: 348, Co. Kerry]

On Guernsey, a tea made from germander speedwell was 'esteemed a valuable remedy for INDIGESTION and pains in the stomach' [Marquand, 1906: 42]. See also SPEEDWELL.

Gethsemane – a Cheshire name for EARLY PURPLE ORCHID.

Gingerbeer plant – see under KARMIC PLANT.

Gis an' gullies – a Shropshire name for SALLOW flowers.

Glasswort – see MARSH SAMPHIRE.

Glastonbury thorn – see HOLY THORN.

Goat's beard (*Tragopogon pratensis*)

[Somerset, 1946:] goat's beard closes its flowers at noon—Jack go to bed at noon. [Leamington Spa, Warwickshire, January 1993]

A close relative of the cultivated vegetable salsify (*T. porrifolius*), goat's beard was formerly used as a food. In 1660 it was recorded that:

A very pleasant dish is made from the roots of this plant cooked in boiling water until they are tender and then served with butter like parsnips, for they have a delicate flavour and yield a juice more health giving than that of parsnip or carrot. The roots are often eaten raw in salads. [Ewen and Prime, 1975: 118]

God's hand leaf – a Gloucestershire name for VALERIAN.

Goldenrod (*Solidago* spp.)

I took some goldenrod to a friend; she went mad, she wouldn't have it in the house at any price, she thought it unlucky to have it in the garden even. [Allenton, Derbyshire, March 1983]

Cure for infected sore places—pull goldenrod when in bloom, hang dry, boil in pan of water for 30 minutes, immerse limb in boil [*sic*] of the solution. [SLF MSS, Aldbrough, East Yorkshire, April 1972]

Good Friday

People like to sow crops, oats, etc., on Good Friday because it is a local belief that whatever is planted on this day will grow. Women generally avail themselves of this belief to plant flowers, make slips, cuttings on Good Friday. [IFCSS 350: 135, Co. Cork]

Good Friday was supposed to be an excellent day for sowing any crop or for planting any tree. Anything planted on that day would grow vigorously and would give abundant return. [IFCSS MSS 450: 167, Co. Kerry]

In Ireland GARLIC planted on Good Friday was believed to be particularly potent when used in herbal remedies.

Good Friday plant – a Somerset name for LUNGWORT.

Good King Henry (*Chenopodium bonus-henricus*). Like the closely related FAT HEN, Good King Henry was formerly valued as a vegetable. In 1660 John Ray wrote:

The younger shoots of this plant put into boiling water and cooked for a quarter of an hour, then eaten with butter and salt, make a pleasant and health giving dish not unlike ordinary asparagus. [Ewen and Prime, 1975: 78]

In the twentieth century:

Mercury—Lincolnshire spinach—or in some parts of the country they call it Good King Henry. Mercury is pronounced marcury in Lincolnshire and used to be very common in gardens. My family have always grown and eaten it. I have quite a large bed of it in my garden; being perennial it needs little attention and no matter the weather it comes up . . . Mercury will fill the gap when we've finished the broccoli, kale, etc. until the peas, beans, etc. are ready. We eat it boiled like spinach, and then I like it hot or cold—also I love the flower-heads and sometimes strip the leaves off and eat it as 'poor man's asparagus'. My grandmother used to tell me because it was so deep rooted it was full of iron and minerals. For many years I've thought it was probably responsible for my good resistance to colds and infection. [Washingborough, Lincolnshire, March 1994].

An Isleham [Cambridgeshire] man declared in the 1930s that, as a boy, he was cured of 'scurvy' or weeping ECZEMA by an old woman . . . 'She told me to ground up markery in water and drink it. That cured the scurvy and cured my sweaty feet too.' Markery, he said, was what 'some folk call fat goose or Good King Henry'. [Porter, 1974: 47]

In the Forest of Dean:

my maternal grandparents (b.1856 and 1858): good king henry—infused fresh leaves and drunk—for bladder [troubles]. [Cinderford, Gloucestershire, November 1993]

Gooseberry (Ribes uva-crispa)

BABIES are found under gooseberry bushes. I was told this by several of my aunts when I was a small child (I was born in 1915), but I don't imagine that they seriously believed it themselves! They said it to avoid having to explain where I really came from and how. [Reading, Berkshire, February 1987]

In July 1975 a colleague who complained that his gooseberry bush had produced only three fruits was humorously reminded that he could hardly expect the bush to be more productive in view of the fact that he had just had an addition to his family. [Streatham, London, September 1992]

Towards the end of 1983 expensive hand–made dolls, known as 'Cabbage Patch Kids' were imported from the United States, where apparently children were told that babies come from the CABBAGE patch. The Kids had to be 'adopted' rather than bought. In December 1983 Pearl's, a shop selling miscellaneous cheap goods, in Mitcham Lane, Streatham, south London, displayed mass-produced rag-dolls in its window, labelled: 'Gooseberry bush doll, £2.50.' [Personal observation]

As the first fruit of the summer, gooseberries were often traditionally eaten at Whitsun or at village feasts and revels.

Lamb and gooseberry, it is well-known, are customary dishes at Whitsuntide. In this city, the usage seems to be religiously kept up. The number of lambs killed here, on Friday and Saturday, was 252; and many besides were sold by country butchers who attend the market. [Lichfield Mercury, 4 June 1830]

At Stoke-sub-Hamdon, in Somerset, villagers climbed the local hill and enjoyed a Gooseberry Feast, described as a 'curious old custom' in 1875 [Pulman's Weekly News, 15 July 1875], but apparently it did not survive until the end of the nineteenth century [Stoke-sub-Hamdon, December 1975]. At Drewsteignton, in Devon, gooseberry pasties and cream are traditionally eaten at 'Teignton Fair, held at Trinity Tide—the first Sunday after Whit Sunday' [Warkleigh, Devon, April

1975]. Helston in Cornwall held a Gooseberry Fair on the third Monday in July [Palmer and Lloyd, 1972: 168], and a similar event was held at Hinton St George in Somerset on the first Sunday after Old Midsummer's Day (5 July) [Watson, 1920: 276].

During the eighteenth century the growing and exhibiting of gooseberries became a passion in Cheshire, Lancashire, and the Midlands, comparable with the present-day enthusiasm for growing LEEKS and PUMPKINS. In the 1740s gooseberry clubs were formed in the Manchester area, and about a century later there were 722 varieties of gooseberry and 171 gooseberry shows. It seems that this enthusiasm was particularly strong among cottage-based handloom weavers. With the development of power-driven looms these weavers moved from their cottages into towns, where space for growing gooseberries was restricted. Few of the gooseberry shows survived the First World War. Today ten shows exist, one at Egton Bridge in Yorkshire and nine in Cheshire. The Egton Bridge Old Gooseberry Society, formed in 1800, currently has approximately 120 members, and holds its show on the first Tuesday in August each year [Smith, 1989: 109].

In Dorset:

My grandmother used to say: 'May the skin of a gooseberry cover all your enemies.' [Thorncombe, Dorset, April 1978]

In Ireland gooseberry thorns were considered to be efficacious in the treatment of STYES.

Stye: pick ten gooseberry thorns, point nine to the eye and throw away the tenth, bury the other nine and when the thorns are withered the stye will be gone. [IFCSS MSS 212: 370, Co. Leitrim]

If you make the sign of the cross with a gooseberry thorn on a stye for nine mornings and then bury the thorn the stye will disappear. [IFCSS MSS 800: 53, Co. Offaly]

Goosegrass (*Galium aparine*)

The sticky burrs of goosegrass, which stick on one's clothes when walking in long grass, are known locally as sweethearts, and are considered certain proof that one has been with one's sweetheart. [Driffield, Humberside, July 1985]

During my childhood in Sussex/Kent in the 1920s and 1930s: if goosegrass was thrown at a girl's back and stuck there without her being aware of it, she had a sweetheart. If she took it off and dropped it, it would form the initial of her sweetheart-to-be. [Farnham, Surrey, December 1985]

Cf. APPLE, BURDOCK, and ORANGE.

A Guernsey name for goosegrass was *la coue* (the tail):

Goosy gullies

This singular name originates in the common amusement of country children on All Fools' Day. They slily stick wisps of this clinging plant on each other's backs, and then start the cry '*La coue! La coue!*' [Marquand, 1906: 42]

As its name suggests, goosegrass was widely fed to poultry.

[Goosegrass], chopped small, is given to goslings in this island [of Wight]. [Bromfield, 1856: 240]

During my childhood in west Dorset in the 1950s, young goosegrass was considered to be excellent food for young POULTRY particularly young turkeys. It was gathered from the hedgerows, and chopped up using scissors. [Streatham, London, December 1983]

When we used to rear turkeys under a hen we scoured the lanes for cleavers (sweethearts) as a source of early greenstuff . . . game-keepers also use it for rearing young pheasants. [Charmouth, Dorset, January 1994]

Goosy gullies – a Shropshire name for SALLOW flowers.

Gorse (*Ulex europaeus*), also known as furze or whin. The yellow flowers of gorse, like those of BROOM, are occasionally considered to be inauspicious when taken indoors.

May [HAWTHORN], of course, should never be brought indoors—also gorse and LILAC—both of these were considered to be unlucky. As a child I was never allowed to bring any of these indoors. [St Peter Port, Guernsey, April 1984]

Gorse, IVY and ARUM LILIES—none of these were ever allowed in the house. [St Aubin, Jersey, April 1984]

More than 60 years ago I lived with my parents in the town of Listowel . . . a couple of miles down river from the town there were acres of shrubland completely covered by . . . furze bushes . . . one early spring I decided to bring a bunch of them to mother who, being a countrywoman, was very fond of wild flowers, but . . . being appreciative of the thought [she] told me to immediately take them out of the house without laying them down and never bring them in again. She told me they were extremely unlucky, and this later in life I found to be the view all over this country. [Ballybunion, Co. Kerry, October 1984]

Some years ago, when in Fifeshire, I plucked a very fine bloom [of gorse] in a bleak season when no other wild flowers were to be seen. Meeting an elderly lady, she exclaimed on its beauty. I, thinking to please her, said. 'You can have it,' at the same time handing it to her. 'Oh,' she said, 'why did you do that? It is very unlucky to give anyone whin blossom; we shall be sure to quarrel.' I laughed and said, 'I never heard of that freit. Perhaps when one does it in ignorance it won't work.' A few days later I had the ill luck to offend the said lady. She was very angry, and gave me her opinion of me in no measured terms, ending in saying, 'That's your present of whin bloom.' [*Weekly Scotsman*, Christmas 1898]

In October 1979 I was told by a London school teacher, then in her 20s, that at the first school which she attended as a child, in Hampshire, children were afraid to touch gorse flowers because it was believed that dragons lived, or were born, in them. [Streatham, London, February 1993]

However, a widespread saying associates gorse flowers with kissing:

Kissing's out of fashion when the whin is out of blossom. [Ballycastle, Co. Antrim, January 1991]

The presence of gorse, like that of THISTLES, is said to indicate rich soil.

[Co. Kerry:] *An t-or fe'n aiteann, an t-airgead fe'n luachair agus an gorta fe'n bhfraoch* (Gold under furze, silver under RUSHES and famine under heath). [Lucas, 1960: 186]

There's a saying around here: 'Where there's BRACKEN there's gold; where there's gorse there's silver; where there's heather there's poverty.' [Newton Rigg, Cumbria, September 1988]

Gorse flowers were widely used as a DYE, particularly for EASTER EGGS.

Whins . . . have a yellow blossom and woollens can be dyed by these blossoms. This is the way it is done. There is some water boiled and when it is boiling the whin blossoms are put in and they let it boil for another while. Then the woollen was put in and it was let take the dye. When it was taken out it is a beautiful yellow colour. [IFCSS MSS 212: 61, Co. Leitrim]

On Easter Sunday we collected all the weans of the village and took them up to a field with a big hill on it. We made our tea after lighting a fire and got all the eggs in a big saucepan to boil them hard. Unknown to the kids we put whin blossom in the water while they were boiling and they came out a lovely yellow colour. The kids thought it was magic. Then up to the top of the hill and roll the eggs down. [Castlerock, Co. Derry, February 1989]

[Burghead, Morayshire, 1920s and 1930s:] for dyeing Easter eggs our mothers might use the outer skins of ONIONS, or whin flowers. [Edinburgh, October 1991]

Although gorse is now considered to be little more than a pest, it was formerly valued as a fuel, a food for livestock, and for providing cover. Lucas (1960 and 1979) provides an extensive survey of the plant's uses in Ireland, and Harris (1992) surveys uses in the East Riding of Yorkshire.

The Normans introduced furze . . . into Ireland to make stock-proof hedges, which it does. [South Stainley, North Yorkshire, March 1992]

I saw an old neighbour using a thick branch of whin to clean his cottage chimney by the simple method of tying a piece of rope to each end of the branch, dropping it down the chimney, coming down from the low roof and entering the kitchen where he caught the rope and brought down the soot and all with the branch of whin. [Glynn, Co. Antrim, February 1992]

Fuzz moots = roots of furze; we used to pull them up and take them home to burn in the kitchen range. Mother preferred them to coal as they burnt with a lovely hot clean flame. This would be around 1935. [Martinstown, Dorset, May 1991]

The Welsh Folk Museum, at St Fagans, has a reconstructed gorse mill from Dolwen in Clywd:

Gorse was a vital part of their [horses'] diet. It was specially grown on a large scale but had to be bruised or crushed to make it fit to eat. Small farmers bruised their gorse by hand, though water-driven mills . . . [such as the one exhibited] were common by about 1800, using heavy metal spikes to crush the gorse. By 1850, however, most farmers were using lighter and cheaper hand-operated machines instead. [William, 1991: 24]

In Ireland gorse was used as a VERMICIDE and to treat JAUNDICE.

Whins . . . are cut up and pounded. Then they are given to horses to take worms out of them. [IFCSS MSS 212: 61, Fenagh, Co. Leitrim]

A handful of whin blossom boiled in milk was strained and given to a child suspected of having worms. [Glynn, Co. Antrim, February 1992]

Furze blossoms are boiled [and] the juice used for yellow jaundice. [ICFSS MSS 500: 76, Co. Limerick]

For a legend concerning St Patrick cursing gorse, see RUSH.

Gout – treated using ALDER, GROUND ELDER, HORSERADISH, and TANSY.

Gout weed – see GROUND ELDER.

Gowk's thumles – a north-east Scotland name for HAREBELL.

Grab – a Devon variant of crab; see CRAB APPLE.

Grandfather's weatherglass – a Somerset name for SCARLET PIMPERNEL.

Granny-jump-out-of-bed, Granny-pop-out-of-bed – names for the LARGE and HEDGE BINDWEEDS.

Granny's toenails – a Kent name for BIRD'S-FOOT TREFOIL.

Grape (*Vitis vinifera*)

Black cats under grapes—people didn't actually go out and kill cats, but if you were lucky enough to find a dead cat, especially a black tom, and bury it under your grape vine it would help your grape grow. Black grapes grew better from black toms. [Wicken, Cambridgeshire, March 1993]

Grape hyacinth (*Muscari armeniacum*)

BLUEBELLS and grape hyacinths – happiness in natural surroundings, dreadful depression in the house. When I was a young nurse I tried to 'crack' this piece of lore, but in fact the flowers must give off some 'essence' which does make people suddenly morose and sullen . . . When I removed the flowers the atmosphere immediately lightened—and I've tested this theory for about 40 years. I've stopped now though and bluebells and grape hyacinth stay outdoors. [Paston, Cambridgeshire, November 1993]

Grass. It is widely believed that an abundance of grass at Christmas foretold a large number of deaths in the following year.

[Dorset:] Ev a chich'ard da look lik' a pastur' veel 'pon C'ursmas Day'll look lik' a plow'd veel avoa Medzumma Day. [Udal, 1922: 267]

A green Christmas, a fat churchyard. Green meaning mild weather, absence of frost and snow. Fat churchyard meaning a full churchyard resulting from many deaths due to a mild Christmas. People preferred hard weather as the frost killed germs, etc. [Daingean, Co. Offaly, January 1985]

The succulent young stems of many grasses were widely chewed by children and countrymen.

[Now an OAP] as a child I was at a prep-school near Budleigh Salterton, Devon . . . We . . . knew about plants 'nice to taste': DANDELION, SORREL, very young grass shoots, BLACKBERRIES and STRAWBERRIES. [Mutley, Plymouth, January 1993]

[I am now 70 years old and have lived in the country all my life.] When out walking we inevitably chewed the succulent ends of grasses. [Corbridge, Northumberland, January 1993]

I am nearly 70 years of age and was born and bred in Norfolk . . . [as children] we chewed the flower stem of grass, if pulled out of its sheath gently it was soft and juicy and a good thirst inhibitor. [Two Locks, Gwent, March 1993]

See also BENT GRASS.

Grass might occasionally be used to treat NETTLE STINGS.

Rub the sting with grass until the grass moistens the sting. Repeat the following:

Nettle come out, grass go in.

I have found this to be a sure cure. [SLF MSS, Scunthorpe, Humberside, November 1969]

Grass leaves could be used to produce whistles.

I never made whistles (always regarded as a boys' activity) but we used to blow a piercing whistle between blades of grass. [Great Bedwyn, Wiltshire, February 1992].

A shrill whistling noise can be made by placing a blade of grass edge-on in the narrow space produced by placing both hands together in such a way that both thumb joints and both thumb bases are pressed together side by side. The grass blade is held in place at these two pressure points. Blowing strongly through the narrow gap can produce a surprisingly loud noise! [Scalloway, Shetland, February 1994]

Blowing through a blade of grass placed between the thumbs in order to create a high pitched whistle or screech, is frowned on generally, as it is said to 'raise the wind' and so endanger boats at sea. [Lerwick, Shetland, March 1994]

Grave flooer – a Shetland name for white NARCISSUS.

Gravel (kidney disease) – treated using PARSLEY PIERT.

Great burnet (*Sanguisorba officinalis*)

[It] is called 'Hot weed' in parts of Brecknock and Radnor: said to cause hay to heat up if present in large amounts. [Llandrindod Wells, Powys, September 1991]

Cf. RIBWORT PLANTAIN.

Greater celandine (*Chelidonium majus*)

The expressed juice or a decoction of the plant is in vogue with the country people of the island [of Wight] as a remedy for infantine JAUNDICE. [Bromfield, 1856: 26]

[In Cornwall] in common with *Ranunculus repens* [BUTTERCUP] the greater celandine enjoys a wide reputation in making ointment for sore EYES, and is frequently called 'Kenning Herb,' from 'Kenning' or 'Kennel', local names for an ulcer on the eye. The yellow latex of the plant is also believed to be a sure cure for warts. [Davey, 1909: 23]

Until about five years ago I had been working for some years in the administration department of one of our large training hospitals. At the time I had a very large WART on the side of my right thumb. As I was right on the spot for treatment many cures were tried, none successfully. On my leaving the hospital, as a final parting gesture, the wart was cut out in the casualty department. In a few weeks it returned.

I had the good fortune some weeks later to meet a man from Worcestershire, who noticed my wart and told me he could cure it. The cure was to rub the sap from the stem of the plant greater celandine on to the wart for five nights. In order that I might do that he sent me some of this plant, on his return to Worcestershire. In three weeks there was absolutely no sign of the wart left, and there has been no sign of any recurrence.

This cure might be of interest to others who have had little success employing . . . 'recognised wart medications'. [Letter from Highgate, London, in *Hornsey Journal*, 17 August 1956]

In Ashford, Kent, greater celandine was much used for the treatment of warts. A stem was broken and the orange sap rubbed on the wart. [Bexhill-on-Sea, East Sussex, February 1991]

The bright yellow sap of the greater celandine contains several alkaloids including chelidonin and chelerythrin [Clapham et al., 1962: 102], and names given to the plant by country people reveal how it is, or was, valued as a cure for warts. Thus in Devon it was known as wart flower, in Gloucestershire as wart wort [Britten and Holland, 1886: 484], and in Somerset as wart plant [Grigson, 1987: 50].

Greater Mexican stonecrop *(Sedum praealtum)*

I have this plant which is quite rare—*Sedum praealtum*— which was sent to me by friends in Brazil. They use it to stop BLEEDING—they even use it for internal haemorrhages. It does work, I've used it on cuts and that sort of thing; you just get a handful, slap it on, and the bleeding stops. [Earls Court, London, October 1985]

Greater plantain *(Plantago major)*. Like BITING STONECROP and WATER FIGWORT, greater plantain was used by children to make 'fiddles'.

[When I was a child at Heston, Middlesex, in the 1930s] a leaf [of greater plantain] was picked and the stalk partly severed to expose the tough veins, these then made a violin (my grandchildren now make guitars!). [St Ervan, Cornwall, February 1992]

Broad-leaved plantain: after making a cut across the stem with the thumb nail, the lower part of the stem could be gently pulled down leaving the veins exposed—a 'banjo'. [Lee, London, April 1993]

Adults used the leaves of greater plantain to treat skin ailments.

My late parents came from Poland after the Second World War, and my mother occasionally used certain plants as herbal remedies . . . a poultice of the leaves of the greater plantain was used for CORNS and ULCERS. [Bromley, Kent, April 1991]

The greater plantain was a good healer; the leaf 'the rough side to draw and the smooth side to heal' was bandaged on a CUT or BRUISE. The seed head was stuck through the bars of a bird cage, and the birds, usually goldfinches, would peck at it. [Lenamore, Co. Longford, April 1991]

Greater plantain = wavverin leaf—used to treat cuts, burns and sores. [Lerwick, Shetland, March 1994]

See also PLANTAIN.

Greater stitchwort

Greater stitchwort (*Stellaria holostea*)

Piskie, Pixie or Pixy—This was the regular name for the stitchwort around Plymouth some years ago. The children still say that if you gather the flowers you will be pixy-led [i.e. hopelessly lost, even in an area which you know well]. [Friend, 1882: 44]

In many parts of Cornwall children refuse to gather this flower, believing that a bite from an ADDER is sure to follow the act. In other districts it is held that the Pixies or 'Piskys' hide during the daytime in the flowers of stitchwort, and that anyone gathering the blossoms after sunset is sure to be 'Pixy-led' and in other ways troubled by the 'small people.' [Davey, 1909: 73]

MOTHER-DIE. Form of mental torture for ultra-sensitive children, especially only children thought to be 'mother's boys'. The child would be told to pick a greater stitchwort or its mother would die and then throw it down again or its father would die. The victims never seemed to appreciate the fallacy for a long time, even when it was pointed out by kinder-hearted children. Used as a *coup-de-grâce* for a child who somehow managed to survive physical bullying. Common in the Denby Dale area in the 1920s and 1930s but I haven't come across it since. [SLF MSS, Welwyn Garden City, Hertfordshire, April 1976]

Greater stitchwort is usually known as snapjacks; children 'snap' the seed capsules. [Thorncombe, Dorset, January 1993]

I was an Examiner for the Naturalist Badge for Guides and Scouts in the 1930s . . . having rhymes and stories attached to plants made them easier to remember, and a lot more fun . . . greater stitchwort—we chewed flowers of this when we got the stitch—most likely mind over matter, I think. [Chard Junction, Somerset, May 1985]

Greater tussock sedge (*Carex paniculata*).
On the Isle of Wight and, no doubt, elsewhere, 'the long tough culms' of greater tussock sedge were used 'as a cheap though inferior substitute for straw for thatching ricks, &c.' [Bromfield, 1856: 553].

Great horsetail (*Equisetum telmateia*)

Great horsetail is uncommon hereabouts, but there is a big patch in Wychwood, and in my boyhood [*c*.1915] I remember seeing a cottager nearby using it for scouring saucepans. [Charlbury, Oxfordshire, February 1991]

Ground elder (*Aegopodium podagraria*)

GOUT: drink an infusion of gout weed twice a day (gout weed's other name is ground elder). An old friend of mine did this successfully within the last ten years. [UCL EFS MSS M4, Kilburn, London, September 1963]

Ground ivy (*Glechoma hederacea*)

When my son went into the Army he did a lot of shooting, and the gun-smoke made his EYES red and sore. He asked us to send something to relieve them, but we didn't know what to send, so my husband went to see a woman of gypsy origin who lived in the village to ask if she could suggest anything. She told us to put a large handful of ground ivy in a saucepan, just cover it with water, and simmer for about 20 minutes. When cool, strain and use to bathe the eyes. We sent some of this to my son and it soon cleared up the trouble. I still sometimes use some myself, as it makes a lovely smooth lotion, almost oily, and has a pleasant smell. [Shipston-on-Stour, Warwickshire, September 1993]

The leaves are much used in villages to make an infusion for COUGHS, and the plant was formerly called ale-hoof or tun-hoof, because their bitter properties rendered them of use in the beer made in the old English households, before hops had become the common growth of our country. Even in recent times a quantity of this plant has been thrown into a vat of ale in order to clarify it, and the ale thus prepared has been taken as a remedy for some maladies of the skin. [Pratt, 1857, 2: 64]

Spring of the year it is the country custom (Berks and Oxon) to make an infusion of ground ivy leaves (Robin run in the hedge), bairns given wineglass full before breakfast—supposed to clear skin and cool blood. [Taylor MSS]

Groundsel (*Senecio vulgaris*)

For a bad CUT: take Ascension, called in towns groundsel, boil for 10 minutes and apply as a poultice. [Taylor MSS, Baconsthorpe, Norfolk]

[Lostwithiel, Cornwall:] for AGUE: put a handful of groundsel into a small linen bag, pricking the side next to the skin full of holes; wear it at pit of stomach and renew every two hours until well. [Deane and Shaw, 1975: 123]

Before castor oil had attained its popularity as a safe and efficient PURGATIVE for children it was the practice in Ireland to add a sprig or two (according to age) of groundsel to the milk, which was then boiled, strained, and given to constipated babies. [Moloney, 1919: 30]

Tuesday we went to see Mr & Mrs Joby House, who used to be at Hewood. [He told us that] for CONSTIPATION you boiled groundsel and lard and take that, and you will 'shit through the eye of a needle.' His sister Lucy had constipation so bad that when the doctor called in the morning he said Lucy will be dead by 5 o'clock. Mrs House went to the gypsies (Mrs Penfold) who lived down Partway Lane, and she told her how to cure her. The doctor came late in the day, and Lucy was running around; there was shit everywhere. The doctor had brought Lucy's death certificate, but he was so mad he tore it up and put it in the fire. [Thorncombe, Dorset, March 1991]

Guernsey lily (*Nerine sarniensis*)

> The Guernsey Lily, *Nerine sarniensis*, has long been regarded as Guernsey's National Flower . . . The legend of its first appearance in the island is part of our fairy tradition. The story goes that when the fairy king won the heart of the beautiful Michele De Garis and persuaded her to go away with him to his far away kingdom, she thought of her family and how they would grieve for her. So she asked her elfin lover to let her leave some small token by which they could remember her. He gave her a bulb which she planted in the sand above Vazon Bay before embarking on the fairy craft taking her away from her island home. Later, when her distraught mother came looking for her missing daughter she found this bulb, now burst into flower—a beautiful scarlet, scentless blossom, sprinkled with fairy gold. [De Garis, 1975: 120]

The history of the Guernsey lily, which is native to South Africa but has been associated with or grown on Guernsey since 1680, has been the subject of considerable debate. Four conflicting explanations have been put forward: it was introduced to Guernsey by General John Lambert who, following the Restoration was held prisoner there from 1661 to 1670; bulbs washed ashore from a wrecked ship rooted on the strand and were taken into cultivation by Charles Hatton, whose father was Governor of the Island from 1662 to 1670; a passenger on a ship from Japan or China who was temporarily stranded on Guernsey made a gift of bulbs to Jurat Jean de Sausmarez (1609–91); or sailors on a ship returning from China gave bulbs to an innkeeper. The first three of these explanations all seem to suggest that the lily was introduced to Guernsey at about the same period, and a hypothetical sequence of events which contains elements of all of the explanations is provided by Ewen and De Carteret, 1974.

Gypsophila (*Gypsophila paniculata*).

Also known as baby's breath, the small white flowers of gypsophila are frequently included in WEDDING bouquets, probably mainly for its decorative qualities, but according to some writers:

> The significantly named baby's breath . . . with a cloud of tiny white flowers, is a bouquet ingredient with obvious fertility connotations. [Baker, 1977: 77]

> *Gypsophila paniculata*, nicknamed baby's breath, is still carried to ensure a fruitful marriage. [Bloxham and Picken, 1990: 82]

H

Hackberry – a name given to BIRD CHERRY in north-east Scotland.

Hairy brome (*Bromopsis ramosa*; syn. *Bromus ramosus*)

I have seen children strip the branches off the culm of *Bromus ramosus* and make a running noose of the thin end with which to catch newts. The newts submitted to having these put round their heads without any sign of fear. [Syston, Leicester, January 1991]

Hairy vetch (*Vicia hirsuta*) – sometimes considered to be the TARES of the New Testament parable.

Half wood – a Warwickshire name for TEAPLANT.

Hallowe'en – associated plants include APPLE, CABBAGE, FLAX, and PUMPKIN; see also ALL SOULS' DAY.

Some people say that if they have not all their fruit preserved before November Eve that Pooka will destroy them. [IFCSS MSS 589: 18, Co. Clare].

A seventeenth-century proverb concerning the planting of APPLES, PEARS, HAWTHORNS, and OAKS advised:

Sett them at All-hallow-tyde, and command them to grow.
Sett them at Candlemas, and entreat them to grow.

[Aubrey, 1847: 105]

Hanging tree – see JOUG TREE and OAK for the legend of the Fort William Hanging Tree.

Hangover – treated using CABBAGE.

Harebell (*Campanula rotundifolia*), also known as bluebell in some parts of Scotland. In north-east Scotland:

The bluebell (*Campanula rotundifolia*) was in parts of Buchan called 'the aul' man's bell,' regarded with a sort of dread, and commonly left unpulled. In other parts it was called 'gowk's thumles.' [Gregor, 1881: 148]

[In north-east England] our children have a custom of blowing into the flower bell; and then, placing it erect on the back of the hand, they make it crack by a smart stroke with the other. [Johnston, 1853: 135]

Cf. FOXGLOVE.

Hart's tongue fern (*Phyllitis scolopendrium*)

In Devonshire the children have a graceful tale about Harts-tongue fern. It was once the pillow for the Son of Man, when He had nowhere to lay His head. In return for this service, He left two hairs of His most blessed and dear head, which the plant treasures in her ripe stem, as His legacy— two auburn hairs which children find and show. [Marson, 1904]

The fresh leaves of the hart's-tongue are applied externally in rustic practice in the island [of Wight] to bad legs! (erysipelatous eruptions) as a cooling remedy. [Bromfield, 1856: 634]

Burn a leaf called hart's tongue and apply it to a BURN and it would cure it. [IFCSS MSS 500: 74, Co. Limerick]

The hart's tongue fern was used as a cure for SCALDS and burns. The underside up it was laid to the scald or burn. Fresh leaves were applied when needed until the cure was complete. [IFCSS MSS 650: 128, Co. Waterford]

Hassocks – made from TUFTED HAIR GRASS.

Hawthorn (*Crataegus* spp.), commonly known as whitethorn in Ireland. When the Folklore Society conducted a survey of 'unlucky' plants between March 1982 and October 1984, 123 (23.5 per cent) of the 524 items collected concerned hawthorn flowers, more than twice the number of items concerning LILAC, the second most feared plant.

Children in Shepherd's Bush who made grottoes [c.1920] would not use lilac or hawthorn blossom to decorate them. [East Bedfont, Middlesex, September 1978]

Just before the last war, I stayed for a brief spell at a boarding house in Torquay, I was a young teenager and had not previously given superstitions any kind of thought. However, one day I picked a lovely spray of fragrant hawthorn blossom to give to my landlady, thinking she would be as pleased as I was with the beautiful flowers; alas, as soon as she caught sight of them she turned on me. I can still see her angry face. 'Throw them out at once' she shouted. 'You are bringing a funeral into the house.' I was amazed and shocked as you can imagine at the hostile reception, and she kept harping on the incident, her husband was poorly, her mother would throw me out (as well as the hawthorn), etc., etc. [Worthing, West Sussex, August 1982]

[According to my gran who lived in Wiltshire] hawthorn (may) if picked would result in a dead child. [Blurton, Staffordshire, March 1983]

When I was a child (I am seventy-three) it was considered unlucky to bring hawthorn blossom into the house. Our old doctor, who was then over eighty, said he thought the superstition had arisen because at the time of the year when may blossom was out there was often a lot of chest and throat ailments because of the pollen, and so people connected their ill health with hawthorn or may blossom that was often brought into the house for decoration. Also these people may have connected it with the unlucky month of May, e.g. Marry in May and you'll rue the day. [Audley, Staffordshire, March 1983]

My parents said it was very unlucky to bring may blossom into the house. On three occasions as a child I brought some into the house, each time I was rushed to hospital, seriously ill within a week . . . Dad's explanation was that Christ's CROWN OF THORNS was made of hawthorns. [Mickleover, Derbyshire, March 1983]

When I moved to a house in rural Cheshire, the farmer from whom I bought the house mentioned [that hawthorn blossom should never be cut] because if you did so you would not get an APPLE crop as you would be depriving the bees of a supply of pollen. [Newcastle-under-Lyme, Staffordshire, March 1983]

When I was a child, living in Sandriacre, Derbyshire (1952–58) I well remember being told by my mother that my younger sister and I should not bring may flowers into the house as they brought bad luck. To bring them into the house would not only bring bad luck, but would ensure that it would rain during the summer months. [Hartshay Hill, Derbyshire, March 1983]

My childhood was spent in the Chigwell, Ongar, Upminster areas of Essex . . . May (*Crataegus monogyna*) . . . must not be brought into the house . . . not necessarily death, but certainly illness [would follow]. It was not lucky to even sit under a may hedge in flower, but quite safe otherwise. [Witham, Essex, May 1983]

When I was at school, I regret over 40 years ago, a very unpopular teacher fell downstairs. It was said that this was because she had vases of hawthorn in her classroom. This was at Redhill, Surrey; I've no idea where we got the idea from. [Anonymous telephone call, July 1983]

I still remember being terrified as a child of about five being told (after the event) that to carry May blossom indoors was certain to cause the death of one's mother—indeed the blossom was known locally as 'MOTHER-DIE'. I learnt of the superstition when we lived in the village of Flixton, now a suburb of Manchester, about 1958 . . . Fortunately, I can tell you that the superstition proved without foundation as today, twenty-five years later, my mother is still fit and well . . . though I never chanced bringing a second bunch of blossom across the threshold. [Chiswick, London, July 1983]

I was born and brought up on a farm in southern Ireland (Longford). Forbidden flowers . . . as I remember from preparing May Altars . . . cutting a lone (single) hawthorn bush—death/illness. [Southfields, London, April 1984]

Cf. LONE BUSH.

Some writers (e.g. Maple, 1971: 31) have claimed that the present fear of hawthorn flowers derives from memories of pre-Christian May Day celebrations in which a May Queen was crowned with hawthorn blossoms before she was ritually slaughtered. Needless to say, there is no evidence to support such speculations.

According to a Cambridge anthropologist:

> It is considered bad luck to bring hawthorn indoors; in contrast to Christmastide greenery and Easter willow, it is a plant kept out of doors, associated with unregulated love in the fields, rather than conjugal love in the bed. [Goody, 1993: 256]

Similarly, 'greene hawthorne' is frequently mentioned in medieval love allegories, where it has been interpreted as being a symbol of carnal as opposed to spiritual love [Eberley, 1989: 41].

Some writers have suggested that hawthorn blossom was associated with devotions to the Virgin Mary.

> Superstition about May dates from the times when Catholics were persecuted for their faith.
>
> During the month of May—which was dedicated to the Blessed Virgin Mary—May blossoms were used to decorate the little shrines which Catholics made in their homes in her honour. If anti-Catholic officials saw May blossom being carried into a house, they recognised the household as a Catholic one and acted accordingly. Hence, to bring these flowers into a house brought 'bad luck' to the owners. [Letter from East Grinstead, East Sussex, in *Sunday Express*, 16 May 1982]

However, historical evidence does not support such ideas:

> May became Mary's month only in the eighteenth century, in Naples, whence it spread to Italy, to Ireland, and all over the Catholic world, encouraged chiefly by the Jesuits. [Warner, 1978: 281]

Similarly:

> In fact 'May Devotions' were only introduced into this country in the middle of the nineteenth century by an Italian priest, Dr Gentili. They were resented for a while as a 'foreign innovation'. The connection between Mary and May was later fostered in the Catholic Schools which developed their own quasi-liturgy with hymns, processions, crownings, etc., none of which had any place in the official liturgy although parochial clergy were often inveigled into taking part. [Portishead, Avon, June 1982]

In 1866 a correspondent of the *Gentleman's Magazine* wrote:

> I have found it a popular notion among . . . country cottagers that the peculiar scent of the hawthorn is 'exactly like the smell of the Great Plague of London'. This belief may have been traditionally held during the last two centuries, and have arisen from circumstances noted at the period of the Great Plague. [Gomme, 1884: 206]

More recently the poet Sylvia Plath referred to the 'death-stench of the hawthorn'.

Two species of hawthorn, which frequently hybridize, are native to the British Isles: the common hawthorn (*Crataegus monogyna*) and the Midland hawthorn (*C. laevigata*, often known in the older literature as *C. oxyacanthoides*). In a letter dated 21 May 1900 the amateur botanist, the Revd R.P. Murray, recorded:

> When in Switzerland we had plenty both of *C. monogyna* and *C. oxyacan-thoides:* the latter flowering a week or two earlier than *C. monogyna*. But I often gathered a lot of *C. oxyacanthoides* for decorative purposes: and tho' in smell quite like the other when gathered, it used to absolutely *stink* of putrid flesh soon after: sometimes within half an hour. I do not remember this ever occurred with *C. monogyna*. [Allen, 1980: 119]

More recently it has been shown that trimethylamine, one of the first products formed when animal tissues start to decay, is present in hawthorn flowers [Challenger, 1955: 266]. Until comparatively recent times corpses were kept in the house for anything up to a week before burial, causing most people to be fully aware of the odour of death and decay. Thus it is not surprising that hawthorn blossoms should have been banned from the home.

There is one odd record of hawthorn blossom being brought indoors to hasten recovery from illness:

> It was said that when there was an outbreak of typhoid in the old Post Office Street [Ayton, North Yorkshire], after eight people had died and several people in one family had had it, the doctor (Dr Megginson) found that they were all very inert and disinclined to rouse themselves; so he told the mother to get large boughs of the flowering hawthorn, and put them all over the house. This was done and the invalids soon began to rouse themselves and made efforts to recover their strength. [Dickinson MSS, 1974: 41]

Another instance of hawthorn being considered auspicious appears to be:

> an old custom in Suffolk, in most farm houses that any servant, who could bring a branch of hawthorn in full blossom on the first of May, was entitled to a dish of cream for breakfast. This custom is now disused . . . it very seldom happens that any blossoms are seen open even on Old May Day. [Forby, 1830: 426]

In Ireland hawthorn was often used to provide protection for the homestead on May Day.

> Long ago on May Day the old people used [to] bring in blossoms of the whitethorn and place them on the dresser. They used [to] leave them there until that day month. They were supposed to have the power of keeping away evil. [IFCSS MSS 413: 35, Co. Kerry]

On May Day . . . sprigs of whitethorn which have been sprinkled with blessed water procured on Holy Saturday are stuck down in the village fields to prevent the 'FAIRIES' from taking the crops, and to produce a good crop. [IFCSS MSS 825: 139, Co. Laois]

Other practices in which hawthorn provided protection include:

Hanging the after-birth of a calf on a thorn is a preventative of fever for the cow. One was seen on a thorn by the [Hampshire] informant in 1939. [Heather, 1940: 406]

[In Radnorshire] the remarkable ceremony of 'the burning bush' was long regarded as essential to the well-being of the wheat crop, providing a safeguard against 'smuts in the wheat'. The bush consisted of a branch of hawthorn pruned to leave four twigs at right-angles. All the men of the farm were out very early on New Year's morning, and armed with bundles of straw and a plentiful supply of beer and cyder, and carrying the bush, they visited each wheat-field in turn. In each field a fire was kindled, over which the bush was hung, to be ignited but not destroyed. The bush, or what remained of it, after all the fires had been lit, was taken to the farmhouse to be preserved carefully until the next New Year's Day . . . It is said that the custom was so widely observed that the whole countryside 'twinkled like stars' in the darkness of the early morning. [Howse, 1949: 206]

A variety of the common hawthorn which produces flowers in winter as well as at the usual time, in late spring, each year is the Glastonbury or HOLY THORN. In Ireland isolated hawthorns are often considered to be fairy trees or LONE BUSHES, which must not be destroyed or harmed.

The multitude of superstitions which surround hawthorn have led to speculation that in pre-Christian times there was a 'thorn cult' in the British Isles [Cornish, 1941], or that the tree was associated with the supreme goddess [Graves, 1948].

The saying 'Cast ne'er a clout 'til May is out' has caused much controversy; does it mean that one should not discard winter clothing until hawthorn is in blossom, or is the end of the month of May intended?

Certainly it is the May or hawthorn and not the month. As a boy here in Devon it was always the way of it and as soon as May blossom showed we were told we could leave pullovers and such off. The old folk would point it out and one felt that spring was here. [Barnstaple, Devon, September 1992]

A letter from Hove, East Sussex, published in the *Daily Telegraph* of 5 June 1993, rejected both the month and may blossom, and claimed:

May was one Mavis (May) Dennison, a 'four-penny drab' who slept out in the Itchy Park area of Spitalfields in the mid-1840s. A cunning old soak, she made it her business to spend each winter in jail, coming out reasonably well-fed and revived for the summer months, about the end of May or early June. It was from this that her contemporaries—most likely jeeringly—took up what has become our most misquoted old saw.

Young hawthorn leaves are frequently eaten by children who know them as BREAD AND CHEESE, and in former times they were eaten by adults in times of hardship. In 1752:

The failure of the harvest was immediately followed by a cattle plague which wiped out many of the local herds. The poor suffered greatly, and the Kingswood Colliers, already outcast, feared and despised, suffered more than most . . . A rumour swept through the Forest that wheat was to be exported from Bristol and this was the spark which lit smouldering unrest into open rebellion. In May 1753, the colliers, many hundred strong, marched on Bristol . . . Ravaged by hunger, they attempted to fill their empty bellies with sprigs of green hawthorn which grew along the way. This, with bitter, irony, they called 'Bread and Cheese'. [Lindegaard, 1978: 8]

More recently:

My mother, who is 86, says she remembers from her childhood in Higham Ferrers, Northants, that . . . the young leaf buds of hawthorn were a delicacy, called 'bread and cheese.' [Waltham Abbey, Essex, March 1991]

The hawthorn was certainly known to me as a lad in Norfolk as 'bread and cheese;' it was also known by this name to my mother, also of Norfolk. We were told by a local old man (now dead) that it was so named because the leaves were the bread and the haw was the yellowish cheese which could (after the removal of the stone) be sandwiched between two leaves. This I now know to be incorrect; it was a quaint reason though. Though I do not like real cheese at all, each year when the hawthorn leaves have just unfurled, I buy some of the Primula brand of cheese, and add a good sprinkling of these leaves to a sandwich. It gives a really nice nutty flavour to it—delicious. [West Stow, Suffolk, May 1991]

I grew up in Leicester . . . we used to eat the new hawthorn shoots—bread and cheese—both raw and together with chopped streaky bacon as a filling for suet roly-poly—very good! [Fleet, Hampshire, April 1994]

Hawthorn fruits—haws—are also eaten occasionally.

My mother, who was born at Buxton, Derbys. in 1901, referred to the fruit of the hawthorn as 'aigie berries' and to its leaves as 'bread and cheese'. Both would be eaten by children when she was young. Not very appetising, but just about edible, I would say. [Bath, Avon, January 1983]

I am an Invernessian . . . The berries of the hawthorn tree were good to eat. They had a thick, sweet skin over a hard stone centre. They were known as 'boojuns'. [Solihull, West Midlands, March 1991]

[In north-east England] boys in autumn go out in groups to gather the ripened haws, and they look out eagerly for those with double stones, which they dignify with the name of Bull-haws. Having sucked the pulp from the stone, they amuse themselves by blowing the latter at each other through their pop-guns, made from the hollow stalks of the hemlock. Haws they believe are apt to fill the teeth with lies; for the number of 'lees' that a boy has told that day is reckoned by the number of black specks on the teeth, and the absence of specks vindicates his innocence. [Johnston, 1853: 78]

Hayfever – cured using MINT.

Hazel (*Corylus avellana*)

Some of the Highlanders, where superstition is not totally subdued, look upon the tree itself unlucky, but are glad to get two nuts naturally con-join'd, which is a good omen. These they call *Cnò-chomblaich*, and carry them as an efficacious charm against witchcraft. [Lightfoot, 1777: 587]

[Radnorshire:] it is . . . thought unlucky to take the catkins of hazel ('lamb's tails') into the house, farmers holding that this will cause a bad lambing season. [Howse, 1949: 207]

Cf. DAFFODIL.

To ensure that the, usually, blue eyes of their newly-born babies would eventually turn brown, they [East Anglian parents] would bind a small hazel twig to the baby's back or hang bunches of twigs in the room in which it was born. [Porter, 1974: 19]

In many parts of the country it was believed

Lots of nuts in the autumn means lots of babies in the spring. [Charmouth, Dorset, January 1994]

Early in the nineteenth century a curious custom was observed in some Surrey parishes:

A ceremony not confined to this parish [All Saints, Kingston-upon-Thames] and consisting in the cracking of nuts by the whole congregation on Michaelmas Eve has scarcely fallen into disuse. The origin or meaning of this absurdity is unknown. Cracknut Sunday, in connection with the election of the bailiffs, is still in the memory of many persons living. [Biden, 1852: 58]

The nuts of wild hazel trees provided a useful source of protein and additional income for people living in areas where such trees were abundant.

At Ashmore and other villages on Cranborne Chase [Dorset] the annual nutting expeditions were great events. The women and girls made them-selves special canvas dresses and the great part of the population went off to the woods, taking their 'nammit' (noonmeat) with them. The nuts were sold to dealers for dessert and also (chiefly) for use in the dyeing industry. Often not less than £200 a year was made by the village during this season, and most families reckoned to pay their whole year's rent, if nothing more, with the proceeds. This custom has now almost come to an end. There is now little sale for the nuts to dyers, and very low prices prevailed in the years between the two great wars so the nutting ceased to be worthwhile. During the wars prices rose again and 6d a lb for slipped nuts was obtained between 1939 and 1945. The price has now fallen to 4d a lb, and during the last decade, it is only the children and the old people who have troubled to carry on the work. [Dacombe, 1951: 44]

It is probable that the economic value of the nut harvest stimulated various taboos to discourage the unscrupulous from nutting at unreasonable times and getting more than their share of the crop. In the north of England unripe nuts were guarded by the goblins Churnmilk Peg and Melsh Dick [Briggs, 1976: 75 and 285]. There was a common, but perhaps not too seriously held, belief that nuts should not be gathered on Sundays, and that those who did so would attract the Devil's attention.

My grandmother . . . a native of Mitcham [Surrey], used to tell of a very wicked man who went into the woods on Sunday to gather nuts. He was terrified to find that as he pulled them off the trees they came again in greater numbers. [Emslie, 1915: 161]

Carefree nutting expeditions sometimes led to a certain amount of horse-play, so nutting, like RUSH-gathering, became a common euphemism for courtship, particularly that of a less restrained nature. In the well-known folksong *The Nutting Girl*:

It's of a brisk young damsel who lived down in Kent,
And she rose one May morning and she a nutting went.

Then a nutting we will go, a nutting we will go,
With a blue cockade all in our hats we'll cut a gallant show.

While she is nutting at this unseasonable time, she hears a young ploughman:

He sung so melodiously it charmed her as she stood,
She had no longer power in that lonely wood to stay,
And what few nuts that poor girl had she threw them all away . . .
So he took her to some shady grove and gently laid her down
She said 'Young man, I think I see the world go round and round.'

The song concludes with a warning:

For if you stay too long and hear the ploughboys sing,
Perhaps a young ploughboy you may get to nurse up in the spring.

[Purslow, 1972: 1]

Ruth Tongue [1967: 54] gave a song reputedly collected from an elderly Somerset servant, in which a girl who went nutting on Sunday took the devil as a lover:

> Oh there was a maid, and a foolish young maid,
> And she went a-nutting on Sunday.
> She met with a Gentleman all in black,
> He took and he laid her a-down on her back,
> All a-cause she went nutting on Sunday.

The outcome of this union was a baby 'which did come before the ring' and was distinguished by the possession of horns and a tail.

Hazel sticks were believed to be poisonous to SNAKES.

> In July and August we were staying at Overton, near Port Eynon, Gower, where this year there happened to be an unusual number of adders, one of which had bitten a sheep . . . When I saw it I suggested that the young farmer should wash it with ammonia; but he replied, 'Oh, I cure it with a poultice made of ground-ash, TANSY, and hazel-leaves.' I asked, 'Why hazel-leaves?' To my amusement he replied, 'Hazel-trees are poisonous to snakes, especially adders. In fact, no creeping thing can live in or near them.' [*Folk-lore*, 7: 89, 1896]

> When people began to emigrate from Ireland to foreign lands (especially U.S.A. and Australia) it was usual for them to bring a bundle of hazel rods with them to kill the snakes. One blow of the rod and the snake was no more! [IFC MSS 462: 310, Co. Carlow, 1937–8]

The flexible and easily split stems of hazel were used in a wide range of woodland crafts.

> [For Irish travellers] tents were the most common shelter of all. There were two types both constructed of bent hazel branches covered with oil-soaked bags or canvas. The smaller variety, no more than waist high at its peak, was known as a 'wattle' or 'bender' tent. [Gmelch and Kroup, 1978: 18]

Forked hazel twigs are frequently used by dowsers, although at least one practitioner [Naylor, 1991: 17] recommends metal rods as being much more sensitive.

> The *virgula divinatoria* is in high repute amongst the Welsh miners; what sympathy there is between a vein of coal or lead ore and a piece of hazle, it would be difficult to say. [Evans, 1800: 404]

> The Isles of Scilly have employed a water diviner after suffering their worst drought. Using a hazel twig, Don Wilkins, from Chacewater, Cornwall, pinpointed two water sources in 100ft deep rock to supply the 70 people on the island of Bryher. [*The Times*, 23 April 1992]

Examples of forked hazel twigs used by Somerset dowsers can be seen in the Pitt Rivers Museum, Oxford.

> To the present day the Irish homespun is DYEd with hazel. [IFCSS MSS 1112: 358, Co. Donegal]

Headache – caused by HERB ROBERT and POPPY; cured using CABBAGE, HENBANE, VIOLET, WILLOW, and YARROW.

Headache flower, headache plant – names for HERB ROBERT.

Headaches – a Northumbrian name for POPPY.

Head lice – killed using PENNYROYAL.

Heartsease – a Lancashire name for COMFREY; also widely used for WILD PANSY.

Heart trouble – treated using DANDELION, FOXGLOVE, ROCK SAMPHIRE, WATERCRESS, and WILD PANSY.

Heather (*Calluna vulgaris*)

The tops of ling heather (*Calluna vulgaris*), *Fraoch*, produce . . . a shade of yellow DYE when boiled in water, in fact the entire plant is wonderfully versatile: it was commonly used for THATCHing houses, and even today the few Highland thatchers that remain will swear it is the best thatch in Gaeldom; it provided beds to sleep on, with the 'tops up and roots down' arrangement of the mattress assuring a pleasantly aromatic and sound sleep; it was used in part of the process of tanning leather; and the fresh, young tops of the heather were (and at times still are) brewed into a kind of ale. Little wonder it is acclaimed in song and story and longed for by the expatriate Scot! [Bennett, 1991: 58]

Mrs Leys [of Ballater, Aberdeenshire] knew all about heather ale, a popular home brew in olden times, which was made in August or September when heather was at its best. They filled a large pan with the purple flowers, covered them with water and boiled them for an hour. This was strained into a large wash-tub, and ginger, hops, and golden syrup were added. Again the mixture was boiled and strained, and yeast was added when the mixture cooled. The liquid after a few days was gently poured off, leaving the barm at the bottom of the tub. [Fraser, 1973: 178]

See also WHITE HEATHER.

Heath rush (*Juncus squarrosus*)

Heath rush = burra—the stalk (burri-stikkel)—is a popular stalk to chew while walking or working on the moorland, but it's said that if you chew too many you'll become a rabbit-mouth, or get a hare-lip. Burri-stikkels were gathered to make fireside brushes well into this century. The heath rush always grows on firm dry ground, hence the saying: 'stramp (step) fair on da burra; keep wide a da floss [soft rush].'

Another use for burri-stikkels was to bind a handful tightly and use as a pot scrubber. [Lerwick, Shetland, March 1994]

See also RUSH.

Hedge bindweed (*Calystegia sepium*)—see LARGE BINDWEED.

Hedge veronica (*Hebe* spp.)
[I used to live in Cornwall.] My family are the only people I have ever come across who have used the leaves of the plant Veronica for DIA-RRHOEA; peel the leaves of the plant down until the smallest pair and eat about six.
  Some years ago, when I lived in Plymouth, I went to an exhibition on healing plants and folklore at the local museum. One of the exhibits was Veronica which, it said, was used by Maoris for stomach troubles . . . I know my great-grandfather sailed on tea clippers, so I wondered if he had also been to New Zealand and maybe brought this idea back with him. [Calpe, Alicante, Spain, November 1991]

Children take the closed leaf tips of Hedge Veronica (*Hebe × franciscana*), the top leaf is curled back to make a sail, leaving the lower leaf as a keel, then they are floated as little boats. [St Mary's, Isles of Scilly, September 1992]

Heead-vahk (headache) – a Humberside name for POPPY.

Hellebore (*Helleborus* spp.), formerly known as bear's foot. On 1 February 1762:
Two young children died at Fisherton Anger [Wiltshire] in a few hours after eating some bears foot, a plant recommended against WORMS. There are two sorts of this plant: 1. Two feet high, dark leaves and whitish flowers a little purpled at the edge, now in flower [*Helleborus foetidus*, stinking hellebore]—this is poisonous: 2. A low plant not a foot high with fish-green leaves and green flowers [*H. viridis*, green hellebore]. This is good against worms. [*Wiltshire Family History Society Journal*, 46: 6, 1992]

Almost a century later, on the Isle of Wight, stinking hellebore
is often seen in cottage-gardens, being a rustic remedy for worms in children, but the employment of so violent a medicine has too often been followed by serious consequences, and its use is now abandoned in regular practice. [Bromfield, 1856: 15]

Hemlock (*Conium maculatum*)
A Suffolk cure for a sore EYE consisted of the leaves of true hemlock . . . chopped finely and mixed with white of egg, bay salt and red ochre. The resulting salve was applied, however, to the sound eye and not to the affected one. [Porter, 1974: 43]

Hemp (*Cannabis sativa*). Formerly grown on a large scale as a fibre crop, hemp continues to be surreptitiously cultivated for use as the illegal recreational drug cannabis, grass, or marijuana. In the nineteenth century hemp seed was widely used in love DIVINATION. In Guernsey in the 1880s:

A vision of your future husband can . . . be obtained by the sowing of hemp-seed. The young maiden must scatter on the ground some hemp-seed, saying:

> Hemp-seed I sow, hemp-seed grow,
> For my true love to come and mow.

Having done this she must immediately run into the house to prevent her legs being cut off by the reaper's sickle, and looking back she will see the longed-for lover mowing the hemp, which has grown so rapidly, and so mysteriously. [Stevens Cox, 1971: 10]

Mrs Calcutt's [of Wolvercote, Oxfordshire] mother was probably the last girl to try the charm of sowing hempseed . . . She, with a girl friend, went to the churchyard one Christmas Eve at midnight, carrying some hemp-seed, while throwing it over her left shoulder said:

> I sow hempseed,
> Hempseed I sow,
> He that is to be my husband,
> Come after me and mow,
> Not in his best or Sunday array,
> But in the clothes he wears every day!

The friend with her was very much frightened; some people said she saw a coffin, but whatever she saw, or thought she saw, it is certain she died soon afterwards, and the people in the village evidently connected her death in some way with the visit to the churchyard, as they forbade their daughters to try this charm any more. [Parker, 1923: 324]

Variations in this custom seem to have been small, the main differences being in the date chosen. Midsummer's Eve appears to have been the time most widely favoured [Wright, 1940: 12], but other suitable nights included St Valentine's Eve in Derbyshire and Devon [Wright, 1938: 152], St Mark's Eve (24 April) in parts of East Anglia [Wright, 1938: 187], and St Martin's Eve (10 November) in Norfolk [Baker, 1975: 36]. A fictional account of hempseed divination can be found in Thomas Hardy's novel, *The Woodlanders*, first published in 1887. Cf. FLAX.

Henbane (*Hyoscyamus niger*). According to John Ray, writing in 1660:

The seed of Hyoscyamus placed on coal gives off a smoke with a very unpleasant smell: when passed through the mouth and nostrils by a tube it drives out small worms (vermiculi) which sometimes grow in the nostrils or the teeth. They can be caught in a basin of water so that they can be seen better. [Ewen and Prime, 1975: 75]

Similarly, in his diary for 17 October 1817 the rector of Wrath, Yorkshire, recorded:

Mr Faber . . . said he heard the TOOTHACHE accounted for in the following manner by a friend and he gave the account as if he believed it. He said that certain minute ephemerae of butterfly species flying about are accidentally taken into the mouth and that they then make a nidus in a rotten tooth where they deposit their eggs which in the process of time are hatched and produce minute grubs which immediately begin feeding on the nerves of the tooth and that the remedy applied by his friend was to procure the seeds of henbane, make them very dry and then set them on fire under a tin funnel, the small end of which is to be directed so that the smoke may issue against the offending tooth which will immediately kill the grubs, and that the friend had ejected several in the saliva after the operation and seen them distinct with a lens. [Aitkin, 1944: 128]

Similarly:

[Henbane] is sometimes smoked like tobacco by country people as a remedy for toothache, but convulsions have occasionally followed its use in this way. [Pratt, 1857, 1: 128]

However, John Gerard was dismissive of such cures.

The seede [of henbane] is used by mountibancke tooth-drawers which runne about the countrey, for to cause woormes come foorth of mens teeth, by burning it in a chafing dish with coles, the partie holding his mouth over the flume thereof: but some craftie companions to gaine money convey small lutestrings into the water, persuading the patient, that those small creepers came out of this mouth or other parts which he intended to ease. [Gerard, 1597: 284]

Vesey-FitzGerald [1944: 25] records that gypsies commonly used henbane as a cure for HEADACHES and NEURALGIA.

Hen's apple – an Inverness name for LIME fruit.

Herb Robert (*Geranium robertianum*). There are scattered records of herb Robert being considered inauspicious because it was associated either with SNAKES or with HEADACHES.

I was born in a village called Hardwicke, near Gloucester, and my memories stem from there. Herb robert was also called Snake Flower and was never picked because snakes would emerge from the stems. [Newcastle-under-Lyme, Staffordshire, March 1983]

Snakes Food, a pink flower with a red stem, we always avoided. [Portland, Dorset, March 1991]

In Ireland herb Robert was occasionally used in folk medicine.

People who suffered from kidney trouble long ago boiled a green weed with a little pink flower on it until all the sap and juice was out of them, the drink was allowed to cool and when cool was drunk by the person. It was always known to remove pain. The name of the weed is herb robert. [IFCSS MSS 975: 27, Co. Cavan]

The herb robert if boiled in milk and the juice given to cattle to drink will cure the murrain. [IFCSS MSS 575: 354, Co. Tipperary]

Hinney flooer – a Shetland name for LOUSEWORT.

Hipseyhaws – an Essex name for both DOG ROSE hips and HAWTHORN berries.

Hoary cress (*Lepidium draba*)

The Smallholders Union omitted from their list of plants proscribed for extermination what is perhaps the most pestilent of all weeds, the whit-low-pepperwort (*Lepidium draba*), which came to us from a district not very distant from French Flanders. When our troops disembarked at Ramsgate after the disastrous Walcheren Expedition of 1809, the straw and other litter on which they had slept aboard ship was thrown into a chalkpit, and afterwards carted into the fields for manure by a farmer called Thompson. A huge crop of the plant, thence named 'Thomson's Curse', sprang up, spread right across England, and is now attacking the North Country. The roots of this terrible pest are many feet in length. [*Westminster Gazette*, 6 April 1915]

Hoary plantain (*Plantago media*) – formerly known as FIRE-LEAVES in Gloucestershire; see under DEVIL'S BIT SCABIOUS.

Hogweed (*Heracleum sphondylium*)

HAWTHORN blossom, LILAC and Devil's Tobacco [hogweed]—all unlucky to have in the house. [Leek, Staffordshire, March 1983]

The stem of hogweed was used here as a cigarette substitute, and 'boys' bacca' was a common term. Gypsies smoked them commonly. [Barnstaple, Devon, September 1992]

[In Cornwall] children are accustomed to make 'skeets' or syringes out of the living stems, and by them the plant is generally spoken of as the 'skeet-plant.' [Davey, 1909: 220]

Holly (*Ilex aquifolium*). Throughout the British Isles the holly is the plant most frequently associated with Christmas and, indeed, in parts of England holly was simply known as 'Christmas' [Grigson, 1987: 115].

I am nearly 70 years of age and was born and bred in Norfolk . . . Holly was never called by name by my grandfather, it was always called Christmas. [Two Locks, Gwent, March 1993]

To a certain extent this association seems to be due to the fact that holly leaves are exceedingly easy to draw, so whenever a notice is needed to announce an office party or a works lunch to celebrate Christmas it is invariably decorated with a sprig of stylized holly. Like 'palm', which should not be taken indoors before Palm Sunday, it is frequently said that it is unlucky to have holly indoors at any time other than Christmas.

> Unlucky to bring holly into the house before Christmas Eve. [St Bride's-Super-Ely, Glamorgan October 1982]

> Rose B said that when her mother was taken ill it was in the summer, and Rose carried some holly indoors and put it up. Someone came to visit her mother, and told Rose it was all her fault that her mother was ill, as she'd brought in the holly. Rose said she was terribly terribly upset to think that she'd made her mother ill, as she was too young to think it rubbish, and she grieved about it for years and years, so she thinks all these things should be forgotten and not remembered. [Thorncombe, Dorset, December 1982]

Occasionally it is believed that holly is unsafe indoors even during the Christmas period.

> We decorated the tractor trailer with holly and ivy . . . and went carol singing. After three nights of singing a piece of holly fell on the trailer floor, and Stewart F. (aged 9) picked it up and asked 'Please could I have it to take home?' I said 'Yes, of course, but if you come tomorrow when we take it all down, I'll give you some more to make a trimming,' and he was so pleased, which we thought was funny for a country child. However, in a few minutes he was back, almost in tears, and threw the holly on the trailer floor saying 'I can't have it, as Mummy says it is unlucky and will not have it indoors.' [Thorncombe, Dorset, January 1983]

> My mother would not have holly in the house. [Allenton, Derbyshire, March 1983]

However, such total prohibitions are rare, and well-berried holly is a valuable commodity in the weeks before Christmas.

> In the principal markets holly has been selling at £1.25 for a generous handful, and £5 for an armload. Supplies come more or less equally from farmers who find a useful supplementary cash crop in their hedgerows, and gypsies who gather it with or without permission where they may.
> Some gypsy families supplying dealers at the Western International Market, Southall, London, reckon to have made as much as £1,500 on holly alone this year . . .
> It seems likely that the total sales of holly this year will exceed £500,000 at wholesale prices. What retailers will take, at 20p to 30p a sprig, is anyone's guess. [*The Times*, 24 December 1980]

Although well-berried holly trees are frequently plundered at Christmas time, there is a widespread belief that holly trees should not be cut down or destroyed.

> Joan . . . who was born, I suspect, about 1910 and has lived her whole life in Hove and Havant . . . states that in her experience farmers find it un-

lucky to cut holly, to the extent that they cut their hedges around it. (I had not myself noticed that in south Hampshire their current machinery is sensitive to that—or any other consideration). [Havant, Hampshire, August 1982]

A holly tree should never be cut down . . . a farmer wanted a holly tree cutting down. He knew he shouldn't do it, so he asked one of his labourers. The labourer refused in spite of being threatened with the sack.

Eventually the farmer found someone to cut the tree down, who did not believe in 'Old Wives' Tales'. This person was dead within three months, even though before cutting the tree down he was perfectly healthy. [Boundary, Staffordshire, March 1983]

In Norfolk it was considered unlucky to cut holly as distinct from breaking off berry-bearing twigs at Christmas time. A tractor driver of my acquaintance, now retired, when using a mechanical hedgecutter, would raise his cutter and give all hedgerow holly a very wide berth. [East Tuddenham, Norfolk, October 1984]

Holly is a frequent hedgerow tree in the north of Worcestershire. This is because it was considered unlucky to cut holly when trimming hedgerows. [Worcester, January 1991]

I won't have holly trees felled unless they are dead. [South Stainley, North Yorkshire, March 1992]

Occasionally a large branch or bush of holly would be favoured instead of a conifer as a CHRISTMAS TREE.

As a child in the late 1920s on a farm in Warwickshire, our 'Christmas Tree' was always a huge bunch of holly hung from a beam—decorated with baubles as the normal tree is. [Mordiford, Hereford, December 1991]

My own mother was a Cornish Bard and greatly concerned in keeping Cornish traditions alive, and we always had a holly bush instead of a pine tree for our Xmas tree; probably fir trees only started getting popular after the 1914–18 war. Two hoops pushed together and bound with holly was also known as a 'bush' and this was actually the traditional Cornish decoration. [Calpe, Alicante, Spain, December 1991]

My maternal grandparents, who lived at Mosterton and later Corscombe, Dorset, in the 1950s and early 1960s always had a large holly bush as their Christmas tree. As the children were given balloons to play with during the afternoon there were usually some tears when these touched the tree and popped. [Streatham, London, May 1992]

The disposal of Christmas holly was subject to various restrictions. As a general rule it should not be burnt.

I am nearly 70 years of age . . . after decorations were taken down after Christmas woe betide anyone who put the holly on the fire in the house;

it was another taboo of my [Norfolk] grandmother, it had to go out on the muck heap. [Two Locks, Gwent, March 1993]

In common with other fruit-bearing trees, a good crop of holly berries foretold a severe winter.

[According to my mother, born in Lichfield, 1916] many holly berries mean a hard winter. [Stratton, Dorset, September 1983]

People used to predict a severe winter if they saw red berries in abundance on holly trees. This was because they considered nature was providing birds with enough food while the snow and frost lasted. [Daingean, Co. Offaly, January 1985]

If a popular theory is to be believed, an abundance of holly berries heralds a hard winter. At this time of year the berries form but go unnoticed because they are green. I have never seen so many as there are in this area this year; one bush in my garden has produced them for the first time ever. [Letter from Reigate, Surrey, in *The Times*, 9 July 1990]

If the holly bush is full of berries at Christmas, it is a sign of a bad winter, nature giving food to the birds. [Maynooth, Co. Kildare, February 1991]

In folk medicine holly was used to treat CHILBLAINS.

A local cure for chilblains—thrash them with holly until they bleed. [Great Plumstead, Norfolk, October 1989]

[Wiltshire:] I have often had powdered holly berries mixed with lard rubbed on my chilblains. [Whitlock, 1976: 167]

Holly was formerly used in the production of bird-lime, a sticky substance used for catching small birds.

Bird-lime is the juice of the holly-bark extracted by boiling, mixed with a third part of nut-oil. [McNeill, 1910: 110]

Holy thorn (*Crataegus monogyna* cv. 'Biflora'). The Holy or Glastonbury Thorn is a variety of the common HAWTHORN which produces flowers in winter as well as at the usual time in early summer. What appears to be the earliest reference to the Thorn is found in a lengthy poem, entitled *Here begynneth the lyfe of Joseph of Armathia*, which is believed to have been written at the opening of the sixteenth century. The poem states that there were three thorn trees growing on Weary-all Hill, just south of Glastonbury in Somerset, which:

> Do burge and bere grene leaues at Christmas
> As fresihe as other in May when ye nightingale
> Wrestes out her notes musycall as pure glas.
>
> [Anon., 1520]

However, there is some slight evidence to suggest that the Thorn may have been in existence almost 400 years earlier. At Appleton Thorn in

Cheshire a custom known as 'Bawming the Thorn' used to be performed each year. Basically the custom consisted of decorating a thorn tree which grows in the centre of the village. Local tradition states that a tree has stood on this site since 1125, when an offshoot of the Holy Thorn was planted by Adam de Dutton [Hole, 1976: 26]. If there is any truth in this tradition, it would imply that there was a thorn tree at Glastonbury early in the twelfth century, when the Benedictine monks at its abbey were busily accumulating their massive, but poorly authenticated, collection of relics, which was destroyed in a disastrous fire in 1184. It is quite possible that a hawthorn which produced flowers at Christmas time might have been added to the attractions provided to stimulate pilgrimages to the abbey.

The lyfe of Joseph gives no information on the trees' origins, and does not mention the production of winter flowers. Fifteen years after its publication, four years before the suppression of Glastonbury Abbey, the Christmas flowering of the Thorn was first recorded. On 24 August 1535 Dr Layton, the visitor sent to the Abbey, wrote to Thomas Cromwell from Bristol, and enclosed two pieces of a tree which blossomed on Christmas Eve.

By this bringer, my servant, I send you Relicks: First two flowers wraped in white and black sarsnet, that on Christen Mass Even, *hora ipsa qua Christus natus fuerat*, will spring and burge and bare blossoms. *Quod expertum est*, saith the Prior of Mayden Bradley. [Batten, 1881: 116]

During the reign of Elizabeth I the Thorn growing on Wearyall had two trunks:

when a puritan exterminated one, and left the other, which was the size of a common man, to be viewed in wonder by strangers; and the blossoms thereof were esteemed such curiosities by people of all nations that Bristol merchants made traffick of them and exported them to foreign parts. [Collinson, 1791: 265]

Or, according to an earlier, more credulous account:

It had two Trunks or Bodies till the Reign of Queen Elizabeth, in whose days a Saint like Puritan, taking offence at it, hewed down the biggest of the Trunks, and had cut down the other Body in all likelihood, had he not bin miraculously punished (saith my Author) by cutting his Leg, and one of the Chips flying up to his Head, which put out one of his Eyes. Though the Trunk cut off was separated quite from the root, excepting a little of the Bark which stuck to the rest of the Body, and laid above the Ground above thirty Years together; yet it still continued to flourish as the other Part did which was left standing; after this again, when it was quite taken away and cast into a Ditch, it flourished and budded as it used to do before. A Year after this, it was stolen away, not known by whom or whither. [Rawlinson, 1722: 109]

Later, during the reign of James I, the Thorn enjoyed some popularity as a garden curiosity, and the aristocracy, including the King's consort, Anne of Denmark, paid large sums for cuttings [Collinson, 1791: 265]. It is possible that this fashion of growing thorns in private gardens saved the plant from extinction, for during the civil unrest later in the century the surviving trunk of the original tree was destroyed by a Roundhead, who 'being over zealous did cut it downe in pure devotion' [Taylor, 1649: 6]. In 1653 Godfrey Goodman, Bishop of Gloucester, lamented: 'The White Thorn at Glastonbury which did usually blossome on Christmas Day was cut down: yet I did not heare that the party was punished' [Rawlinson, 1722: 301].

In 1645 the Revd John Eachard described the Glastonbury Thorn, which was then much mutilated by visitors who cut off pieces of it for souvenirs, as being of the kind 'wherewith Christ was crowned'. An elaboration of this belief relates how St Joseph of Arimathea brought two treasures to Glastonbury: silver containers holding the blood and sweat of Christ (which seem to have become confused or equated with the Holy Grail) and a thorn from Christ's Crown of Thorns, which grew and proved its holiness by flowering each year at the time of Christ's birth [Hole, 1965: 39].

Seventy years after Eachard wrote, an oral tradition collected from a Glastonbury inn-keeper explained how the Thorn had grown from a STAFF carried by St Joseph of Arimathea [Rawlinson, 1722: 1]. According to tradition, the Apostles divided the world between them, St Philip being sent to Gaul, accompanied by St Joseph of Arimathea, who is usually considered to be an uncle of the Virgin Mary. After some years Joseph left the Apostle and accompanied by eleven others set out for Britain, arriving at Glastonbury, and eventually founding the first church to be built on British soil, in AD 63 [Hole, 1965: 35]. When Joseph reached Glastonbury he rested on Wearyall Hill and thrust his staff into the ground, where it grew and became the original Holy Thorn [Rawlinson, 1722: 2]. Some writers have asserted that it was this miracle which caused Joseph to settle in Glastonbury.

A second version of the legend relates how St Joseph landed on the Welsh coast, or possibly at Barrow Bay in Somerset, but found the natives hostile. He continued his wanderings and reached the land of King Arviragus. Although Joseph was unable to convert the monarch, he made a sufficiently good impression for land at Ynyswitrin—Glastonbury—to be granted to him and his companions. However the local inhabitants showed little enthusiasm for the new faith. It was not until Joseph fixed his staff in the ground and prayed, whereupon it immediately produced blossoms, that people began to pay serious at-

tention to the missionaries' preaching [Anon., n.d.: 6 and 23]. It is
sometimes claimed that Joseph performed this miracle on Christmas
Day and hence the Thorn has flowered on this day ever since [Wilks,
1972: 98].

Some recent writers have asserted that there is some truth in the
various legends and suggest that the Thorn originated from stock
brought from the Holy Land, or at least a country bordering the Mediterranean. The winter flowering of the tree is explained by the suggestion that it belongs to a variety of hawthorn native to the Middle
East [Batten, 1881: 125]. The Revd Alan Clarkson, Vicar of St John's
church in Glastonbury, in a pamphlet produced in 1977 in aid of
church restoration funds, claimed that: 'Whatever the legend may say,
a Thorn has been growing here for 2,000 years and it came from Palestine.' A recent study of hawthorns states:

> In North Africa, flowering in late autumn and early winter is known also
> in populations of C[rataegus] monogyna that are morphologically fairly
> similar to the Holy Thorn of Glastonbury. [Christensen, 1992: 111]

A young leafy shoot of hawthorn, labelled 'Oxyacantha autumnalis,
from Wells, Joseph of Arymathaea rod', is preserved in the herbarium
of the Natural History Museum in London. This specimen was included in a collection given by the London apothecary Robert Ni-
cholls to the Apothecaries' Company in 1745, and was part of 'a
valuable series of plants' presented by the Company to the Museum in
1862 [Vickery, 1991: 81].

It is told that, in the eighteenth century, a miller walked all the way
from his home in Wales to visit the Thorn. His English vocabulary
was restricted to three words, 'Staff of Joseph', but these were sufficient to ensure that he reached Glastonbury, and he was able to
proudly carry home a sprig from the tree [Bett, 1952: 139].

When the calendar was reformed in 1752 the Holy Thorn attracted
considerable attention, for people watched the trees to see if they
would produce their Christmas blossoms according to the new or old
calendar. The *Gentleman's Magazine* of January 1753 recorded that on
Christmas Eve, 24 December 1752, hundreds of people gathered at
Glastonbury to see if the several Thorn trees growing there would
produce flowers. No flowers appeared, but when the crowds reas-
sembled on Old Christmas Eve, 5 January 1753, they were rewarded
and the trees blossomed, confirming the onlookers' doubts about the
validity of the new calendar. Later in 1753 a correspondent of the
Magazine stated that, after reports of the Thorns' flowering on Old
Christmas Eve had been printed in a Hull newspaper, the vicar
of Glastonbury had been questioned. According to him, the trees

blossomed 'fullest and finest about Christmas Day New Style, or rather sooner' [*Gentleman's Magazine*, 1753: 578].

At Quainton in Buckinghamshire over two thousand people gathered to watch a thorn they remembered as being a descendant of the Glastonbury tree:

> but the people finding no appearance of bud, 'twas agreed by all, that December. 25 N.S. could not be Christmas-Day and accordingly refused going to church, and treating their friends on that day as usual; at length the affair became so serious, that ministers of neighbouring villages, in order to appease the people thought it prudent to give notice, that old Christmas-Day should be kept holy as before. [*Gentleman's Magazine*, 1753: 49]

Until early in the present century people continued to visit Holy Thorns on Old Christmas Eve.

> It is believed that the Holy Thorn blossoms at twelve o'clock on Twelfth Night, the time, so they say, at which Christ was born. The blossoms are thought to open at midnight, and drop off about an hour afterwards. A piece of thorn gathered at this hour brings luck, if kept for the rest of the year. Formerly crowds of people went to see the thorn blossom at this time. I went myself to Wormesley [Herefordshire] in 1908; about forty people were there, and as it was quite dark and the blossom could only be seen by candle light, it was probably the warmth of the candles which made some of the little white buds seem to expand. The tree had really been in bloom for several days, the season being extremely mild. [Leather, 1912: 17]

A thorn in the garden of Kingston Grange in Herefordshire was annually visited by people who came from miles around, and 'were liberally supplied with cake and cider' [Leather, 1912: 17]. However, such convivial gatherings sometimes gave way to unruly behaviour, and some people destroyed thorns growing on their property so that unwelcome visits might be stopped. Near Crewkerne in Somerset, in January 1878:

> Immense crowds gathered at a cottage between Hewish and Woolmingstone to witness the supposed blooming of a 'Holy' thorn at midnight on Saturday. The weather was unfavourable and the visitors were impatient. There were buds on the plant, but they did not burst into flower as they were said to have done the previous year. The crowd started singing and then it degenerated into a quarrel and stones were thrown. The occupier of the cottage, seeing how matters stood, pulled up the thorn and took it inside, receiving a blow on the head from a stone for his pains. A free fight ensued and more will be heard of the affair in the Magistrates' Court. [*Pulman's Weekly News*, 10 January 1978]

Similarly:

A Holy Thorn made a brief appearance in Dorset in 1844 in the garden of a Mr Keynes of Sutton Poyntz. It was rumoured that it had grown from a cutting of the famous Glastonbury Thorn and was expected to blossom at midnight on Old Christmas Eve. 150 people turned up to see the event. Violent scenes took place, the fence was broken down and the plant so badly damaged that it died. [Waring, 1977: 68]

Not surprisingly, tales were told of misfortunes (many of which were very similar to those which befall people who destroy LONE BUSHES in Ireland) which happened to those who attempted to cut down Holy Thorns. An early attempt to destroy a tree resulted in thorns flying from the tree and blinding the axeman in one eye, so that he was 'made monocular' [Howell, 1640: 86]. A man who attempted to cut down a tree that grew in his garden at Clehonger in Herefordshire was more lucky and was let off with a warning: 'blood flowed from the trunk of the tree and this so alarmed him that he left off at once!' [Leather, 1912: 17]. A farmer who destroyed a thorn at Acton Beauchamp in Worcestershire was successful, but within a year he broke an arm and a leg, and part of his house was destroyed by fire [Lees, 1856: 295].

Shortly before Christmas each year sprays from a Thorn tree which grows in St John's churchyard in Glastonbury are sent to the Queen and Queen Mother. In 1929 the then vicar of Glastonbury, whose sister-in-law was a lady-in-waiting to Queen Mary, sent a sprig to the Queen, reviving, according to some writers, a pre-Reformation custom [Anon., 1977]. A report in the *Western Daily Press* of 20 December 1973 stated that the custom started in Stuart times, and it is recorded that James Montague, Bishop of Bath and Wells, sent pieces of the Holy Thorn and Glastonbury's miraculous WALNUT tree to Queen Anne, consort of James I [Rawlinson, 1722: 112]. About a week before Christmas a short religious service is held around the Thorn. Children from St John's Infants' School sing carols and play their recorders, and the vicar and mayor of Glastonbury cut twigs from the tree. It is said that the Queen has her sprays placed on her breakfast table on Christmas morning, while the Queen Mother has hers placed on her writing table. Letters sent by ladies-in-waiting to the vicar, asking him to convey thanks to the people of Glastonbury, are pinned on the church notice board [Vickery, 1979: 12].

The tree in St John's churchyard which had been used for this ceremony died early in 1991, but fortunately there is a younger tree growing in the churchyard, and other Holy Thorns may be found in the Abbey grounds, outside St Benedict's church, and in private gardens in Glastonbury.

Honesty (*Lunaria annua*)

A bunch of dried honesty is hung inside a wardrobe for good luck in some Guernsey homes. I was told at a W.I. meeting in 1973 by a member that when she got married a local lady visited her and was very concerned to find that the new bride had no honesty to hang up. She brought her some straight away. My informant said that she still has this original honesty in her wardrobe although she has changed house several times since then. She had made enquiries from time to time and discovered that quite a lot of people who know the custom themselves keep honesty in their homes for good fortune. This corroborated by other women at the meeting. [De Garis, 1975: 119]

Money-in-both pockets = the honesty plant. [Headcorn, Kent, January 1993]

However:

I am from Yorkshire. Another odd dislike is honesty. My father is very against it, saying it brings all kinds of bad luck. He won't even have it in the garden, never mind in the house. A pity, since the seed pods are so pretty, but I can't bring it in knowing it will make someone uneasy. [Stetchworth, Cambridgeshire, December 1991]

A name for honesty used in the Ashford area of Kent: Devil's Ha'pence. [Bexhill-on-Sea, East Sussex, January 1991]

Honey-sookies – a Shetland name for LOUSEWORT.

Honey suck – a Dorset name for RED CLOVER.

Honeysuckle (*Lonicera periclymenum*), also known as woodbine. The sweetly scented flowers of honeysuckle were occasionally banned from being taken indoors.

The flower was never brought into a Fenland home where there were young girls; it was thought to give them erotic dreams. If any was brought indoors, then a wedding would follow. [Porter, 1969: 45]

Until recently my home was in Scotland . . . Honeysuckle was never taken indoors, it was very unlucky for the family, and should not be worn either. [Apples, Switzerland, February 1983]

When Mrs Evans moved to a house in rural Cheshire, the farmer from whom she bought the house told her that honeysuckle should never be cut, because if you did you would not get a second crop of hay. [Newcastle-under-Lyme, Staffordshire, March 1983]

A local country fellow of this village was an amateur but knowledgeable herbalist. He said that you should never bring honeysuckle indoors because it gave you a sore throat. [Capel Hendre, Dyfed, September 1983]

As its name suggests, the flowers of honeysuckle can be sucked for their nectar.

> As children (I was born in 1943) we used to pick honeysuckle, remove the tip at the base of the flower and suck the juice (nectar). [Clevedon, Avon, March 1993]

In Ireland honeysuckle was used to cure JAUNDICE.

> The bark of woodbine is a good cure for jaundice. [IFCSS MSS 190: 167, Co. Leitrim]

> Jaundice is cured by Mrs Caffrey, at first she chews woodbine, and rubs it to the patient's forehead and says some prayers. [IFCSS MSS 800: 122, Co, Cavan]

In parts of Ulster the FUCHSIA is known as honeysuckle.

Honeysuckle stick. In Sussex:

> The possession of a 'honeysuckle stick' is a guarantee of good luck, especially to a young man in his courtship of the lady of his choice. These sticks were 'bats' of HAZEL around which honeysuckle has entwined itself and which, when the bind has been removed, have a twisted appearance. To carry one of these when calling upon your lady love predisposes the lady in your favour and your suit will be successful. [Williams, 1944: 59]

Hop (*Humulus lupulus*)

> [Herefordshire:] Rain on Good Friday and Easter Day
> A good crop of hops, but a bad one of hay.
> [Leather, 1912: 245]

> [Gypsy remedies:] an ounce of hops to a pint of boiling water taken some time before meals is a good cure for loss of APPETITE. a poultice of the tops will relieve sciatica or LUMBAGO. An infusion of the flowers will cure WORMS in children. Put hops into a muslin bag and use the bag as a pillow and you will cure INSOMNIA. [Vesey-FitzGerald, 1944: 25]

Horehound (*Marrubium vulgare*)

> [Derbyshire gypsies;] infusion of leaves cures COUGHS and colds . . . is a good tonic. [Thompson, 1925: 162]

Horse bean – see BROAD BEAN.

Horse chestnut (*Aesculus hippocastanum*). The horse-chestnut tree, a native of the Balkans, was introduced to western Europe in 1576 [Bean, 1914, vol. 1: 170], and by 1699 large plantings were being made at Windsor [Hadfield, 1957: 392].

However, it seems that the use of horse-chestnut seeds in the game of conkers did not become popular until much later. When Britten and Holland were preparing their *Dictionary of English Plant-names* (1878–86) the game seems to have been known only in a few scattered localities. Although Britten organized boys' clubs, and Holland was the father of a large family, their knowledge of the game seems scanty, and not based on first-hand experience. The *Dictionary* gives two references to the name conker.

CONQUERORS—The fruit of *Aesculus hippocastanum* L.—Ches[hire], where children thread them on strings and strike them one against each other. The one remaining unbroken is the 'conqueror'.

KONKER-TREE – *Aesculus hippocastanum* L.—Som[erset], 'A game known as Konkers is played with the fruits.'

Additional information is given under the name 'Oblionker', the material being taken from *Notes and Queries*, 5 ser. 10: 378, 1878:

Having heard this word [oblionker] as being in common use at Ledbury in Herefordshire, I wrote to Mr Piper, of that town—a gentleman who takes great interest in the antiquities of that county. His reply was:- Oblionker is a game played by boys with horse chestnuts: each of the two contending players passes a piece of string a foot or so in length, and having a knot at the end to prevent its escape (a with of yellow willow answers equally well), through a chestnut. They then strike alternately at each other's nut whilst held suspended, and he who succeeds in breaking that of his adversary is the winner. The first who utters the following rhyme has the right to begin:

'Obli, obli, O,
My first go.'

And on striking it is customary to say:

'Obli, obli, onker,
My nut will conquer.'

The chestnut that has demolished the greatest number of its congeners acquires proportionate reputation, and the successes theretofore scored by the vanquished opponent are added to the achievements of the victor. Doubtless the Cymric boys of pre-Roman times played at oblionker.

The name oblionker continued in use until at least the 1940s.

When I went to live in Worcestershire after the last War, I found that conkers were always called Obly-Onkers, and Worcestershire children preceded the game with the solemn chant:

'Obly, obly-onker
My best conker,
Obly, obly O,
My best go!'

[Sidmouth, Devon, October 1991]

By the second decade of the twentieth century the game seems to have become popular and widespread, so that in 1914 it was recorded that:

They [horse-chestnut trees] have such an extraordinary fascination for boys in furnishing material for the game of 'conkers' (conquerors) that the value of the species as a communal tree in some districts is seriously diminished by their efforts with sticks and stones to bring down the nuts before they naturally fall. [Bean, 1914, vol. 1: 170]

This problem continues to cause concern:

Isn't it about time the Town Council got rid of the conker trees in Queen's Road Tewkesbury? Every year we get the hazard of children throwing sticks and bars at the chestnuts, which is only natural, but I wonder who would pay the bill for any damage caused to car drivers and their cars. They are a real menace. [Letter in the *Gloucestershire Echo*, 12 October 1989]

Although it is generally assumed that the word conker is a corruption of 'conqueror', some writers have disputed this.

At Woodstock Road School there was a resident caretaker who told us that the game of conkers was originally played, not with horse chestnuts, but with the shells of snails and winkles. (A conker is a little conch.) I once heard him telling a group of boys how you could make the string-hole in such a shell by using a red-hot meat-skewer held in a thick cloth. But we had an Uncle George in our family, a man with his own conker-tree, an acknowledged authority on the conker, who remembered that in the original game you had to press the apexes of the contesting snail-shells together between your palms, with your fingers interlocked—and go on pressing harder until one shell broke. [Rolph, 1980: 33]

Similarly:

[The game of conkers is] the descendant of an earlier game in which snails' shells were crushed; the origin of the name is therefore the same as that of 'conch' and not connected with 'conqueror'. [Hadfield, 1957: 392]

However, speculation about the origin of the word conker is of little or no interest to players of the game, who are more concerned with methods by which they can obtain potential champions.

[Ayton, North Yorkshire:] Conkers: you are sure to have obtained a 'hundreder' if the chestnut was caught falling from the tree before it touched the ground. [Dickinson MSS, 1974: 38]

[In the Northam district of Southampton in the 1930s] recipes for hardening winners were varied; it might be to part-bake the conker, or soak it in paraffin. Ginger Blake, Ken's friend, said his Dad recommended soaking them in the 'Po' overnight before baking. Ken confided to me that he didn't really want to win Ginger's current prize conker. [Sharman, 1977: 60]

I recently caught my seven-year-old son using a microwave oven to harden his conkers before combat! [Letter from Stoke Poges, Buckinghamshire, in *The Times*, 28 September 1987]

However, most children do not bother with any preparations, and are content to use fresh, untreated nuts. At Shipley in West Yorkshire in the 1940s:

> In October most boys collected horse chestnuts or 'conkers'. The term 'conking' covered both casually looking for them and undertaking exhaustive searches at weekends. On these expeditions much expert knowledge of the peculiarities of local trees and park-keepers was amassed. Trees with pink flowers tended to produce the inferior 'water conk', which was useless for the game of 'conkers', having nothing but fluid inside. Most park-keepers or 'parkies' objected to small boys in general, and the sport of knocking conkers off the trees with stones and sticks, or 'throwing for conks', in particular. Conkers were collected partly for their own sake; they are attractive objects and anyway small boys will collect almost anything. But they were collected ostensibly for the sake of the game.
>
> For 'conkers', large conkers had holes driven through them, and were threaded on strings. One player challenged another and perhaps claimed the right to begin by calling 'fuggy smack'. The opponent then held up his conker, dangling on its string, for the first player to aim a smack at it. They continued, aiming alternate smacks and probably watched by an excited crowd, till one conker disintegrated. The winning conker was then nominated a 'oner'. If it won again it became a 'twoer', and so on. Any score accredited to a beaten conker was passed on to the winner; thus, if a 'twoer' beat a 'fiver', it became an 'eighter'. In this way champion conkers sometimes built up large if somewhat exaggerated scores. They were carefully examined for signs of wear and tear, and maybe rethreaded to make them more secure. If the outer shell had been largely knocked off, but the kernel remained, it might be soaked in vinegar to make it harder than ever. These champion conkers could be swapped for quantities of sweets, or marbles, bits of liquorice root, and so forth, but they were usually preserved by their owners. Crowds gathered to watch games in which such battered relics were concerned.
>
> As with all games there were ways of cheating at conkers. The most diabolical was to aim at your opponent's string, rather than at his conker, in the hope of pulling it out of his hand and dashing it to the ground. Such treatment would obviously do no good, and one could always claim it had been an accident. Sometimes unfair play of this kind was penalised; if the offended party called 'strings' he was awarded a free smack. There was an understandable but mistaken feeling that it was an advantage to have the smack; if your conker was cracked it would as soon break up from hitting as being hit. Sometimes, as bits of shattered conker flew everywhere, you thought you had won, only to find on looking at your string that it was your conker that was finished. Sometimes both players let go of their strings in the excitement, especially if they had become entangled; and then a dispute would arise, very serious to the players but amusing to the crowd, over which fragments belonged to which party.

The conking season came to an end in mid-October when most boys' energies were absorbed in 'progging' for 'Plot Night', that is, collecting wood and other combustible materials for bonfires on 5th November. Some far-sighted boys would store champion conkers for next season, when they would be brought out as 'last-yearers', 'eighteeners' or whatever, very hard and venerable. [Ogden, 1978: 71]

Sometimes the game of conkers is taken up by adults who organize championships to raise funds for charity. The best known of these events is the World Conker Championships, held in the village of Ashton, Northamptonshire. These started in 1965, and form the central attraction at a fête held on the village green. Between 1965 and 1989 the Championships raised almost £45,000 for charity. The main competition is the men's, for which the rules are:

1. The contest is to take place on the green at Ashton on the second Sunday in October.
2. The number of contestants is limited to 128.
3. All conkers and strings are to be supplied by the Ashton Conker Club.
4. Each competitor is to take three alternate strikes until one of the conkers is shattered.
5. The contestant with a conker intact is declared the winner, but if either or both conkers are dislodged by a snag [i.e. the strings becoming entangled] the game is declared void and restarted.
6. Three snags will lead to the disqualification of a contestant.
7. The length of lace in play must be no less than 8 inches on strike.
8. There will be two stewards in charge of each game and their decision will be final.

There are also smaller competitions for women (started in 1988) and children (started in 1986). At the conclusion of the 1990 competition the 'Champion Conker' was auctioned, raising £45 [personal observation, 14 October 1990, and World Conker Championships Programme, 1990].

In 1973 a conker championship held at Goodleigh in Devon attracted 485 entries.

Former title holder Gordon Hill faced tough opposition from Mrs Margaret Bleloch in the final of the Goodleigh conker championships.

Swinging hard and accurate, Mrs Bleloch looked at one stage as if she might score another feminine victory in the annual charity event in the north Devon village. Two years ago, Mrs Alison Bidgood outswung Mr Hill, a local man, to become the first woman champion. But Mr Hill finally triumphed in this year's competition. [*Western Morning News*, 6 November 1973]

Nine years later the licensees of the New Inn at Goodleigh reported that the competition, which started in the 1960s, continued, and was played over two weekends in late October or early November each year. The licensees and a few customers who organize the event provide each competitor with a conker which has been drilled, stringed, and numbered. Play continues until only one conker, the winner, survives. Each contestant must pay a 15p entry fee, and the proceeds derived from these are donated to local charities.

In 1982 a smaller event was reported in London:

> An autumnal boom in good old-fashioned conker fights was predicted last night by David Evans, landlord of The Sun in Splendour in Portobello Road, Notting Hill, after hosting his second annual conker championships.
>
> 'So many people turned up that the bar was jammed solid and we had to use the beer garden for the contest. It's all done in great sporting spirit. All the spectators take sides for each fight but there's no trouble on the terraces like football, no fights and no bad feelings. It's a game that involves everyone in the pub, which is more than can be said for the electronic games.'
>
> London arts dealer Norman Twohig, 35, walked off with the champion's title and his one and a half gallons of beer first prize after six gruelling rounds. [*Evening Standard*, 30 September 1982]

It appears that the game of conkers is rarely met with outside the British Isles.

> On a recent visit to Gjirokaster in southern Albania, I was enthusing over the use there of *Aesculus hippocastanum* as a street tree, and our guide told me that Albanian children play 'conkers'. [Akeroyd, 1990: 20]

> Hungarian schoolchildren collect horse chestnut nuts and make toy animals out of them, but the game of conkers is unknown. [Budapest, October 1984]

> I spent much of the autumn of 1983 teaching two sons of a visiting American colleague how to play conkers, as they had not previously come across it. [Exeter, Devon, October 1984]

> Nothing strikes me as more odd, in the Grand Duchy of Luxembourg, than the sight of countless boys and girls walking past horse chestnut trees completely oblivious to the thick carpet of conkers under their feet.
>
> My own children, however, pounce on them excitedly, much to the consternation of passers-by, one of whom recently admonished my son with the words 'Oh, but you must not eat them.' [Letter from Luxembourg, in *The Times*, 27 October 1989]

Like their Hungarian counterparts, British children also enjoy making toys from conkers.

> As a child I myself had quite a different use for chestnuts. They came in very handy for making furniture for my dolls' house.

A plump, shiny chestnut was an excellent seat for a dining-room chair, while very long pins with glass heads formed legs, and slats for the backs interwoven with wool. I was very proud of my work (age 7). [Letter from Norwich, Norfolk, in *The Times*, 27 October 1989]

Less frequently played are games using the stalks of horse-chestnut leaves. Around Norwich the leaf stalks were known as knuckle-bleeders, and

Boys try to get one another to allow them to hit them over the knuckles with the end which grows next the branch. [Britten and Holland, 1886: 292]

A game was played in Chesterfield, Derbyshire, in the 1950's with the leaf stalks [of horse chestnut]. A stalk was held at each end by one person and another person would place a similarly held stalk behind it at right angles. Each would then pull in an attempt to break the other's stalk. The winner would then be challenged with another fresh stalk. [Llandrindod Wells, Powys, September 1991]

During the First and Second World Wars conkers were collected for military purposes. Early in the First World War, in 1915, the need for acetone essential for the manufacture of cordite caused concern in Britain. The usual American sources had become erratic and costly, so it was necessary for a British source to be found. Lloyd George requested Chaim Weizmann, then professor of chemistry at the University of Manchester, to investigate ways in which acetone could be manufactured. Initially Weizmann produced a method of making acetone from maize, but

the shipping shortage in 1917 which forced us to restrict all unnecessary imports, introduced yet another experiment. In the autumn of that year, horse chestnuts were plentiful, and a national collection of them was organised for the purpose of using their starch content as a substitute for maize.

When Lloyd George suggested to Weizmann that he should receive an honour for his work, Weizmann replied that he wanted no personal honour, but spoke of his 'aspirations as to the repatriation of the Jews to the sacred land they had made famous'. Lloyd George discussed Weizmann's hopes with his Foreign Secretary, A.J. Balfour.

Dr Weizmann was brought into direct contact with the Foreign Secretary. This was the beginning of an association, the out-come of which, after long examination, was the famous Balfour Declaration which became the charter of the Zionist movement [and in 1948 led to the establishment of the state of Israel]. [Lloyd George, 1938: 349]

An advertisement published in the magazine of the National Federation of Women's Institutes in 1942 pleaded:

Horse chestnuts (without the outer green husk) are urgently needed. Collection is sponsored by The Ministry of Supply (Directorate of Medical Supplies). Collecting groups are being organised in your district.

Groups of scholars, Boy Scouts, etc., are being organised to collect the 'conkers'. Receiving depots are being opened in most districts. All schools, Women's Institutes, W.V.S. Centres and Boy Scout Leaders will advise you of the address of your nearest depot where 7/6 per cwt. is being paid for immediate delivery of the Chestnuts (without the outer green husk). The collection is valuable war work and very urgent.

Please encourage it.

Landowners please encourage this collection on your land. [Kitchen, 1990: 69]

More recently, it was reported in *The Times* of 28 October 1993:

Landowners may soon be growing horse chestnuts as a cash crop to sell to the international pharmaceutical industry.

Forestry Commission scientists in Edinburgh have been commissioned by a German pharmaceutical company to study which strain of horse chestnut produces most aescin, a natural chemical found in conkers. It is used on the Continent for treating SPRAINS and bruising and is particularly useful in treating sports injuries.

The chemical was first used by the Turks to treat bruising in horses, which, according to the commission is how the horse chestnut got its name.

Other uses of conkers include preventing PILES and RHEUMATISM, and keeping moths away from clothes.

[In Somerset, in c.1970] old Bill, he'd had these piles for years . . . tried all manner of things, but it was just the same . . . one day this fellow got an idea about carrying a conker in your pocket, so old Bill . . . said he'd give it a go . . . He carried the conker in his pocket just like he was told, and tried to forget about it. Would you believe, after a few days they started to go down, and soon they were all better. Well, he goes to the doctor to show him, and the fellow doesn't believe his eyes . . . old Bill won't be caught without his conker now—never on your life. [K. Palmer, 1976: 113]

Carry a conker in your pocket to prevent rheumatism. [Kensington, London, October 1979]

I must collect some conkers, I haven't done it yet this year, but I get fresh ones each year and hang them up in my wardrobe to keep moths away. [Bayswater, London, October 1980]

About the efficacy of conkers (horse chestnuts) as a protection against moths, this was recommended to me some 15 years ago, and I have not seen a clothes moth since. As advised, I keep conkers in small plastic bags, closed with a knot, among my woollens and fastened to a fur coat. During the year, the conkers shrivel, so I presume they emit a vapour undetectable to humans, but inimical to moths. The conkers need to be intact when packed, not bitten by squirrels, etc., or they will rot. [Letter from Bath, Avon, in the *Independent*, 31 October 1990]

During the German Occupation of Guernsey, dried horse-chestnut leaves were used as a substitute for TOBACCO [McClintock, 1975: 99].

Horseradish (*Armoracia rusticana*)

A simple method of determining the sex of an unborn baby was for a Fenland couple to sleep with a piece of horse-radish under each of their pillows. If the husband's horse-radish turned black before his wife's, then the expected child would be a boy, and vice-versa. [Porter, 1969: 12]

Horseradish leaves, which are superficially similar to DOCK leaves, can be used as a substitute for dock in the treatment of NETTLE stings.

If by chance you did sting yourself with a nettle, rubbing dock leaf on the spot helped (as kids we always called the horse-radish leaf a dock leaf, which isn't strictly correct). [St Osyth, Essex, February 1989]

Other uses included:

[In the Fens] horse-radish, applied to a cut, would stop bleeding and draw the edges of the wound together leaving little scarring . . . Horse-radish was considered an effective cure for stomach cramp. [Porter, 1958: 118]

[According to my grandparents, b. 1856 and 1858] horse-radish was grated and you inhaled the vapour for heavy COLDS. Horse-radish root was dug up, boiled, and taken for worms—a common complaint in those days of insanitary cottages. [Cinderford, Gloucestershire, November 1993]

Gypsy's remedy for sciatica and GOUT: scrape fresh horse-radish—soak in white vinegar—bathe the affected parts in liquor and use the radish as poultice. [Taylor MSS]

Horse wort – a name for PARSLEY PIERT.

Hottentot fig (*Carpobrotus edulis*)

The Hottentot figs (*Carpobrotus edulis* and *C. acinaciformis*)—both garden escapes growing abundantly wild—can be used medicinally. The cut fleshy leaf is juicy and can be rubbed on SUNBURN for relief. [St Mary's, Isles of Scilly, November 1992]

Hot weed – a name used for GREAT BURNET in Brecknock and Radnor; cf. FIRE GRASS.

Houseleek (*Sempervivum tectorum*)

Old wryters do call it Iovis barba, Iupiter's Bearde, and holde an Opynion supersticiously that in what house so ever it groweth, no Lyghtning or Tempest can take place to doe any harme there. [Bullein, 1562; quoted in Grigson, 1987: 183]

[In Kent] to ensure a house from fire: Before going into a new house, plant the day previously, a root of houseleek; the leaves too, of which are regarded as a remedy for burns. [*N & Q*, 4 ser. 4, 507 1869]

Ireland shared fully in the very common European belief that the houseleek (*Sempervivum*) protected the house from conflagration and LIGHTNING, and the growing of this plant on the roofs of thatched houses, or in specially made niches or nooks in or about the roofs or porches of houses covered with other materials, was known in every Irish county. The plant is known by various names: 'houseleek' is widespread, but 'roofleek' occurs in parts of county Cork, *buachaill ti* in Galway and Mayo, *luibh a' toiteain* in west Limerick and Kerry, *toirpin* in Clare and Tipperary, and 'waxplant' in Offaly and Westmeath. Besides its virtues as a protection against FIRE it was also valued as a medicinal herb. [Ó Danachair, 1970: 25]

Ice plant or houseleek: if it grows on your roof you will never be entirely without money. [Rushmere St Andrew, Suffolk, February 1989]

Houseleeks were widely used in traditional medicine.

In Cornwall the leaves of the houseleek are made into a poultice for the extraction of CORNS. [Davey, 1909: 193]

Willoughton [Lincolnshire].—An application of houseleek is good for BURNS . . . Sore lips—a leaf of houseleek held between the lips, and bruised so that the 'cream' comes out will be found of great use. An application of houseleek is good for any SORE place. [Rudkin, 1936: 27]

The way they used to cure sore eyes was they used to have a lot of houseleek growing on their houses and they would squeeze it into a cup and rub it with a cloth into their eyes and it would cure them. [IFCSS MSS 50: 298, Co. Galway]

My initial acquaintance with it [houseleek] occurred when I was about fifteen years. It was a beautiful summer's day when I joined a group of men of my village before a traditional type whitewashed cottage with thatched roof. The thatch was terminated at either end of the cottages by 'barges' of flagstones set in lime-mortar. (In modern building terminology, this word would be 'verges'.) An old man had died in this cottage the previous day and the village folk and I were attending the funeral. While we waited for the coffin to be carried to the awaiting side-car I found myself intrigued by a clump of plants growing on one of the 'barges'.

'What are the plants growing on the barge?' I asked my neighbour, an elderly man.

'That,' he said 'is *Buachaill a'tighe*.' I remarked that I had never before heard of it. For a little while he was silent. Then turning towards me he spoke in lowered tone. 'It's a strange plant, that. Now if a young girl got into "trouble" (unwanted pregnancy), her mother would take some of those plants, boil them, and give the water to her daughter to drink. Later on, she would tell the girl to climb up on a high wall and jump down. That would make the girl alright.'

When, a few years ago, I related this story to a young farmer in this locality, he answered:

'It's quite true. I saw these plants tested only a short time ago. Walter C— came to me, and asked me if I had anything to give his cow that had retained the "cleansing" (afterbirth) after calving. I made up a bottle for him with *Buachaill a' tighe*. Walter took it home and gave it to his cow. A few hours later she passed the "cleansing" and was alright.'

Buachaill a'tighe is one of several names that Irish has for *Sempervivum tectorum*. I should translate it as 'the warden of the house'. [Kiltimagh, Co. Mayo, April 1983]

At the turn of the century my parents were farmers. My then 4- year-old brother had his hand bandaged. A gypsy came to the door and she asked what was wrong with the wee boy's hand. My mother said 'RINGWORM from the cattle.'

The gypsy said 'You have the cure on your wall. Take the Leek, boil it, then dab the boy's hand with the water.' It was also used for WARTS. [Armathwaite, Cumbria, October 1988]

My father-in-law was brought up in Norfolk. When he was suffering from impetigo a visiting gypsy woman recommended breaking off a piece of houseleek and rubbing the sores with it. The houseleek was growing on the cottage roof. My father-in-law (who is still alive) says the cure did work. [Bexhill-on-Sea, East Sussex, February 1991]

Hungry-grass. In Ireland there was a widepread belief that there was a certain grass which if trodden on would cause immense fatigue. This grass has sometimes been identified as QUAKING GRASS, but it seems more probable that hungry-grass cannot be identified with any particular species. It appears that people were particularly prone to stepping on hungry-grass when they were returning from events at which alcohol was consumed, so it is possible that the fatigue was alcohol-induced.

Fairgurtha or hungry-grass. Tufts of a peculiar grass that grows on the mountains, on which if anyone tread he immediately becomes faint and hungry and incapable of walking. People found dead in the hills are said to have had the *fairgurtha*, that is, they stood on a tuft of this grass and lost the power of going on. [Kinahan, 1881: 109]

People used to bring a handful of oaten meal when walking lest they should walk on *fear gorta* [IFCSS MSS 232: 21, Co. Roscommon]

The Hungry Sod is situated on the lands of Macetown. One day when the late Mr George Carr and other men were enjoying a day's hunting . . . they were returning home, and they were taking their time on the way and Mr Carr stepped on the sod. With the hunger he was unable to go home. His companions had to carry him home. When they reached the house Mr Carr fainted and he was put to bed and after a good feed he recovered. [IFCSS MSS 790: 65, Co. Dublin]

People used to get *feur-zorca* or get weak coming home from markets and fairs. This grass, if you walk on it you will not be able to go any further without eating something. There is *feur-zorca* at Mamore, at Slavery, and many other places.

My grandfather, William McLaughlin, Carva, said that one day he and a young man were coming from Clonmany and the man got weak at this spot and he had a few cakes in his pocket and he gave them to him to eat and he got right again. [IFCSS MSS 1112: 390, Co. Donegal]

Hydrangea (*Hydrangea macrophylla*).

A superstition seems to have grown up in recent years that the potted hydrangeas sold by florists are unlucky if brought into the house. This belief has been three times recorded in Cambridge and once in Chatteris. The blue flower seems to be considered more unlucky than the pink. [Porter, 1969: 45]

[I'm now well into my sixties, born in Mitcham] My grandma's horror of hydrangeas in the house is carried on by me. [Paston, Cambridgeshire, November 1993]

Hydrangea flowers, which are available in many colours and are relatively tough and long-lasting, are a favourite material used in Peak District WELL-DRESSINGS and were formerly much used to decorate floats in Jersey's BATTLE OF FLOWERS.

Hydrophobia – treated using BUCK'S HORN PLANTAIN and ELECAMPANE.

I

Ice plant – a widespread name for HOUSELEEK and similar succulent plants.

Impetigo – treated using HOUSELEEK.

Impotence – cured using ASH.

Indigestion – treated using DANDELION.

Infertility – overcome using pieces of a BLACK POPLAR tree growing at Ashton-on-Clun, PENNYROYAL, or walking around a YEW tree at Stoke Gabriel, Devon; in women, cured using DOCK.

Influenza – treated using ELDER and YARROW.

Insanity – caused by BUTTERCUP.

Insomnia – prevented using HOP and LETTUCE.

Iris – see STINKING IRIS and YELLOW IRIS.

Irish moss – see CARRAGEEN.

Irish spurge (*Euphorbia hyberna*), also known as yellow root plant.

> In Galway people consider it [Irish spurge] a 'grand physic', and give it to horses and cattle, but think it too strong for human patients; nevertheless it is sometimes given, generally to the unknowing by way of a practical joke. I was told of one individual in Gort who was dosed with it a couple of years ago, and a spectator assured me that he 'ran up and down the street like a madman, and swelled so big that his friends had to bind him with hay-ropes lest he should burst'. The country people have a quaint notion of the way in which this medicine is to be extracted. They take about an inch of the root (in which its strongest properties lie) and scrape it into some boiling liquid, generally tea, which draws out its essence; but they firmly believe 'that if it be scraped up it will work upwards, but if you scrape it down it will work downwards, and if it is scraped both up and down it will work in every way and burst you!' [Hart, 1873: 339]

> I have seen the country people in the Blackwater valley crushing quantities of this plant between stones and then throwing the mass into the river to poison the salmon and trout. [NHM MSS, herbarium H.J. Ryden, fl. 1860s]

Irish spurge, *Baine caoin*, is well known in Kerry and West Cork and is used to poison fish. The plant is pulled from the habitat, the river bank, and thrown into the stream or river. The white exudate (common to many spurges) contains saponins which destroy the gill tissues and prevent respiration. [Dublin, March 1992]

In the yellow root plant there is a hole through the middle and if you bruised it white stuff like milk would come out of it, and if it went on your hands it would blister them. It was used here by old people for colouring wool for frieze coats. It was also used to catch fish. It was put into a tin box and the juice let go out into the water and it would poison the fish and they would easily be caught. They would come up to the top of the water and the boys would 'suil' them out and bring them home. It was also used for hens having the sickness. [IFCSS MSS 450: 90, Co. Kerry]

Although plants are used in this manner to poison fish in many parts of the world, especially in the tropics, no other plant has been recorded as being used for this purpose in the British Isles.

Irish tea – a County Carlow name for dried BLACKTHORN leaves, used as a substitute for TOBACCO.

Italian weed – a Yorkshire name for YELLOW CORYDALIS.

Ivy (*Hedera helix*)

[According to my 73-year-old mother from Rothes, Morayshire:] the following plants are strictly forbidden in the house . . . ivy—very dangerous. [Stanton-on-the-Wolds, Nottinghamshire, January 1983]

Ivy . . . should not be used in CHRISTMAS decorations. HOLLY was placed over shelves and in vases, but not ivy. [Witham, Essex, May 1983]

I never have ivy in the house—always considered it unlucky. [Cleethorpes, Humberside, February 1991]

More usually ivy is forbidden indoors at any time other than Christmas.

HOLLY and ivy must not be taken in house until Christmas Eve and must be removed by January 6th. [Boundary, Staffordshire, March 1983]

The Irish ivy (*Hedera helix* ssp. *hibernica* 'Hibernica') differs from the common ivy in having larger leaves. In Rosneath, Dunbartonshire:

in the 1940s schoolgirls took a leaf of garden Irish ivy . . . off the wall near the church, slipped it inside their blouses and sang:

Ivy ivy I love you,
In my bosom I put you,
The first young man who speaks to me
My future husband he will be.

[Helensburgh, Dunbartonshire, February 1991]

Cf. ASH.

Ivy was widely used on washdays.

We had to pull a big bunch of coarse ivy leaves. Chop them up and stew them until soft. Keep the juice and put in an old container. Discard the leaves. With an old clothes brush take your husband's serge suit and proceed to brush in the liquid, especially [into] the lapel and neck and cuffs. Then take a clean cloth and iron it all over. It's like new. A lot cheaper than dry cleaning. [Castlerock, Co. Derry, February 1989]

Stewed ivy leaves, or rather the water therefrom, were used in my own youth in Dorset to take the shine out of navy-blue serge. [Sidmouth, Devon, November 1991]

Ivy has been widely used in folk medicine, particularly to treat CORNS.

Boiled ivy leaves for corns is not just a Cornish recipe; when we lived in north Wales during World War II the old Welsh lady with whom we shared a house boiled these leaves for a corn my mother had developed, the poultice should have stayed in place for five days but on the third day when my mother thought her complete toe was being drawn from her foot, she removed the bandage and away came the painful corn, never to return. [Calpe, Alicante, Spain, November 1991]

[In the 1970s] I met a young woman in Fairlie, Ayrshire coast, who made a concoction of ivy leaves for her corns with vinegar—she pointed to 'Irish' as the type used. [Helensburgh, Dunbartonshire, February 1991]

I am in my mid 70s now. When a child of about 2 years I fell on a fire and was badly burned in my face (so my mother, R.I.P., often told me), likely a travelling woman offered to bring her ointment that would cure the BURN and leave no mark; she wouldn't reveal what it was. In desperation my mother used it and it worked. T.G. I haven't a mark.

It took 30 years before I discovered the cure. When I came to live here a very old lady lived near me. I got friendly with her and discovered she worked near my home town (Kanturk) in her youth, and made, as she called it, a plaster for burns. She gave me instruction . . . on how to make it. This is it: You choose good green ivy leaves, wash them and dry them; boil in fresh lard enough leaves to turn the lard a rich green colour—they crisp up in boiling. The lard can then be strained and stored in jars and will keep for years. I have seen it used with great success. [Ballyclough, Co. Cork, October 1990]

An 'Ivy Cap' used to be made by joining the leaves together, and put on the heads of children who had some disease of the scalp (a sort of rash). It had good healing powers. [Lenamore, Co. Longford, April 1991]

I have a cure using tendrils of ivy. 33 years ago [in Derbyshire] my son suffered from ECZEMA. We met the 'Grandma Gypsy' from a local gypsy group . . . one day she said that she could help 'calm that skin'. She went into the undergrowth and brought back a pile of ivy tendrils with leaves. She called it Robin-run-in-the-hedge. My instructions were to boil the lot for three hours, and then leave the lot for 24 hours. I was then to wipe the 'gunge' over the affected places. This I did to please the old lady, and was surprised to find that it did indeed cool the skin. [St Mary's, Isles of Scilly, September 1992]

In Warwickshire it was recommended that ivy should be given to sick SHEEP. 'If they will not eat ivy, they are going to die' [Wharton MSS 1974: 196].

During the German Occupation of the Channel Islands (1940–5) ivy berries were boiled and eaten [Bonnard, 1993: 26].

Ivy-leaved crowfoot (*Ranunculus hederaceus*). On Colonsay, in the Inner Hebrides, ivy-leaved crowfoot pounded between stones 'was used as one of the principal ingredients in poultices for KING'S EVIL' [McNeill, 1910: 95].

Ivy-leaved toadflax (*Cymbalaria muralis*)

'This [ivy-leaved toadflax] is what we call wall rabbits.'
'Why do you give it that name?'
'Because if you turn the flower upside down, and squeeze its sides, like this, it looks like a rabbit's head.' [Abbotsbury, Dorset, May 1983]

Other names which refer to this feature include the Somerset monkey-jaws and monkey mouths; the Devon nanny goat's mouths, rabbit-flower, and rabbits [Grigson, 1987: 297].

J

Jack-go-to-bed-at-noon – a name for GOAT'S BEARD.

Jack in the Green, a man or youth enclosed in a wooden or wicker conical framework covered in leaves, was formerly a widespread feature of May Day celebrations, being particularly associated with the May festivals of urban chimney-sweeps.

It was once fashionable to regard Jack in the Green as a manifestation of the foliate head motif which is a common ornament in medieval churches [Raglan, 1939], or as a rare and curious survival of an extremely ancient rite—'the annual victim of the vegetation drama' [James, 1961: 288]. In the 1970s it was shown that the association between Jack in the Green and the foliate head could not be justified [Basford, 1978], and that Jack evolved towards the end of the eighteenth century as one of a variety of begging activities practised on May Day [Judge, 1978]. However, the old ideas about the origin of Jack in the Green continue to be repeated by some of the groups which have revived the figure.

The Hastings Jack in the Green can be seen in Hastings every May Day Bank Holiday, together with morris dancers from all over the country. (48 teams this year!)

It is a 10 ft high bush, made from leaves and topped with a crown of flowers. It has a man inside and is paraded around all day with 'Green Man Keepers'. At the end of the day it is 'killed' to 'release the spirit of summer', and flowers and leaves are distributed to the crowd for good luck. [Hastings, East Sussex, March 1993]

Jacks – a name given to WILD GLADIOLUS on the Isles of Scilly.

Jade plant – a name for MONEY TREE.

Japanese knotweed (*Fallopia japonica*). Originally introduced to the British Isles as an ornamental, Japanese knotweed started escaping from gardens in the 1880s and is now a common plant on waste ground.

[In Wales] Japanese knotweed was increasingly being used for making peashooters from the 1920s onwards . . . In some parts of north Wales this plant had no name and it was referred to generally as a form of wild rhubarb. However by the 1930s it was being referred to generally as a *cegid* or *cecs* [i.e. a plant with a hollow stem] which might indicate its acceptance into Welsh plant folklore—or at least children's folklore! As a child in north Wales in the 1950s this plant featured in our efforts at making pea-shooters—we called the plant *the peashooter*, a name which persists as in 'there are peashooters growing down by the river'. However, fieldwork amongst school-children in the 1980s in north Wales failed to elicit one example of such use. [Cardiff, January 1994]

Jaundice – treated using BARBERRY, BOGBEAN, BROOM, CHICORY, COWSLIP, DANDELION, ELM, GARLIC, GERMANDER SPEEDWELL, GORSE, GREATER CELANDINE, HONEYSUCKLE, NETTLE, and PRIMROSE.

Jaundice tree – a Cornish name for BARBERRY.

Jenny or Jinny Greenteeth – a NURSERY BOGEY associated with DUCKWEED-covered pools, or a name for duckweed.

Jersey lily (*Amaryllis belladonna*)

My mother's family were of Kent origin, and she seemed to be steeped in superstition . . . it was supposedly unlucky to bring what we call pink bel-ladonna lilies (*Amaryllis*), also known, I believe as naked ladies, into the house. [Nicholson, Victoria, Australia, July 1983]

Petals of Jersey lily, cover with brandy, add a little camphor and leave in a screw-top jar for about a month; it was used here . . . in the old days to treat bad CUTS by taking one leaf and putting over the wound, it stings but works. [St Lawrence, Jersey, April 1993]

Jew guts – a Devon name for TRAVELLER'S JOY.

Johnsmas-flooer – a Shetland name for RIBWORT PLANTAIN.

Joseph and Mary – a Dorset name for LUNGWORT.

Joseph's coat of many colours – a south London name for LUNG-WORT.

Joug tree. In Scotland trees used by feudal barons as their gallows were known as joug, or dool, trees. These were usually SYCAMORES, and could also function as PROPHETIC TREES.

The Joug Tree was the local laird's gallows, for in Scotland the feudal lairds had right of life and death. By a kind of revenge, these trees became ominous to the family, and when a limb fell off a death followed. [Briggs, 1971: 541]

See also OAK for the legend of the Fort William Hanging Tree.

Judas Iscariot – associated with ELDER.

Jump-up-and-kiss-me – a Munster name for GERMANDER SPEED-WELL.

Juniper (*Juniperus communis*), formerly also known as saffern, SAF-
FRON, and savin.

> People said that he who cut down a juniper would die within the year.
> For this reason, in many parts of Wales, aged junipers are carefully
> preserved, and it is customary to 'let it die of its own will', or a natural
> death.
>
> Twenty years ago an old farmer living in Glamorgan asserted that three
> deaths in his family followed by disaster happened when 'the old juniper
> was cut down'. [Trevelyan, 1909: 105]

Juniper was widely used to produce abortions, a Somerset name for
the plant being bastard killer [Grigson, 1987: 24]. In the court of Mary
Queen of Scots (1542-87) there were four ladies-in-waiting, all
named Mary. One of these, Mary Hamilton, became pregnant and in
desperation resorted to juniper—savin—as an abortifacient. In the
words of one of the many ballads telling of Mary Hamilton's tragedy:

> She's gane to the garden gay
> To pu' of the savin tree;
> But for a' that she could say or do,
> The babie it would not die.

[Child, 1889: 387]

In the Pitt Rivers Museum, in Oxford, is a specimen of 'about five
sprigs of "saffron" [i.e. juniper], around 4.5 inches in length,'
presented to the Museum in 1914. A note by the donor explains:

> *To prevent conception.* When a woman notices that she has missed a period
> she puts about the same quantity of saffron as this envelope contains into
> a pint jug; pours half a pint of *boiling* water on to it, covers the jug's mouth
> with muslin and puts a saucer on the top. She leaves the saffron to soak
> and, when cold, strains it through the muslin and drinks a wineglass-full
> for four consecutive mornings. She puts one sprig of saffron into each
> boot and wears it for *nine* days. The idea of this being that as the feet get
> hot the saffron soaks through the stocking into the foot. The sprigs here
> contained have been worn in the boots [of an] Oxford [woman].

More recently:

> I asked a local chemist if he had been around long enough to have heard
> of juniper pills—'The Lady's Friend': typical advertisement in small print
> in ladies' journals: 'Late? Worried? Take Juno juniper pills.' 'Yes,' he said,
> he remembered them in little brown and green boxes . . . He said he hadn't
> seen them for five or six years; he then looked in his pharmaceutical trade
> book, and said, 'Yes, they're still available, Juno juniper pills.' . . . still
> needed even in the day of the pill. [Great Bedwyn, Wiltshire, July 1993]

In south-west Lincolnshire:

> [Saffern] was often given by farm servants to their horses to make their
> coats shine. [Wright, 1905, 5: 200]

K

Karmic plant

It's known as an Egyptian, cosmic, or karmic—as in karma— plant. It sits in tea, splits into two, then you lift the top one—the daughter—off. It's stringy, membrane-like. Put it in another dish and feed on tea, at the end it's quite heavy and caramel or skin coloured. On Monday give the daughter plant away to three others—like a chain letter—who keep the plant for three weeks and then pass on the daughters. Keep the mother plant dried in linen as a protector—a talisman. While growing in the tea—which should have half a teaspoonful of sugar added, it occasionally gives off a vinegar-like smell and tiny air bubbles. Any little insects which fall in while it is growing become coated in a film of flesh. The plant is said to be 5,000 years old. [Wandsworth, London, October 1992]

This mysterious 'plant' seems to be similar to the 'gingerbeer plant' which can be used to produce a children's drink, and is composed of a yeast and a bacterium. Possibly it is the same 'plant' as that used to produce tea-cider,

which has become very popular in parts of the orient [and] is made by fermenting sweetened tea by a 'mould' of which the chief constituents are . . . yeast and a bacterium. A heavy gelatinous scum forms on the surface. [Ramsbottom, 1953: 213]

Karo (*Pittosporum crassifolium*)

[On the Isles of Scilly] *Pittosporum* fruits, which are sticky when ripe, are called 'pobbles' and collected by children for 'pobble fights'. [Woodnewton, Northamptonshire, June 1992]

Kell (kale) – a Shetland name for CABBAGE.

Kennel herb – a Cornish name for BUTTERCUP.

Kenning herb – a Cornish name for both BUTTERCUP and GREATER CELANDINE.

Kidney bean – see RUNNER BEAN.

Kidney troubles – treated using ANNUAL KNAWEL, DANDELION, HERB ROBERT, and PELLITORY OF THE WALL.

Kidney vetch (*Anthyllis vulneraria*). On the Channel Islands kidney vetch leaves were used to check BLEEDING from wounds [Bonnard, 1993: 23].

Kill-your-mother-quick – an Essex name for COW PARSLEY.

Kingcup – see MARSH MARIGOLD.

King's evil (scrofula) – treated using IVY- LEAVED CROWFOOT and OX-EYE DAISY.

Kiss me quick – a Dorset name for RED VALERIAN.

Knapweed (*Centaurea nigra*)

> In Bucks, I find that the young people still make use of love-DIVINATION by means of the knapweed . . . The florets should all be stripped off, and the rest of the flower-head placed in the bosom. If, on being withdrawn, one of these spikes, of which three should be employed, is found to have grown, that one represents the true lover. [Friend, 1884: 14]

On Guernsey knapweed was known as *herbe de flon*:

> *Flon* has two different meanings. *Un flon* signifies a boil or wen on the human body; but *le flon* is a disease of cows, which causes the induration of the udder after calving. To cure this, a handful of black knapweed is boiled for half an hour, and the affected part is bathed with it. [Marquand, 1906: 41]

Knuckle-bleeders – a Norfolk name for the leaf stalks of HORSE CHESTNUT.

Kolanut (*Cola* spp.). The author Buchi Emecheta was born in Nigeria and came to London at the age of 17 in 1962. When her second book was published, in 1975, she held a party:

> Mr Enenmoh shocked my guest when he took a copy of *Second-Class Citizen*, poured half a bottle of whisky over it, broke a kola-nut on it, and commanded our Western Ibo gods through prayers to make me the greatest black writer Britain has ever seen, and to make all my children greater still . . . All Mr Enenmoh was doing as the oldest male present was to represent my father, and knowing that I intended to make writing my career, was thanking our ancestors for revealing my vocation to me, and praying to them to make me use my gift responsibly. [Emecheta, 1986: 185]

Cf. COCONUT.

Konker-tree – a Somerset name for HORSE CHESTNUT.

Ku-tree – a Cornish name for TREE MALLOW.

L

Laburnum (*Laburnum anagyroides*)

Laburnum winter—a cold spell of weather coinciding with the flowering of the laburnum. [Great Bookham, Surrey, October 1979]

Lad's love – a name for SOUTHERNWOOD.

Lady's bedstraw (*Galium verum*). As several local names, such as the widespread cheese RENNET and the Gaelic *lus an leasaich* [Grigson 1987: 343] indicate, infusions of lady's bedstraw stems were widely used for curdling milk.

> In Arran, and some of the Western islands, the inhabitants make a strong concoction of this herb, and use it as a runnet to curdle milk: and in Jura, Uist, and Lewis, &c I was inform'd they used the roots to DYE a very fine red. [Lightfoot, 1777: 116]

> The people in Cheshire, especially about Namptwich where the best Cheese is made, do use it in their Rennet, esteeming greatly of that Cheese above other made without it. [Gerard, 1597: 968]

> Maidens hair = lady's bedstraw—occasionally used by grandma [b.1858] to curdle milk for cheese when rennet was not available. [Cinderford, Gloucestershire, November 1993]

In 'darkest Berkshire':

> The only plant still in general demand is *Galium verum* which dried between sheets of newspaper is used for lining wardrobes and clothes-chests to deter MOTHS. [Oxford, December 1993]

Lady's lace – a name for COW PARSLEY.

Lady's milksile – a Cheshire name for LUNGWORT.

Language of Flowers. During the nineteenth century many books were produced on the Language of Flowers, whereby sentiments could be expressed by the presentation of suitably chosen blossoms. Although these books were popular, and their attractive illustrations ensured that they survived rather better than many other publications of the period, it appears that they were merely glanced through, rather than being actually used. Indeed, as different books often ascribed different meanings to different flowers, any attempt to convey sentiments by such means was liable to be misunderstood.

The Language of Flowers is often said to have been of Turkish origin, introduced by Lady Mary Wortley Montagu. However, the method of communication by flowers and other objects which she described in her letters from Turkey was a mnemonic system, which gives no meanings to flowers, and is of no relevance to the development of the Language [Halsband, 1965: 387-9 and 464-5].

The Language first appears in Charlotte de La Tour's *Le Langage des Fleurs*, published in Paris in 1818. Subsequent books on the subject are derived from this work. Some plants retained the meanings ascribed to them by La Tour, even though these might be inappropriate in Britain. Others changed their meanings due to the French work being incorrectly translated, and others had their meanings changed to take into account Shakespearean and other traditions. Thus ROSEMARY, which according to La Tour meant 'your presence revives me', was associated with 'remembrance' in British publications. Other flowers had to have their meaning changed to take account of religious beliefs. La Tour and some British writers state that the PASSION FLOWER meant 'faith'. Other British writers ascribed 'religious superstition' to the flower, while *The Catholic Language of Flowers* by 'the young ladies of Gumley House', published in London in 1861, associated the flower with 'meditation'.

During the 1870s there was a revival of interest in the Language of Flowers, stimulated by the publication of John Ingram's *Flora Symbolica* in 1869. Publications of this decade reflect the great increase in the number of ornamental plants brought into cultivation during the earlier part of the century, and drew from a wide range of sources, with the result that some flowers had more than one meaning ascribed to them [Elliott, 1984: 63].

Books on the Language of Flowers continue to be published, and it would be interesting to know who buys them. The Language also gets mentioned in popular works on the folklore of plants:

> The white hollyhock symbolizes female ambition . . . In the Language of Flowers it [HONEYSUCKLE] means 'I will not answer hastily'. [Addison, 1985: 135 and 137]

However, it appears that the Language was an entirely literary tradition which had little, if any, influence on the 'folk'. For a survey of the development of the Language in France and the United States of America see Goody, 1993, chapters 8 and 9.

Large bindweed (*Calystegia silvatica*) and **Hedge bindweed** (*C. sepium*); also known as CONVOLVULUS.

When you squeeze the green bit at the bottom of a convolvulus flower saying 'Granny pop out of bed' the white petals pop off. This came from my mother and aunt in London. [Hampstead, London, September 1987]

From Emily Dimmer (aged 7) who had it from a friend at school, autumn 1988: the calyx and bracts of bindweed—*Calystegia sepium* or *silvatica*—are squeezed so that the corolla jumps out, and one repeats 'Grandmother, Grandmother, jump out of bed.' [Girton, Cambridge, May 1989]

Squeeze bindweed flowers saying 'Granny jump into bed, Granny jump out of bed.' [Sittingbourne, Kent, August 1991]

The children's game with convolvulus is known here, but with the slight variation: 'Granny jump out of the rocking chair.' [St Mary's, Isles of Scilly, November 1992]

Around Inverness:

The flower of the trailing plant convolvulus was called bee traps because as children we would watch a honey bee enter the flower when we would imprison it by holding the opening of the flower between finger and thumb, and listen to the insect wriggling and trying to get out and could feel the vibrations of its movements. May I say when it got too fierce we allowed the bee to escape, and stood well back. We never killed one. [Solihull, West Midlands, April 1991]

Laurel (*Prunus laurocerasus*), also known as cherry laurel.

[Horseheath, Cambridgeshire:] a test for true love was to prick our the sweethreat's name on a laurel leaf and wear it next to your heart; if the writing turned red all was well, but if it turned black, the young man loved you not. [Parsons MSS, 1952]

Picked laurel leaves and with a thorn pricked our name on the back, put them inside our vests, the warmth brought out our name clearly. [Plymstock, Devon, January 1993]

In the past we used laurel leaves for 'secret letters'—the message pricked or sratched on the back of the leaf went brown—and also for putting in tobacco tins for killing and relaxing butterflies for our collection. [Woodnewton, Northamptonshire, June 1992]

Laurel leaves were formerly used to flavour milk dishes.

One old lady put laurel leaves in the milk when she made corn flour moulds—'Gave a lovely almond flavour'—I never tried it! [Plymouth, January 1993]

Occasionally laurel is used to decorate greengrocers' and, more rarely, butchers' shops at Christmas time [personal observation, Chelsea, Streatham, and Tooting, December 1983].

Wreaths of laurel leaves are often used in ceremonies that commemorate the well-loved dead. In January each year nurses from St

Thomas's Hospital place a laurel wreath at the base of the statue of Edith Cavell, at the south end of Charing Cross Road, in commemoration of her execution in Brussels in 1915. On the last night of the BBC Promenade Concerts, held at the Royal Albert Hall in London on the second Saturday in September, two promenaders place a laurel wreath on a bust of Sir Henry Wood (1869–1944), the founder of the Concerts [personal observation, 11 September 1993]. Each year on 21 October, the anniversary of the Battle of Trafalgar, a laurel wreath is placed on the quarter deck of Lord Nelson's ship the *Victory*, now docked in Portsmouth Harbour [Boase, 1976: 175]. It appears that these wreaths have almost entirely supplanted the BAY wreaths used to crown victors in classical times.

> Boil and strain laurel leaves, mix the juice with lard, and use as a cure for BURNS. [IFCSS MSS 575: 324, Co. Tipperary]

> RINGWORM used to be a common complaint in the country and the cure for that was an ointment made from unsalted butter and the juice extracted from laurel leaves. [Glynn, Co. Antrim, February 1992]

In the British Isles laurel leaves are sometimes used in place of MANGO leaves at Hindu wedding celebrations.

Laver (*Porphyra umbilicalis*)

> Of the finer seaweeds gathered locally for food, the best known is laver. This is eaten after prolonged boiling, seasoned with lemon juice, oil or butter. Or it is incorporated in scones or girdle cakes . . . In Devon some people enjoy it boiled and hot . . . others prefer it cold as salad.
>
> Large quantities are gathered in Cornwall, Devon, and Pembrokeshire, and in Scotland the same weed is called slaak, and in Ireland sloke. The miners of South Wales are the biggest laver eaters in the country, and freshly made laver bread is almost always on sale in Cardiff Market. [Yarham, 1944: 814]

> The thin delicate red seaweed, Porphyra or laver, is still a culinary dish in certain parts of South Wales, Devon and Cornwall. It is eaten either as salad or, more usually, is cooked and made into a breakfast dish . . . In the 18th century it was stongly recommended as a suitable dish for crews of whaling boats. It requires to be fried in a great quantity of fat. [Chapman, 1950:152]

> During summer holidays [Minehead, Somerset] laver (seaweed) was collected from the seashore, taken home and washed in the bath and kitchen sink, dried and fried with bacon for breakfast, called laverbread. [Felmersham, Bedfordshire, March 1993]

Leaf

> [In West Sussex] if you catch a falling leaf, you will have twelve months of continued happiness. [Latham, 1878: 9]

Leek

[In my schooldays about 60 years ago, it was believed that] if a falling leaf lands on your clothes you should not throw it away but keep it carefully in your satchel and it will bring you good luck. [Great Bookham, Surrey, November 1979]

[As a child in Nottinghamshire in the 1920s] to catch a falling leaf was very lucky. [Oban, Argyll, October 1990]

The short-lived leaves of deciduous trees have been considered to be symbolic of man's mortality. In the words of the hymn-writer W. Chalmers Smith (1824-1908):

> To all life thou givest—to both great and small;
> In all life thou livest, the true life of all;
> We blossom and flourish as leaves on the tree,
> And wither and perish—but nought changeth thee.
>
> [*New English Hymnal*, 1986, no. 377]

Or, according to a south of England folk song:

> What's the life of a man any more than a leaf,
> For a man has his season and why should he grieve?
> Below in the wide world he appears fine and gay,
> Like the leaf he shall wither and soon fade away.
>
> [R. Palmer, 1979: 216]

Leek (*Allium porrum*). For the Welsh the leek shares with the rather more ornamental and easily worn DAFFODIL the honour of being a national symbol, worn on St David's Day (1 March) and other occasions when such symbols are considered to be appropriate. Why the leek should have been chosen for this role is a matter for speculation.

I will not presume to enter a controversy . . . by suggesting that . . . it may have become amalgamated into Druidic theology with a degree of sanctity, according to Latin writers, similar to that which rendered the leek so sacred a symbol amongst the ancient Egyptians, that to swear by these plants was considered equivalent to swearing by one of their gods, but will pass on to tell how Owen, otherwise a good antiquary, actually derives it from a prevalent Welsh custom, called *Cymhortha*, by which neighbours assemble, at seed-time, or harvest, to assist each other in completing the labour of the day; at which gathering each man contributes, by a sort of complimentary usage, a leek to the broth which forms the dinner on the occasion; and as these leeks, he assures us, might naturally be carried in the band of the hat, he supposes the nation assumed them as a badge! . . .

King James in his *Royal Apothegms* says, that it was chosen to commemorate the lamented Black Prince; but what connection subsisted between that gallant youth and the ill-scented plant, he does not inform us, Nor do the old Welsh records approach much nearer to the truth. Their general testimony appears to be in favour of some battle, in which the Welsh were victorious, having been fought in a garden of leeks, from which each man gathered and wore one, to enable his countrymen to distinguish him from the enemy; to whom they had pre-determined to grant no quarter. This battle is variously stated to have occurred under the leadership of St David at the close of the fifth century, or commencement of the sixth century; or under that of Cadwalladr, in the year 633, when he defeated the Saxons near Hethfield, or Hatfield, in Yorkshire. It is needless to say that the idea is imaginary. [Wilkinson, 1858: 137]

However, despite such unsatisfactory explanations, the symbol is firmly established.

St David's Day Custom.—In Anglesey it is the custom for boys to wear leeks up to twelve mid-day only, after that hour girls are supposed to deck themselves with the emblem of St David. Should a boy be seen without a leek in the morning, or with one after mid-day he is mercilessly pinched, and the same rule applies, vice versa, to the girls. [N & Q, 5 ser. 7: 206, 1877]

A favourite photograph in newspapers on the day after St David's Day shows a small girl in traditional Welsh costume stretching up to present a neatly trimmed leek to a tall guardsman.

Colour Sergeant Phil Atweel, of Merthyr Tydfil, receiving a leek from Joanne O'Driscoll, aged four, of Bridgend, during St David's Day celebrations yesterday hosted by the 1st battalion of the Welsh Guards at their barracks at Pirbright, Surrey. [The Times, 2 March 1989]

The annual Rugby Union International between England and Wales provides the rival supporters with an opportunity to demonstrate their support by decking themselves with appropriate symbols.

The essential item of clothing is, of course, a woollen scarf with stripes of the Welsh team's colours, red and white. Other items worn by supporters included flags depicting Welsh dragons, draped over the shoulders; and leeks or daffodils. Some supporters wore real leeks; one particularly well equipped individual wore a red-and-white scarf, a flag, and a miner's helmet with a leek attached to the back. Some of the older men had miniature leeks made from knitting wool pinned to their lapels, and some groups of youngsters carried home-made leeks up to 3 or 4 feet high, made from white cardboard, green crêpe paper and other materials. [Personal observation, 16 February 1980]

The growing of giant leeks for exhibition at autumn leek shows has been a favourite pastime throughout much of north-east England since the mid-1880s. Thus in 1893 the sixteen-member 'Pot and Glass' Leek Club at Crossgate Moor held its seventh annual show with the first prize being a pair of blankets and a picture [Calderbank, 1984: 11]. In 1895 a show was held at Mr Lumsden's hostelry at Crossgate:

Three leeks comprised a stand. W. Golightly took first place and a prize of £1 15s (£1.75p); W. Robson, second, (£1 and a sheep's heart), and T. Stewart third 15 shillings (75p) and a 'beast's heart'. A special prize was awarded to Mr Robson for the best single leek in the show. [Calderbank, 1984: 12]

Two main types of leek are commonly exhibited: long leeks which resemble the ones commonly seen in greengrocers' shops, being long and narrow, and pot leeks which are shorter and stouter. Some shows also have classes for intermediate leeks.

However, there is some confusion about the length at which a pot leek becomes an intermediate, and an intermediate becomes a long leek. [Calderbank, 1984: 9]

Each exhibit ('stand') usually consists of a pair of leeks, and it is the pot leeks which usually create most excitement. Traditionally, judges at northern leek shows considered the cubic capacity of the leeks displayed to be of greatest importance, but the Royal Horticultural Society in its guidelines for judges has stipulated that leeks should be judged according to their condition, solidity, and uniformity (i.e. the shape of the leek and how well it compares in shape and size with its companion or companions, making up a stand). Most northern judges take the RHS guidelines into consideration, but also pay considerable attention to the size of the leeks in a stand. As leek-growers themselves they are fully aware of the amount of effort which must be put in to produce good large leeks, whereas it is comparatively easy to produce perfect smaller specimens.

From mid September until late October newpapers in the north of England, and in some other areas where leek-growing has become popular, contain numerous reports and photographs of local leek shows. On 14 September 1974 the *Rugeley Times* reported:

Almost £500 worth of prizes went to this year's 29 entries at the Poplars Leek Show held last weekend at the Poplars Inn, Handsacre . . . Each person submitted three leeks, all of which were grown with the use of 'recipes' formulated by the grower himself, and usually not divulged to others . . . On Monday a 'glutton's supper' was held at the Poplars, where leek soup, leek sandwiches and other food made from leeks were served to members and their families in celebration of a successful competition.

Results were as follows: 1. A. Clarke, sewing machine; 2. S. Bolt, dressette; 3. C. Jessop, chest of drawers: 4. E. Fitch, quilt, blankets and sheets; 5. B. Jones, table lamp . . . 24. S. Davies, iron. The next five entrants all won £6 cash.

Further north, where shows are much more common, reports tend to be shorter, often consisting of a couple of introductory sentences followed by a list of winners.

Blanchland Leek Show produced an impressive display of vegetables and flowers with a mammoth leek measuring 145.1 cu ins taking the top trophy.

Benched by Mr P. Everitt, it was judged best in show over his nearest rival Mr K. Heppel who, to make up for his second placing, went on to win first prize in the intermediate leek class. In the flower classes the Rev. John Durnford had his prayers answered when he won first prize for his collection of flowers. [*Hexham Courant*, 21 September 1990]

In 1992 it was reported that:

the National Pot Leek Society, with 1,000 members . . . now has branches from Scotland to Somerset . . .

The Newcastle Exhibition World Open leek show, with a £1,300 first prize, is at the Northern Club, Ashington, on September 26-27. The event includes the Newcastle Brown Ale Heaviest ONION Challenge with an £850 first prize. [*Hexham Journal*, 12 September 1992]

Lemon (*Citrus limon*)

We used to save lemon rinds after the juice had been squeezed out, put them in a jug with a bit of honey and pour boiling water over them . . . at least one lemon to a pint of water. Leave it overnight and then drink it, as much as you want and as often as you want. You can also make it with cold water, but you have to leave it to steep longer. Spots and PIMPLES will go in a couple of days. [Chard, Somerset, March 1991]

Lemon balm – see BALM.

Lemon verbena (*Aloysia triphylla*)

A Northam [Devon] woman told me that 'anyone who can make cuttings of lemon verbena grow will not die unmarried', adding with a twinkle in her eye, 'I don't think it's always true, because I can make it grow.' [Chope, 1929: 126]

Lemon-scented verbena leaves used to make a refreshing tea that cleanses the system. [Plymouth, April 1993]

Lesser celandine – see CELANDINE.

Lesser spearwort (*Ranunculus flammula*). On Colonsay, in the Inner Hebrides, lesser spearwort was used as a substitute for RENNET in cheese-making [McNeill, 1910: 96]. On the Channel Islands water distilled from lesser spearwort 'is said to have been the preferred local method of causing instant vomitting in cases of poisoning' [Bonnard, 1993: 13].

Lesser yellow trefoil (*Trifolium dubium*). According to a survey conducted in 1893, lesser yellow trefoil was the species which was most popularly believed to be the true SHAMROCK, with 51 per cent of

correspondents considering it to be the real plant [Colgan, 1893]. A similar survey conducted in 1988 produced a similar result with 46 per cent of the participants believing it to be the true shamrock [Nelson, 1990].

Lettuce (*Lactuca sativa*)

Lettuces . . . were formerly believed to have magical and healing properties, including the power of arousing love . . . in medieval times they were often included in love-potions and charms. They were also said to promote child-bearing if eaten in salads by young women, or taken in the form of decoctions made from the juice or seeds.

Some years ago, what seems to be a confused and inverted version of this last belief was recorded at Richmond in Surrey, where it was stated that too many lettuces growing in a garden would stop a young wife having children. In 1951 the *Daily Mirror* printed some letters on this subject, in one of which (published on 20 July) the writer asked whether it was true that eating the plant was bad for brides. In another letter (26 July), a woman wrote: 'After being childless for a number of years, I was advised by a specialist to eat plenty of lettuce, and to give my husband some too. In less than six months, my first baby was on its way.' [Radford, 1961: 217]

Sleeplessness: eat lettuces for supper. [Taylor MSS, Ashby Norfolk]

Liberty cap (*Psilocybe semilanceata*). The liberty cap toadstool, also known as the magic mushroom, is occasionally collected for the hallucinatory drug psilocybin which it contains.

A former soldier who ran a sabre through his girlfriend's heart was jailed yesterday for manslaughter

The attack by farm worker Paul Albiston came after he had drunk a magic mushroom brew . . .

He had drunk only modestly—but went beserk after drinking his own brew . . . from liberty cap magic mushrooms. [*Daily Mail*, 5 June 1992]

It appears that the use of magic mushrooms is particularly prevalent in the Edinburgh area. In the south of the city:

I know of several locations where they collect magic mushrooms. There's the Hermitage, directly opposite the Klondyke Garden Centre; along Frogstone Road West, directly opposite the Princess Margaret Rose Hospital, in a walled field usually grazed by ponies; and off Braid Road, right along Blackford Hill in a field open to the public grazed by cows. You see three or four people looking for them for drug use. [Edinburgh, November 1993]

Other species of *Psilocybe* are widely used as hallucinogens in many parts of the world [see Guzmán, 1983: 33].

Lichens – *Parmelia caperata, P. saxatilis,* and *Xanthoria parietina* used in WELL-DRESSING; according to the DOCTRINE OF SIGNATURES *Usnea* spp. are recommended as being good for hair. Lichens were formerly valued as sources of DYES.

[North Wales:] the L[ichen] *omphalodes* [now known as *Parmelia omphalodes*] the natives steep in urine, and form a paste, which they dry in the sun; and with the addition of alum make a brown dye. This, and the *L. tartarius* [now *Ochrolechia tartarea*] are so abundant, that the poor people employ themsleves in gathering them for the use of the dry salters, at the low price of one penny per pound. They will, however, collect from twenty to thirty pounds a day. From these a beautiful dye called arcell, or archil, is prepared as follows:- The lichens, when dry, are placed under a large indented stone, with a circular motion, and bruised; they are then thrown into capacious vats, and mixed with lime and urine. Here they are permitted to remain six months, but stirred every day; and the materials thicken as the humid particles evaporate. In this part of the process the substance appears like mire; afterwards like the husks of grapes. When it has acquired the latter consistency, it is cut small, dried in a spacious room, sometimes reduced to powder, and packed in barrels for use; the most beautiful colours, such as purple, pink, greys, and pompadour, are obtained from the composition. [Evans, 1800: 197]

[Shetland:] old granny's scrottyie is the famous brown crotal used for Harris tweed. It gives a chestnut colour with almost the glow of purple . . .

These brown crotals (*Parmelia saxatilis, P. sulcata* and *P. omphalodes*) are the foremost natural dyestuffs of the north, some of the oldest, and simplest and most plentiful . . . they flourish like terrestrial seaweeds . . . it was a simple matter to gather a gallon panful. The old folks used a shell as a scraper . . . The only tricky part of the job was to spread the hanks of yarn evenly amongst the lichen gruel so that they came out all the same colour . . .

The grey-beard lichen *Ramalina scropulorum* [now *R. siliquosa*] is equally plentiful . . . this lichen is as simple to work as crotal but much milder in its effects. [Venables, 1956: 138]

To the present day Irish homespun is dyed with . . . crotal. Crotal is got growing on the rocks at the shore, but it is very hard to get, and there is a cure for BURNS and CUTS in it, and when it is made it is called goldenbrand. There are two kinds of crotal, one of which dyes green and the other kind dyes yellow. The crotal also grows on stones and on some kinds of trees. [IFCSS MSS 1112: 54, Co. Donegal]

Lightning – plants which are said to protect against it include BITING STONECROP, ELDER, HOUSELEEK, and ST JOHN'S WORT.

Lightnings – a Northumbrian name for POPPY.

Lilac

Lilac (*Syringa vulgaris*). Flowering lilac is widely believed to produce misfortune if picked or taken indoors.

> I remember visiting an old lady, about 1970, who had a lovely white lilac in her garden. Something she said about it being difficult for her to get into the garden made me offer to go and pick her some lilac, as it was in flower. She made all sorts of excuses to stop me, and finally said it was unlucky to bring it indoors. She was from Lancashire originally, but had lived in Worthing for very many years. [Worthing, West Sussex, February 1982]

> I've always heard that lilac's unlucky. It has such a strong scent; it's alright for us, but for people who are sick it's too much. Also bees don't like lilac. [Tunbridge Wells, Kent, March 1983]

> I always admired a lilac tree that was growing in a lady's garden near my home, and in the month of June it was alive with lovely purple flowers. One day I plucked up courage to ask the lady for a bunch of lilac flowers. She looked at me and she said 'Child, I'll give you a bunch of any other flower in the garden, but not lilac—it always bring bad luck.' [Ballaghadereen, Co. Roscommon, October 1984]

> My father told me people won't have lilac in the house because it was used for lining either coffins or graves, I'm not sure which. [Gorleston, Norfolk, April 1991]

When lilac is in flower it is a bad time to buy calves.

> I don't know if we have ever said for farming: 'Never buy calves when the lilac is out as it is the dearest time, and they are most likely to SCOUR.' This seems to be true, but I suppose the scour part comes in as cows are then on lush grass and the milk is richer. [Thorncombe, Dorset, May 1982]

In Wales:

> Lilac blossoms were supposed to indicate changes in the WEATHER. If they kept closed longer than usual, fine weather might be expected. If they opened rapidly rain would fall soon. If the lilacs quickly droop and fade, a warm summer will follow. Late flowering lilacs indicate a rainy season. [Trevelyan, 1909: 96]

Other flowers which are 'unlucky' when taken indoors include FORSYTHIA, HAWTHORN, and SNOWDROP.

Lily – see ARUM LILY, JERSEY LILY, MADONNA LILY, and ORANGE LILY; STAR OF BETHLEHEM was sometimes thought to be the biblical 'lily of the field'.

Lily of the valley (*Convallaria majalis*). Like many other white flowers, such as HAWTHORN, the lily of the valley is sometimes considered to cause misfortune if taken indoors.

Lily of the valley: lucky to grow in garden, but not to bring into house—reason not known. [Driffield, Humberside, March 1985]

It is unlucky to take lily of the valley into the house. [Dunkineely, Co. Donegal, February 1986]

In Sussex:

A very long-standing legend asserts that he [St Leonard] did actually live in St Leonard's Forest, near Horsham, and moreover that he once killed a dragon there. The battle was long and ferocious, and as a reward for Leonard's courage, Heaven granted that wild lilies of the valley would spring up wherever his BLOOD had sprinkled the earth. [Simpson, 1973: 34]

At Helston, in Cornwall, lily of the valley flowers are traditionally worn by participants in the annual Furry Dance, normally held on 8 May, unless that day falls on a Sunday or a Monday (the local market day).

At seven o'clock the Early Morning Dance, the first of the day, begins. This is for the young people who, like their elders later on, dance through the narrow streets and in and out of the gardens and houses, all of them wearing lilies of the valley, the particular flower of the festival. [Hole, 1976: 75]

Occasionally lily of the valley was used in folk medicine.

A neighbour of ours, probably in his late 70s or early 80s, described to me how his mother, who lived locally, used to treat CUTS and abrasions, including apparently quite serious ones, successfully by covering them with fresh lily of the valley leaves held in place by a bandage. [Girton, Cambridge, August 1989]

Lime (*Tilia × vulgaris*)

I am an Invernessian . . . the fruit of the lime tree was soft and sweet; it was known as hen's apples. [Solihull, West Midlands, March 1991]

I was taught by other children in my Dorset village seventy-odd years ago to produce an ear-splitting WHISTLE from a leaf of common lime. Leaves were at their best for this purpose in June, when fully developed but flexible. I recently demonstrated to impressed grandchildren that I have not lost this art. The leaf is held taut against the lips. [Sidmouth, Devon, December 1992]

Ling – see HEATHER.

Livelong – a name for ORPINE.

Live-long-love-long – a Sussex name for ORPINE.

Liver fluke – in sheep, treated using MALE FERN.

221

Lone bush

Lone bush or Fairy tree

> Except perhaps for raths, duns, and lisses—the fairy forts of legend—
> nothing in Ireland is more closely associated with the fairy folk than are
> certain types of tree. Wherever one goes in the country one does not have
> far to look to see some lone thorn bush growing in a field. The thorn bush
> is locally reputed to be under fairy protection. [Mac Manus, 1973: 51]

Although these trees are usually HAWTHORNS, other isolated trees are
sometimes considered to be lone bushes.

> In Ireland [the greatest rivals to hawthorn as lone bushes] are, in order of
> merit, the HAZEL, the BLACKTHORN, the bourtree—which is the English
> ELDER—the sally [SALLOW], the ALDER, the HOLLY, the BIRCH, the OAK—
> especially the twisted mountain oak—the BROOM, and the SCOTS FIR; also,
> to my personal knowledge, in at least two instances, the ROWAN or moun-
> tain ash. [Mac Manus, 1973: 52].

Numerous accounts of lone trees were contributed to the Irish Folklore Commission's archives as a result of its 1937-8 Schools' Folklore
Scheme.

> In the neighbourhood of my uncle's farm at Ballyduff, there is a lone bush
> growing in the middle of a big field belonging to Mrs Smythe.
> The people said it was not right to cut this bush. One day a man, who
> wanted to fence a gap in a ditch, came with his saw to cut it down.
> When he got inside the bark, he heard a voice saying, 'If you go farther
> with it you will be sorry,' and he kept cutting away. When he had it half
> cut blood began to shoot out, still he cut another little bit.
> Then he thought of himself and he fled leaving the saw stuck in the
> bleeding bush. This man died inside a week.
> The bush is there still and from the cut up is decayed, but the stump is
> quite sound. [IFCSS MSS 717: 103, Co. Meath]

> There is a field beyond there in Kilquiggan in which there is a rath. In the
> rath there was a bush (and it is said that it is unlucky to touch a bush which
> stands alone in a rath). Well this man cut the bush to use it for fencing and
> when he came home after cutting it he found his horse dead in the stable.
> [IFCSS MSS 919: 216, Co. Wicklow]

> A lone bush was growing on the [Ulster] Canal bank and when the com-
> pany was making the canal, a man was sent to cut the tree. He began cut-
> ting, but the chips would fly out and immediately fly back again. The man
> gave up the job.
> This bush was a great inconvenience to the company. When the horses
> came to it with the pull boats the men had to loose the cable and put it
> inside the bush, causing a great loss of time. The company offered £10 to
> anyone who would cut the bush, but no one accepted it, and the bush
> remains standing to this day. [IFCSS MSS 1020: 243, Co. Cavan]

> I have returned from a holiday in Donegal, Ireland, and spoke to an old
> aunt of mine, regarding 'fairy trees'. According to local tradition, one

should not interfere with these trees, as it is unlucky. She told me some years ago, when her sons were out playing, they brought home some things that looked like bean pods, which they found at the bottom of the fairy tree. My aunt opened one of them and found a little fairy man inside. He was like a little doll dressed in red cap, green jacket and trousers. She was very cross with the children and made them return to the tree all the strange beans which they had removed. She was extremely annoyed with the children, so much so that they never again repeated that offence. [Bracknell, Berkshire, August 1984; when visited in 1991 the tree was found to be a hawthorn]

Such stories, in which the fairies are actually seen, are rare. More common are accounts of lights being seen in the vicinity of lone bushes.

I have lived in London for almost 30 years, but I did live in Glenties, Co. Donegal, where I was born, and fairy trees are very common in that part.

I lived near a house that one of these trees was cut down to build and every man that lived in it went mad, but women came to no harm. I remember lights round the house at night, but no one lives there any more, so no lights appear. But these things are still going on over there. [London, September 1984]

This tale is reminiscent of English stories of hauntings which are supposed to have been put about by smugglers to discourage other people from venturing near their hiding-places. It seems probable that at least some lone bushes originated as markers of sites where people gathered for illicit activities. Such an explanation is perhaps hinted at in at least one nineteenth-century account:

There was such a tree on the lone mountain road between Feakle and Gort near the mearing of Clare and Galway. When a boy my attention was directed to it by the parson of Feakle, who said it was considered a fairy bush, and pointed out the worn spot under it where they danced. The fairies were said to have left the country during the famine years (1848–52) as the grass grew on the bare spot, but they returned afterwards. [Kinahan, 1888: 266]

Cf. HOLY THORN and MONUMENT BUSH.

Long purples – a plant mentioned in Shakespeare's *Hamlet*, usually identified as EARLY PURPLE ORCHID or LORDS AND LADIES.

Lords and ladies (*Arum maculatum*), also known as cuckoo pint and wild arum.

As a child I was told by a nurse-maid not to pick [lords and ladies], as adders got their poison from eating it. It was called in North Tawton [Devon], SNAKES' MEAT. In 1939 . . . a Portuguese lady told me that as a child she had been told not to pick the plant for the same reason, by a Portuguese nurse at Figerira de Foz, in Portugal. [Brown, 1952: 298]

Our parents would tell us that adders ate wild arum berries to obtain the poison for their fangs. The plant was always 'parson in the pulpit' or 'snakefood' down here, and of course despite the fact it wasn't true it served to remind us that the berries are poisonous to humans. [Barnstaple, Devon, May 1991]

It was believed in eastern Cambridgeshire that cuckoo pints, if brought into the house, gave TUBERCULOSIS to anyone who went near them. [Porter, 1969: 42]

When we were very young at school (and innocent) we used to say you (girls) should never touch a cuckoo pint; if you did you'd become pregnant. Where that silly idea started I do not know. [Thorncombe, Dorset, March 1982]

Presumably the association of lords and ladies with PREGNANCY is suggested by the somewhat phallic-shaped spadix of the flower, which led to the plant being considered to be an APHRODISIAC. In his play *Loves Metamorphosis*, published in 1601, John Lyly, who used the plant's older name of wake robin, wrote: 'They have eaten so much of wake robin, that they cannot sleep for love' [Grigson, 1987: 430].

Lords and ladies also had phallic associations in Warwickshire in the 1940s and 1950s.

Cuckoo pint in seed caused great mirth amongst children as this was nicknamed dog's dick and we all thought it very daring to look at one. [Aldershot, Hampshire, April 1994]

The leaves of lords and ladies, like those of the EARLY PURPLE ORCHID, are said to have become stained with Christ's BLOOD.

There is a popular superstition in North Wales that this plant grew at the foot of our Saviour's cross, in consequence of which the leaves became spotted . . . [There is] a beautiful allusion to this singular legend in a poem by . . . the late lamented Mrs Hemans.

> Yes, these deep inwrought marks,
> The villager will tell thee (and with voice
> Lowr'd in his true heart's reverend earnestness),
> And the flower's portion from th' atoning blood
> On Calvary shed. Beneath the cross it grew;
> And the vase-like hollow of the leaf,
> Catching from that dread shower of agony
> A few mysterious drops, transmitted thus
> Unto the groves and hills, their sealing stains,
> A heritage for storm or vernal shower
> Never to blow away.

[Bromfield, 1856: 529]

In the Cambridgeshire Fens lords and ladies was associated with St Withburga.

Old Fenmen in the last century . . . held the traditional belief that when the nuns came over from Normandy to build a convent at Thetford in Norfolk they brought with them the wild arum or cuckoo pint. When the monks of Ely stole the body of St Withburgha from East Dereham and paused, on their way back, to rest at Brandon, tradition has it that the nuns of Thetford came down to the riverside and covered the saint's body with the flowers. During the long journey down the Little Ouse of the barge bearing St Withburgha several of the lily flowers fell into the river, where they threw out roots. Within an hour they had covered all the banks as far as Ely with a carpet of blooms and, more remarkable still, these flowers glowed radiantly at night. Fenmen old at the turn of the century could recall that, when a new church was consecrated in the newly formed parish of Little Ouse, the Bishop of Ely in his sermon warned his congregation against all Romish superstitions and practices and stressed that there was no factual foundation to the story of St Withburgha and the lilies.

The pollen of the flowers does, in fact, throw off a faint light at dusk and when the Irish labourers came in large numbers to find work in the Fens during the famines in their own country during the last century, they named the lilies Fairy Lamps. The Fen lightermen had long called them Shiners. [Porter, 1969: 41]

St Withburgha's body on its barge covered with flowers is reminiscent of John Everett Millais' famous painting *Ophelia*, which is now in the Tate Gallery, London. This depicts Ophelia's death by drowning in Shakespeare's *Hamlet*, act V, where the coronet which Ophelia made from WILLOW branches and wild flowers is described:

> Therewith fantastic garlands did she make
> Of crow-flowers, NETTLES, DAISIES, and long purples
> That liberal shepherds give a grosser name,
> But our cull-cold maids do dead men's fingers call them.

Although many commentators agree that long purples were EARLY PURPLE ORCHIDS, at least one Shakespearean scholar has concluded:

> Shakespeare was thinking of the wild arum or cuckoo pint . . . judging both by the appearance of the flower itself, and by the consistency with which—at least from the thirteenth to the nineteenth centuries—it has been known, in England and elsewhere, by 'grosser' phallic names. [Wentersdorf, 1978: 417]

In the sixteenth century lords and ladies was valued as a source of the STARCH needed for the elaborate ruffs then worn by the aristocracy. In about the 1560s 'tubs and other utensils necessary for the preparation of starch which are nowadays banished to the laundries, were to be seen in the most aristocratic residences. Washing, drying, hanging out and ironing were performed in the presence of nobles as today are music and arts' [Prime, 1960: 37]. Gerard [1597: 686] observed:

The most pure and white starch is made of the rootes of Cuckowpint; but most hurtfull to the hands of the laundresse that hath the handling of it, for it choppeth, blistereth, and maketh hands rough and withall smarting.

Soon after this time the use of starch from lords and ladies began to decline, due to the severe blistering of its users' hands. However, in 1797 the making of lords and ladies starch was rediscovered. In that year the Royal Society of Arts offered its gold medal or thirty guineas for the discovery of a method of manufacturing starch from a material not used as food for man. This was won by Mrs Jane Gibbs of Portland, Dorset, whose

> starch, or arrow-root, as it is usually called, was prepared by her by crushing in a mortar the corms of the *Arum maculatum*, stirring the mass with water, and straining off the liquor, from which the fecula was allowed to subside; this was again washed and afterwards dried. She stated, and the statement is confirmed by the then Rector of the island, that she had in her possession 2 cwt of the starch; and was ready to supply any quantity of the same, whenever required, at 11d per lb. [*Phytologist*, 4: 1030, 1853]

In 1824 a visitor to Weymouth recorded that:

> in the island [of Portland] the roots [of lords and ladies] are dug in large quantities and when made into powder, many hundredweights are sold in Weymouth for starch and nourishment for invalids, and it is also used in pastry, soups, puddings, etc. [Prime, 1960: 50]

However, by the mid-nineteenth century only one elderly woman continued to make arrowroot.

> My informant tells me she obtains, on an average, 3lbs from a peck of corms; more in June, less in May. During the whole season she considers three dozen lbs to be a good average quantity to obtain; and for this she asks 1s 4d per lb. It is highly valued by the Portlanders, who say that it is good for sick people. [*Phytologist*, 4: 1031, 1853]

Lousewort (*Pedicularis sylvatica*)—known as bee-sookies or honey-sookies in Shetland, due to its 'nectar-filled flower-tubes' [Tait, 1947: 79]. Other Shetland names—sookies, and hinney flooer [Lerwick, March 1994]—seem to imply that children sucked the flowers for their nectar. Cf. WHITE DEADNETTLE.

Lukki-minnie's oo – a Shetland name for COTTON GRASS.

Lucy arnits, arnots, or **barnuts** – Scottish names for PIGNUT.

Lucy locket – a Derbyshire name for CUCKOO FLOWER.

Lumbago – cured using AGRIMONY and HOP.

Lungwort (*Pulmonaria* spp., especially *P. officinalis*), also known as liverwort. Lungwort has characteristic cream-coloured spots on its dark green leaves, and produces flowers which are pink when young and become blue as they age. These characteristics have led to the plant being given a large number of local names.

> Lungwort is associated with the Virgin Mary because it has blue and pink flowers—these two colours being the colours of the Virgin's clothes in medieval paintings. [Bratton, Wiltshire, April 1983]

> Dr T.W.N. Smart writes from Salisbury: 'I had an old woman weeding in my garden, and proposed to her to turn out a plant or two of it [lungwort], to which she strongly objected, and said, 'Do ee know Sir, what they white spots be?' 'No, I don't.' 'Why, they be the Virgin's Mary's Milk! so don't ee turn em out, for it would be very unlucky!' [Britten and Holland, 1886: 481]

The Monmouthshire name, Virgin Mary's milk-drops, and the Cheshire name, Lady's milksile [Britten and Holland, 1886: 481] provide indications of the wide distribution of this belief.

> At Osmington [Dorset], and no doubt at other places in our county, there is a survival of a sweet, simple, old-world piece of folklore about the spotted liver-wort. The cottagers like to have it in their gardens, and call it 'Mary's Tears'. The legend is that the spots on the leaves are the marks of the tears shed by ST MARY after the crucifixion. Farther . . . her eyes were blue as the fully opened flower, and by weeping the eyelids became red as the buds. [Udal, 1922: 17]

Good Friday plant, a south Somerset name for lungwort [Macmillan, 1922: 128] presumably refers to a similar legend.

> I was born in 1948 in Ferndown . . . the old local name for lungwort was Joseph and Mary. [Hamworthy, Dorset, June 1991]

> Years ago I was given (and still have) some *Pulmonaria officinalis* by relatives living at Kington, Herefordshire, near the Welsh border. They called it Spotted Mary. [Rhymney, Powys, March 1991]

> 'Do you know the real name of this plant? I've always called it Joseph's coat of many colours.' [Southfields, London, June 1985]

> When I was a child, in the 1950s, my grandmother grew lungwort as an ornamental in her garden at Mosterton, on the Dorset/Somerset border; the family knew it as Soldiers and Sailors. [Streatham, London, November 1991]

Lusmore – a County Antrim name for FOXGLOVE.

M

Madonna lily (*Lilium candidum*). In common with other white flowers (such as LILAC and SNOWDROPS), the Madonna lily is sometimes considered to be inauspicious.

> White lilies are a sign of a funeral. Whilst in Malaya during the early 1950s the local Chinese 'gentry' had to be dissuaded from sending this particular flower to the local British Military Hospital, as they upset so many people. [Chester, Cheshire, April 1984]

> The large white lilies that grow in cottage gardens mean death if brought into the house . . . My husband was going to the solicitor to make his will—a daunting task! and as he was driving along he could smell a strong smell that reminded him of funerals; he stopped his vehicle and took a look in the back, and there was a bunch of lilies that an aunt had given to me the night before—I did not want them in the house because of the smell—anyway he threw them over the hedge—and felt much happier. [Brize Norton, Oxfordshire, August 1992]

> A man came to the house and noticed a lily in the garden. Said it should not be brought into a house where there was an unmarried girl, or she would never get married. [Swansea, West Glamorgan, April 1984]

As its name suggests, the Madonna lily is a well-established emblem of St Mary the Virgin, and is particularly associated with Our Lady of Walsingham, who is usually depicted as seated and holding a lily. St Anthony of Padua is often depicted 'as a rather "soft" young man, carrying the child Jesus and a lily' [Attwater, 1970: 51].

Madonna lilies were valued for healing CUTS.

> Some of the older women of Great and Little Waltham still use the petals of madonna lilies on bad cuts and say they heal quickly. [Little Waltham, Essex, January 1978]

> When we had a cut or wound we used to put something out of a bottle on, it was a green glass bottle; we were told it was lily leaves in brandy. This happened in 1911, as I am 87 years old now. [Stowmarket, Suffolk, February 1989]

In Dorset the price of WHEAT could be foretold by examining Madonna lilies: 'a . . . calculation is made from the number of the blossoms as shown on the majority of its spikes, each blossom representing one shilling per bushell' [Udal, 1922: 257].

Magic mushroom – see LIBERTY CAP.

Maidens' hair – a Gloucestershire name for LADY'S BEDSTRAW.

Malaria – see AGUE.

Male fern (*Dryopteris filix-mas*, agg.)

Male fern is used as medicine for cattle and sheep. The roots are boiled and strained and given to animals as a cure for fluke. [IFCSS MSS 232: 129, Co. Roscommon]

Some flockmasters used to treat their LIVERfluked sheep with a weekly dose of 4oz of salt or a monthly treatment of male fern. [Barrington, 1984: 50]

Mallow (*Malva sylvestris*), also known as marsh mallow.

As children playing in the fields we would eat the 'fruit' of wild mallows—the seeds—and call them cheeses. [Christchurch, Dorset, May 1991]

[Around Burghead, Morayshire] biscuities were the little seed-heads from a mauve-flowered plant, which we ate, but never knew its name! [Edinburgh, December 1991]

Willoughton [Lincolnshire] . . . 'Marshmallow' used to be grown in gardens because it was so useful in cases of BLOOD POISONING. 'Pancake' is another name that it is known by owing to its 'pie'-shaped seeds. (This is the common mallow). [Rudkin, 1936: 27]

SPRAINS and stiff joints: a good remedy for these complaints was to boil marsh mallow and to rub well into the affected places. [IFCSS MSS 350: 182, Co. Cork].

Get marsh mallows and boil them, then bathe the place where you have RHEUMATISM and it will cure it. [IFCSS MSS 700: 121, Co. Meath].

My aunt, in Notts in the 1920s, used to send us out to gather the leaves of mallow; she made a wonderful ointment—but no one ever knew the recipe. This was useful for SORES, grazes and BRUISES. I got in touch with my aunt's daughter (well over eighty) and she remembered her mother making it when she was a child. She's sure she simmered the leaves with lard until it turned pale green, then it was strained and put into jars. She tells me a similar salve was made using ELDER flowers. [Oban, Argyll, October 1990]

A large colony [of common mallow] around a farmyard at Llanfaredd, Radnor—said by the owner to have been used as a leaf poultice to cure sprains of horses' legs. [Llandrindod Wells, Powys, September 1991]

I was born and lived as a child in Crowborough which is in Sussex although right on the Kent border . . . Mallow was used by the family as a cure for CUTS. An uncle whilst in Australia was bitten by a snake (species unknown!) and swore he had recovered through using mallow on it, whilst a cousin who jumped onto an upturned nail with the wound turning bad was nursed by my grandfather with mallow on the wound, which healed beautifully to the surprise of the doctor. [Pershore, Worcestershire, October 1991]

[In Cornwall] when we were young mother . . . bathed our eyes with the liquid from the boiled leaves of mallow, if we had any eye complaints. [Calpe, Alicante, Spain, November 1991]

See also TREE MALLOW.

Mandrake (*Mandragora officinarum*)

There used to be this chemist—well pharmacist—in Aberystwyth—he was the top chemist in the town—who had a mandrake plant in his garden. When he died, about ten years ago, he bequeathed it to the College Botanic Garden in his will. Quite a party of people gathered to remove the plant—my father was one of them—but they hesitated before digging it up, because it was supposed to be unlucky. They joked about getting a starving dog to pull it up, but the College gardener said he didn't worry. so he dug it up. He did so, and he is still alive and happy. [Kew, Surrey, July 1984]

In classical times there was a great deal of superstition surrounding the digging of mandrake roots. One of these was that the root should be attached to a starving dog to pull it up when enticed by having meat thrown towards it. It is probable that such ideas were invented by herb-gatherers who wanted to protect their livelihoods. [Stearn, 1976: 290]

In England roots of WHITE BRYONY were commonly used as a substitute for mandrake.

Mangel wurzel – see MANGOLD.

Mango (*Mangifera indica*). Town-dwellers often observe pieces of string hung with leaves placed above the front door of Hindu homes. Traditionally these leaves, which are put in place when a wedding is celebrated, should be of mango, but in the British Isles substitutes such as LAUREL or spotted laurel (*Aucuba japonica*) are frequently used.

Villagers in India believe that the mango tree puts forth fresh green leaves at the birth of a son. So a tradition is being perpetuated and mango leaves are festooned across the doorways of a house where a son is born. The plant being considered auspicious, its leaves are also hung over the doorways of a house where marriage ceremonies are performed, perhaps in the hope that the young married couple would beget a son. [Gupta, 1971: 61]

Mangold (*Beta vulgaris*, cv.). Although lanterns made by children at Hallowe'en time can be made of TURNIPS or swedes (or in recent years PUMPKINS), the large, orange roots of the mangold are preferred. The

top of the mangold is cut off to form a lid, the inside hollowed out, and holes cut, usually to make a face. Then a candle is fixed inside, and usually a string is attached so that the lantern can be carried.

In parts of the country where Hallowe'en was not traditionally celebrated, the mangold lanterns—commonly known as punkies—provided light on Bonfire Night, 5 November.

> In the Wiltshire village of my boyhood . . . we had a communal bonfire on the high hill that overlooks the village. We ran about with blazing besoms that had been dipped in tar. We made lanterns of hollowed-out mangolds or turnips with grotesque faces and stumps of candle fixed inside. [Whitlock, 1978: 145]

> [In west Dorset in the 1950s] on Guy Fawkes' Night a bonfire of hedge-trimmings was lit and fireworks let off. On the day before the fire my brother and I would each make a punky by placing a piece of candle inside a hollowed-out mangold on which a face had been carved. These were proudly carried to the bonfire in the evening. [Vickery, 1978: 156]

At Hinton St George, in Somerset, the children carry punkies around the village on the last Thursday in October. According to local tradition punkies

> were first used by the worried wives of Hinton to look for their husbands who had gone to Chiselborough fair and got drunk.
>
> The women hollowed out mangolds and made them into lanterns to search for their wayward husbands in the dark. [*Pulman's Weekly News*, 31 October 1972]

According to an 85-year-old local woman interviewed in 1988, in her childhood:

> We used to go to the big houses, knock on their doors and say 'give us a candle, give us a light' and they used to give us a penny or a piece of candlewax, which we used a lot in those days . . . At that time Punky Nights were not the organised affairs as they are now—the village children just got together and went off on their own. [*Chard & Ilminster News*, 9 November 1988]

In recent years the children have formed part of an organized procession.

> We went to Hinton St George for Punky Night this year. We got there at about 6.30 p.m. There were a few people standing along the streets, so we wandered along to the village hall, where there were lots of people. The children carrying the punkies were very small; one child had a punky made from a swede, but the others all carried mangolds—the designs included dragons, primroses, and houses. They stood around for about threequarters of an hour, then a tractor pulling a decorated trailer drew up. On the trailer were a punky king and queen, and

prince and princess—all very young children, and a man playing a guitar. On the front of the trailer the words of the punky ditty were written out:

It's punky night tonight,
It's punky night tonight . . .

The procession was formed, led by a man dressed in a white smock and top hat who rang a bell, followed by the tractor and trailer, and the children carrying their punkies. There were so many adults looking after the small children that you couldn't really see the punkies. You couldn't really hear the singing either. They went all round the village, knocking on some doors, and collecting . . . Then they returned to the hall for a social gathering at which the punkies were judged. [Thorncombe, Dorset, November 1982]

These days, the whole event is staged for the children of Hinton St George, who get a Christmas party, a summer coach trip and a sports day out of it and this year it made a £125 profit—the best for several years. [*Pulman's Weekly News*, 31 October 1988]

Marigold (*Calendula officinalis*). Formerly known in Wiltshire as MEASLE-flower:

The dried flowers having some local reputation as a remedy. Children, however, have an idea that they may catch the complaint from handling the plant. [Dartnell and Goddard, 1894: 101]

Marigold tea for measles: 1 doz. heads of marigolds in full flower, 1 pint boiling water; let it stand, give to child in wineglass three times a day. [Taylor MSS, Yoxford, Suffolk].

See also AFRICAN MARIGOLD.

Markery – an East Anglian name for GOOD KING HENRY.

Marlie – a Shetland name for EELGRASS.

Marram grass (*Ammophila arenaria*)

Marram grass—bent—used for high quality ROPES and BASKET-making. [Lerwick, Shetland, March 1994]

Marsh mallow – a widespread name for common MALLOW (also a book-name for *Althaea* spp.).

Marsh marigold (*Caltha palustris*), also known as kingcup. In Ireland and on the Isle of Man, the golden flowers of marsh marigold were used as a source of protection on MAY EVE (30 April).

As a 4-year-old in Portaferry, County Down, (1910!) I remember seeing cottage roofs strewn with 'May' on the appropriate day . . . it was not HAWTHORN but marsh marigold. [Charlbury, Oxfordshire, January 1991]

Over 30 years ago, when I was a small boy, it was a tradition here in our village to gather kingcups from our local meadow on 30 April in late afternoon. Then before nightfall I put a kingcup in the letterbox of each house in the village. This supposedly kept evil fairies from entering the house before May Day, 1 May. Many people, especially the elderly, were very superstitious concerning this custom, and would remind me beforehand not to forget to pay them a visit. This was also a good source of a bit of pocket money as some people were very pleased to receive their May flowers as they were called. I carried on this custom into my teens. [Carnlough, Co. Antrim, January 1989]

It was the kingcup or marsh marigold that was most sought after as a source of protection against witches. One of its Manx names was *Lus y Voaldyn*, the Herb of Beltain (though it was commonly called the *blughtan*), and as it was essential that it should be among the flowers gathered on May Eve, the first signs of its flowering or 'breaking' were anxiously looked for. A farmer in Kirk German, who kept a diary over a number of years in the late eighteenth century, noted down the breaking of the blughtan each spring. Sometimes it was late, and there was a growing note of anxiety in his April entries: 'The blughtan not broke yet,' 'No sign of the blughtan breaking.' Then at last, almost at the end of the month, 'The blughtan broke'—but only just in time for its flowers like small golden suns to add their brilliance to the May rites. [Killip, 1975: 173]

Cf. PRIMROSE.

In south-west Wiltshire the marsh marigold was sometimes known as BULRUSHES, 'from some nursery legend that Moses was hidden among its large leaves' [Dartnell and Goddard, 1894: 19].

Marsh samphire (*Salicornia* spp.). Although species of *Salicornia* are commonly given the name glasswort in books on the British flora, people who live along parts of the coast of England usually call them samphire, samfer, or samper. Samphire has long been gathered as food.

Sampion . . . a corruption of Samphire—Chesh[ire], about Runcorn, Helsby, and the neighbourhood, where it is hawked about by cart-loads for pickling. [Britten and Holland, 1886: 414]

Villagers living near the river [Humber] gather plants for their own use. The plants are either boiled and served with butter, or pickled. Marsh samphire is served in at least one local pub, but as far as I know it is not marketed in these parts. [Hull, Humberside, May 1988]

There is a plant on the east coast of Northumberland called samphire or samfer which is picked and either eaten raw after being washed in seawater, or boiled and pickled in vinegar. It is a succulent and the way you eat it is to pull it through your teeth to remove the tough stringy stem, and it is delicious. I have never seen it sold in shops though. [Hexham, Northumberland, May 1988]

In East Anglia and parts of Lincolnshire samphire has traditionally been harvested for sale in local markets.

> I have been buying samphire in the markets of King's Lynn annually for over 40 years, more recently in Cambridge Market and in France. [Letter from Cambridge, in *The Times*, 29 July 1988]

In June 1990 a fish stall in King's Lynn market, Norfolk, offered samphire for sale, labelled:

> Samphire is an edible seaweed
> Wash then boil for 15 mins.
> Eat by pulling the green from
> the roots, dip in vinegar or
> butter, nice with cold meat
> and brown bread and butter.
> 70p per lb.

> [Personal observation]

In recent years samphire has enjoyed wider popularity as a delicacy, having been served at the wedding reception of the Prince and Princess of Wales in August 1981, and now being sold by up-market fishmongers around the country.

Samphire
Sea-weed
£1.20 ½ lb.
[Guildford, Surrey,
personal observation, June 1990]

Samphire Grass
75p a ¼lb.
[Chichester, West Sussex,
personal observation, August 1991]

However, it seems that this delicacy may be in danger, for in June 1991 it was ruled in King's Lynn that under the Wildlife and Countryside Act of 1981 the collectors who uprooted samphire without the landowner's consent risked prosecution, although at least one major landowner along the Norfolk coast is willing to support the collectors' traditional rights:

> The National Trust owns a seven-mile stretch of coast from Stiffkey to Salthouse. 'Eating samphire is an age-old tradition,' said Joe Read, the trust warden. 'It is such an abundant crop and only [such] a relatively small amount is taken that we do not think it much of a problem at present. Clearly if it became a big commercial operation we would have the power to stop it.' [*The Times*, 25 June 1991]

Marsh woundwort (*Stachys palustris*), formerly known as clown's all-heal.

> [c.1683:] Lady Swan of Southfleet in Kent hath cur'd many deplorable and dismal sores in the legs and other parts with this made into an Ointment with Hog's Grease. [Newton MSS]

Mary's tears – a Dorset name for LUNGWORT.

Mass bush

Mass bushes are still treated with reverence in Ireland. These are usually HAWTHORNS and are said to have been places where Mass was celebrated by hunted priests in the period of Catholic repression. The Bush Road near Mullinscross and Stabannon in mid Louth is so named for that reason. In the garden of Mr Ambrose Congreve in County Waterford there is a Mass Bush, a hawthorn, which local men are reluctant even to prune. This tree has been carefully tended and protected over the years and is a prominent feature in the garden although it looks a little incongruous in the more exotic surroundings. [Synnott, 1979: 42]

Cf. St Newlina's FIG tree, LONE BUSH, and MONUMENT BUSH.

Mat grass (*Nardus stricta*)

I used to see doormats made . . . from flat sods of mat grass (*Nardus stricta*) in northwest Yorkshire, some sixty years ago. [Teulon-Porter, 1956: 91]

May – a name commonly given to blossoming HAWTHORN; also given to MARSH MARIGOLD in Ireland.

May-birchers

In Cheshire in the earlier part of the nineteenth century were groups known as May Birchers, who . . . coming to a house after dark on MAY EVE, they would quietly leave a branch of some tree or shrub on the doorstep, to be discovered by the inhabitants next morning; this conveyed a message, complimentary or insulting, according to the plant chosen. The code was based on rhyme; NUT for a slut, PEAR if you're fair, PLUM if you're glum, BRAMBLE if you ramble, ALDER (pronounced 'owler') for a scowler, and GORSE for the whores. There was also HAWTHORN, which did not rhyme with anything but counted as a general compliment. [Simpson, 1976: 148]

May Eve (30 April) – associated plants include MARSH MARIGOLD, PRIMROSE, and ST JOHN'S WORT

May flower – an Irish name for MARSH MARIGOLD and PRIMROSE, also given to both CUCKOO FLOWER and marsh marigold on the Isle of Man.

May garlands. The custom of children taking around garlands on May Day was formerly widespread in England.

The May garland is a summer emblem of very great antiquity, which has given to May Day the secondary name of Garland Day. It has always varied considerably in form and shape, ranging from a simple bunch of flowers tied to the top of a long staff, or a pole wreathed with flowers, to the elaborate double-hoop garland, densely covered with spring flowers of every kind, or the less usual pyramid, also thickly covered by blossoms, and usually very tall, often rising to a height of 5 or 6 ft. Sometimes there is a May Doll seated in the centre of a hoop garland, or fixed upon the front of a pyramid. [Hole, 1975: 58]

Children carried these garlands around the village, outlying farms, and big houses; the more wealthy members of the community were expected to donate money to the carriers. An account from the carriers' point of view is given in Flora Thompson's *Lark Rise* (1939: chapter 13).

An account from another vantage point is provided in the memoirs of Princess Alice, Duchess of Gloucester (b. 1901). At Boughton, Northamptonshire, one of her childhood homes:

> Four villages stand at the edge of the park . . . From each of them, on May 1, would come in turn separate groups of children, the girls garlanded and the boys holding bunches of spring flowers as they carried their May Queen on a throne smothered in blooms and leafy branches. After singing songs they would dance around the maypole and then to the delight of all, we showered them with well-polished pennies, thrown as far as possible to cause the greatest chase and scramble. [Gloucester, 1983: 34]

Garlands continue to appear in one or two places, but they rarely appear on May Day and, although carried by children, are usually made by mature women. At Abbotsbury, Dorset, two garlands are paraded around the village early in the evening of 13 May. In 1983:

> On the evening of 12 May suitable flowers were gathered and placed in water in an outhouse ready for the following day. Work on decorating the garlands started at about 2 p.m. on the 13th. The woman, aged about 35, working on one of the garlands explained that as they would not be taken around the village until 5.30 this year they were being decorated in the afternoon, instead of on the previous evening, when they used to be decorated. As Abbotsbury no longer has its village school, the local children are not allowed a day off, so the garlands have to be displayed after school hours.

> It takes 3–4 hours to decorate each garland. The frames are made, by a local maker of lobster-pots, from rigid blue plastic tubing, the older wooden frames having been abandoned in 1982. The frames first have a covering of ELDER leaves tied to them. Then generous bunches of flowers—each bunch containing flowers of only one species—are tied on to cover the leaves. About four decorators work on the garlands, starting at the top of each garland, so that the stalks of each bunch of flowers are covered by the heads of lower bunches.

> Two garlands are made. One contains wild flowers: BLUEBELLS, COW PARSLEY, COWSLIPS, pendulous sedge, PRIMROSES (only available when it is a late season—'only once or twice since I've been making them'), and a few cultivated flowers—LILAC, APPLE blossom and flowering currant. The other contains cultivated flowers: LILAC, STOCKS, WALLFLOWERS,

rhododendron, camellias, and pieris foliage, some of them donated by the owner of the Abbotsbury Sub-tropical Botanical Gardens.

At about 4.45 p.m. there was a panic when it was discovered that there were insufficient flowers for the wild garland, so more cow parsley and bluebells had to be gathered. The decorating was completed by about five o'clock, when the decorators and watching children took a break before reassembling about twenty minutes later. The children, aged from 8 to about 15, were split into two groups each of about eight, each group taking a garland. They were told to call on every house, and instructed not to take their bicycles with them (apparently they had upset some householders by doing this in 1982). The children were left to their own devices, with no adult accompanying either party. The reaction of people whose houses were visited varied: some people simply passed over a coin or two without taking any interest in the garlands, others examined the garlands closely, and a few were actually waiting for the garlands to be brought around. At least one woman, an apparently wealthy individual who had recently had a house built in the village, lectured the children severely and refused to give anything unless they could prove that the proceeds would be given to a worthwhile charity. Donations varied from a couple of pence to a couple of pounds.

The children took it in turn to carry the garlands, and, although the two garlands took slightly different routes, in theory at least each house in the village was visited by both garlands. The children appeared to be very proud of their tradition, which they claimed was very old, and only carried on in Abbotsbury. It was described as a 'tradition to bless the sea'. Although Abbotsbury garlands are mentioned in most books on traditional customs, they do not appear to attract a significant amount of outside attention; only three 'outsiders' appeared to be present.

The knocking on doors continued for about three hours, during which time the garlands became increasingly limp and dishevelled. It was possible to trace the garlands' progress around the village by following the trails of fallen blooms.

It is said that the garlands used to be thrown into the sea, but since the plastic frames were introduced the garlands are now left in the churchyard. The present vicar of the village does not approve of the tradition, and the village children appeared to be divided into two groups: one group of 'respectable' children who went to choir practice—'they're paid to go', the others explained, and a less 'respectable' group who carried around the garlands.

At the end of the evening the collected money was shared between the children who had accompanied the garlands. [Personal observation]

Although these garlands survive only at Abbotsbury, they were formerly made at other Chesil coast fishing villages [Robson MSS, 1988: 217–80].

Mazeerie

At Bampton in Oxfordshire garlands are carried around the village early in the morning on the Late Spring Bank Holiday. In this locality the garlands have become loosely associated with the better known morris dancing, which formerly took place on Whit Monday and later moved to the Bank Holiday. Although the garlands are carried by children, and they are judged with a prize being awarded to the best, they are made by adults. As an observer in 1984 put it: 'there was the usual number of garlands, made by the usual number of old ladies.'

Mazeerie – a Lincolnshire name for MEZEREON.

Meadow foxtail grass (*Alopecurus pratensis*)

In north Derbyshire in the 1950s, the flowers would be stripped off the stalk of meadow foxtail grass, leaving the stem with the floret stalks. This would be quietly twiddled into the hair of the child sitting in the desk in front. A swift yank would speedily remove all the hair attached. Very painful. [Llandrindod Wells, Powys, September 1991]

Talking of Chinese haircuts brought back painful memories of my War-wickshire preparatory school in the early Forties. In my experience it was invariably Meadow Foxtail that was used. It produces flower heads in time to function as an instrument of torture at the start of summer term, deployed on heads intently watching cricket. [Winchester, Hampshire, September 1991]

As a child, evacuated to Elgin, Scotland, during World War II . . . one grass we would not even pick was the meadow foxtail, *Alopecurus praten-sis*—because it was said to be infested with fleas! [Stevenage, Hertford-shire, January 1993]

Meadowsweet (*Filipendula ulmaria*), also known as queen of the meadow.

Our border matrons say that, if smelled too much, the Queen-of-the-Meadow will cause people to take fits. [Johnston, 1853: 59]

Meadowsweet is regarded as a fatal flower in Wales. There is an old story to the effect that if a person falls asleep in a room where many of these flowers are placed death is inevitable . . . it is considered quite dangerous for anybody to fall asleep in a field where it is to be found in abundance. [Trevelyan, 1909: 96]

Eastbourne, 1941 (wartime). I was a keen collector of wild flowers at that time and brought back large armfuls of exceptionally fine sprays of 'Queen of the Meadow', also known as 'Meadowsweet', I believe. I brought it into the house where my mother and I were staying as guests, and met our hostess, a woman of fifty or more (unpleasant, petty-minded and very violent R.C. convert and very superstitious) who promptly told me not to bring it into the house. 'Why ever not ?' Whereupon the woman nearly became crazy, she was screaming at me in the end. Ghastly bad luck would descend on the house if I did; I thought it too foolish for words and tried to persist in bringing it in. She was beside herself and screamed that she would throw my mother and me out if I did. In the end my mother intervened and begged me to leave it outside. I kept one bit secretly for my collection and left the rest outside, frightful waste. The silly woman calmed down but talked of it for the rest of the evening, as far as I could see she was afraid of general disaster rather than death hitting the house. [Kensington, London, January 1983]

Although meadowsweet has all the characteristics of flowers which are considered to be 'unlucky'—a sweet scent, creamy-coloured flowers, and small petals which fall, creating a mess—records of it being banned from being taken indoors are vague and few. Further evidence of meadowsweet being considered inauspicious occurs in a name given to the flower by a 79-year-old Nottingham woman in October 1985:

As children we always called meadowsweet 'old man's pepper'.

The 'old man' in plant-names is generally assumed to be the devil.

In the Retford district of Lincolnshire:

Meadowsweet they used to smoke like TOBACCO. They dried out the flowers. [Cottam MSS, 1989: 50]

Measle-flower – a Wiltshire name for MARIGOLD.

Measles – cured using, or caught by handling, MARIGOLD; treated using COWSLIP, MISTLETOE, and RED DEAD-NETTLE.

Meldi – a Shetland name for CORN SPURREY.

Mercury – a name for GOOD KING HENRY.

Mezereon (*Daphne mezereum*). In Willoughton, Lincolnshire, the berries of 'mazeerie' (mezereon) were taken and swallowed like pills as a cure for PILES [Rudkin, 1936: 26].

Michaelmas – associated plants include APPLE, CARROT, and CRAB APPLE.

Midsummer men – a name for ORPINE.

Midsummer's Eve – associated plants include ORPINE and ST JOHN'S WORT.

Milkies – a Morayshire name for WHITE CLOVER.

Milkwort (*Polygala vulgaris*) – known as *herbe de paralysie* on Guernsey, and used to prevent or cure paralysis and strokes; see TORMENTIL.

Mimosa (*Acacia dealbata*)

> My mother was very superstitious about flowers: May blossom, LILAC and mimosa . . . The mimosa was considered a forewarning of disaster, as I found out to my cost when I purchased a bunch out of my first week's earnings and it was promptly thrown into the dust bin (much to my disgust), but I never could find out why. [Bayswater, London, July 1983]

Minerac herb – a Co. Offaly name for SELF-HEAL.

Mint (*Mentha spicata*)

> I've been told by many an old lady that when you leave your home to go on holiday mint should be picked from the garden and put in water and placed in a room. This apparently is supposed to keep the air fresh while the house is closed up. I don't know how true this is, I've never tried it. [Churchdown, Gloucestershire, January 1988]

> A vase of mint in the kitchen keeps away flies. [Rushmere St Andrew, Suffolk, February 1989]

> We put mint on windowsills to keep flies from the house. [Barnstaple, Devon, May 1991]

> When visiting a friend in Aldershot a few years ago, she told me that for many years she suffered from hayfever. One year when it was very bad a gypsy called at the house and after looking round the garden said: 'You have the cure here. Pick some fresh mint every day and put it in a muslin bag. Put it in your pillow and inhale the scent during sleep. Also wear some during the day.' My friend did so and was permanently cured. [UCL EFS MSS M22, St Leonard's on Sea, East Sussex, October 1963]

Miscarriage – prevented using RASPBERRY.

Mistletoe (*Viscum album*). Pliny the Elder (AD 23–79) recorded:

> The Druids hold nothing more sacred than mistletoe and a tree on which it is growing, provided it is Valonia oak . . . Mistletoe is, however, rather seldom found on Valonia oak, and when it is discovered it is gathered with great ceremony, and particularly on the sixth day of the moon (which for these [Gallic] tribes constitutes the beginning of the months and the years) . . . Hailing the moon in a native word that means 'healing all things,' they prepare a ritual sacrifice and banquet beneath a tree and bring up two white bulls, whose horns are bound for the first time on this occasion. A priest arrayed in white vestments climbs the tree and with a golden sickle cuts down the mistletoe, which is caught in a white cloak. Then finally they kill the victims, praying to God to render his gift propitious to those on whom he has bestowed it. They believe that mistletoe

given in drink will impart fertility to any animal that is barren, and that it is an antidote for all poisons. [Rackham, 1968: 549]

Largely as a result of this passage, more nonsense has been written about mistletoe than any other British plant.

As neither tree nor shrub, mistletoe symbolises freedom: this might explain the custom of kissing under the mistletoe, an act of liberation from usual restraint . . . it was the feminine to the masculine of the oak. At the winter solstice it symbolised new life. [Caption in an exhibition '150 Years of the Christmas Card' at the Victoria & Albert Museum, London, November 1993–January 1994]

Because of its Druid, pagan associations mistletoe is traditionally banned from churches.

Mistletoe has been banned from a church this Christmas because, says the vicar, it is 'a pagan decoration'.

But—a sprig will hang in the vicar's home.

The ban announced by the Revd H.R. Joyce applies to St Thomas's Church, Derby.

He has invited parishioners to decorate the church with HOLLY, but has told them: 'Mistletoe is a pagan decoration and under no circumstances should it be hung in a Christian church.'

He explained yesterday: 'Mistletoe has strong connections with the Druids, who were the pagan leaders of the Ancient Britons.' He added: 'I have nothing against mistletoe in the home—I enjoy kissing pretty girls under it as much as anyone else.' [*Daily Mirror*, 8 December 1958]

[Basingstoke area, Hampshire:] mistletoe—a pagan plant, so must never be taken into a church. [Maida Hill, London, December 1982]

However, mistletoe usually finds a ready sale for decorating homes at Christmas.

[Mistletoe] is carryed many miles to set up in houses about Christmas time, when it is adorned with a white glistening berry. [Coles, 1656: 41]

Mistletoe grows very freely in the HAWTHORNS and other trees in Grimsthorpe Park, Lincolnshire, though it is not to be found elsewhere in the neighbourhood. People have been accustomed to come from long distances, especially from London and Manchester, in order to gather the mistletoe, and have brought with them carts to carry off the spoil. Besides thus committing a trespass, they disturbed the red deer in the park, and greatly damaged the trees. Lady Willoughby de Eresby has, therefore, been compelled to protect her property by employing additional watchers in the park during the month before Christmas, in order to prevent the mistletoe from being interfered with and stolen. During this past December 14 extra watchers were engaged. [*N & Q*, 5 ser. 5: 126, 1876]

Mistletoe . . . is available at greengrocers this Christmas at 10p a sprig, but it is imported in cauliflower crates from France and Belgium.

Mr Peter Heyes, of the fruit and vegetable wholesellers, the House of Heyes, expects to have handled 1,000 crates by Saturday, when as far as he is concerned this most seasonal of trades finishes.

He says the best comes from Belgium, where the foliage is deeper green and the berries larger and more numerous. [*The Times,* 11 December 1979]

Formerly—at least earlier in the twentieth century in northern England—the name mistletoe was also given to a form of Christmas decoration.

[I'm now 70 years old] in addition to the Christmas tree, my grandfather made what he called a 'mistletoe'. This consisted of two wooden hoops (obtained from the grocer—taken from a butter cask, no prepacked butter then). The two hoops were criss-crossed and tied in position, and coloured papers, greenery and small presents were added and all finished off with a bow, holly berries and mistletoe. [Corbridge, Northumberland, January 1993]

One of the attractions of hanging mistletoe up indoors is the custom of kissing beneath it. This custom is said to be unique to Britain or, at least, to have originated in Britain.

A man's objection to his wife being kissed under the mistletoe on Christmas Eve in a public house bar in Staines Road, Hounslow, it was stated today at Brentford, ended in a fight among the customers, in which two women were injured and taken to hospital. [*Star,* 21 January 1947]

Covent Garden traders report that this year's sales of mistletoe are the worst for years. One trader said: 'It's a different sort of age. When they strip off naked in Leicester Square you can see why. They don't need mistletoe today.' [*Guardian,* 20 December 1972]

For about the last week the girls and boys in my [4th year, secondary school] class have been chasing each other around with mistletoe. If a girl catches a boy she gives him a kiss. [Streatham, London, December 1990]

What should be done to mistletoe once the Christmas period is over varies.

[Mistletoe] should always be kept hanging till the Christmas following. It is believed around the Chudleigh district that it will prevent the house from being struck by LIGHTNING. At Ottery they say it will assure that the house will never be without bread. [Brown, 1955: 355]

[Moretonhampstead:] Never take down mistletoe until next Christmas. [Brown, 1972: 267]

[Eccleshill, Bradford, 1962:] A piece of mistletoe must be kept to be burned under the SHROVE TUESDAY pancakes.

[Conisbrough:] A piece of mistletoe must be kept from one year to the next because while mistletoe stays in the house love also stays. [McKelvie MSS, 1963: 176]

Mistletoe . . . kept to be burnt on the fire when cooking pancakes on Shrove Tuesday. A sprig kept hanging on the beam until next Christmas 'to keep the witches out'. [Addingham Moorside, West Yorkshire, April 1993]

In 1856 a German visitor to Conway asked a woman living in the decayed remains of a sixteenth-century mansion if she was ever afraid of ghosts:

'Iesu!' cried the woman, 'no, we don't think of that!' But the schoolmaster showed me the fireplace into which, according to the custom of the Welsh, a bunch of mistletoe had been stuffed for the summer, still possessing the aura of secret powers from the time of the Druids. 'That'll keep all evil spirits away,' he said. The woman smiled, and looked as if she was a little ashamed in my presence. [Linnard, 1985: 34]

Although some Devon people believed that mistletoe indoors ensured sufficient food and prevented the house from being struck by lightning, other people in the county regarded the plant with caution.

[According to a servant maid in Torquay:] mistletoe is the poison of the apple tree. It comes up out of the roots. That is why when there are many apple trees together, they don't grow well unless there's mistletoe on them. [Chope, 1926: 110]

[Newton Abbot:] If you plant mistletoe and it grows, your daughters will never marry. [Brown, 1959: 200]

In traditional medicine:

[c.1683:] in Essex . . . about little Bentley and Tendrill in Tendrill Hundred where People give it to Cows after they have newly calv'd to ym cleanse well. [Newton MSS].

Mistletoe from a hawthorn bush for MEASLES; this was made into tea (horrible). [Yeovil, Somerset, October 1975]

Mock orange (*Philadelphus coronarius*)

My other story concerns an elderly patient in this little nursing home [in Eastbourne, Sussex in 1941], a very sick old lady who had been in India nearly all her life as the wife of a soldier or official. I used to go and talk to her . . . However, I put my foot wrong with her as I marched into her room with a bunch of Philadelphus, vulgarly and erroneously known as Syringa, hoping it would cheer her up. 'Take that out of my room !' was all the welcome I got ! 'But it has such a lovely smell' I wailed. 'That's just what I can't stand,' she shrieked. 'If you leave it outside the door I'll tell you why I don't like it.' The story was that during her days in India

Hindus put Philadelphus all over the dead bodies before they were cremated. On account of the heat corpses were burnt very soon after death, but in the really hot season four or five hours, which is what it took to arrange a cremation, often wasn't quick enough, and the mock orange's powerful scent masked the smell of decay. This old lady associated this lovely flower with death, which was a shame. It could be that she had, in fact, smelt the smell of decay through the smell of the Philadelphus. [Kensington, London, January 1983]

[According to my grandparents, b. 1856 and 1858] we were not allowed to bring into the house: SNOWDROPS, may blossom (HAWTHORN) and mock orange (philadelphus). [Cinderford, Gloucestershire, November 1993]

Mogue Tobin – a County Carlow name for CORN MARIGOLD.

Moles – deterred using CAPER SPURGE.

Molucca bean – see SEA BEANS.

Money-in-both-pockets – a Kent name for HONESTY.

Money tree (*Crassula ovata*). In January 1978 a woman interviewed on the BBC television programme 'Nationwide' explained how her luck had dramatically improved since she had acquired a 'Money Tree' which she exhibited for viewers to see. This interview caused a minor sensation, and the 'Tree' was eventually identified as the common succulent houseplant *Crassula ovata* (also, but incorrectly, known as *C. argentea* and *C. portulacea*). Other names given to the plant include 'Jade Plant', 'Tree of Happiness' [Wimbledon, London, November 1983] and 'Tree of Heaven'. By August 1978 many London florists were stocking small rooted cuttings of the money tree, priced from 50p to £1.50 each [personal observation]. Reference books published earlier than 1978 do not give money tree as a name for *Crassula ovata*. Although the name was known earlier:

My mother has had one of those Money Trees . . . for about 15 years, and she's always called it a Money Tree. [Barnes, London, February 1986]

it appears that it was not widely known until being mentioned on television. However, *C. ovata* is now commonly known as money tree, and provides an interesting example of how television, often regretted as a destroyer of folklore, can act as a super-efficient spreader of folk beliefs, particularly when these beliefs also feature in a popular daily newspaper.

Joyce Brown proved money DOES grow on trees when she won £20,000 on The Sun's bumper bingo competition.

Three weeks ago her sister Maureen gave her a money plant—told her if she talked nicely to it she would have a win.

Last week Mrs Brown, 60, of Norwich, Norfolk, won £70 at a local bingo club.

'I said thank you very much to my plant, went to bed and the next morning my husband Neville woke me up shouting "You've won on The Sun!" ' [*Sun*, 23 August 1982]

Similarly:

Green-fingered granny Clarice Cowell celebrated a £40,000 Sun Bingo win in champagne style yesterday—and said a big thank you to her lucky money plant!

For clever Clarice believes the house plant helped her join our list of super Sun Bingo winners . . .

'It's an old wives' tale, but if you talk to them they are supposed to bring you luck. I am always talking to mine. I was making a fuss of it only the other day and I swear that's why I won.' [*Sun*, 24 January 1983]

If a money tree is given away, its owner's luck goes with it.

We bought this plant at a hospital fair two years ago, when we asked what it was, we were told it was a Money Tree. It would bring us good fortune, but if we ever gave the whole plant away the good luck would go with it. It's alright to give away cuttings. My wife has just won a Grand National sweepstake. [Holborn, London, April 1983]

Monkey-jaws, monkey mouths – Somerset names for IVY-LEAVED TOADFLAX.

Monkey puzzle tree (*Araucaria araucana*). Since its introduction from Chile in the late eighteenth century, the monkey puzzle tree has become associated with the devil and misfortune.

There is a Fenland belief that if a monkey puzzle tree was planted on the edge of a graveyard it would prove an obstacle to the Devil when he tried to watch a burial. Many elderly Cambridgeshire people believe that the tree is an unlucky one. [Porter, 1969: 63]

A widespread belief among children was that one should keep silent while walking under a monkey puzzle tree.

In the 1930s I well remember the massive monkey puzzle tree which stood in Peterborough Recreation Park. As we children walked beneath its mis-shapen boughs we believed that penalties worse than death would befall us if we spoke so much as one word! I wonder if our hands clapped over our mouths had any connection with the monkey's 'speak no evil'? [Peterborough, Cambridgeshire, June 1981]

Similar beliefs have been recorded from Forfar, Angus, 1954 [Opie, 1959: 218] and Ealing, London, in 1979, while at Coulsdon, Surrey, in 1960 an 11-year-old schoolgirl explained:

Monk's hood

If you talk as you go under a monkey puzzle tree it means you'll have bad luck for three years. [Opie and Tatem, 1989: 260]

Monk's hood (*Aconitum napellus*)

A woman I was visiting near Poole once told me that her name for monk's hood was 'Old woman in her bed,' adding, as she pulled the covering petals off, 'with her shoes on', the feet being represented by the deformed anthers. [Linton, 1908: 15]

Montbretia (*Crocosmia* spp.)

Montbretia leaves were used as whistles, different tones were produced depending on the breadth of the leaf. [Larne, Co. Antrim, October 1993]

Monument bush or tree

Canon O'Hanlon, writing . . . in 1870, states that monument bushes: 'are found for the most part, in the centre of road crossings' and that unbaptised children and abortions are generally buried under them. 'It would,' he continues, 'be considered profanation to destroy them, or even to remove any of their branches.' That the term 'monument' is equivalent to 'memorial' in this context is apparent from information recorded in Cappanarrow, Co. Laois, in 1939: 'Long ago when a person would be killed in an accident there would be a small tree planted in that place. There is a monument tree over in Strahane. Usually it is a whitethorn [i.e. HAWTHORN] tree planted. Nobody ever touches a monument tree.' Such trees were to be found at Coolrain, and Longford, in the barony of Upperwoods, Co. Laois, and at Skirk in the same county. There were others at Rosenallis and Arless where they were said to mark places where Mass was said in the time when the penal laws against Catholicism were rigidly enforced, but this is perhaps a later tradition grafted on to them. Monument bushes were also known in Cos Longford and Westmeath. At Corlackan, Ballymoe, Co. Galway, 'Dolly's Bush,' a whitethorn by the roadside, commemorated a woman who met her death at the spot. [Lucas, 1963: 43]

Cf. LONE BUSH, MASS BUSH.

Moon

When to plant or sow to get the best results by the moon: PEAS, BEANS, flowering vegetables and plants which produce fruit above the ground should always be sown when the moon is going to the full. POTATOES and root crops should always be sown when the moon is low and below the earth. [*Foulsham's original Old Moore's Almanack for the year* 1989]

Seeds for vegetables which grow above ground sow at New Moon. Seeds for vegetables which grow below ground sow at Full Moon. [Stockport, Greater Manchester, April 1991]

[East Anglia:] Sow when the moon is waxing: weed when it is waning. [Evans, 1971: 142]

In olden times twigs were harvested for baskets during November Dark Moon [i.e. while the November moon is waning]. [Roaring Water Bay, Co. Cork, January 1993]

[Herefordshire:] Sow BEANS when the moon is round, they'll pod down to the ground. [Leather, 1912: 15]

Never start to sow, plant or harvest a crop if the moon is waning. It won't thrive. [Lerwick, Shetland, March 1994]

See also TIDE.

Morel (*Morchella* spp.). Even before the current vogue for eating wild fungi, morels were occasionally gathered and eaten in some rural areas.

In 1921 I visited the home [Whittlesford, Cambridgeshire] of my future husband . . . I was very intrigued by festoons of what looked like very dusty crumpled balls of dead brown leaves threaded on strings and festooned along the beams . . . [I] discovered later that one of my father-in-law's favourite dishes was steak and kidney pie and these objects were always added and cooked in the gravy. The resultant pudding was excellent as I can testify. My father-in-law called these things murrels . . . He used to collect them on his way home from night shift. [Maulden, Bedfordshire, April 1993]

Moss

Hair moss [*Polytrichum* spp.] and thyme thread moss [*Mnium* sensu lato spp.]—believed to be unfriendly for some reason, and occasionally called poisonous spittle. [Lerwick, Shetland, March 1994]

See also SPHAGNUM MOSS.

Moth – deterred using BOG MYRTLE, HORSE CHESTNUT, LADY'S BED-STRAW, and TANSY.

Mother die – a name given to flowers which are reputed to cause the death of one's mother, or simply cause misfortune, if picked or taken indoors. Such flowers include: COW PARSLEY, FOOL'S PARSLEY, HAW-THORN, HEMLOCK, PLANTAIN, RED CAMPION, ROSEBAY WILLOWHERB, UMBELLIFERS, and YARROW. GREATER STITCHWORT was said to cause the death of one's mother if it was *not* picked.

Mothering Sunday. The fourth Sunday in Lent is celebrated as Mothering Sunday when, largely as a result of commercialization in comparatively recent times, it is customary to take gifts or send greeting cards to one's mother. It is believed that this custom has its origin in pre-Reformation times when 'on Mid-Lent Sunday devout parishioners went to the Mother Church of the parish, or to the Cathedral of the diocese, to make their offerings' [Hole, 1976: 142]. Later it became a time for family reunions, when servants were allowed home to visit their mothers. By the mid-twentieth century many parish churches held Mothering Sunday services, at which posies of flowers were distributed to mothers.

Many churches give flowers (VIOLETS or DAFFODILS or PRIMROSES) for children to give their mothers. [SLF MSS, Fulwood, Sheffield, May 1969]

At the family Communion service at St Mary's Church [Marston Magna, Somerset] on Mothering Sunday the tradition of distributing posies to the children of the Sunday School and other children in the congregation was carried out by the Rector, the Rev. H. de Jersey Hunt. Some 30 posies were given out. [Western Gazette, 30 March 1979]

Not long after Mothering Sunday became commercialized, so that it is now, along with Valentine's Day, a major source of income to florists.

Mothering Sunday is often referred to as Mother's Day, a name which more properly belongs to the second Sunday in May. Since 1914 this day has been observed throughout the United States of America, and to a lesser extent in Canada and parts of Latin America [Hole, 1976: 143]. On this day CARNATIONS are worn—'you wear a red flower if your mother's still alive, a white one if she's dead' [Malibu, California, July 1990].

Mother's Day – see MOTHERING SUNDAY.

Mother's-heart – a Lancashire name for SHEPHERD'S PURSE.

Motherwort (*Leonurus cardiaca*)

Vervine (Yn Lhus) was, and is, the great magical and apotropaic herb in Man. It is usually known simply as 'the herb'. The officinal VERVAIN is uncommon in the Island, and the plant one is commonly shown is motherwort. Sometimes the two were distinguished as he- and she-vervine, but it has proved impossible to discover which was which. The two have similar powers. The best day to acquire vervine roots to grow was St John's Eve, but they should not be asked for directly, although it is permissible to hint that you need the plant. Some people assert that, as with a spoken charm, the donor and the recipient should be of opposite sex. [Garrad, 1984: 78]

Mountain ash – see ROWAN.

Mourning – see DEATH and FUNERAL FLOWERS.

Mouse-ear chickweed (*Pilosella officinarum*)

Mouse's ear is a weed or herb that grows in grassy banks, dried, and after been thoroughly dry, is made into a tea, is used for children in cases of WHOOPING COUGH. [Taylor MSS, Blythburgh, Suffolk]

Herbal cures used in the Ashford area of Kent: my father boiled the roots of 'mouse ear' (as he called it) with chemists' liquorice to make a mixture for taking to alleviate COUGHS and colds. It tasted vile and we were glad to get better! [Bexhill- on-Sea, East Sussex, February 1991]

We used to collect mouse-ears from the common years ago and my mother made a cough mixture with it. [Itchen, Hampshire, June 1993]

Muckies – an Inverness-shire name for DOG ROSE hips.

Mugger – a Cornish name for MUGWORT.

Mugwort (*Artemisia vulgaris*). On Colonsay:

The leaves when young and tender are frequently made use of by the highlanders as a pot-herb. [Lightfoot, 1777: 469]

The leaves [of mugwort] were smoked by old people. [McNeill, 1910: 137]

[Shortlane End School, near Truro, 1934–1938:] mugwort—mugger— smoked by schoolboys. [St Day, Cornwall, January 1994].

On the Isle of Man:

5 July is the day on which the Tynwald, or Manx parliament, transacts its business in the open air at St Johns, as it has done for over a thousand years . . . A well attested custom, revived by Archdeacon Kewley in 1952, is the wearing of sprigs of mugwort (*Bollan Bane* or *Bollan feailleoin*) at Tynwald . . . Some of the older accounts emphasise that soldiers wore mugwort when attending Tynwald, and it may be that mugwort is a typical Norse sign of loyalty to the king, or that it was the plant badge of the Kings of Man. [Garrad, 1984: 76]

Mulberry (*Morus nigra*)

In the Western Counties it is asserted that frost ceases as soon as the mulberry tree bursts into leaf. [Dyer, 1889: 120]

The mention of mulberry in the children's game 'Here we go round the mulberry bush' has excited a great deal of speculation, especially as the mulberry is a tree rather than a bush. Sometimes it is stated that the game is derived from prisoners taking exercise in a prison yard.

Silver medal in the gardens category at the Chelsea Flower Show has gone to two inmates of Leyhill Open Prison. The men, guarded by two burly prison officers, have clearly been enjoying themselves in the Chelsea sunshine . . . The Leyhill Garden, entitled 'Here we go round the Mulberry Bush', is a representation of the old-fashioned exercise yard at HM Prison, Wakefield. At its centre is a fine specimen of *Morus nigra*, the bush around which the men used to walk on their daily exercise—hence the nursery rhyme. [*The Times*, 20 May 1992]

The game is curiously absent from Alice Bertha Gomme's 1894 and 1898 collection of traditional games, and although the Opies include the game in their 1985 study of singing games, they do not mention prison-yard mulberries. According to them:

> An ingenious joke-history for the 'Mulberry Bush' was going the rounds in 1978. The knights who were intent on killing Thomas à Becket first hung their swords on a mulberry tree, still, of course, extant. They scalped the Saint singing 'this is the way we do our hair.' They washed their hands afterwards to get rid of the guilt, and said their prayers round the body. [Opie, 1985: 291]

The Opies also list some of the other plants which have been used in place of mulberry bush in the words of the game. These include BAR-BERRY bush (recorded in the USA, 1882 and c.1900) BRAMBLE bush (recorded in 1849), GOOSEBERRY bush (known by Thomas Hardy, born in Dorset in 1840), HOLLY bush (Nottinghamshire, 1894), IVY or ivory bush (Norfolk, 1894), and prickly pear (known by T.S. Eliot, born in St Louis, Missouri, in 1888). Of these bushes probably only the bramble or blackberry is worthy of further consideration.

> I have been unable to find any attempt to explain why blackberries were known as mulberries in East Anglia. It is true that there is a species of bramble with a bigger berry than most others and that is given the name of mulberry by some East Anglian countrymen even today, but I believe there is another explanation, as the phrase *going a-mulberrying* was used for gathering blackberries of all sizes and species . . . Only people of substance had their mulberry trees. The ordinary people had to be content with the bramble. It is probable that the blackberry was referred to ironically as the mulberry because it was the poor man's fruit . . . One further piece of evidence does suggest that this meaning of mulberry was linked particularly with the ordinary country people. This is the action rhyme: *Here we go round the mulberry bush*. Genuine mulberries grow on trees, therefore this mulberry bush must have been a bramble. [Evans, 1969: 13]

The confusion between mulberry and balckberry is long-standing. In classical Latin the same word *morum* was used for both, by Horace for mulberry and by Vergil and Ovid for blackberry. In this context it is also worth considering the various cures which were effected by crawling around, or more usually under, brambles: did these have any connection with the origin and evolution of the game?

In East Anglia mulberry was used as a 'sure cure' for DIARRHOEA:

> Boil the green leaves from the mulberry tree and drink the infusion. [Taylor MSS, East Harling, Norfolk]

Mullein (*Verbascum thapsus*)

[In Guernsey, in the 1880s] for cows which were attacked by stranguary [difficulty in passing urine] the following remedy was used:

Take the leaves of mullein; chop them up very fine, mix them with bran and water, and then give the whole to the cow. [Stevens Cox, 1971: 6]

For BRONCHITIS and ASTHMA: the leaves of the mullein plant, dried, and put in a clay pipe and smoked like tobacco, the smoke to be inhaled. [IFC MSS 36: 252, Co. Laois, *c*.1930]

The mullein plant . . . is boiled and the juice is strained off. The drink is used as a cure for a COLD and also CONSUMPTION and other diseases of the lungs. [IFCSS MSS 660: 347, Co. Louth].

I recall Bob Penfold [a gypsy] showing me mullein out on Braunton Burrows and calling it cough flannel, from the leaves which were, I understand, used for a COUGH mixture, as good as 'ammonia and ipecac'. [Barnstaple, Devon, May 1991]

Mumps – treated using PRIVET.

Murrain – cured using HERB ROBERT.

Murrel – a Cambridgeshire variant of MOREL.

Mushroom (*Agaricus campestris*). Although mushrooms thrive on well-rotted horse manure, according to folk belief in parts of Yorkshire it is the semen of a stallion which really stimulates mushroom growth.

Keeping horses (especially a stallion) in a field is likely to result in the development of mushrooms . . . There is a popular association between stallions and mushrooms—the latter are supposed to develop from the ejaculated sperms of the horse. [SFL MSS, Walkley, South Yorkshire, October 1969]

There is a belief that a good crop of mushrooms will come from a pasture in which a male breeding animal is kept. The belief is that the stallion, bull or ram crops the mushroom with his semen. [SFL MSS, Epworth, Humberside, May 1971]

Mutton rose – a Cornish name for WHITE CLOVER.

Myrrh – a name for SWEET CICELY.

Myrtle (*Myrtus communis*)
Myrtle was much esteemed in Wales, where they say that if it grows on each side of the door the blessings of love and peace will never depart from the house. To destroy a myrtle is to 'kill' both love and peace. Sprigs of myrtle, with its blossoms, were not only used by brides, but in some parts of Wales they were worn in the girdle or bodice of young girls when going to their first Holy Communion. Sprigs were also placed in cradles to make babies happy. [Trevelyan, 1909: 105]

Myrtle

In Britain the association of myrtle with weddings was started or, at least, made popular by Queen Victoria, who carried myrtle in her bouquet when she married in 1840. Old myrtle bushes are often said to have grown from or be descended from sprigs of myrtle used in the Queen's wedding bouquet.

When Princess Anne married Captain Mark Phillips on 14th November 1973 . . . the princess's bouquet contained a sprig of myrtle grown from myrtle used in the wedding bouquet of Queen Victoria . . . Miss B.D. Hadow, manager of Moyses Stevens Limited, florists to the Queen and makers of Princess Anne's bouquet [commented] . . . 'We do not find that myrtle is asked for very much these days for bridal bouquets. On the few occasions that we have used it, it has nearly always been because the bride's grandmother or some other relation had some growing in their garden and wished it to be put into the bouquet for sentimental reasons.' [Baker, 1974: 28]

When I was a child I lived in an old house on the outskirts of Belfast, and on a south-facing wall outside my nursery there grew a fine myrtle bush which flowered freely. According to local tradition this bush grew from a sprig from Queen Victoria's wedding bouquet. [Broomborough, Merseyside, November 1990]

About four years ago an elderly lady came to the shrub nursery for which I am propagator asking me to give a good home to a potted myrtle plant (*Myrtus communis*) as she was moving away from the area into a flat. She said it was reputedly grown from a cutting from Queen Victoria's wedding bouquet and thought we might like to propagate from it. [Verrall, 1991: 28]

N

Naked ladies – a name for JERSEY LILY.

Nanny goat's mouths – a Devon name for IVY-LEAVED TOADFLAX.

Narcissus (*Narcissus* spp.)

The sweet-scented old fashioned white narcissus, also called scented lily or white lily—known as grave flooers and unlucky to take indoors, but favoured for the garden. [Lerwick, Shetland, March 1994]

See also PRIMROSE PEERLESS.

National emblems. The following plants are considered to be national emblems of the British Isles:

DAFFODIL or LEEK: Wales.

FLAX: Northern Ireland.

GUERNSEY LILY: Guernsey

RAGWORT (Manx: *Cushag*): Isle of Man—'Of no great antiquity; reputedly a sarcastic Victorian Governor-General said it must be, there is so much in the fields' [Union Mills, Isle of Man, June 1994].

Red ROSE: England

SHAMROCK: Republic of Ireland, which also has OAK as its national tree.

THISTLE: Scotland.

For a more extensive list of such emblems see Asch (1968).

Navelwort – see PENNYWORT.

Nerves – DANDELION good for them.

Nettle (*Urtica dioica*)

Nettles in many parts of Scotland were till not very many years ago used as food, and were looked upon as a wholesome diet. The young and tender leaves were gathered, boiled, then mashed . . . mixed with a little oatmeal, and reboiled for a short time. They were cooked in the same way as 'greens', which were and are still thought to possess medicinal virtues. In the north such a dish went by the name of 'nettle kail', as the dish of 'greens' went by that of 'chappit kail'. But the nettle . . . was used as a medicine, under the form of 'nettle ale,' for the cure of JAUNDICE. The ale was prepared in the following manner: a quantity of nettle-roots was gathered, thoroughly washed, and then boiled for hours in water till a strong extract was got. This extract was then treated with yeast, 'barm,' fermented,

Nettle

'vrocht,' and bottled. A man whose mother was in the habit of making this ale lately told me he had often drunk it, and found it quite palatable.

In one district at least the medicinal virtue of the nettle lay in its being 'unspoken,' i.e. no one must speak to the gatherer of it, and collected at the hour of midnight. The following story [set in Kincardineshire] . . .

'Geordie Tamson, who lived near Jollybrands on the south turnpike, not far from the toll-bar, lay sick. After weeks of treatment by the doctor, Geordie lay ill, without the least token of improvement. A "Skeely woman" from the Dounies, a village not far off, was called in. She at once prescribed a supper of "nettle kail," and added that the dish must be made of "unspoken nettles," gathered at midnight. That very night by eleven o'clock three young men, friends of Geordie's, from Cairngrassie, were on their way to the Red Kirkyard of Portlethen, where there was a fine bed of nettles . . . the nettles were gathered, carefully taken to the sick man, cooked of course, and given to him. A complete and speedy recovery followed.' [Gregor, 1884b: 377]

Particularly in Ireland, the use of nettles as a health-giving food continues to be recorded.

Then there were the nettles, we had to gather them to make soup, oh, it was lovely. [Castlerock, Co. Derry, February 1989]

From my mother: when she was a child, approximately seventy years ago, she was given (or forced to take!!) three meals of boiled nettles in the month of March to clear the BLOOD. [Danesfort, Co. Kilkenny, April 1991]

Eat three feed of boiled young nettles in the springtime and it will keep you free of disease for the rest of the year. [Ballymote, Co. Sligo, May 1994]

To boost blood iron drink water from boiled nettles, or eat young nettle leaves. [Llanuwchyllin, Gwynedd, April 1991]

Once nettle flowers start to develop, and the leaves begin to get coarse, the plant becomes unsuitable for eating.

The springtime nettle of the [New] Forest was . . . said to be unfit for eating after a certain date . . . tradition claims that on May Day the Devil gathered the nettles to make his shirts. [Boase, 1976: 115]

Nettles are considered to be good food for young turkeys:

Back in the 1930–40 period people who reared flocks of turkeys used to feed them with nettles. They put an old stocking on their hand, took a knife and went out to the fields to cut nettles; some people even cut them by the sack full. They made a pot of Indian Meal gruel (maize). Then the nettles were chopped fine. My aunt used to take a big handful in her bare hands and squeeze them (this way they didn't sting) and cut them up with a sharp knife. Then they were put into the boiling gruel and stirred around. When the mixture cooled it was thick and the nettles were cooked. [Lenamore, Co. Longford, April 1991]

My next door neighbour who rears just a few turkeys for Christmas feeds them on nettles, or, I should say, includes nettles in their diet. [West Stow, Suffolk, October 1992]

Nettle beer was a favourite home-made drink, especially at Heysham in Lancashire.

In August 1988 I visited the Old Rectory Tea Garden in Heysham, to try their 'traditional' nettle beer—a pleasant, refreshing, slightly ginger-flavoured drink. A man at the next table had bought a bottle full of it, and explained he had fond memories of thirty years ago, when he used to enjoy the nettle beer which an old lady sold from her cottage in the village. [Streatham, London, November 1992]

Nettles were particularly valued as a cure for rheumatism.

I am informed by some maiden ladies living in Torquay that nettle-stings are a cure [for RHEUMATISM]. The nettles must be applied to the affected parts. [Chope, 1935: 138]

[Around Moretonhampstead, Devon, it is said that stinging nettles] infused are good for rheumatism. Used successfully in past five years. [Brown, 1972: 267]

From an old herbalist who used to be in Exmouth: As a cure for rheumatism take a good bunch of stinging nettles, about 8 inches long, and with it beat the affected part. [Budleigh Salterton, Devon, February 1976]

Other remedies which employed nettles included:

For BRONCHITIS: Dry nettles and burn them in a closed room over hot embers. Breathing the pungent aroma will relieve bronchitis and ASTHMA attacks. [Langtoft, Humberside, July 1985]

Nettle tea was made and drunk for stomach complaints. [Histon, Cambridgeshire, January 1989]

Ointment for easing pain: Chop nettles, add good measure of salt, 3 tablespoons of vinegar, mix in 2 oz of pure lard, when well mixed spread good portion on piece of brown paper and apply to troubled area, fix with firm bandage. [Stockport, Greater Manchester, April 1991]

A friend, now over 80 years old, who came from Fife recalled being told how her father was cured of a frozen shoulder when nettles were put on the bare skin of the shoulder area and kept on for, probably, several days.
When the nettles were removed, and despite the blisters caused by them and the pain suffered, the man was cured, for all time. [Edinburgh, January 1992]

Nettles boiled, and the resultant liquid drunk, is a cure for 'Lily Rash'. Lily Rash is the result of juice from the DAFFODIL family—usually making sore and itching fingers. This is usually when the skin is irritated when either picking or packing flowers during the season for market. [St Mary's, Isles of Scilly, September 1992]

Wild nettles if boiled are good for ARTHRITIS. [Clonmel, Co. Tipperary, February 1993]

There is one record, from a New Forest gypsy in 1952, of nettles being used as a contraceptive. A man should lay nettle leaves thickly as a sole inside his socks and wear them for 24 hours before engaging in intercourse. The gypsy claimed to have tried this, and proved its effectiveness [Macpherson MSS].

Stinging with nettles was a traditional punishment for children who failed to wear OAK on Oak Apple Day. In some areas at least it is probable that the custom owed its survival to fun involved in chasing non-wearers with nettles rather than any pro-royalist patriotic feelings.

A custom now dying out existed in Nottinghamshire on the twenty-ninth of May, or 'Oak and Nettle Day', as it is termed in Nottinghamshire. The rising generation sally out in the morning, their caps and buttonholes adorned with sprigs of oak. They also provide themselves with a bunch of nettles. They request all persons whom they meet to 'show your oak.' If a single leaf even is produced they are permitted to pass unmolested, but supposing they are unprovided with the necessary sprig or leaf their face, neck, and hands are well 'nettled'. When the punishment has been bestowed for disloyalty, a slip of oak is presented to the offending party, who is thus provided with protection from the next gang of youths and lads they meet. [E., 1884: 381]

At Common Moor, near Liskeard, Cornwall, 1 May was known as Stinging Nettle Day.

[I am 84 years of age, I went to live in Cornwall when I was about four and a half years old.] Stinging Nettle Day was celebrated there on May 1st. On our way to school on that day we would pick a small DOCK leaf and then a leaf from a stinging nettle, wrap it in the dock leaf and eat it. This was supposed to keep you from harm until the next Stinging Nettle Day. [Teignmouth, Devon, November 1984]

In parts of south Devon and Cornwall and around Cromer in Norfolk [Chandler 1993: 11] 2 May was Sting Nettle Day.

I was born in Brixham, Devon, and we had a little rhyme which goes:

> 1st of May Ducking Day
> 2nd of May Sting Nettle Day
> 3rd of May Petticoat Day

1st of May we carried water about with us to fill our water pistols which we squirted at people. (Ducking). In the evening the fire brigade went to the harbour and with their hoses washed down the monument of William Prince of Orange. After that to the Town Hall to do the same. 2nd of May we chased the girls with sting nettles. 3rd May we chased the girls and tried to lift up their dresses. [Paignton, Devon, November 1984]

May 1st was a great day for us youngsters 50 years ago, it was Ducking Day
. . . but Sting Nettle Day followed (May 2nd). The boys used to collect
stinging nettles and chase all the girls trying to sting their legs; of course,
they hardly ever caught us and there was much laughter. The boys were
not bad even if they caught you, they would think twice about stinging.
May 3rd was Petticoat Day . . . the boys would chase after us, trying to
see what our petticoats were like. [Brixham, Devon, November 1984]

A trick played by adults on children, or by country children on unsus-
pecting town children, is to claim that 'nettles don't sting this month'.

They say 'Nettles don't sting this month', and confirm their statement by
grasping a nettle leaf firmly. The 'towney' touches the leaf gingerly and
cries out with pain, whereupon the country child jeers, 'Nettles don't
sting this month—but they do sting you!' [Opie, 1959: 61]

Nettles were used as a dyestuff, and were collected for this use by
schoolchildren during the Second World War.

The people long ago also dyed wool with nettles. First the wool was put
into water and potash and it was boiled for some length so that it would
take a good dye. Then a lot of nettles were pulled and they were boiled in
some clean water. Then the juice was taken off the nettles, and the wool
was put in to this and it was boiled again for about one hour. When the
wool had taken a green colour it was taken out and it was washed to get
all the pieces of nettles off it and it was dried and spun. IFCSS MSS 212:
79, Co. Leitrim]

When the war began, the claims long held by country people as to the
value of the nettle were investigated, and County Herb Committees were
asked in 1942 to collect 100 tons of it. Over 40 tons were gathered
throughout the country in that year; some of this was used for the extraction of the dark green dye for camouflage, and the chlorophyll for tonic
and other medicines. [Ranson, 1949: 84]

Erica collected both rose hips and nettles for the Guides in about 1940 . . .
The nettles were dried on the lawn and tied into bundles . . . she never
knew about their eventual fate. Erica's guides were the 2nd Heaton Moor
Company, near Stockport. [Girton, Cambridge, June 1989]

I well remember one hot summer being organised in parties from our
school in Sussex to go out foraging for stinging nettles during World War
II. We returned with massive bunches and innumerable stings, and
covered the playing fields with them—cricket was abandoned for that
week. After drying they were gathered up and despatched to we know
not where. It was all terribly hush-hush and we weren't allowed to write
home about it . . . Somebody much later suggested they were used for
making green 'blanco' for the use of His Majesty's Forces. It does not
sound improbable, but why all the secrecy? [Hexham, Northumberland,
August 1989]

Nettle stings

When I was at school during the war we used to collect things—LIME flowers, stinging nettles and [DOG] ROSE hips. They used to dry the stinging nettles, laying them out on sort of big canvas sheets. I didn't like collecting stinging nettles. On the list of clothing we had to take to school were stinging nettle proof gloves—they were terribly difficult to get. [Chiswick, London, February 1991]

Occasionally nettles were used as a fly deterrent.

[When I was a child in the 1920s] a freshly gathered bunch of nettles hung up in the kitchen or larder was supposed to keep flies away. [Larne, Co. Antrim, November 1991]

Nettles were hung up to deter flies (they didn't). [Woodnewton, Northamptonshire, June 1992]

Nettle stings – treated using DANDELION, DOCK, GRASS, and HORSE-RADISH.

Neuralgia – cured using HENBANE.

New Year's Day – associated plants include DAISY and HAWTHORN.

Nipplewort (*Lapsana communis*)
In some parts of England the common people boil them as greens, but they have a bitter and not agreeable taste. [Lightfoot, 1777: 445]

No blame – an Irish name for BIRD'S-FOOT TREFOIL.

Norway spruce (*Picea abies*) – the tree most popularly sold as CHRIST-MAS TREES.

Nosebleed – a name for YARROW.

Nosebleeds – caused by POPPY and YARROW; stopped using YARROW.

Nursery bogies
There is a group of spirits that seem as if they had never been feared by grown-up people but had been invented expressly to warn children off dangerous ground or undesirable activities. [Briggs, 1976: 313]

Such bogies include Awd Oggie and Lazy Laurence who protected APPLES; Churnmilk Peg and Melsh Dick who protected unripe HAZEL nuts, and Jenny Greenteeth who grabbed children who ventured too near DUCKWEED-covered pools.

Nut
[Childhood memories from c.1935–45:] If one finds a nut with two kernels (common in almonds), one gives one kernel to someone else. As soon as the two people who have shared the nut see each other again on the next day (or when they next meet) they must say 'Philip!' If

one forgets the other claims a forfeit. I think this is a French custom; my Belgian mother taught it to us. [Worthing, West Sussex, January 1989]

See also HAZEL.

Nutmeg (*Myristica fragrans*)

A nutmeg carried in the pocket is a cure [for RHEUMATISM]. [Chope, 1935: 138]

[West Riding of Yorkshire:] A nutmeg threaded and worn on the braces will prevent rheumatism. [McKelvie MSS, 1963: 265]

A nutmeg carried in the pocket wards off the rheumatics. (Firmly believed in the Doncaster area today. I have been given one for each of my pockets by an earnest well-wisher). [CECTAL SLF MSS, Doncaster, South Yorkshire, April 1968]

Sometime ago I asked an elderly lady who was born in Suffolk what treasures she had in a under pocket which she always wore . . . a well-worn quite small thing, which looked like a small bean, and she said that it was her nutmeg. I said 'why in the world do you carry that,' oh she said her mother gave it to her when she was about 17 years of age to always carry in her pocket, to ensure good health . . . she died three years ago in Brighton aged 91. [Taylor MSS, Debenham, Suffolk, April 1925]

Cf. POTATO.

O

Oak (*Quercus petraea* and *Q. robur*). Although the oak tree is an unofficial emblem of England (for example, it appears as a 'national' plant, equivalent to the FLAX, LEEK, and THISTLE on pound coins) and has been adopted as the national tree of the Irish Republic, it is not the focus of a great deal of folklore. Such folklore as exists is concentrated around three themes: weather rhymes concerning the oak and the ASH, the wearing of oak on Oak Apple Day (29 May), and legends concerning individual trees.

Versions of the weather rhyme are widespread, but its interpretation can cause confusion.

An old labourer who frequently visited my parents [in west Dorset] would recite:

> If the oak is out before the ash,
> We shall surely have a splash.

Then he would scratch his head and remark 'but there's another way of saying that:

> If the ash is out before the oak,
> We shall surely have a soak.'

He believed that both rhymes implied wet summers. [Vickery, 1978: 157]

However, it is generally agreed that if the ash produces leaves before the oak the summer will be wet.

> If the oak before the ash,
> Then we'll only have a splash.
> If the ash before the oak,
> Then we'll surely have a soak.
> [Ballycastle, Co. Antrim, January 1991]

In this part of England we say:

> Oak before ash—splash;
> Ash before oak—soak.
> [Letter from Enmore, Somerset, in *The Times*, 20 March 1990]

Regarding the unreliability of weather predictions based on the oak and ash adage . . . there is a corollary which I have only heard within the boundaries of Dorset:

> If oak and ash leaves show together,
> Us may fear some awful weather.

This be a sight but seldom seen
That could remind we what has been.
[Letter from Marnull, Dorset, in *Daily Telegraph*, 27 June 1987]

29 May was known as Oak Apple or Royal Oak Apple Day, and commemorated the restoration of the monarchy in 1660. King Charles II,
who triumphantly entered London on 29 May, is probably best
known for the way in which he escaped capture after the battle of
Worcester by hiding in an oak tree at Boscobel (see below). At one
time Charles II considered setting up a new order of chivalry, the
Knights of the Royal Oak, but the project was abandoned as it was
thought likely 'to keep awake animosities which it was part of wisdom
to lull to sleep' [Yallop, 1984: 29]. However, until well into the twentieth century oak (or occasionally FIELD MAPLE) leaves, and, if possible,
oak apples, were worn on 29 May.

> When I went to school, 60 odd years ago, there was one day we used to
> call 'Oak Ball Day.' We were supposed to wear an oak leaf or oak ball on
> our coats and if we didn't the other kids used to attack us with stinging
> NETTLES. [Letter from Church Gresley, Staffordshire, in *Daily Mirror*,
> 1 November 1973]

> [During my childhood in East Cowes, 1920s and 1930s:] Oak Apple Day
> (29 May) wear a sprig to get luck—an oak apple makes you even luckier.
> [Ryde, Isle of Wight, November 1988]

> [Macclesfield area, Cheshire:] my grandmother, born in Adlington in
> 1873, sent me to school wearing oak leaves in 29 May on at least one oc-
> casion, *c.*1946. [Skipton, North Yorkshire, November 1991]

The oak apples worn on Oak Apple Day were not the hard globular
oak apples which are familiar to us today, but the larger, less regular
spongy galls which rapidly grow on oak trees in May and mature in
June or July. The gall-wasp responsible for the smaller globular oak
apples was deliberately introduced from the Middle East to Devon in
about 1830, so that its galls, which contain 17 per cent of tannic acid,
could be exploited for dyeing cloth and ink-making [Darlington and
Hirons, 1975: 151].

In some places the use of oak sprigs on Oak Apple Day has become
rather more formal. At the Royal Hospital, in Chelsea, London, oak
sprigs are worn by the pensioners and their guests on Founder's Day,
which is held on or near 29 May each year. The Royal Hospital was
founded by King Charles II in 1682, as a home for old soldiers, and the
Founder's Day Parade, at which a member of the Royal Family or a
high-ranking army officer takes the salute, has been held without a
break since 1692. In addition to oak being worn by the participants,
the Grinling Gibbons statue of Charles II at the hospital is also decked

with, and almost concealed in, oak branches on this day [Brentnall, 1975: 122]

Elsewhere oak branches were hoisted to the top of church towers on Oak Apple Day. At Castleton, Derbyshire, a garland ceremony takes place on 29 May; for this the church tower is 'decorated with branches of greenery (usually oak),' and 'sometimes the children dance back through the village [from the church] and all the parents who have ever taken part in the ceremony dance behind wearing oak sprays' [Lester, 1972: 2].

In Cornwall:

> An oak branch is still placed on the top of the tower of the parish church of St Neot on Oak Apple Day. St Neot was, of course, a royalist parish during the Civil War. The oak bough is always supplied by Lampen Farm. The bough is hoisted up the outside of the tower. When in place, the vicar says prayers. I always used prayers for the Royal Family and for the government of the day, and closed with the Lord's Prayer and a blessing.
>
> In addition, the St Neot Women's Institute holds an Oak Apple Day fair. [The Revd E.G. Allsop, former vicar of St Neot, November 1989]

In recent years the environmental organization Common Ground has actively promoted Oak Apple Day. A card produced by the organization in 1991 carried the exhortation: 'Revive an ancient festival—wear the oak on the 29th of May.'

As oak trees are relatively long-lived and can attain a massive size, it is, perhaps, inevitable that some individual trees have become the focus of legends.

Gospel Oaks still exist in some localities, or are remembered as place-names. It is said that these trees marked spots where the Gospel was read during beating the bounds ceremonies which perambulated a parish's boundaries on Rogation Day. The most famous of these Gospel Oaks was the one which stood near the church at Polstead, Suffolk.

> Tradition gives the Gospel Oak an age of over 1300 years, attributing its earliest use to the Saxon missionaries led by Bishop Cedd in the mid-seventh century. [Harley, 1988: 5]

This tree eventually collapsed in 1953, but it has been replaced by a young tree, 'which may be presumed self-sown from the now dead tree'. Since 1910, or possibly earlier, an annual service—the Gospel Oak Service—is held beside the oak tree on the first Sunday in August. The music is provided by the local Salvation Army band, there is a guest preacher, and an expected congregation of seventy or more [the Revd G. Marsden, Rector of Polstead, September 1993].

The Major Oak in Sherwood Forest—which got its name from the local antiquary Major Hayman Rooke—is popularly associated with Robin Hood and his merry men who 'are said to have hatched their projects for the redistribution of wealth' beneath its branches.

> The Major Oak . . . lies half a mile north of Edwinstowe. Its age is difficult to estimate, but it is not thought to be older than the sixteenth century. Now one of the centres of Robin Hood tourist commerce, this part of Sherwood Forest owes its prominence and all its supposed detailed associations with the legend to the romantic interest in Robin which developed in the nineteenth century. [Holt, 1983: pl. 10/11]

In recent years there has been considerable concern about the Oak's health.

> The Major Oak in Sherwood Forest, Robin Hood's legendary hide-out, is being drenched daily with thousands of gallons of water because of fears that during the hot, dry weather it could be destroyed by fire or drought. [*The Times*, 30 August 1990]

> The ancient oak in Sherwood Forest in which Robin Hood is said to have hidden has been cloned in a test tube so that exact copies of the tree will be growing when it dies . . . Dr Wright received a £23,000 grant from Nottinghamshire County Council to produce identical replicas of the tree.
> The Robin Hood legend is an important money-spinner for the authority, which runs Sherwood Forest country park where the 80ft high oak with its 240ft spread is a main attraction. The plan is to plant a copy to replace the Major Oak when it dies. Dr Wright and the council think that many of the one million visitors to the forest each year would buy small versions of the oak to plant at home. [*The Times*, 21 May 1992]

The oak tree in which King Charles II is said to have hidden after the Battle of Worcester in 1651 can still be seen in the grounds of Boscobel House in Shropshire. However, there is some doubt whether this is the original tree or a younger one that has taken its place.

> Immediately the story of Boscobel became known people flocked to see the house and the oak, and almost at once the tree was injured by souvenir hunters removing its young boughs. The damage was so great that before 1680 the owners of Boscobel, Basil and Jane Fitzherbert, were forced to crop part of the tree and protect it with a high brick wall . . . In 1706 John Evelyn wrote that he had heard that the 'Famous Oak near White Ladys' had been killed by people hacking the boughs and bark', and six years later William Stukeley described the tree as 'almost cut away by travellers'. He also remarked that a 'young thriving plant from one of its acorns' was growing 'close by the side'. [Weaver, 1987: 29]

A Leicestershire legend explained the presence of 'top-less' trees—presumably trees which had formerly been pollarded—in Charnwood Forest.

> In the spring of 1893 I was told by my driver, hired from Loughborough, that the old oaks were said to have lost their tops when Lady Jane Grey, who resided at Bradygates Hall in the neighbourhood, was beheaded. A curious argument from analogy. [Skipwith, 1894: 169]

Similarly:

> According to a local tradition still current in Newtown Linford when I was a boy, all the oak trees in Bradgate Park were pollarded as a sign of mourning when [Lady] Jane [Grey] was executed. [R.Palmer, 1985: 17]

In Fort William, Inverness-shire, an oak tree known as the Hanging Tree was cut down 'amid controversy and protest' in 1984–5 to make way for a new public library. This tree is believed to have been a JOUG TREE on which the local chief hanged wrong-doers. As a result of its destruction it is believed that

> there has been a sequence of unexplained incidents at the library, trivial in themselves and not on the face of it connected. These happenings have, however, become associated in people's minds and are now explained as the work of restless or mischievous spirits. There have been no apparitions, only a series of 'accidents'. A flower pot was found one morning having fallen for no apparent reason . . . a very heavy and cumbersome chair was discovered to have been turned over . . . the Chief Librarian's word-processor produced an upside-down print-out. [Douglas, 1989; Fort William, Inverness, October 1993]

There are occasional records of oak being used medicinally.

> DIARRHOEA: grate a ripe acorn into warm milk and give to patient. [Taylor MSS, Woolverstone, Suffolk].

> RINGWORM: get six leaves of an oak tree, boil them and drink the water in which they were boiled. [IFCSS MSS 800: 219, Co. Offaly].

> Oak bark was commonly used as a cure for sore shoulders in horses. The bark was boiled and the sores washed with the water. [IFCSS MSS 1075: 135, Co. Donegal].

See also CORK OAK.

Oar weed (*Laminaria hyperborea*)

> As children we also were told we could (and occasionally did) eat bits of the hold-fasts of one of the bigger seaweeds—*Laminaria hyperborea* (or perhaps one of the other Laminarias) I think—I cannot remember. [Ballycastle, Co. Antrim, January 1991]

Oat (*Avena sativa*)

> Oats were to be sown by *Ffair Garon* (Caron Fair) [Tregaron, Cardiganshire], on the 15th of March, although *Ceirch du bach* (little black oats—a primitive local type of oat) did not have to be sown until the 21st of the month. Adverse climatic conditions in the uplands of north Wales led to

later sowing there, and the favoured dates for sowing oats in those districts were *tridiau y deryn du, a dau lygad Ebrill* (the three days of the blackbird, and the two eyes of April), which are taken . . . to refer to the last three days of March and the first two of April according to the 'old calendar', i.e. from the 10th to the 15th of April. [Williams-Davies, 1983: 229]

Considerable care was needed to ensure that sheaves of oats were sufficiently dry before they were stacked.

They always used to say about oats, three Sundays after it was cut. Whether it was cut on the Friday before the first Sunday or the Monday before the first Sunday, they always used to say it had to be left out for three Sundays. [Thorncombe, Dorset, March 1975]

Oats should have the church bells rung over them three times after they have been cut, i.e. must be left while the bells are tolled on three successive Sundays. Otherwise there will be sickness in the village. [Woodstock, Oxfordshire, January 1983]

Oblionker, obly-onker – names for HORSE CHESTNUT seeds.

Oil-seed rape (*Brassica napus* ssp. *oleifera*)

The origin of the phrase Lincolnshire Yellow Belly is much discussed amongst Lincolnshire people—various ideas are upheld by various people.

The following is the most recent [1988] version that I have encountered. In a three person conversation on cultural tradition, between an Indian doctor, a psychiatric nurse (resident of Kintan in Lindsey, but Nottinghamshire born) and myself, the doctor asked: 'Why do they call them Lincolnshire Yellow Bellies?' With an expansive sweep of her arms indicating the breadth and shape of Lincolnshire's farmland, the nurse replied: 'It's because of all the oil-seed rape they grow in Lincolnshire—it's the yellow belly of Lincolnshire.' [Barton upon Humber, Humberside, February 1992]

Old man – a name for SOUTHERNWOOD; when 'Old Man' occurs in plant-names it is generally assumed to be a euphemism for the DEVIL.

Old man's beard – an alternative name for TRAVELLER'S JOY.

Old man's pepper – a Nottinghamshire name for MEADOWSWEET.

Old woman in her bed – a Dorset name for MONK'S HOOD.

Onion (*Allium cepa*). A cut onion in the house was believed to absorb germs, but opinion as to whether or not this was desirable seems to vary.

SCARLET FEVER broke out at Whitechurch [Warwickshire] in the autumn of 1915. One young mother assured me she had taken away the chance of

infection by peeling some onions and burying the peelings. At Stratford
an onion was often suspended in a dwelling under the idea that it would
turn black if the house was infected. [Bloom, 1930: 245]

On one occasion some other children in the house contracted scarlet
fever, and as a result mats outside the doors were covered with raw Spanish onion, my mother claiming that any germs would be attracted to it.
Anyhow, we did not get fever. [UCL EFS MSS M13, Carshalton
Beeches, Surrey, October 1963]

According to my grandmother who was born in Lancashire in 1897, a cut
piece of onion should never be kept as it will attract all the bad from the
air into it. [St Andrews, Fife, September 1988]

A half of onion was hung in the house every winter; a cut onion was supposed to take the germs. [Hill, Worcestershire, October 1991]

An onion cut in half and kept in the house was supposed to kill germs.
[Pimperne, Dorset, January 1992]

During the disastrous outbreak of foot-and-mouth disease on British
farms in 1968, on one Cheshire farm which escaped, although in the
midst of raging infection, the farmer's wife laid rows of onions along all
the windowsills and doorways of the cow-sheds and attributed the farm's
escape to this. [Baker, 1975: 53]

It has been stated that the inhabitants of God's Providence House in
Chester were spared from the plague due to their having placed
onions at the entrances to their home [Jeacock, 1982]. However, historical evidence does not support this. The last outbreaks of plague in
Chester occurred in 1605 and 1647–8, but the house was not built
until 1652, following the extensive damage to the centre of Chester by
artillery bombardment during the Civil War siege of the city.

The legend concerning the House's escape from the plague, without
mentioning onions, is commonly given by both printed and two-legged
guides, and can be traced back to George Batenham's *The Stranger's
Companion in Chester*, published in 1821. Presumably this is inspired by
the House's name. The words 'God's providence is mine inheritance'
were used by Richard Boyle, Earl of Cork, to adorn buildings erected
by him . . . but there does not appear to be any connection between
the Earls of Cork and Chester's God's Providence House. [Chester,
Cheshire, November 1993]

The growing of mammoth onions has its enthusiasts, although onion
competitions are far rarer than LEEK shows. In 1991 Dewsbury Onion
Fair in West Yorkshire was revived after a gap of 101 years:

The record-setting 29lb 4oz trio [being] grown in 11 months by Peter
Glazebrook, of Newark, Nottinghamshire, who won £50. [*The Times*,
14 October 1991]

The National Kelsae Onion Championship takes place at the Great Autumn Flower Show, Harrogate, North Yorkshire, in September each year. In 1992 the winner was an 11lb 2oz onion—said to be the biggest in the world—exhibited by Robert Holland of Cumnock, Strathclyde [*The Times*, 22 September 1992]. In 1993 Mr Holland failed to beat this, with his prize-winning exhibit weighing a quarter of an ounce less than the one he exhibited the previous year [*Harrogate Advertiser*, 24 September 1993].

Onions were widely used in folk medicine.

'If an onion is eaten every morning before breakfast, all the doctors might ride on one horse' was a local saying [around Horseheath, Cambridgeshire]. [Parsons MSS, 1952]

In the late twenties and thirties onions, chopped and stewed in milk, were used to cure colds and COUGHS. [Ryde, Isle of Wight, November 1988]

The onion had many uses. The inside of an onion skin placed on CUTS and scratches acted as a type of elastoplast . . . An onion placed on a wasp or a bee STING soon took the pain away. A mixture of onions and sugar in water was a cure for WHOOPING COUGH. Rubbed on the head it was believed a cure for BALDNESS. [St Osyth, Essex, February 1989]

To cure BALDNESS: cut and bruise an onion. Rub the sap mixed with a little honey into a bald patch, keep on rubbing until the spot gets red. This concoction if properly applied would grow hair on a duck's egg. [IFCSS MSS 175: 313, Co. Sligo].

[Around Chipping Ongar, Essex] RHEUMATISM may be warded off by carrying a small onion in the pocket. [Smith, 1959: 414]

When picking fruit in an orchard my father always carries half a raw onion in his pocket and rubs this on any place where a wasp has stung him. He always maintains this alleviates the pain of the STING, and I have often seen him do it. [SLF MSS, Sheffield, November 1966]

Severe bruising—rub gently at regular intervals with a slice of raw onion. [Stockport, Greater Manchester, April 1991]

For CHILBLAINS: rub feet with half a peeled onion. [Llanuwchylln, Gwynedd, April 1991]

Hot roasted onion for EARACHE. [St Davids, Dyfed, October 1991]

[I am 88] as a small child I remember a small hot onion being put in my ear to soothe earache. Probably the heat was the effective part of the remedy—the onion was heated in the oven. [Maulden, Bedfordshire, 3 April 1993]

My maternal grandmother came from the then rural area of Middlesex. Her cure-all was onion syrup made by slicing onions and covering the slices with brown sugar over night. The resulting brown liquid was distributed to us children quite liberally at the slightest sign of a cold or sore throat. [Taunton, Somerset, January 1992]

An old Irish remedy for PILES was the application of a poultice of boiled onions. [Glynn, Co. Antrim, February 1992]

Onion skins provide a favourite DYE for colouring EASTER EGGS.

In our childhood days of the 20s and 30s in and around Burghead, Moray . . . for the dyeing of Easter eggs our mothers might use the outer skins of onions, or whin (= GORSE) flowers. [Edinburgh, October 1991]

Schoolboys recommended that if an onion was rubbed on a hand before it was caned the pain would be alleviated [Opie, 1959: 375].

The schoolboy . . . does not fail to make use of the time-honoured charm against the sting of the cane, viz. the rubbing of an onion on the palm of the hand. [Gutch, 1912: 31]

For wild onion see CROW GARLIC.

Opium poppy (*Papaver somniferum*). Although commercially produced laudanum was frequently used to provide relief from pain and hunger (cf. Mrs Gaskell's *Mary Barton*, 1848), home-made remedies derived from opium poppies were also utilized.

The universal pain-killer for RHEUMATISM and, indeed, for all muscular and nerve pains, was opium, freely obtainable in the poppy tea which every Fen housewife could make from the white poppies . . . she grew in her garden. She took it herself, gave it to her husband and even to the children, down to the youngest baby with TEETHING troubles. [Porter, 1969: 85]

Sleep in children: A decoction of poppy heads. You will see poppies growing in many cottage gardens, where they are cultivated it is always for this reason—it saves the mothers a great deal of trouble. Forty years ago many of our farm labourers used to take laudanum regularly, it was easier to carry about than the home decoction—an old man of nearly 80 years always had 4oz a week of the very strongest. [Taylor MSS, Norwich, Norfolk].

Orange (*Citrus sinensis*). Occasionally orange peel was used instead of APPLE peel by girls wanting to find out the initial of their future husband's name.

I used to toss long strips of orange peel to find out the initial letter of my future husband when I was about 5–6. The peel was cut by a grown-up of course, but we were given the peel. It always ended up as a curved letter—C, G and S—so this was a source of some anxiety to me as I was affianced to my beloved sweetheart whose name began with D; no way could you produce D, so I gave up doing it. But it was popular among little girls of our group; apple peel was used too, but often broke. This was early 1930s in south England. [Great Bedwyn, Wiltshire, November 1988]

Orange blossom, usually artificial rather than the real thing, is frequently used in WEDDING bouquets, or to decorate wedding cakes. The history of this use in the British Isles is vague, but it appears that the custom originated in the Mediterranean region.

The orange tree, simultaneously bearing golden fruit, sweet-scented flowers and leaves—typifying fertility, through this abundance—is a traditional ingredient in love charms and marriage luck. Saracen brides wore its flowers as a sign of fecundity and crusaders are said to have carried the custom to the west. [Baker, 1977: 78]

The MYRTLE was rivalled in popularity in the nineteenth century by the orange blossom, which seems to have been introduced to Britain from Spain in the 1820s. Oranges are said to have been the golden apple given by Juno to Jupiter on their wedding day, and the blossoms symbolize good luck, fertility and happiness. [Bloxham and Picken, 1990: 82]

Egg-rolling was a popular Easter-time activity in many parts of the British Isles for many years [Newall, 1971: 335], and a peculiar version of this custom which used oranges instead of eggs took place on Dunstable Downs, Bedfordshire, on Good Friday. In 1972 it was stated that:

Hundreds of children gather on Dunstable Downs and roll oranges down Pascombe Pit. This is said to be symbolic of the stone being rolled away from Jesus's tomb. [Palmer and Lloyd, 1972: 137]

However, a few years later:

Good Friday: Orange-throwing for the children has always been traditional on Dunstable Downs . . . but has lapsed in the last year or two after a hooligan threw an orange at the Mayor. [SLF MSS, Wood Green, London, March 1977]

Orange lily (*Lilium* spp., especially *L. × hollandicum*) On 12 July each year the Ulster Orange Lodges march in commemoration of the defeat of King James II by King William III (commonly known as William of Orange) at the Battle of the Boyne, fought in 1690.

Our banner poles are decorated with orange lilies and SWEET WILLIAM. If the traditional orange lily is not available substitutes such as the Peruvian lily or one of the new lily hybrids are used.

The orange lily is traditionally the symbol of the Orange Order and this is traced to orange lilies growing at the site of the Battle of the Boyne (similar in concept to the Flanders poppies). [Belfast, May 1994]

However, throughout William's lifetime and until the mid-eighteenth century it appears that the ORANGE tree, rather than the orange lily was used by his supporters. On 12 July 1812 a traveller found Tandragee, County Armagh, to be

> a perfect orange grove. The doors and windows were decorated with garlands of the Orange lily. The bosoms and heads of the women and the hats and breasts were equally adorned with this venerated flower. [Loftus, 1994: 16]

> In the Twelfth celebrations in Belfast in 1857 orange lilies decorated windows, arches and buttonholes . . . Today it flourishes in cottage gardens and country graveyards, on banner-poles and in the painted decoration of lambeg drums. [Loftus, 1994: 16]

In the Republic of Ireland:

> There are many kinds of poultices for drawing out BOILS or SORES, but the best is the orange lily. The roots are dug out of the ground, washed clean, and cut. Then they are boiled in water and the water turns into [a] substance like cornflour. Then it is applied to the boil or CUT and draws out all the matter and cleans it up. [IFCSS MSS 1100: 248, Co. Donegal].

Oregon weed – a name for PINEAPPLE WEED.

Orpine (*Sedum telephium*). John Aubrey (1626–97) wrote:

> Also I remember, the mayds (especially the Cooke mayds and Dayry-mayds) would stick-up in some chinkes of the joists, etc., Midsommer-men, which are slips of Orpins. they placed them by Paires, sc: one for such a man, the other for such a mayd his sweet-heart, and accordingly as the Orpin did incline to, or recline from ye other, that there would be love or aversion; if either did wither, death. [Aubrey, 1881: 25]

> In one of the tracts printed about 1800 at the Cheap Repository, was one entitled Tawney Rachel, or the Fortune-Teller, said to have been written by Hannah More. Among many other superstitious practices of poor Sally Evans, one of the heroines of the piece, we learn that 'she would never go to bed on Midsummer Eve without sticking up in her room the well-known plant called Midsummer Men, as the bending of the leaves to the right, or to the left, would never fail to tell her whether her lover was true or false . . .'

> On 22nd of January, 1801, a small gold ring . . . was exhibited to the Society of Antiquaries by John Topham, Esq. It had been found by the Rev. Dr. Bacon, of Wakefield, in a ploughed field near Cawood, in Yorkshire, and had for a device two orpine plants joined by a true-love knot, with this motto above: 'Ma fiance velt;' i.e. My sweetheart wills, or is desirous. The stalks of the plants were bent to each other, in token that the parties represented by them were to come together in marriage. The motto under the ring was, 'Joye l'amour feu.' From the form of the letters it appeared to have been a ring of the fifteenth century. [Brand, 1853: 329]

Although this passage has been frequently repeated, it should be treated with caution. The present whereabouts of the ring is unknown, but what was considered to be a similar one was in the Ralph Harari collection of finger rings. The bezel of this ring was 'engraved with a device of two plants, joined by a tasselled cord'. The collection has been dispersed and the plants cannot be identified from its illustrated catalogue [Boardman and Scarbrick, 1977], but they are certainly not orpine.

> Wednesday 11 June [1873]. In Gander Lane we saw in the banks some of the 'Midsummer Men' plants which my Mother remembers the servant maids and cottage girls sticking up in their houses and bedrooms on Midsummer Eve, for the purpose of divining about their sweethearts. [Plomer, 1977: 234]

> When we were children, we made Midsummer Men. These were two pieces of orpine, known to us as 'Live-long-love-long'. These we pushed through two empty cotton reels and took them to bed with us. One reel was given the name of our particular boy friend and the other was ourself. In the morning we looked at the reels. If the plants had fallen towards each other, all was well. If they had fallen one in one direction and the other in the opposite, then our love would not be true. [Simpson, 1973: 123]

Oxalis spp. – sold as four-leafed CLOVER; sold as SHAMROCK for St Patrick's Day in the USA.

Ox-eye daisy (*Leucanthemum vulgare*)

> As children we used to make chains from dog daisies. (I don't know the correct name for this plant. They are similar to the daisy but much larger and are usually found in meadows.) This plant or flower was also used in a game where one would pluck a petal each time as he/she recited: she/he loves me, she/he loves me not, until all the petals were gone. [Daingean, Co. Offaly, January 1985]

> There was the big white daisies . . . called Dog Daisies. I remember my own hands all big blisters, we were not allowed to touch them. [Castlerock, Co. Derry, February 1989]

> [On Colonsay ox-eye daisy] was esteemed as an excellent remedy for KING'S EVIL. [McNeill, 1910: 136]

For further information on daisy chains see DAISY; other plants used in love DIVINATION include ASH and HEMP.

Oxlip (*Primula elatior*)

> Many people in East Anglia (where the oxlip is a rare native) believe that the plant began its decline with the extinction of the wild boar. They say that the plant depended upon the droppings of these creatures, and the only reason they have survived in the area is because the oxlip woods, largely left to their own devices, still contain the last cases of wild boar dung! [Stevenage, Hertfordshire, January 1993]

P

Paigle – a name for COWSLIP and, more rarely, PRIMROSE.

Palm Sunday (also known as FIG Sunday and FLOWERING SUNDAY)—plants used as palm include BOX, CYPRESS, SALLOW, and YEW.

> People put blessed palm in the cow-houses so that the cows would get no disease. They also put it behind pictures to keep evil spirits away from the house. If you did not burn last year's palm, the old people said misfortune would befall you. If a person eat three pieces of palm he will get no sickness during the year. [IFCSS MSS 656: 67, Co. Tipperary].

Pancake – a Lincolnshire name for MALLOW.

Pansy (*Viola* × *wittrockiana*)

> My grandmother had a pansy game or story which goes like this: There were these five lovely daughters and they all went to the ball in the most lovely velvety ballgowns. My grandmother would pick off the five petals and hand them to me to admire the gowns. Then she would say—but they left their old mither (she was a Scot, my gran!) all alone sitting with both her legs in one stocking! Then she would show me the two spindly plant parts from which she had pulled a little green covering. I was always fascinated that this was so. And even now, I often pull apart a fading flower just to repeat my gran's story! [Long Melford, Suffolk, November 1993]

In the 1920s 'pansy' became slang for a male homosexual, particularly one of a rather effeminate nature. Any association between the flower and homosexuality is unclear, and it has been said that pansy is a corruption of the earlier 'nancy' which was in use towards the end of the nineteenth century, and was in turn derived from the 'Miss Nancy' which was used in the 1820s.

See also WILD PANSY.

Paralysis – prevented or cured using MILKWORT and TORMENTIL.

Parsley (*Petroselinum crispum*). With the possible exception of APPLE, parsley is the focus of more superstitious beliefs than any other plant commonly grown in gardens. In common with other herbs, such as SAGE, it is said that parsley grows best where the wife is dominant.

> Where parsley stays green all the year round the wife wears the trousers. [Wimbledon, London, November 1983]

My late husband, an officer and later Merchant Navy master . . . found it difficult to settle ashore.

In his allotment, he planted parsley which came up in abundance and he was delighted, but a few days later a neighbour told him that if parsley flourished the wife was the boss in the house. He dug it up. [Letter from Barry, South Glamorgan, in the *Daily Mirror*, 7 June 1989]

Parsley will grow where the wife wears the trousers. [Parkstone, Dorset, June 1991]

[In the Fens] in the years of economic depression, boys were far more welcome than girls . . . for this reason parsley . . . was never allowed to grow too high or too thick. If it did so this signified that the wife's influence in the home was stronger than her husband's, and so her children would probably all be female. [Porter, 1958: 113]

Alternatively parsley grew best for whoever was the dominant partner in a marriage.

Amongst people of the same background as my wife and myself it is thought that parsley should be sown by the head of the household. [Purley, Surrey, January 1978]

Whoever grows the parsley will be head of the house. [Reading, Berkshire, February 1987]

[From my family which originated from the village of Whitwick, near Coalville, Leicestershire:] the person who wears the trousers needs to set the parsley. [Hornchurch, Essex, August 1992]

More rarely it is thought that people who can grow parsley are malevolent.

Parsley flourishes only when sown by a rogue. [Letter from London, NW1, in the *Daily Mirror*, 26 May 1962]

Only a witch can grow parsley. [Waltham Abbey, Essex, March 1991]

In Somerset:

Parsley must be planted on a holy day or the fairies will get it. [Tongue, 1965: 33]

More usually GOOD FRIDAY is specified as being the day for sowing parsley.

A belief prevails in this district [Great Torrington, Devon] that . . . to have your parsley all the year round it should be sown this day [Good Friday]. [Amery, 1905: 114]

A north-country saying is that parsley will grow best if sown by the lady of the house before twelve noon on Good Friday. I do it and it works. [Letter from Orpington, Kent, in the *Daily Mirror*, 26 May 1962]

[In Sussex] Good Friday is the traditional day for . . . the sowing of parsley . . . if it is sown on this holy day, not only will it sprout quickly, but it will come up curly. [Simpson, 1973: 113]

We had to sow parsley seed on Good Friday because it had to go three times to the DEVIL before it germinated. [Hamworthy, Dorset, May 1991]

The idea that parsley seed 'visits' the devil was widespread, the number of visits made differing in different parts of the country.

[In Devon] parsley goes three times to the Devil before it comes up. [Chope, 1932: 155]

[In Sussex] some people say its roots go seven times to Hell and back before it will sprout. [Simpson, 1973: 113]

[In Walton-le-Dale, Yorkshire] parsley seed after being sown went seven times to the devil before it came up. [N & Q, 4 ser. 6: 211, 1870]

There is a saying in the North Riding of Yorkshire that 'parsley seed (when it has been sown) goes nine times to the devil.' [N & Q, 6 ser. 11: 467, 1885]

[In Herefordshire, parsley] is said to 'go to the owd 'un nine times afore it comes up.' [Leather, 1912: 21]

Cf. PARSNIP.

There is a widespread belief that parsley should not be transplanted or given away.

A poor woman near Morwenstow attributed a sort of stroke which had affected one of her children after whooping-cough to the moving of the parsley-bed; and in a neighbouring (Devonshire) parish, the parish clerk, it was believed, had been bed-ridden 'ever since the parsley-mores were moved'. [King, 1877: 90]

[Around Ilmington, Warwickshire] parsley must not be transplanted. If it is a member of the family in whose garden the parsley plants are set will die within the year. [*Folk-lore*, 24: 240, 1913]

[In west Dorset] in 1958 my father's mother died, and we moved from the cottage into the farmhouse. This entailed the transplanting of plants from one garden to the other. Parsley plants were amongst those moved, and, as she transplanted these, my mother lightheartedly said: 'Transplant parsley, transplant death.' These words were remembered a few days later when an elderly uncle of my father died. [Vickery, 1978: 158]

Many years ago an 80-year-old neighbour told me, 'Never transplant parsley, it always brings bad luck!' Being a trainee gardener, young and sceptical, I took no notice. When the time came I transplanted what was required. In three weeks I lost my job (no fault of mine), accidentally killed my cat, and lost a sum of money. [Truro, Cornwall, November 1993]

Although I transplant parsley, I do not offer seedlings to anyone in case they are superstitious about it. [Vale, Guernsey, April 1984]

A friend, a native of the south of Hampshire, tells me that it is the belief of the peasantry in his part of the country that it is very unlucky to give parsley. Last year his grandfather gave my friend's mother some which she planted. The latter was telling her washerwoman of this, when the woman exclaimed, 'Oh, ma'am, you have not taken the parsley? Then your father will die within the year.' Unfortunately this prediction was verified, so, doubtless, the woman is more than ever convinced of the truth of her absurd superstition. [N & Q, 4 ser. 11: 341, 1873]

Someone gave me a root of parsley and a neighbour said it was unlucky. Anyway, I tossed my head and thought 'so what'. Not long after my husband died. So that's the last I will grow. [Portland, Dorset, March 1991]

At the last whist drive at Holditch Mrs Harris picked some parsley, brought it up and gave it to me (as we haven't any). Phyllis Down was horrified as she said all sorts of awful things would befall me; I should have gone down to Gardners Farm and stole it; you should never have parsley given to you. Two nights later was when I was taken ill, so there's proof for you! [Thorncombe, Dorset, November 1984]

Children were told that babies came from parsley-beds.

Inquisitive children with us are usually told that babies are dug up from the parsley-bed, and sometimes it is vexatiously added that the boys are dug up from beneath a GOOSEBERRY bush. [N & Q, 4 ser. 9: 35, 1872]

[On Guernsey in 1882] the origin of babies was variously accounted for ... they are brought over in band-boxes from England in the mail packets ... are dug out of the parsley beds with golden spades. [Stevens Cox, 1971: 7]

In traditional medicine parsley was valued for gynaecological matters.

Take plenty of parsley to recuperate quickly after childbirth. This was told to me by my mother in the 1920s/30s, as told to her by her grandmother in 1890, and practised by her mother (who had 23 surviving children) in Berkshire in the mid-nineteenth century. [Farnham, Surrey, December 1985]

[From a London woman, aged about 20, 1982] if you want to bring on your period put a sprig of parsley inside your vagina for 12 hours—your period should start 24 hours later. [Opie and Tatem, 1989: 299]

[Fenland] village girls who became pregnant before marriage had faith in parsley, eating it three times daily for three weeks. [Porter, 1958: 113]

Parsley breakstone – a name for PARSLEY PIERT.

Parsley piert (*Aphanes arvensis*), also known as parsley breakstone.

[Gypsy remedy:] parsley piert . . . also called horse wort: infusion of the dried herb is good for gravel and other bladder troubles. [Vesey-FitzGerald, 1944: 27]

Parsley breakstone, washed and boiled, then drunk (by my mother) for gravel in the kidneys. [Quinton, West Midlands, April 1993]

Parsnip (*Pastinaca sativa*)

Old farmers used to say, with regard to digging the ground for their parsnip crop, that they should begin it whilst eating the bread baked at Christmas. [*Report and Transactions of the Guernsey Society for Natural Science*, 2: 276, 1893]

[Guernsey:] The seedlings germinate slowly and irregularly, and it was said the parsnip goes three times to the devil before it comes up four to six weeks after sowing. [De Garis, 1975: 121]

Cf. PARSLEY.

Parson in the pulpit – a widespread name for LORDS AND LADIES.

Pasque flower (*Pulsatilla vulgaris*). The rare and beautiful pasque flower, which is restricted to chalk grasslands in central and eastern England, is said to grow on the sites of battles, usually against the Danes.

On the dry chalk lands is found . . . the pasque flower, which is . . . traditionally associated with the Danes. It is supposed to grow only where their BLOOD has been shed and is known in Hampshire as Danes' blood. One of the few places where its purple bell-like flowers can be seen is on the Downs dividing Hampshire from Berkshire—curiously enough, the site of King Alfred's battlefield. [Boase, 1976: 115]

When we used to live in that area [Berkshire Downs, on the Oxfordshire border in the 1950s] we were told a story that the pasque flower grew on the sites of battles. The Danes planted these flowers where they fell in battle. [Anonymous telephone call, April 1991]

Passion dock – a Yorkshire name for BISTORT.

Passion flower (*Passiflora caerulea*)

Another flower which is traditonally associated with the Crucifixion is that called the Passion-flower . . . the Spanish friars in America first called it 'flower of the passion' (*flos passionis*), and, by adding what was wanting, made it an epitome of our Saviour's Passion . . . The name was given by the superstitious in former times, who saw in the five anthers a resemblance to the five wounds received by Christ when nailed to the cross. In the triple style are seen the three nails employed; one for each of the hands, the other for the feet. In the central receptacle one can detect the pillar of the cross, and in the filaments is seen a representation of the crown of thorns on the head. The calyx was supposed to resemble the nimbus, or glory, with which the sacred head is regarded as being surrounded. [Friend, 1884: 192]

Passion Sunday – PEAS eaten on.

Pea (*Pisum sativum*)

[Cambridgeshire] farmers used to say that it would be a good year for peas if the hedges dripped on St Valentine's morn. [Parsons MSS, 1952]

Peas were widely used in love DIVINATION:

[In Co. Cavan] if you put a pod with nine peas in it up over the door the first person who enters will have the same name as your 'future'. [Jones, 1908: 323]

[In Horseheath, Cambridgeshire] when peas were being 'coshed' or shelled, a keen look out was kept for a 'cosh' holding nine peas and when a girl found one she would hang it over her doorway in the belief that she would marry a man with the same initial as the first person who passed under it. [Parsons MSS, 1952]

Alternatively:

[In West Sussex] if you find nine peas in the first pod you gather, it bodes you good luck. [Latham, 1878: 9]

In parts of northern England peas are traditionally eaten on Passion or Carling Sunday.

In north-east England peas or BEANS fried in butter with vinegar and pepper are still served in many houses on Passion or Carling Sunday. There is considerable doubt as to the meaning of the word 'carling;' in the Midlands the day is called Care Sunday, a name which is supposed to refer to the sorrow or care of Our Lord's Passion. [Hole, 1950: 42]

Here in the fastness of East Cleveland this [Carling Sunday] is still observed in the old mining communities. It, in fact, takes place on the fifth Sunday in Lent, Passion Sunday, not on the fourth.

Carlings are no delicacies, either. They are black peas, usually reserved for pigeon food, soaked like mushy peas and eaten with salt and vinegar.

To the uninitiated they are utterly vile, tasting neither like peas nor anything else, but to the East Cleveland carling enthusiast they are something to be looked forward to.

The name for the Monday which follows Carling Sunday I would not mention to your reader's delicate ears! [Letter from Boosbeck, Cleveland, in *The Times*, 3 April 1985]

Carling Sunday: 3 weeks before Easter; where I live now in Cumbria a kind of brown dried pea, usually given to pigeons, soaked and boiled with molasses is eaten. Not a family tradition with me, but I eat them now— OK once a year. [Townhead, Cumbria, August 1989]

Peach

Peach (*Prunus persica*). Peach blossom is occasionally associated with Chinese New Year celebrations.

> It is the custom for Chinese families to go out into the market on New Year's Eve to buy peach blossoms to decorate their homes. The blossoms signify spring, which also means the beginning of the New Year in the lunar calendar and this is why the New Year Festival is often termed the Spring Festival. This is still the practice in Hong Kong and also in certain Chinese communities here in the UK, where imported blossoms are available. [Soho, London, February 1991]

The association of peach blossom with New Year festivities 'seems to have held only for some forty years'. In earlier times the hanging bell-flower (*Enkianthus quinqueflorus*), a wild bush in south China, was used.

> With the Japanese occupation of most of Guangdong province in 1938 supplies dried up and local residents looked for alternatives. Some skilled nurserymen sought refuge in Hong Kong where they introduced the art of growing peach blossom. In post-war years the hanging bellflowers made a temporary comeback. But in 1949 the changes in landownership and in marketing in producing areas . . . led to its final demise for the New Year. [Goody, 1993: 394]

Today the production of peach blossom is a highly skilled occupation 'for their growth requires great care to make them bloom at the right moment and so ensure good fortune for the coming year. If they come on too soon, steps are taken to discourage their growth and the early blooms are nipped off or salt water sprayed over them. If too slow, the leaves are plucked off earlier rather than later to encourage the flowers, and the trees wrapped in plastic to keep off the wind.'

The buying of peach blossom also requires some skill, as the branches have to be in bloom on New Year's Day, but not too advanced, so that they remain in blossom throughout the fifteen-day New Year season [Goody, 1993: 389–94].

Peanut (*Arachis hypogaea*)

> An old aunt, born 1870s, Warwickshire, advocated eating peanuts for DIABETES. [Mordiford, Herefordshire, December 1991]

Pear (*Pyrus communis*)

> [An Irish belief:] it is unlucky to bring pear blossom into the house. It signifies a death in the family. [SLF MSS, Birmingham, September 1977]

> George Broun, 10th Laird of Coalstoun, who died in or before 1524, married Marion Hay, daughter of the second Lord Hay of Yester. The dowry of this lady consisted, in part, of what has long been known as the Coalstoun Pear. Hugo de Gifford of Yester, her remote ancestor, famed for his necromantic powers, was supposed to have invested this Pear with

278

the extraordinary virtue of securing for the family which might possess it unfailing prosperity. This Pear is preserved at Coalstoun with the care due to so singular an heirloom, which, regardless of the superstition, must be esteemed a very wonderful vegetable curiosity, having existed for more than 500 years . . .

Sir George Broun of Coalstoun, Bart., married Lady Elizabeth M'Kenzie . . . and this lady is reported to have bitten a piece out of the famous Pear. It was to be expected that some calamity would follow on such an outrage . . . Accordingly, in 1699, Sir George was constrained by the pressure of incumbrances to sell the estate; but he was fortunate in meeting with a purchaser in the person of his brother, Robert Broun . . . However, a much greater calamity soon befell . . . the Laird of Coalstoun and both his sons were drowned on the 5th of May 1703, and Coalstoun passed to an heiress. [*Scottish Antiquary*, 5: 181, 1891]

Pearlwort (*Sagina procumbens*). On Colonsay, in the Inner Hebrides, pearlwort

is said to have been one of the plants that were formerly fixed over doors for good luck. [McNeill, 1910: 105]

Cf. ROWAN.

Peashooter – a north Wales name for JAPANESE KNOTWEED.

Pee-beds, pee-in-bed, pee-in-the-bed, pee-the-beds – names for DANDELION.

Pellitory of the wall (*Parietaria judaica*)

[Guernsey:] a tisane made from this plant is used in cases of DIABETES. [Marquand, 1906: 44]

[Gypsies use] juice from leaves as an ingredient of ointment that cures ULCERS, running sores and PILES . . . Infusion of the leaves allays all bladder troubles. Infusion of leaves and wild CARROT is good for DROPSY. Ointment made from crushed root is good for piles. [Vesey-FitzGerald, 1944: 27]

My father boils . . . pellitory of the wall and drinks the brew thus obtained. He says it's good for the KIDNEYS. It acts against kidney stones as far as I remember. [Skibbereen, Co. Cork, April 1994]

Pennyroyal (*Mentha pulegium*)

Pouliet or *Poue-ye* . . . pennyroyal . . . so called at the Vale [Guernsey] and said to be efficacious in destroying vermin on children's heads. These parasites are known by the name of *pouas*. [Marquand, 1906: 45]

More usually pennyroyal was used as an ABORTIFACIENT. According to an early eigthteenth-century author, the liquid juice and oily tincture of pennyroyal would 'provoke the terms in women, expel the birth,

dead child, and afterbirth'. However, the 'potestates or powers' prepared from the same plant had the ability to cure INFERTILITY in men
and women, while the essence would 'much increase the seed in both
sexes and strongly provoke lust' [Salmon, 1710: 846].

Until the First World War pennyroyal syrup was valued as an abortifacient by the poor of Salford [Roberts, 1971: 100], and in a North
Riding sword-dance play, collected in 1926, a man–woman, who is
killed, simulates labour and is revived after being treated with
'oakum-pokum pennyroyal' [Helm, 1981: 26]. A nurse training in a
London hospital in the 1940s found that one of her patient's records
revealed how she had suffered a miscarriage after swallowing a box of
pennyroyal pills [Shepherdswell, Kent, October 1979]. About fifteen
years later, pennyroyal extracts were resorted to by Halifax telephone
operators. If there was a strong minty smell in the workroom, someone would be sure to say 'Hallo girls, who else has been got now?' for
bottled pennyroyal was commonly used as 'a standby for girls who
missed a period', and worked in some cases, 'when it probably would
have worked anyway' [Leeds, October 1981].

Pennywort (*Umbilicus rupestris*), also known as navelwort.

> Among my childhood group in mid-Devon in the 1930s navelwort was
> quite the most favoured agent of weather forecasting. One selected two
> large leaves, spat liberally into them, pressed them together and threw
> them into the air. Should they continue to adhere when striking the
> ground rain would ensue, should they part dry weather could be ex-
> pected. Being Devon, it usually rained, but, on reflection, I incline to the
> view that the liberality of spittle was the main determinant of the outcome
> (but this, of course, was the main fun involved!). [Salisbury, Wiltshire,
> January 1992]

More usually pennywort is used in folk medicine.

> Pennywort which grows along hedges is a cure for CORNS. [IFCSS MSS
> 925: 6, Co. Wicklow]

> Lard and wall pennywort are pounded together for the treatment of saddle
> sores. [Douglas, Isle of Man, August 1979; originally collected 1965]

> I was told by a lady that when a child, in the 1950s, she and her friends
> used the leaves of Cornish Pennywort (*Umbilicus rupestris*) to treat spots
> and pimples. Pennywort is very common here, on our Cornish walls. I
> feel sure that the use of round leaves is a modern 'DOCTRINE OF SIGNA-
> TURES' prompted by the resemblance to first aid adhesive patches. [St
> Ervan, Cornwall, February 1991]

> Mix pennywort and butter (unsalted) for BURNS. [Llanuwchylln, Gwy-
> nedd, April 1991]

A local farmer tells me he always uses pennywort if he gets a thorn or splinter in his fingers. He peels the 'skin' from the back of the leaf before applying and 'tis drawn out in a day or two. [St Ervan, Cornwall, February 1992]

Occasionally pennywort is eaten.

Young fleshy leaves [of wall pennywort] can be found early in the year, and small amounts chopped into salads. [St Mary's, Isles of Scilly, September 1992]

Peony (*Paeonia* spp.)

On the death of a friend in the summer, an old lady, a relative, who was on a visit of condolence to the widow, went quietly into the garden and counted the flowers on the peonies. On her return . . . [she] said she had counted the flowers on the peonies in the garden, and there was an odd number on each plant, which was a sure sign of death in the house before the year was out. [*N & Q*, 4 ser. 12: 469, 1873]

If there are odd numbers of flowers on a peony it is a sign of a death. [Taylor MSS].

[The peony] is called 'sheep-shearing rose' by many from the rough joke of filling the folds of the petals with pungent snuff or pepper at sheep-shearing feasts in order to enjoy the torments of those who innocently smell it at that period. [*N & Q*, 5 ser. 9: 405, 1878]

[In West Sussex] a necklace turned from the root of the peony is worn by children to prevent CONVULSIONS, and aid dentition. [Latham, 1878: 44]

Periwinkle (*Vinca minor*, lesser periwinkle, and *V. major*, greater periwinkle). A widespread rhyme which describes a bride's apparel is:

> Something old, something new,
> Something borrowed, something blue.

Near Cheltenham in Gloucestershire:

The 'something blue' that a bride wears is the blue periwinkle. One informant told me that it must be worn in the garter for fertility. [Hammond MSS, 1970: 28]

In Wiltshire:

Many old cottages have periwinkles along the garden banks. These were often planted when a newly-married couple took possession of the cottage, in the belief that the periwinkles would ensure a lucky and happy marriage. [Whitlock, 1976: 163]

Similarly, in Cambridgeshire:

Fen people believed that if a young married couple planted a patch of periwinkles in the garden of their first home their life together would be a happy one.

The periwinkle is one of the flowers held by many Cambridgeshire people to wither quickly if worn as a buttonhole by a young girl of a flirtatious nature or by an unchaste wife. [Porter, 1969: 47]

Popular works of the sixteenth and seventeenth centuries mention periwinkle as a promoter of conjugal love. First published in English in c.1550, *The Book of Secrets*, falsely attributed to Albertus Magnus (1193–1280), stated that when periwinkle was 'beaten unto a powder with worms of the earth wrapped around it, and with an herb called *Semperviva*, in English HOUSELEEK, it induceth love between man and wife, if it be used in their meats' [Best and Brightman, 1973: 8]. Culpeper [1652: 170] claimed that the periwinkle was owned by Venus, and that 'the leaves eaten by man and wife together causeth love between them.'

In west Dorset the wild periwinkle is associated with St Candida (also known as St Wite), to whom the church at Whitchurch Canonicorum is dedicated. St Candida has been variously identified as the Breton princess, St Gwen (or St Blanche), a monk named Witta who accompanied St Boniface, and a local Saxon holy woman who was martyred by Danish invaders. The Saint's shrine remains intact in the church, and is the focus of a growing cult. In pre-Reformation times:

> After venerating the shrine, our pilrim made his way to the saint's well, about a mile away at Morcombelake. The waters of St Wite's Well enjoyed a reputation as late as the 1930s as being 'a sovereign cure for sore eyes' . . . The wild periwinkles that carpet nearby Stonebarrow Hill every spring, are still known locally as 'St Candida's Eyes'. [Waters, 1987]

In nineteenth-century Oxfordshire the greater periwinkle was known as cutfinger:

> The leaves are commonly applied to chapped hands, and are said to have healing properties. [Britten and Holland, 1886: 139]

Peruvian lily (*Alstroemeria aurea*)—used for decorating banner-poles at Orange Order marches, if ORANGE LILIES are not available.

Petty spurge (*Euphorbia peplus*)

[Andreas, Isle of Man, June 1929:] *Lhuss-ny-fahnnaghyn*—used for WARTS. [NHM MSS, herbarium C.I. Paton]

> When I was a very young boy (about 5 years old) I went to a gypsy camp close to Bodmin. There was a lady there complaining that the elderly lady had failed to 'charm' a very disfiguring WART on her face. The gypsy said she had another way provided she was given silver. Wartweed was produced and the 'milk' was applied to the wart, and she was told to do this daily. The husband refused to pay. The gypsy then cursed him and rubbed his forehead with wartweed.

Later that day we saw the husband in Bodmin and there was a bright red cross on his forehead. I was very interested and tried putting it on the back of my hand. It soon started to sting quite badly. [Truro, Cornwall, December 1993; specimen of plant sent and identified].

See also SPURGE.

Phacelia (*Phacelia tanacetifolia*)

Phacelia was originally reported in Jersey in the mid eighties as being sown after the POTATO crop had been lifted to deter eelworm in the soil. Now grown similarly as a green manure. [St Saviour, Jersey, May 1993]

Pharoah's pea – a Northamptonshire name for EVERLASTING PEA.

Pignut (*Conopodium majus*)

My mother and her peers used to eat Lucy Arnots (Arnuts?) and SOORICKS . . . Lucy Arnots were the root of some plant that grew along the banks . . . I never ate them. [Whitfield, Dundee, November 1988]

Pignut: we used to dig the roots in the First World War and eat the noodles [i.e. nodules] at the end of the root! [Didcot, Oxfordshire, February 1991]

[As a child at Wimborne St Giles, Dorset, over sixty years ago:] the tubers of pignut were dug up with flints, and eaten, but we washed them in the river. [Sidmouth, Devon, October 1991]

Pigtoes – a Kent name for BIRD'S-FOOT TREFOIL.

Pig weed – a Gloucestershire name for COW PARSLEY.

Piles – treated using CELANDINE, CHESTNUT, ELDER, HORSE CHESTNUT, MEZEREON, ONION, and PELLITORY OF THE WALL.

Pilewort – a name for CELANDINE.

Pimples – treated using LEMON and PENNYWORT.

Pin bur – a Bedfordshire name for CORN CLEAVERS fruits.

Pine (*Pinus* spp.). On Guernsey:

Pines are very unlucky trees indeed. Whoever planted a row of them ran the risk that the property on which they stood might change hands, or pass from their rightful heir to a younger branch of the family. My grandmother always said that if you fell asleep under a pine tree you would not wake up. [De Garis, 1975: 117]

However, elsewhere:

A remark made to me the other day by a friend who said a parent had been advised to take his ailing son for a fortnight's holiday at a spot on the Welsh coast where pines are plentiful. 'Get the child into the smell of the pines for an hour or two every day', the serious advice ran. And he did, and the child, by all accounts, was cured. [*Times Weekly Review*, 31 May 1956]

See also SCOTS PINE.

Pineapple (*Ananas comosus*). Stone pineapples are often seen decorating the entrances to even quite modest homes.

> Members of the British East Indies Company brought the plants to England where they were cultivated in 17th century hot houses. Only the very rich could afford the fruit, so it became synonymous with opulence and high living. Middle-class party givers had to be content with renting the fruit for centrepiece displays. American sea captains gave the custom a new twist during the era of New England's great sailing ships. When a captain arrived home from the tropics he brought pineapples with him. He placed one on the newel (post) of his front stairway to let everyone know he was home and waiting for his friends to visit. [*Miami Herald*, 4 February 1984]

This explanation appears to be less than totally correct for, although pineapples are now widely cultivated throughout tropical Asia, the plant is of New World origin and the first fruits to reach Britain came from the West Indies [Raphael, 1990: xxxii].

Pineapple weed (*Matricaria discoidea*)

> Rayless mayweed, also known as pineapple weed or Oregon weed—gives a yellow-orange DYE. [Lerwick, Shetland, March 1994]

Piskie, pixie, pixy – Devon names for GREATER STITCHWORT.

Piss-i-beds, pissimire, piss-in-the-beds, pisterbed – names for DANDELION.

Plaguewort – a Cornish name for BUTTERBUR.

Planets – plants under the dominion of, see ASTROLOGICAL BOTANY.

Planta genista. The identity of *planta genista*, which gave its name to the Plantagenet royal house that ruled England from 1154 to 1399, has caused considerable speculation, but it is usually considered to be BROOM. The family's name is said to have been derived from the habit of Geoffrey, Count of Anjou, of wearing a piece of the plant.

> A sprig of *genista* was adopted as his badge by Gefroi, Duke of Anjou, father of Henry II. He gathered that wild flower . . . when passing through a rocky pathway; he saw on either side bushes of yellow broom clinging with firm grasp to the huge stones, or upholding the crumbling soil: 'And thus' (said he) 'shall that golden plant ever be my cognizance, firmly rooted amid rocks, and yet upholding that which is ready to fall. I

will bear it in my crest, amid battlefields if need be, at tournaments, and when dispensing justice.' Thus saying, the warrior broke off a branch, and fixing it in triumph on his cap, returned to his castle. [Friend, 1884: 390]

Plantain (*Plantago* spp.)

We called all plantains MOTHER-DIE and this was purported to happen if you took one indoors. [Stockport, Greater Manchester, March 1994]

What happened was that an elderly man doing some gardening cut his thumb badly. He refused all first aid, picked a plantain leaf—I think from the edge of the lawn—bit it in several places (with his front teeth) bound the leaf over the cut, assuring us that it would heal quickly and cleanly, which it did. [Diptford, Devon, February 1979]

[She] picked the leaves of a variety of this plant from her garden and told me it would stop bleeding in a few minutes. When her husband cut himself when shaving she always got the leaves for him to put on. He himself would go and get a cobweb and put it on, and she said 'Of course that would stop the bleeding too.' [Andreas, Isle of Man, May 1963; Manx Folklife Survey].

See also BUCK'S HORN PLANTAIN, GREATER PLANTAIN, HOARY PLANTAIN, and RIBWORT PLANTAIN.

Planting times

It is . . . believed that flowers or shrubs set or transplanted in January, February, March, April, September, October, November and December are sure to grow, but if set in other months (those without the letter R) will not grow. [IFCSS MSS 350: 356, Co. Cork]

It is considered, by farmers, unlucky to begin any work such as ploughing, sowing or mowing on Saturday. [IFCSS MSS 225: 347, Co. Leitrim]

See also GOOD FRIDAY.

Plant of friendship – a name for ROSEMARY.

Pleurisy – cured using field scabious.

Plum (*Prunus domestica*)

'A good WHEAT year, a fine plum year.' This is a prevailing saying in N. Notts, and one which I have heard from many persons this year, the crops of both being very good. [N & Q, 7 ser. 4: 485, 1887]

Pneumonia – cured using ELDER.

Pobbles – a name given to the fruit of KARO on the Isles of Scilly.

Poison spittle – a Shetland name for hair MOSS and thyme thread moss.

Polypody

Polypody (*Polypodium vulgare*)

An old woman [in Co. Galway] informed me that this [polypody] was an excellent physic. 'It was to be pulled,' she said, 'in the full moon, and the roots of it buried in porridge and left there for the night; but,' she said 'if you do place the root this way (as it grows) it will work you downwards, and if you place it upside down it will work you upwards, but if you put it both ways it will work you up and down, and it is the best physic that grows.' [Hart, 1873: 339]

The crushed roots, used [by gypsies] as a poultice and applied to the seat of the pain, is a good remedy for RHEUMATISM. An old country name for the plant is rheum-purging polypody, which indicates that the properties have long been known in a wider circle. But this name has long since died out. [Vesey-FitzGerald, 1944: 27]

Pontius Pilate – associated with a YEW tree at Fortingall, Perthshire.

Poor man's asparagus – a Lincolnshire name for cooked stalks of GOOD KING HENRY.

Poor man's weatherglass – a widespread name for SCARLET PIMPERNEL.

Pop dock – a Cornish name for FOXGLOVE.

Poplar (*Populus* sp.)

When I was little [c.1940s] my older relatives urged me to collect poplar catkins and put them in a little saucer, carefully mixed with water for the fairies to eat at night (while I was asleep!) Needless to say the catkins had all gone by morning . . . I believe it was a fairly common practice among children earlier this century. [Sutton, Surrey, August 1993]

See also BLACK POPLAR and WHITE POPLAR.

Poppy (*Papaver rhoeas*)

About Wooler [Northumberland] it was wont to be called the Thunder-flower or Lightnings; and children were afraid to pluck the flower, for if, perchance, the petals fell off in the act, the gatherer became more liable to be struck with lightning; nor was the risk small, for the deciduousness of the petals is almost proverbial. [Johnston, 1853: 30]

The red poppies that grow in cornfields in Ireland are in the counties of Carlow, Wexford, Wicklow and Waterford called 'Headaches', and are particularly obnoxious to females, the more so to young unmarried women, who have a horror of touching or being touched by them. The flower is sometimes used with logwood and copperas to DYE wool and yarn black, but otherwise the weed is considered posionous. [*N & Q*, 3 ser. 8: 319, 1865]

The popular name for field poppies, as well as cultivated ones, in this district [Worksop] is 'earaches' . . . It is said that if they are gathered and put to the ear a violent attack of EARACHE will be the result. [*N & Q*, 5 ser. 9: 488, 1878]

Blind Eyes—*Papaver rhoeas*, there is a belief in Yorkshire that if placed too near the eyes it will cause BLINDNESS. [Britten and Holland, 1886: 50]

Cornish people believe that if freely handled the corn poppy will produce WARTS; hence it is often called the 'Wart Flower'. [Davey, 1909: 19]

[In Horseheath, Cambridgeshire] children were taught that they should avoid smelling the flowers of the Common Red Poppy which were believed to cause NOSEBLEEDS, which could be stopped however by putting cobwebs up the nostrils. [Parsons MSS, 1952]

Poppy—called the 'heead-vahhk' (HEADACHE)—because it gives you one. [Driffield, Humberside, March 1985]

As a boy I was told not to sniff poppy flowers as to do so would give you a headache. [Histon, Cambridgeshire, January 1989]

It is probable that at least some of these beliefs were propagated to discourage children from gathering the attractive flowers, and thereby causing damage to crops. Cf. BINDWEED. However, it appears that there may be an element of truth behind the idea that poppies could cause headaches and blindness. According to a veteran of the First World War, who described long marches through fields of red poppies, the flowers 'was so bright they affected our eyes—we could see red for days' [Hewins, 1981: 147]. Similarly in the nineteenth century, London tailors found that:

Of all colours scarlet, such as used for regimentals, is the most blinding . . . there's more military tailors blind than any others. [Quennell, 1984: 167]

However, sometimes children seem unaware of poppies being inauspicious, and use them in games.

The dollies I remember from the cornfields . . . were the little ballerina poppy dollies that our mother taught us to make from the scarlet poppies . . . Tiny features were marked with a pin or a pencil point on the green seed capsule which wore its own natural flat ribbed cap; a few stamens were removed in front of the face, the remaining ones forming an impressive Elizabethan-type ruff. The petals were turned down and tied tightly at the waist with cotton or a blade of grass. A length of stalk was pushed between the petals for arms, and, if fussy, another piece could be pushed up into the waist to make a second leg. [Hersom, 1973: 79].

[We were perpetually on the move during my childhood, but 50 years ago, probably in Staffordshire] we made Chinese-men poppy dollys. The petals were turned back. Two pieces of stalk were used, one as a cross-piece for the arms, and another to add to the still attached stalk to make a second leg. A piece of wool gave a waist to the poppy petal dress, and a Chinese face drawn on the exposed seed box. [St Mary's, Isles of Scilly, September 1992]

When my children were at school in Craigavan, Northern Ireland, c.1969, they used to say to me 'Do you want to see the fairies dance?' They would pull a flower—either field poppy or lesser bindweed—and pull the petals back over the stem to make a 'skirt', and holding the stem between thumb and forefinger just behind the flowerhead (within the skirt) move the finger to and fro to cause the flowerhead to partially rotate and return—this caused the 'fairy' to dance. [Barton upon Humber, Humberside, February 1992]

Since early in the nineteenth century poppies have been associated with those who have died in battle.

The red poppies which followed the ploughing of the field of Waterloo after the Duke of Wellington's victory were said to have sprung from the BLOOD of the troops who fell during the engagement. [Dyer, 1889: 15]

In the twentieth century the poppy has become a symbol of remembrance of those who died in the First World War and subsequent wars. During the second Battle of Ypres, in May 1915, a Canadian doctor, Colonel John Macrae, wrote:

> In Flanders fields the poppies blow,
> Between the crosses, row on row
> That mark our place; and in the sky
> The larks still bravely singing fly
> Scarce heard amid the guns below.
>
> We are the dead. Short days ago
> We lived, felt dawn, saw sunset glow,
> Loved and were loved, and now we lie
> In Flanders fields.
>
> Take up our quarrel with the foe;
> To you from failing hand we throw
> The torch; be yours to hold it high,
> If ye break faith with us who die
> We shall not sleep, though poppies grow
> In Flanders fields.

Published in *Punch* in December 1915, the poem caught the eye of, and inspired, an American woman, Moina Michael, who produced a poem which took up the poppy motif:

> We cherish, too, the poppy red
> That grows on fields where valor led,

> It seems to signal to the skies
> That blood of heroes never dies,
> But lends a lustre to the red
> Of the flower that blooms above the dead
> In Flanders fields.

Miss Michael took to wearing a poppy to 'keep faith in those who died', and in November 1918 a French woman, Madame Guerin, intrigued by the poppy, asked Miss Michael what it meant. Madame Guerin decided to get poppies manufactured in France and sell them, with any profits going to assist people returning to war-devastated areas. Thus when the British Legion organized its first Poppy Day, in 1921, it used poppies imported from France. The first appeal raised £106,000, and the Legion thought it desirable to find a British source to supply poppies.

By June 1922 Major George Howson had established a poppy factory, which employed five disabled men, in east London. Initially only lapel poppies were made, but in 1924 the making of wreaths was added to the factory's activities, the first large wreath being laid by the Prince of Wales on 11 November 1924. By 1925 Hewson's workforce had grown to fifty, so it was necessary to search for larger premises, which were eventually found at Richmond, Surrey.

Until 1975 only ex-servicemen, with preference being given to the disabled, were employed making poppies, but since then the pool of potential recruits has expanded to include ex-servicewomen and the widows and disabled dependants of ex-servicemen. In July 1989 the factory provided work for 130 employees, 80 per cent of whom were disabled. An additional forty-five or so workers, who were aged, severely disabled, or in poor health, assembled poppies in their own homes. Each year the factory produces approximately 36 million poppies (which are sold by some 250,000 volunteers), 75,000 wreaths, and 250,000 remembrance crosses. In 1988 the Poppy Appeal, which exists to help all ex-service personnel and their dependants, raised over £10 million [Royal British Legion Poppy Factory, December 1989].

Since 1933 white poppies have also been worn during the Remembrance Day period. Initially these were promoted by the Co-operative Women's Guild as 'a pledge to peace that wars must never happen again'. It was intended to extend 'the narrow nationalistic and militaristic view of Remembrance to remembering all the dead in wars, irrespective of nationality, civilians as well as those in the armed forces'. The use of white poppies reached its peak in 1938, but they continued to be used sporadically until 1980, when they were adopted by the Peace Pledge Union. The Union organizes an alternative wreath-laying ceremony at the Cenotaph in Whitehall, London, at which a wreath of white poppies is used. In 1988 the Union expected to sell 50,000 white poppies [leaflets produced by the PPU, 1988, and Seed, 1988].

See also OPIUM POPPY and YELLOW HORNED POPPY.

Potato (*Solanum tuberosum*). On Looe (or St George's) Island off the south coast of Cornwall:

> We had been told that it was tradition to plant early potatoes on Boxing Day. As it was now February it seemed a matter of urgency to sow them as soon as possible, and I was determined to get started at once. [Atkins, 1986: 23]

Elsewhere planting was delayed until later in the year. In some parts of Ireland:

> Early potatoes: it was believed that this crop should be sowed before ST PATRICK'S DAY. [Daingean, Co. Offaly, January 1985]

> Potatoes should be planted . . . about St Patrick's Day, when he 'turns up the warm side of the stone'. [Lisburn, Co. Antrim, March 1986]

However, the common date for planting potatoes was GOOD FRIDAY, which can fall on any date between 20 March and 23 April, when at least token plantings would be made.

> [Warcop, Cumbria, c.1920] On Good Friday only essential work on farms was done, but everyone with a garden set his potatoes no matter how late or how early Easter came. [Short, 1983: 118]

> [In Ireland] most farmers would, however, plant a small quantity of grain or potatoes on this blessed day, thus invoking a blessing on the crops. [Danaher, 1972: 71]

> [In Rutland and south-west Lincolnshire before the 1939 war] Potatoes (first crop) must be planted on Good Friday (believed to be symbolical of the Resurrection after three days, thus promoting the growth of the buried tubers). [Frome, Somerset, June 1978]

> The planting of our potatoes, it was always on Good Friday. 'They' seemed to think because it was a Holy Day the potatoes would be better, and in our case the potatoes were great. [Castlerock, Co. Derry, February 1989]

In County Mayo seed potatoes 'are dressed during planting, with a pinch of salt and human excrement'; in Kerry 'a piece of CYPRESS is stuck into the ridge on planting day, and on harvesting a branch of the same is burnt' [Salaman, 1949: 117].

It was reported in 1836 that in County Mayo:

> The digging of potatoes for daily use commences after Garlick Sunday [the first Sunday in August], but not to such an extent as to prevent a great rise in price. [Danaher, 1972: 165]

Elsewhere in Ireland:

> Garland Sunday, being the last in July, is in Galway the day on which the first digging is permitted. In Kerry the date is 7 July, the day of the local patron saint. In Cork, some potatoes, however few, should always be dug on 29 June. In Mayo, in every home the end of the potato harvest is celebrated by a feast. In Tipperary, when new potatoes first appear on the table, it is usual for each to say to the other: 'May we all be alive and happy this time twelve months.' [Salaman, 1949: 117]

Garlick or GARLAND SUNDAY are two of several recent names given to the ancient Celtic festival of Lughnasa, which was formerly celebrated to welcome the first fruits of the harvest. In many parts of Ireland the day was known as the Sunday of the New Potatoes [Ó Suilleabhain, 1967: 68].

Wishes were often made when the first new potatoes were eaten (cf. FRUIT).

> There is an old saying that you'll get what you wish for when you are sitting down to your first dinner of new potatoes. [IFCSS MSS 232: 269, Co. Roscommon]

> It is a custom to wish when eating the first new potato. [IFCSS MSS 800: 14, Co. Offaly]

Potatoes are used to prevent RHEUMATISM or, more rarely, CRAMP.

> I knew a clergyman in the North of England, a graduate of Oxford, who used to carry in his trousers pocket, and recommend to others, a potato as a cure for rheumatism. [N & Q, 8 ser. 9: 396, 1896]

> It is a common custom in this neighbourhood [Mere Down, Wiltshire] for a person suffering from rheumatic afflictions to carry a potato in his pocket. I have known several individuals try the experiment, and have seen the potatoes, after being carried in their pockets, perhaps, for months, dried up and shrunk to about the size of a large marble. Whilst some believe it to be a certain cure—one man, in particular, says he was a martyr to the complaint for years, but since he has carried a potato has not felt a twinge—others say they derive no benefit from it. [N & Q, 8 ser. 9: 396, 1896]

> [Somerset/Devon:] a potato carried until it gets hard in the pocket of the patient, is firmly believed in as a cure for rheumatism. It is supposed to 'draw the iron out of the blood': too much iron, and consequent stiffness, being the root of the complaint. [Whistler, 1908: 89]

> A cure for rheumatic pains, sciatica and lumbago, is carry in your pocket a Champion potato which you stole from your neighbour's pit. [IFCSS MSS 812: 110, Co. Offaly]

> It is an ordinary eating potato which is two years old. He has kept it in his trouser pocket, so near the skin (his I mean) as possible, as years ago he was

told by a gypsy by doing that it will prevent rheumatism. He hasn't it and is now eighty years of age. [Altarnun, Cornwall, April 1986]

A potato in the bed helps do away with cramp. [Rushmere St Andrew, Suffolk, February 1989]

Occasionally a potato may be used to provide more general protection, or even to attract good luck.

In May 1978, when discussing the football pools with a group of middle-aged women working in South Kensington, they mentioned some of the 'lucky charms' which they hoped would bring them luck. These included short lengths of string, pressed four-leaved CLOVERS, and tiny withered potatoes, all of which they carried around in their purses. [Streatham, London, October 1991]

Other medical uses included:

A sore throat was cured by roasting potatoes and putting them into a stocking, and tying them around the neck. [IFCSS MSS 212: 10, Co. Leitrim].

Sliced potato to be rubbed on the CHILBLAIN every night for three times and in a short time the chilblain will be cured. [IFCSS MSS 790: 34, Co. Dublin].

I have been assured by an elderly neighbour, a lady, that a certain cure for leg ULCERS and other hard-to-heal lesions is obtained by simply grating a portion of raw potato over the sore. She has used the treatment herself in the past with complete success. [Glynn, Co. Antrim, February 1992]

Being readily available, potatoes were used in children's toy-making and games.

Tattie craa—Choose a nicely rounded potato, then collect some stout wing feathers from a large bird such as the herring gull or crow. Insert the points of the feathers (using 3 or 4) slightly angled and splayed out into the end of the potato, then throw it high in the air, and as it descends it twirls around very fast making a loud whirring noise. The positioning of the feathers and the number used can be experimented with, adding interest to the game.

Staelin swine – A player sits on a stool with a cloth in his hand, and four to six potatoes lie before him on the floor. The second player approaches and recites:

> A'm, come fae da high laands,
> Gyaan ta da low laands,
> Seekin swine, geese an gaeslins.
> We lost a peerie aalie pootie,
> An me midder pat me ower ta see
> If he wis among your eens.

The seated player then replies: 'Look du, du's welcome' whereupon the other starts to turn over the potatoes, examining them carefully, and saying: 'Hit's no dis een, an no dis een.' The aim of the game is to get one of the potatoes in his hand and escape before the other player touches him with the cloth. [Lerwick, Shetland, March 1994]

In Horseheath, Cambridgeshire, and no doubt in many other places:

> For laundry, water in which potatoes had been boiled was frequently used as a substitute for the expensive and perhaps better known flour STARCH. [Parsons MSS, 1952]

Poultry-keeping – associated plants include DAFFODIL, DANDELION, GOOSE GRASS, IRISH SPURGE, NETTLE, PRIMROSE, SALLOW, TANSY, and WHITE DEAD-NETTLE.

Pregnancy – caused by touching LORDS AND LADIES; herbs used during it include RASPBERRY.

Prick-timber – a seventeenth-century name for SPINDLE.

Primrose (*Primula vulgaris*). Primroses, like DAFFODILS, were associated with POULTRY-KEEPING.

> In East Norfolk some old women are still found who believe that if a less number of primrosen than thirteen be brought into a house on the first occasion of bringing in, so many eggs only will each hen or goose hatch that season. When recently admitted into deacon's orders, my gravity was sorely tried by being called in to settle a quarrel between two old women, arising from one of them having given one primrose to her neighbour's child, for the purpose of making her hens hatch but one chicken out of each set of eggs. And it was seriously maintained that the charm had been successful. [*N & Q*, 1 ser. 7: 201, 1853]

> Never look for early primroses, because if you pick them and take them into the house it affects the fertility of the eggs the hens are sitting on at that time, and however many primroses (and it's usually one or two at first) you pick that is the number of chicks (ducks or whatever) that will hatch out of each clutch. She has had many 'a clout around the yer' for that, but if her sister and her wanted to please their mother they would hunt around and try to find a nice lot (say a dozen or more) and then her mother would be really pleased. [Thorncombe, Dorset, February 1983]

> I have always heard that it was unlucky to take primroses indoors before April, particularly if one had fowl hatching! [Cappamore, Co. Limerick, October 1984]

> 'Of course you had to bring at least thirteen primroses into the house. Do you bring less, it were no use; it didn't serve. Thirteen was the number or more. It didn't matter if you had more; but you dursn't have less.' The

rationale of the custom was then immediately clear as one of the old people pointed out; thirteen was the number traditional to a clutch of eggs placed under a hen during the spring. Each yellow primrose was, therefore, the analogue of a young chick which would eventually emerge from the egg. If one grants that like produces like—an unquestioned assumption of the primitive mind either in Britain or in Borneo—it is folly then to bring in fewer primroses than you hope to have healthy young chicks. [Evans, 1971: 68]

There are also hints that primroses might in some way be connected with the health and well-being of humans. In the mid-nineteenth century it was reported that at Cockfield in Suffolk there were no primroses:

Nor, it is said, do they thrive when planted, though they are numerous in all surrounding villages, which do not apparently differ from Cockfield in soil. The village legends says here, too, they were once plentiful, but when Cockfield was depopulated by the plague, they also caught the infection and died, nor have they flourished since that time. [*N & Q*, 1 ser. 7: 201, 1853]

An old Cheshire name for a primrose was paigle. If it bloomed in winter, it was an omen of death. [Hole, 1937: 47]

[Lake District, *c.*1930s:] a single primrose brought into a house is a sign of a death in the family. [Metheringham, Lincolnshire, April 1994]

On the Isle of Man:

MAY EVE, as its Manx name *Oie Voaldyn* indicates was the eve of the festival of Beltaine. As elsewhere in Europe, yellow blooms and green branches were used to decorate and protect the house and cattle. Primroses (*sumark*) and MARSH MARIGOLDS (*Lus vuigh ny boaldyn, Lus airh ny lheannaugh, bluightyn*) were the favoured flowers. This use gave the name Mayflowers—also shared in Man with the lady's smock [CUCKOO FLOWER]—to the latter. Primroses and marsh marigolds still appear in jars of water on May Day, even on office windowsills and shop counters in the towns. [Garrad, 1984: 76]

Similarly, in Ireland:

Though it is dying out now, but still surviving in this district, a custom was to scatter primrose or COWSLIPS outside the front door on May Day. [IFCSS MSS 700: 186, Co. Meath].

In years gone by people used to throw a primrose in the byre door [on May Eve] so that the FAIRIES would not take away the milk from the cows for the year. [IFCSS MSS 1112: 441, Co. Donegal].

In some parts of Ireland this custom has been Christianized.

Primroses, or mayflowers, always used here to decorate the May altar, dedicated to Our Blessed Mary. [Ballymote, Co. Sligo, May 1994]

In Humberside primroses are associated with St John of Beverley.

Since 1929 a Patronal Festival in honour of St John of Beverley has been held at St John's Well at Harpham, the saint's birth-place.

Children from the village pick primroses in the nearby woods and place bunches of them on the saint's tomb during the Patronal Festival at Beverley Minster. [Burton Agnes, November 1988]

The Primrose League was formed in 1883 in memory, and in support of the political ideas, of Benjamin Disraeli (1804–81), who served as prime minister in 1868 and 1874–80. Primroses are said to have been the statesman's favourite flower, and the League promoted the wearing of primroses on the anniversry of his death (19 April).

We have had an opportunity of seeing how flower-lore originates and grows, for we have recently added to our calendar, in connection with the late Lord Beaconsfield [i.e. Disraeli], a new festival, under the title of Primrose Day. [Friend, 1884: 7]

The future historian will probably not find it very easy to establish the connection between the memory of Lord Beaconsfield and the primrose, or to say why the modest yellow flower should be accepted as the symbol of a political career, more bold, brilliant, and strange, perhaps, than any other of its time in England. But if the primrose is to become symbolic, like the PLANTA GENISTA and the *Fleur de lis*, the ORANGE LILY and various other plants and flowers, it must be admitted that its purpose was well served at the unveiling of his statue. [*Daily News*, 20 April 1883]

[If the newspapers are correct] we shall have this day [Primrose Day] commemorated, as Royal OAK Day has been, for many years. Ladies will wear primroses in their head-dresses, and gentlemen sport them in button-holes, and wreaths will still be consecrated at the Earl's shrine. [Friend, 1884: 7]

The enthusiasm demonstrated on Primrose Day in the decade after Disraeli's death was not maintained, and today it passes virtually unnoticed.

Tories steeped in the 'One Nation' tradition who thought the pendulum had swung back their way have suffered a setback: an acute shortage of primroses on Primrose Day . . . Alas, members of the Primrose League, including about 30 Tory MPs, who had hoped to be sporting buttonholes today are finding them in short supply. The early spring has meant that in most places, Disraeli's favourite flower has long since bloomed and wilted. [*The Times*, 19 April 1990]

An occupation which has fascinated many generations of children is the attempted production of pink or red primroses. James Britten [1869: 122] recorded that around High Wycombe in Buckinghamshire it was commonly believed that 'spring flowers'—primroses with bright purplish flowers—could be produced by planting a primrose in cow dung. Polyanthuses could be obtained by placing a COWSLIP root upside down in soot. Similarly:

> When I was about nine or ten, I remember my father telling me that if you planted a primrose upside down it would produce red flowers. I tried doing this but the plants invariably died, so I never produced any red flowers. This was in west Dorset in about 1956 or '57. [Streatham, London, April 1991]

Such beliefs have been the subject of a scientific paper 'On the variability and instability of the coloration of flowers of the primrose (*Primula vulgaris*) and of the cowslip (*P. veris*)'. According to this, the belief that the flower-colour of primroses and cowslips could be changed by such methods as those recorded by Britten had 'long been held by practically all country people throughout Britain'. The evidence assembled in the paper varied: some people transplanted pink-flowered wild primroses into their gardens and were surprised when these later produced yellow flowers; others found primroses retained their colour no matter how and where they were transplanted, and others claimed to have induced plants to change their flower-colour from yellow to pink. The author concluded that it was possible to make a normal primrose plant produce pink flowers if it was transplanted in a well-manured, rich soil [Christy, 1928]. However, his evidence seems weak.

The belief seems to be stimulated by the fact that pink-flowered primroses do occur quite frequently, and are presumably the result of hybridization between wild primroses and garden polyanthuses. It is noteworthy that primrose plants bearing pink or reddish flowers also have a tendency to produce several flowers on each stalk, thus pointing to a polyanthus as an ancestor. Such hybrid seedlings are likely to colonize areas where the soil has been disturbed, where a ditch has been redug or a hedge repaired. The conclusion is that during this work a primrose root had been inadvertently upturned, thus 'proof' for the belief is provided.

The 'primrose path', defined by the *Oxford English Dictionary* as 'a path of pleasure', but often used to mean a way to a rather illusory or uncertain pleasure, seems to have first appeared in Shakespeare's *Hamlet* I. iii: 50 (1602):

> Doe not as some ungracious Pastors doe,
> Shew me the steepe and thorny way to Heauen;
> Whilst like a puft and recklesse Libertine
> Himselfe the Primrose path of dalliance treads.

Similarly in English traditional song primroses are frequently associated with courtship.

As I walked out one midsummer morning
For to view the fields and to take the air,
Down by the banks of the sweet prim-e-roses
There I beheld a most lovely fair.

[Copper, 1971: 219]

And when we rose from the green mossy bank
In the meadows we wandered away;
I placed my love on a primrosy bank
And I picked her a handful of may.

[Karpeles, 1987: 64]

In folk medicine:

The primrose . . . cure for yellow JAUNDICE. Boil the roots in water and preserve the liquid in bottle and take a wine glass full each morning. [IFCSS MSS 750: 293, Co. Longford].

A gypsy cure for skin complaints on the face: take three primrose leaves and boil them in a pint of water, drink the water. [Corscombe, Dorset, March 1975]

I am 87 years old now. Mother used to make a healing ointment, also a mixture for curing RINGWORM. The ointment was made with pork lard and primrose leaves. [Stowmarket, Suffolk, February 1989]

A lady who lived near here had the 'Burn Cure' . . . I don't know the recipe, but the primrose was one of the plants used, and she had to dig for the roots winter-time. It was an ointment made with beef or mutton suet, and was very good. It was used to treat even quite bad cases of BURNS and scalds, and was always successful. [Lenamore, Co. Longford, April 1991]

Primrose peerless (*Narcissus* × *medioluteus*). The narcissus primrose peerless, formerly a much cultivated garden ornamental, is widely naturalized in the British Isles. Until about 1920, when it was exterminated by heavy grazing, a large colony of the plant, covering about half an acre, grew in a field between the vicarage and the church at Churchill in north Somerset. An elderly man still living in 1965 could recall how he used to pick bunches of the flowers and sell them at Weston-super-Mare market [Churchill, Avon, June 1978].

The tale is a sad one.

A Crusader came home to Churchill after years of heat and bloodshed in the Holy Land. He had gone away rich—he came home poor, but he had brought his beloved wife a carefully cherished present—two bulbs of the Primrose Peerless. She had always loved rare flowers.

Alas, when he reached Churchill the primroses on her grave were blooming for the fourth time. In despair he flung the precious bulbs over the churchyard wall and, falling beside his lady's grave, died of a broken heart.

Throughout the centuries the bulbs have grown and flourished and kept his memory alive. [Tongue, 1965: 202]

Privet (*Ligustrum ovalifolium*). In common with other white, strongly scented flowers (such as LILAC), privet flowers are sometimes banned from being taken indoors.

I remember in about 1963, when we were living in South Shields, that my mother would not allow privet flowers in the house. [Ealing, London, May 1982]

In London during the first decade of the present century, privet was associated with DIPHTHERIA.

When I was in hospital I heard much gossip about various sources, previously thought innocuous, from which you could now 'catch the fever': privet leaves, putting an iron key in your mouth, passing a smelly drain without a handkerchief to clap over your mouth and nose. [Rolph, 1980: 56]

Records of privet being used in folk medicine are rare.

To cure sore lips get some privet leaves and chew them and let the juice flow over the sore lip. The pain will be intense but the lip will undoubtedly get better. None of the juice should be swallowed. [IFCSS MSS 775: 83, Co. Kildare].

[A cure for mumps:] Put privet berries in a pan with water to cover. Boil till the juice is out of the berries and tip juice into a small bottle, together with cream from top of the milk. Leave berries in a jar with enough water to cover. Do not take till it has cooled for at least three hours. Dose: teaspoon of juice and one berry, once daily and after food. [Macpherson MSS, Wiltshire].

Prophetic trees. Certain landed families had trees growing on their land which foretold deaths in the family by shedding a branch; such trees include a CEDAR tree at Bretby, Derbyshire; see also JOUG TREE.

Pudding bags – a Bedfordshire name for CAMPION.

Puff-ball (*Lycoperdon* spp.)

One way to stop BLEEDING is to get a blind-ball. It is like a mushroom and it grows in the field. Put the spongey part of it to the cut and it stops bleeding instantly. [IFCSS MSS 717: 151, Co. Meath].

[Suffolk:] In the autumn or late summer the large puffballs were in great demand by country butchers. These were not allowed to get ripe and become dust-like, but cut in slices and kept in the slaughter house . . . When a butcher cut his hand or arm a slice was put on immediately. They were supposed to stop bleeding and prevent infection. [UCL EFS MSS M42, Carshalton Beeches, Surrey, October 1963]

[Owston, Leicestershire, 1916:] We were helping one of the local farmers in the hayfield, when he cut his thumb rather badly . . . He held his thumb to staunch the bleeding and went in search of a puffball. He selected a very ripe specimen, the interior of which consisted of brown powder. Bursting the puffball, he tore off a piece of the outer skin and used this as a plaster, placing the inner side of the peel in contact with the wound. In . . . less than a week the wound had completely healed. [UCL EFS MSS M53, Leicester, November 1963]

Pumpkin (*Cucurbita maxima*). Until comparatively recently pumpkins have entered British consciousness mainly as providing the fruit which Cinderella's fairy godmother turned into a golden coach to take her to the palace ball. The popular story-book and pantomime versions of this tale are derived from Charles Perrault's *Histoires ou Contes du temps passé*, first published in 1697.

Her Godmother, who was a Fairy said, 'You want to go to the Ball, isn't that it?'

'Yes' sighed Cinderella.

'Well, if you're a good girl, I shall send you,' said her Godmother.

She took her into her own room and told her, 'Go into the garden and bring me a pumpkin.'

Cinderella went straight and picked the finest she could find, and took it to her Godmother, without the least idea how a pumpkin could help her go to the Ball. Her Godmother scooped it out to a hollow skin, then tapped it with her wand, and the pumpkin was instantly turned into a beautiful gilded coach. [Philip, 1989: 11]

However, in recent years pumpkins have become increasingly familiar. The rapidly growing fruits of the pumpkin have a fascination which can become an obsession for the enthusiasts who enter competitions to see who can grow the heaviest fruit. Only LEEK shows generate similar passion.

This year has been murder for British pumpkins. Even so, if the fairy godmother took her wand to Mrs Linda Withers's prize specimen she would end up with something like a troop carrier rather than a mere coach and four.

This year's summer reduced almost 200 inquiries about the British National Pumpkin Championship, held yesterday at Ashby-de-la-Zouch, Leicestershire, to a mere dozen entries. Telephones were abuzz with stories of fast-growing monsters ruined by hail, or rotted by rain . . .

Nevertheless . . . Mrs Withers's premier pumpkin this year weighed in at 284.2 lbs, winning her a £200 prize, and a trip, with her pumpkin, to the United States for the world pumpkin festival. [*The Times*, 13 October 1987]

Since 1967 the Greyhound Pumpkin Club, which has its headquarters at the Greyhound pub in Broughton, Hampshire, has held an annual

Pumpkin

show, which in 1990 attracted a record 84 entries [*The Times Saturday Review*, 27 October 1990]. Although the club holds other competitions throughout the year, starting with a competition for the heaviest stick of RHUBARB in June, and finishing with a competition for the longest blanch LEEK in December, it is the pumpkin competition which provides the club with the primary reason for its existence. The 24th show, held on 6 October 1990, had thirteen classes, including: the heaviest pumpkin grown by a Broughton resident under 11 years, novelty decorative pumpkin, best matched pair over 25 lbs, and pumpkin pie. The prizes included four trophies and prize money ranging from £2 to £12, with 'further prize money for the three heaviest pumpkins exhibited at the show, to be raised to a total of: 1st £100, 2nd £25, 3rd £12.50'. The club is affiliated to the International Pumpkin Growers' Association, which has branches in the USA, Canada, Australia, and Japan, and the Greyhound is the official United Kingdom weigh-off site for the Association [Jack Orrell, Chairman, Greyhound Pumpkin Club, November 1990]. In 1990:

Ian Hatcher's pumpkin tipped the scales at an amazing 423 lb to scoop the first prize . . .
Ian, 34, took second place with another entry—just over 390lb—collecting £112 in prize money in addition to the trip [to a pumpkin festival in California] . . .
He has been growing pumpkins since 1983 and entering competitions for the past five years.
The secret of producing a whopper pumpkin? 'Plenty of muck and water,' advises Ian. [*Southern Echo*, 9 October 1990]

During the 1980s HALLOWE'EN, the celebration of which had previously been largely restricted to the northern part of Britain, became increasingly popular in southern England. This spread of the custom seems to have come about from a combination of the spread of American culture and the opportunity to create another commercially exploitable festival. During the mid and late 1980s pumpkins began to appear in greengrocers' shops in October, and pumpkin lanterns began to be made in homes. Cheap plastic toys, often in the shape of pumpkins and imported from the Far East, appeared in shops, and the popular women's magazine *Family Circle* in its November 1990 issue included a 'Hallowe'en Special', which contained instructions on how to make a pumpkin cake (i.e. a cake decorated to look like a pumpkin), pumpkin pie, and a pumpkin jack o'lantern. Even when pumpkins are not present or represented in Hallowe'en decorations, orange, the colour of pumpkins, has become one of three colours—together with the white of ghosts and the black of the 'tradi-

tional' witches' clothing—associated with the festival [personal observation, Uttoxeter, Staffordshire, and London, October 1993].
Cf. MANGOLD and TURNIP.

Punky – a lantern made from a hollowed-out MANGOLD.

Purgatives – plants used include FAIRY FLAX, GROUNDSEL, and STINKING IRIS. See also CONSTIPATION.

Purple moor grass (*Molinia caerulea*)
The fishermen in the isle of Skie make ROPES for their nets of this grass, which they find by experience will bear the water well without rotting. [Lightfoot, 1777: 96]

Purple moor grass: referred to as disco grass in Rhayader, Radnor area. When you walk through the tussocks you stagger about and look as if in a disco, I presume.
Also still cut as rhos hay in mid and west Wales in September. [Llandrindod Wells, Powys, September 1991]

Q

Quakers – an Oxfordshire name for QUAKING GRASS.

Quaking grass (*Briza media*)

> Respecting the notions which used to be entertained of the virtues of plants, I have quite recently come across two or three interesting illustrations. In Oxon and the neighbouring counties the pretty Shaking-grass (*Briza*) is called Quakers, from its constant quivering. Now in the DOCTRINE OF SIGNATURES, that which shakes is good for the shaking complaint, and AGUE is not uncommon in some low-lying districts, the people maintain that if you keep Quakers in the house you will be free from the quaking complaint. [Friend, 1884: 8]

In Yorkshire quaking grass was known as 'Trimmling Jockies' or 'Doddering Dickies,' and it was said:

> A trimmling jock i' t' house
> And you weeant hev a mouse.

> Dried in bunches, with its brown seeds on a tall stem, it was commonly stuck on the mantel-shelf, as believed to be obnoxious to mice. [Gutch, 1901: 61]

In the Cambridgeshire Fens:

> It was an old belief that it [maidenhair or quaking grass] grew only in places where a young woman had drowned herself—usually on account of some unhappy love affair—and so it was considered unlucky to bring the grass indoors. In W.H. Barrett's [born 1891] boyhood the old people used to declare that they noticed maidenhair grass flourished particularly well wherever a corpse, dragged from the river, had been laid on the bank. He himself noticed, when minding cows as a young boy, that the beasts would never eat or trample on maidenhair grass. [Porter, 1969: 45]

In Dorset:

> [Often growing near bee orchids] is a form of grass called 'Wiggle woggles'. Unlucky to have in house. [Portland, Dorset, March 1991]

The mysterious Irish plant known as HUNGRY-GRASS, *fairgurtha*, or *fairgorta* is sometimes considered to be quaking grass.

> *Fear gorta(ch)*: quaking grass, a mountain grass supposed to cause hunger-weakness when trodden on, hence a violent hunger, abnormal craving for food, diabetes . . . it is prevented by carrying food and cured by a grain of OATS . . . it occurs on Mt Brandon and in mountains near Omeath between two cairns which peasants will not pass without carrying food. [Dinneen, 1927: 436]

Queen Anne's lace – a name for COW PARSLEY.

Queen Mary's thistle – a Northamptonshire name for COTTON THISTLE.

Queen of the meadow – a name for MEADOWSWEET.

Quinsy – cured using TORMENTIL.

R

Rabbit-flower, rabbits – Devon names for IVY-LEAVED TOADFLAX.

Radish (*Raphanus sativus*)

> A curious annual custom, dating from time immemorial, was celebrated at Levens Hall . . . near Kendal . . . known as the Radish-feast . . . [it] is attended by the mayor and corporation of Kendal and most of the gentry . . . who partake of radishes and oatbread and butter . . . After the repast . . . [there are] drinking . . . and . . . athletic competitions. [*N & Q*, 5 ser. 8: 248, 1877]

The Feast was formerly held on 12 May when the nearby village of Milnthorpe used to hold its fair. The right to hold the fair was granted in 1280, and it is believed that the feast dates from late in the seventeenth century, when it was said that the owner of Levens Hall wanted an entertainment which would attract greater attention than that provided by his neighbour at Dallam Tower [Wilson, 1940].

> After the repast came the 'colting' of new visitors. These neophytes were brought into a ring, or 'haltered' . . . when they were required in turn to stand upon one leg and drink what was called the 'constable', a weighty glass filled with half a pint of Morocoo [a strong ale brewed at the Hall]. This had to be emptied at one draught, pledging at the time the ancient house in the words, 'luck to Levens as long as the Kent flows.' Declining or failing to accomplish this feat, the forfeiture of a shilling was required for the benefit of the under gardeners, and well they deserved it, for it is said that it took a full day's work for four men to clean the radishes eaten at this festival, which were conveyed to the tables in wheelbarrow loads. [Curwen, 1898: 36]

The feast is not currently celebrated and has not been since well before the war [Levens Hall, November 1993]. Elsewhere radish feasts seem to have been associated with parish elections. In Oxfordshire:

> The annual meeting for the election of churchwardens . . . will be held in the vestry of the Parish Church on Easter Tuesday . . . The Radish-feast will be at the New Inn, New Street, immediately after. [*N & Q*, 1 ser. 5: 610, 1852]

At Andover, in Hampshire:

> The [radish]feast was usually held on the day of the election of officers, and the person who supplied it was chosen by ballot. [*N & Q*, 5 ser. 8: 355, 1877]

Ragwort (*Senecio jacobaea*), formerly also known as ragweed. After the Battle of Culloden in 1746 the victorious English are said to have renamed the attractive garden flower SWEET WILLIAM, in honour of their leader, William, Duke of Cumberland. The defeated Scots retaliated by naming the obnoxious weed ragwort stinking Willy [letter from Upholland, Lancashire, in the *Daily Mirror*, 21 September 1984]. Alternatively, the Scots maintain that the spread of ragwort in Scotland was due to the forage used by the Duke of Cumberland's troops during the Culloden campaign [Grigson, 1975: 389].

Throughout Scotland there was a belief that witches and fairies travelled on ragwort stalks.

> Tell how wi' you on ragweed nags
> They skim the muirs an' dizzy crags
> > [Robert Burns, *Address to the Deil*, verse 9, 1785]
> On auld broom-besoms, and ragweed naigs,
> They flew owre burns, hills, and craigs.
> > [Henderson, 1856: 59]

It is regarded as unlucky to take into your hands the ragwort plant, also known as *boholàun*. In rural Ireland you were likely to be reminded not to strike a beast with a *boholàun* as this action would bring misfortue to the beast. There was an old saying around here: 'Don't call it a weed though a weed it may be, 'tis the horse of the fairies, the *boholàun buidhe*.' [Ballymote, Co. Sligo, May 1994]

On the Hebridean islands ragwort was used in the children's game *Goid a' Chruin*, according to a description recorded in Gaelic in 1953:

> Well, we played it during the interval at school when I was a little boy. You had always to be on a level piece of ground . . . we had an excellent stretch of green sward a short distance from the school, and we gathered there. And it was always in autumn that this game was played because we had a sort of plant that is very common then, we call it *buaghallan* in Gaelic [ragwort]. And that was plucked out by its roots, and two rows were set up on the green; boys and girls were in each row. *An Crun* [the Crown] was one of those *buaghallans*, one of those plants. It was thrown there on neutral territory between the two ranks and the person who was successful in breaking through and taking up the crown and running right down . . . round, circling their opponents, and right round and coming back, without being caught, that person was successful. But he always had to give the next, his companion, a chance, and he himself just looked on. But if he was caught with the *buaghallan*, with the crown, by his opponents before he circled them and came back to his own allies . . . then he had to go outside the camp, and he was called a *cnoimheag* [maggot!]. Now the side that had more failures (or more *cnoimhags*) was the side that lost, and the row that had less, of course, was the one that was successful. And that was the game! [Bennett, 1991: 59]

Ramsons (*Allium ursinum*)

[Reminiscences of her aunt, licensee of the Halfway House, between Douglas and Peel, who died in 1973, aged 90]. In the 1930s the pub had a garden/orchard. *Allium ursinum* grew at one end of the orchard. Bulbs were dug when they first sprouted in spring, washed and dried in the sun on a clean tea towel. Then packed into a wide-mouthed glass jar with dark brown sugar. Light Jamaica rum was poured over and the whole was stored in a cool dark place—e.g. wardrobe—until the following winter, when it was used for chesty colds and COUGHS. [Contributed to the Manx Folklife Survey, October 1991]

According to a seventeenth-century proverb:

> Eat LEEKes in Lide [March] and ramsins in May,
> And all the yeare after physitians may play.

[Aubrey, 1847: 51]

See also GARLIC.

Rashes – treated using CHICKWEED.

Raspberry (*Rubus idaeus*)

Raspberry leaves for easing labour pains. A preparation made from these leaves is sold in the Bradford herbalists' shops under the title 'Mother's Friend'. [McKelvie MSS, 1963: 273]

[From Mrs Newsam of Dore, Sheffield:] Raspberry leaf tea: 1 oz. raspberry leaves (wild or cultivated) to two cups of water.
Dose: 2 cups a day during the last month of PREGNANCY to give an easy delivery.
Also mentioned in the Sheffield area for preventing MISCARRIAGE, increasing mother's milk, for painful menstruation, DIARRHOEA, and as an eye-wash for sore EYES. After being soaked to the skin, to avoid a COLD take raspberry leaf tea and go to bed. [Steele MSS, 1978: 81]

Rat leaf – a Lancashire name for BUTTERBUR.

Rats – deterred using WHITE BRYONY.

Rayless chamomile – see PINEAPPLE WEED.

Red and white flowers. The belief that red and white flowers together in a vase cause misfortune or death is widespread, but apparently not very old. According to the *Sunlight Almanac* (1896) a dream of red and white flowers foretold death. However, the belief in its present form does not appear to have evolved until the twentieth century.

I have just retired but started nursing during the war. I found that red and white flowers in the same vase made some patients uneasy; they would mutter 'Red and white, someone will die.' If the colours were separated into a vase of red and one of white this was acceptable. [Penicuik, Midlothian, April 1982]

As a Parish Priest in England and Wales over 40 years I have grown to fear, as a result of personal experience, red and white flowers on the Altar as usually followed by an *unexpected* death, even in parishes with only four or five funerals a year, e.g. Arthog Church—red and white flowers on Altar seen at 7 p.m. on Saturday, put on by elderly spinster. Next morning before 8 a.m. celebration at Farbourne Church in same parish, 'Rector please pray for the soul of Schoolmaster—he fell downstairs at 2 a.m. and broke his neck.' I am also coming, for a similar reason, to dislike *artificial* red and white flowers in houses. [Aberystwyth, Dyfed, January 1983]

It is extremely unlucky to have red and white flowers together in a vase. (I once took some red and white carnations to my mother in hospital and the nurse snatched them from me and eventually returned with them in a vase to which she had added some cornflowers!) [Aberdovey, Gwynedd, July 1983]

The family of a friend of mine went to visit their mother in hospital in Galashiels. When they got there they were very upset to see a vase of red and white flowers placed on the locker beside her bed. They complained to the sister, and told her that they would rather be told that the hospital thought that their mother was going to die, instead of having them dropping hints. They thought that the red and white flowers indicated that the hospital had given up hope with their mother. [Notting Hill Gate, London, May 1985]

Most often this belief is explained by stating that the red flowers symbolize blood and the white bandages.

Red and white flowers: must not have these together in the house or hospital, as they represent blood and bandages. [Shelton Lock, Derbyshire, March 1983]

Recently I heard that red and white flowers are considered unlucky as funeral flowers . . . I asked my florist a few months ago, when sadly ordering a funeral spray, whether it was true . . . 'Oh yes' he replied cheerfully, 'They are known as "Blood and Bandages"—nurses hate them—say it is so unfeeling to send them if a person died in hospital.' [Kensington, London, January 1983]

However, red and white flowers are not always considered to be inauspicious:

At WHITSUN many Anglican churches decorate with red and white flowers—the symbolism of the fire and the wind of the Holy Spirit. [Catford, London, September 1984]

Red and white are the colours of the City [of London], so when there are events at the Guildhall there are always masses of red and white flowers. [Fleet Street, London, August 1983]

Chinese brides in London often carry bouquets of red and white flowers, thus combining the wedding colours of two cultures.

Red campion (*Silene dioica*). In nineteenth-century Cumberland red campion was known as Mother Dee (i.e. MOTHER DIE).

> There is a superstition amongst Cumberland children that if they pick the flower some misfortune will happen to their parents. [Britten and Holland, 1886: 342]

More recently red campion has been associated with FAIRIES, SNAKES, and THUNDER.

> [On the Isle of Man] red campion, being the fairies' flower, *Blaa ny Ferrishn*, was unlucky and should not be picked. [Garrad, 1984: 79]

> *Blodwyn Neidr* (snake flower)—red campion—used to be one of my favourite flowers, but my grandmother was convinced that I would be attacked by a snake if I brought it into the house. [Bow Street, Dyfed, March 1984]

> In Cnwch Coch, near Aberystwyth, in about 1921–1931, we called red campion *Blod Trane* (*Blodyn Taranau*: Thunder Flower) as it was believed that a storm of thunder and lightning would follow if it was picked. [Garth, Gwynedd, April 1984]

See also CAMPION

Red clover (*Trifolium pratense*)

> We used to pull out the petals of pink clover and suck the ends, because they were sweet. [Glencruitten, Argyll, October 1990]

> Red clover: sweet flowers picked by us, as children [I am now 43], called 'honey suck'. [Christchurch, Dorset, June 1991]

In 1988 7 per cent of the specimens obtained in response to an appeal for examples of 'true SHAMROCK' were found to be red clover [Nelson, 1990: 34].

Red dead-nettle (*Lamium purpureum*)

> When children had MEASLES they used to boil the red dead-nettle roots in sweet milk and give it to them to drink so as to bring out the measles. [IFCSS MSS 717: 352, Co. Meath]

Red flowers. Although it has been suggested that red flowers are inauspicious [Opie and Tatum, 1989: 325], the evidence for this is weak. Three of the four examples given to support the belief are unconvincing. In two of the examples red ROSES which are being worn disintegrate and fall to the ground, causing their wearers to expect misfortune. Surely it is the disintegration of the flowers, rather than their colour, which is considered inauspicious. A third example concerns the picking of POPPY flowers, which, if the petals fall, is supposed to cause the picker to be struck by lightning. This belief was widespread, but relates only to poppies, and not to red flowers in general. The fourth example is more convincing, but perhaps concerns only one species rather than red flowers in general:

> I have always understood that a red rose was considered unlucky. [N & Q, 7 ser. 8: 265, 1889]

Conversely, according to an Irish correspondent:

> Red flowers, symbol of the blood of life, are always lucky, however bringing bunches of RED AND WHITE [flowers] together into a hospital forebodes death. [Kiltegan, Co. Wicklow, November 1984]

Red-hot poker (*Kniphofia* spp.)

> If the brilliant red or yellow flowers known as red-hot poker or torch lily, blooms twice in one year, it is an omen of death for someone in the family of the garden's owner. [Radford, 1961: 282]

Red-rot – a name for SUNDEW.

Redshank (*Persicaria maculosa*); also known as spotted persicaria. In Gaelic-speaking areas of Scotland redshank was known as *Am boinne-fola* (the blood-spot) or *Lus chrann ceusaidh* (herb of the tree of crucifixion):

> The legend being that this plant grew at the foot of the Cross. [Cameron, 1883: 61]

> A few old folk may still be found in west Cornwall who believe that the spotted persicaria grew at the foot of the Cross and that the dark markings on the leaves are due to drops of BLOOD falling from our Saviour's body. [Davey, 1909: 389]

> There is a flower called the redshank and it is said that it got its colour when Our Saviour was dying on the cross. That flower was near the cross and a drop of blood fell on it and that is how it got its name and colour. [IFCSS MSS 375: 90, Co. Cork]

Elsewhere redshank was associated with the Virgin Mary or an unnamed murderess.

> The Oxonian, however, says that the Virgin was wont of old to use its leaves for the manufacture of a valuable ointment, but that on one occasion she sought it in vain. Finding it afterwards, when the need had passed away, she condemned it, and gave it the rank of an ordinary weed. This is expressed in the local rhyme:
>
>> She could not find in time of need,
>> And so she pinched it for a weed.
>
> The mark on the leaf is the impress of the Virgin's finger, and the persicaria is now the only weed that is not useful for something. [Friend, 1884: 6]

Red snot

Herbe traitresse . . . this name originates in a Guernsey legend to the effect that a woman who had committed a murder, wiped her blood-stained fingers on the leaves of the plant, which betrayed her, and led to her detection. Ever since then the leaves have been marked in the centre by a dark spot. [Marquand, 1906: 42]

In the Shetland Islands ALPINE MEADOW-RUE is known as redshank.

Red snot – a Kent name for YEW fruits.

Red valerian (*Centranthus ruber*)

Red valerian: 'Kiss me quick', not advisable to take in the house as it smells quite a lot when cut.

Dried valerian stems [were] used as pea shooters with ripe vetch seeds. [Portland, Dorset, April 1991]

Reflexed stonecrop (*Sedum rupestre*)

[Guernsey:] this plant, mixed in certain proportions with garden THYME, is prepared as a tisane and used in cases of DIABETES. [Marquand, 1906: 41]

Rennet – substitutes include BUTTERWORT, LADY'S BEDSTRAW, and LESSER SPEARWORT.

Restharrow (*Ononis repens*)

The roots are very sweet, and, when young, have the flavour of liquorice. The writer was informed by some workmen . . . that they and their fellow labourers were accustomed to suck the juice from these roots, in order to assuage the thirst induced by hard toil under summer sun. The young shoots are also sweet and succulent, and in some country places they are boiled and eaten. [Pratt, 1857, 2: 37]

Reglisse or *Reclisse*, restharrow . . . old people [on Guernsey] still remember as children eating the roots of this plant, which are said to taste very much like liquorice root. The same thing is done in the north of England, where restharrow is called wild liquorice. [Marquand, 1906: 46]

Rheumatic fever – cured using TORMENTIL.

Rheumatism – prevented using ALDER, DOG ROSE moss galls, HORSE CHESTNUT, and POTATO; cured using BLADDER WRACK, BOGBEAN, BROOM, BURDOCK, BUTTERCUP, CELERY, CHICKWEED, DOCK, ELDER, NETTLE, POLYPODY, ROWAN, ROYAL FERN, SUN SPURGE, WATERCRESS, and WOOD SAGE; alleviated using OPIUM POPPY.

Rhubarb (*Rheum × hybridum*)

A slice of rhubarb placed at the bottom of the 'dibbed' hole will prevent club root in brassicas [i.e. CABBAGES]. [Horsted Keynes, West Sussex, February 1991]

Old remedies for a COLD: eating an ONION, rhubarb and spirit of nitre . . .
[Llanuwchyllyn, Gwynedd, April 1991]

Boyes [1991: 44] in a brief survey of colour in 'mock-obscene' riddles
gives the following:

What's long and thin and covered in skin
Red in parts, stuck in tarts?
Answer (which is usually chanted as part of the rhyme) Rhubarb!

Early in 1992 'greetings' cards with this riddle were on sale in south
London.

In some parts of Wales JAPANESE KNOTWEED is known as wild rhubarb.

Ribgrass – an Irish name for RIBWORT PLANTAIN.

Ribwort plantain (*Plantago lanceolata*), known as Johnsmas-flooer
on the Shetland Islands:

The local name refers to an ancient Scandinavian custom which also had
a place in the folklore of Orkney and Faeroe. We cannot do better than
quote from Hoeg (1941): 'In these parts of the country [south-west and
west Norway], and only here, it has been (and partly still is) common to
foretell the future by means of that plant, by taking one or two flowering
spikes of it on St John's Eve, picking off the stamens, and keeping the
spike over night, usually under the pillow: If new stamens were developed in the morning (as will generally be the case), certain wishes
would be fulfilled, mostly concerning matters of life and death, or
love.—Similar customs and names of the plant are known from the Faroes
and the Shetlands, and must consequently be assumed to be very old, no
doubt from before the year 1468.' This custom was still providing amusement in Shetland as late as the 1920s. [Scott and Palmer, 1987: 274]

More widespread is another children's game:

Children everywhere play with the flower-stems of ribwort plantain,
striking one against the other until the loser's breaks, like CONKERS. Plymouth kids call this game 'Kings'. [Plymouth, Devon, May 1986]

As children we played a game called 'Fighting Cocks' with the long-
stemmed seed heads of ribwort plantain. Two children each took a 'cock'
and they kept hitting them against each other until the head was knocked
off one. Then 'My cock won.' [Lenamore, Co. Longford, April 1991]

[Memories of Aberdeen in the 1930s:] CARL DODDIES is the name of a
game played by children with *Plantago lanceolata*. The name has extended
from the game to the plant itself. During the 45 rebellion supporters of
Charles, the Young Pretender, were known as Carls, and supporters of
King George were known as Doddies—Doddie being the local name for
George. Children emulated their parents and took sides, hence the
game's name. [Limpsfield, Surrey, June 1993]

Ribwort plantain

This game, which is also known as Blackmen, Cocks and Hens, Hard Heads, Knights [Opie, 1969: 226], and, in parts of north Wales, *ceiliogod* (cocks) or *taid a nain* (grandfather and grandmother) has a long history.

> In the historical poem *Histoire de Guillaume le Maréchal*, written soon after 1219, the story is told how the boy William Marshall, later to become Earl of Pembroke and Regent of England, but then not ten years old, was detained as a hostage in the king's camp, while Stephen was besieging Newbury. One day the boy picked out the plantains (*les chevaliers*) from the cut grass strewn on the floor of the tent, and challenged the king, 'Beau sire chiers, volez joer as chevaliers?' The challenge being accepted, William laid half the 'knights' on the king's lap, and asked who was to have the first stroke. 'You' said the king, holding out his knight, which the small boy promptly beheaded, greatly to his own delight. King Stephen (strictly in accordance with the rules of the game) then held out another plantain, but the game was interrupted. It matters not whether the story is apocryphal; as early as the thirteenth century a poet has shown himself to be familiar with the game. [Opie, 1969: 226]

In another game:

> The stem and flowering heads of the plantain were used as a missile, by somehow knotting and flicking the ripe seed head. [Ringwood, Hampshire, November 1990]

> Friends who lived in Dumfriesshire many years ago reminded me that a game was played in this way: Take a long, strong stalk of plantain, loop it over the head of the flower, pull it quite tightly so that the head shoots off. The winner is the one whose plantain head travelled furthest. [Edinburgh, December 1991]

> I was born in 1948 in Ferndown, before it was built up, and our playground was the fields, common and forestry around our home . . . Ribwort plantain (bootlace): tie in a knot then quickly shoot the end off. [Hamworthy, Dorset, May 1991]

According to Mont Abbott, a farm labourer born at Enstone, Oxfordshire, in 1902, when he was a young man on summer evenings young men would cycle to neighbouring villages to view the girls:

> gals was dotted about like daisies . . . We foreigners 'ud pull up on our bikes within winking or aiming distance, picking the Daisy we fancied from the bunch by looping the pliant stem of a plantain into a catapult and pinging her bare neck with its . . . seedhead. [Stewart, 1987: 96]

Leaves of ribwort plantain were used in folk medicine.

> When a person got a cut and was BLEEDING profusely, he pulled some *slanlus* (rib grass) leaves, chewed them in his mouth and then placed the pulp on the wound. This always stopped the flow of blood. [IFCSS MSS 450: 55, Co. Kerry]

Rib grass is chewed and put on a wound to stop bleeding. [Daingean, Co. Offaly, January 1985]

Too much ribwort plantain in a hay rick could cause the rick to overheat.

When building a hay rick in rather showery unsettled weather, old Durrant would casually mention 'There's a fair bit of fire grass hereabouts Gaffer' and again the Manager knew that the rick was in danger of beginning to overheat. 'Better put a chimney in Durrant,' he would say. Fire grass was the name given by the older men to the ribwort or narrow-leaved plantain, which holds quite a bit of moisture in its leaves. [Nixon, 1977: 181]

See also GREATER PLANTAIN, HOARY PLANTAIN, and PLANTAIN, cf. GREAT BURNET.

Rickets – cured using BLADDER WRACK.

Ridin' girse – a Shetland name for field gentian.

Ringworm – cured using GARLIC, HOUSELEEK, LAUREL, OAK, and PRIMROSE.

Robin-run-in-the-hedge – a Derbyshire name for IVY; also a widespread name for GROUND IVY.

Rock samphire (*Crithmum maritimum*)

Semper grows[s] in the cliffs by the sea . . . eaten in its raw state relieves pain in the HEART. [IFCSS MSS 1121: 425, Co. Donegal]

[On Colonsay] samphire is much sought after for pickling sometimes at the risk of human life (men being suspended from the rocks by ropes). [McNeill, 1910: 128]

Rock samphire is not very succulent on the isles, but it is used—pickled, as a relish with meats. [St Mary's, Isles of Scilly, September 1992]

Rogues – a name given to WILD GLADIOLUS on the Isles of Scilly.

Romans – associated plants include CLARY, FAIRY FOXGLOVE, WINTER ACONITE, and YELLOW CORYDALIS.

Roofleek – a name given to HOUSELEEK in Co. Cork.

Ropes – made from MARRAM GRASS and PURPLE MOOR GRASS.

Rose (*Rosa* cv.). The red rose is considered to be a symbol of England, where it is occasionally worn on St George's Day, and love. It has also been used as a symbol of the Labour Party.

Roses are not naturally available at the appropriate time of year, and the English, unlike the Welsh and Irish, have never had to assert their nationality. Consequently red roses have never been commonly worn on St George's Day (23 April), and the practice is mainly restricted to televison newsreaders and a few private individuals. However, even this restricted use was sufficient to cause unease when the Labour Party adopted the red rose as its symbol in 1986.

> The colour of the rose for St George's Day became an important issue at Common Council [of the City of London] last week, as the Court strove to prove that it was non-political.
>
> A motion was tabled by Mr Brian Boreham that all Common Council-men should wear a red rose provided by the Corporation for their meeting on St George's Day. However, Mr Norman Harding said that he would be voting against the motion since the red rose was now an emblem of a political party. His reasoning was that the Court should remain apolitical. [*City Recorder*, 9 April 1987]

> The Common Council can't make up its mind what colour rose should be worn on St George's Day—but the City of London branch of the Royal Society of St George has no doubts . . . Mr John Minshull Fogg, Hon. Secretary and chairman-designate of the branch, said this week, 'The red rose is the rose of England, and that's what we shall be wearing. We always have done and always will.' [*City Recorder*, 16 April 1987].

> It has been my custom, in previous years, to wear a red rose on April 23—a custom shared with many of my fellow countrymen and women. However, I am a Civil Servant and as such must show no tendency to favour any individual political party.
>
> Given that the rose has become the symbol of one of our major political parties I wonder if any of your correspondents could suggest what, if anything, would be appropriate wear on St George's Day? [Letter from Tunley, Avon, in *The Times*, 14 April 1989]

Following the Labour Party's defeat in the 1992 general election the use of its red rose symbol has been less flamboyant.

The Royal Northumberland Fusiliers wore a red and a white rose on St George's Day.

> St George's Day was their regimental day, when all ranks wore a red and a white rose. This tradition is now continued by all battalions of the Royal Regiment of Fusiliers. The roses are thought to symbolise the unity of the houses of Lancaster and York. [Letter from Bristol, Avon, in *The Times*, 22 April 1989]

Since 1975 1 August has been designated as Yorkshire Day.

> August 1 is Yorkshire Day, an event established by the Yorkshire Ridings Society in 1975 to act as a focal point for county pride, because on this day in 1759 soldiers from the Yorkshire regiments who had fought in the Battle of Minden in Germany picked white roses, the county emblem, from nearby fields as a tribute to fallen comrades. The society was formed

after the local government changes to ensure that the county's identity was not lost. [*The Times*, 1 August 1990]

As symbols of love, red roses are in great demand on St Valentine's Day.

The annual Valentine red roses spree was in full swing again yesterday.

And prices of our favourite bouquet went through the roof as florists cashed in on love . . .

Shop owner Ian Duncan blamed worldwide demand. 'The trouble is that Valentine's Day falls on the same day everywhere, unlike occasions like Mother's Day,' he added. In Birmingham, where some shops were charging £3 a bloom angry wholesalers said their price was only 65p–75p. 'We're fed up with it,' said one. 'It happens every year.'

At Sally's, in Dulwich, South-East London, a dozen red roses had soared 300 per cent from £9 to £36. The assistant was frank. 'It's Valentine's now, so everything has gone right up,' she said. [*Daily Mail*, 14 February 1991]

Today most of the roses sold on Valentine's Day are imported from Colombia. In 1994 it was reported that although the 450 rose-growers on the plains around Bogota had suffered their most severe frost for many years, this year they expected to export more than 375 million flowers. Valentine's Day roses account for between 30 and 70 per cent of a grower's annual income.

For Valentine's Day, staff levels can quadruple, as farms work 24 hours a day to meet the demand. Teams of workers will pick and pack by hand 150,000 stems in an eight-hour shift. After 24 hours in cold storage, the flowers are then transported to the airport in locked, refigerated lorries. [*Daily Telegraph*, 12 February 1994]

Since Roman times rose petals have been showered on important people or on religious statues. The *Daily Mail* of 12 June 1928 reported:

A shower of thousands of rose petals greeted Miss Joy Kennerley Rumford, the tall young daughter of Dame Clara Butt, when she was married yesterday to Major Claude Cross at Holy Trinity, Brompton.

These petals were softly tinted tissue paper and have been supplied by the Disabled Men's Industries for most of the big society weddings. Princess Mary and the Duchess of York ordered them for their weddings . . .

The petals are cut out of rice paper with a steel cutter, and then sprayed with colour, put in an oven to crisp and dry, and finally made up in boxes ready for despatch. Millions are sent out every week, some having even travelled to Borneo, the Secretary of the organisation said.

The petals are made in pink shading to white and orange shading to cream. Boxes of separate colours can be had for 1s 6d a thousand petals, but most brides choose mixed colours.

Besides having the advantage of giving work to disabled men, the petals make a prettier and more delicate show than confetti, and do not stick so tenaciously to clothes and carpets. They are not wasteful nor do they sting like rice.

At St Albans in Hertfordshire roses are placed on the shrine of St Alban, England's first Christian martyr, on the Sunday nearest his feast day, 22 June. Sunday school children from all over the diocese gather at the cathedral to take part in a simple, joyful service, at which the church is usually packed. Simple hymns are sung, and the entire congregation, led by the bishop who has his staff decorated with roses, processes down the aisle to place roses on the martyr's shrine. One of the lesser known hymns sung at the service, and presumably written for it, is sung to the tune of *The Battle Hymn of the Republic*, and includes the verse:

> It was here, a British hillside, green and beautiful with flowers,
> That the martyr made a stand for Christ against those evil powers;
> So in Christ's name we shall witness and his triumph can be ours.
> His glory marches on . . .

Although it appears that the service is of comparatively recent origin, information on its early history is vague. According to J.R. Kell, the Cathedral Warden, writing in October 1977:

> I don't know when it started . . . The first I was taken to as a child some 70 years ago being a small thing, mainly for children. I should say it was instigated by Dean Lawrance, who came here in 1868 as rector and became archdeacon and in 1904 dean.
>
> The earliest record of the martyrdom of Alban records that he was led up the hill from the Roman city of Verulamium, across the River Ver, and the hill was covered in 'various kinds of flowers'. From this it seems that the idea of roses arose, they being most prolific in June. The blood of martyrs has always been signified by the colour red—the liturgical colour for Saints' Days—and hence red roses are considered appropriate for St Alban. At the Patronal Festival the shrine is always decorated with red roses. . . .
>
> Dean Lawrance's grand-daughter, who still lives in St Albans . . . agrees that the Rose Service probably started around the turn of the century, no earlier.

However, according to another member of the cathedral staff, writing in October 1990:

> The actual Rose Service was started in the 20s by the dean as a way of celebrating St Alban's Day. For many years people remember it as a small abbey service attended by children and their abbey families . . . In the 70s the Diocesan Sunday School Adviser suggested that it should be broadened out to become an opportunity for children from all over the diocese

to attend their mother church to celebrate St Alban's Day. Many Sunday schools join in a course, which includes details of the life and death of St Alban, for six weeks before they come to the Service, and when they come each child is asked to bring a rose to put at the shrine during the processions. These flowers are subsequently taken out to the housebound people in the parish.

During the Service the words 'Among the roses of the martyrs, Brightly shines St Alban' are used, although I have not been able to trace their origin.

To go back further, the account of St Alban's journey up the hill from Verulamium to the site of his martyrdom mentions flowers springing up on the hillside as he passed, but does not stipulate roses!

In Unitarian chapels roses are often used in children's naming ceremonies. Unitarians reject the doctrine of original sin. Therefore most of them consider the use of water in naming or christening ceremonies to wash away sin to be unnecessary.

We prefer the symbolism of the rose, chosen because of its beauty and its thorniness. The words generally spoken are some version of:

'[Name] we give you this rose today,
We have taken the thorns off it for this occasion.
But we know that, even if we would, we cannot remove the thorns from your life.
Therefore we hope that your life, like this rose, will be beautiful in spite of the thorns.'

We then stroke the child's face with the rose petals, not necessarily with any deep theological meaning, other than connection with life itself, but more for the pleasure of it. If the child is old enough (four months on) they generally try to eat it, which is alright too. [Hampstead, London, October 1993]

Rosebay willowherb (*Chamerion angustifolium*)

[From a woman in Coreley, Shropshire, 1981]. Of course you never picked rosebay willowherb that was a 'MOTHER-DIE' flower. We used to call it 'mother-die'—means you think your mother would die. I wouldn't pick it for anything. [Opie and Tatem, 1989: 267]

[In the Macclesfield area of Cheshire during my childhood in the 1940s it was believed that] rosebay willowherb should not be picked, otherwise a THUNDER storm will ensue, or, more horrifically, your mother will die. I think we called this plant 'thunderflower'. [Skipton, North Yorkshire, November 1991]

[As boys in the Thetford area we] at times used to smoke the fluffy down from the rosebay willowherb, but it was a very hot and strong smoke. [West Stow, Suffolk, November 1992]

Rosemary (*Rosmarinus officinalis*)

> [Stockleigh Pomeroy, Devon:] If you had a rosemary bush growing near the house no WITCH could harm you. [Brown, 1971: 268]

Alternatively:

> You always had to plant rosemary in your garden, so that you wouldn't be short of friends. [Streatham, London, July 1992]

> In Hampshire rosemary was known as friendship bush. Every house had one; I can't remember seeing a house that didn't have one. [Streatham, London, April 1993]

> I have always referred to rosemary as the plant of friendship. [Charmouth, Dorset, January 1994]

In common with other herbs, such as PARSLEY and SAGE, rosemary was reputed to grow best where the wife was dominant.

> There is also a saying in Yorkshire that rosemary will not grow in the garden of a house unless the woman is master. [*N & Q*, 5 ser. 11: 18, 1879]

> A woman came to ask me with many apologies whether I would plant some rosemary cuttings; she did not wish to be rude, and Mrs Wist had said it was a very delicate thing to ask anyone to strike rosemary cuttings, but she did want a bush so badly. I said I did not mind doing it for her, why should it be such a delicate thing to ask anyone. She replied 'Don't you know it only strikes in the house where the mistress is master, and if it won't grow here, it won't grow anywhere.' So I got 14 shoots off the branch, 11 grew, three didn't. My husband was so interested that he went to look at the cuttings every day, and said the three that did not grow were evidently where he got a look in. [Taylor MSS, Norwich, Norfolk]

> In any marriage there is a dominant member, and as often as not it was the wife. In Hertfordshire one traditional outward sign of this was a thriving rosemary bush in the garden. 'That be rosemary sir,' said a cottager . . . 'and they do say that it only grows where the missus is master, and it do grow here like wildfire.' This belief is still current in most rural parishes. [Jones-Baker, 1977: 69]

Various legends associate rosemary with the Holy Family's flight to Egypt.

> When I was five or less I heard that rosemary flowers, which were formerly white, became blue after the Virgin Mary stopped to do some washing on the way to Egypt and hung her robe to dry on a rosemary bush. [Wicken, Cambridgeshire, April 1994]

At Stratford-upon-Avon rosemary is worn or carried on the anniversary of the birth of William Shakespeare, 23 April.

> Rosemary, DAFFODILS and PANSIES (see Hamlet, Act IV, Scene V) feature in the Shakespeare Birthday Celebrations every year, worn as buttonholes

or carried as posies in the procession through the town which ends at Holy Trinity Church. Here all the flowers are put in the chancel round Shakespeare's tomb. . . . The celebratory procession was started about 1898–1900 by the headmaster of the King Edward VI Grammar School, where Shakespeare is said to have been a pupil. The boys took evergreens including rosemary to the church on Shakespeare's birthday, and this became an annual event. It is now an international celebration of a great dramatist. [Stratford-upon-Avon, Warwickshire, February 1994]

Most of the people taking part in the 1994 Shakespeare Birthday Celebration procession wore sprigs of rosemary, but the flowers carried to be placed around the memorial in Holy Trinity Church seemed to be readily available seasonal or florists' flowers having no particular associations with the dramatist [personal observation].

Infusions of rosemary are valued as a hair rinse.

Rosemary for a rinse after shampooing hair. [Bangor, Gwynedd, March 1993]

Rosemary leaves in the bath revives, and strained off, having been in hot water, make a nice rinse for hair and leaves it shiny. [Sutton, Surrey, August 1993]

Rot-grass – a name for BUTTERWORT.

Rowan (*Sorbus aucuparia*), also known as mountain ash, quickbeam, and whitty tree. Throughout the British Isles, but especially in Ireland and the Highlands and Islands of Scotland, rowan was valued for its protective powers.

Whitty-tree . . . in Herefordshire they are not uncommon; and they used, when I was a boy [1630s], to make pinnes for the yoakes of their oxen of them, believing it had the vertue to preserve them from being forespoken, as they call it; and they used to plant one by their dwelling-house, believing it to preserve from witches and evill eyes. [Aubrey 1847: 56]

[The Scots] believe that any small part of this tree carried about with them will be a sovereign charm against all the dire effects of witchcraft. Their cattle also, as well as themselves, are supposed to be preserved by it from evil; for the dairy-maid will not forget to drive them to the shealings or summer pastures with a rod of the roan-tree, which she carefully lays up over the door of the sheal boothy, or summer-house, and drives them home again with the same. In Strathspey they make, for the same purpose, on the first day of May, a hoop of the wood of this tree, and in the evening and morning cause all the sheep and lambs to pass through it. [Lightfoot, 1777: 257]

In 1945, the new owner of a croft in a remote part of north-west Scotland was warned against destroying a clump of rowans which obscured the view from her kitchen window:

'Ach—but you must no' be cutting them all down, whateffer!' She exclaimed 'You must be leaving one . . . because a rowan tree near the house keeps evil spirits away. It's good to have a rowan tree in your garden, and if you hang a wee sprigie of it over the byre door, your beasts will be well too, and bad luck willna come to themselves.' [Armstrong, 1976: 36]

Similarly:

A rowan berry tree is good to have growing in the garden, or nearby, because it wards off the influence of WITCHES. [Ashreigney, Devon, July 1983]

The rowan or mountain ash tree is said to be the home of good FAIRIES. I have one growing in my garden, given to me by my mother after I got married. [Dromsally, Co. Limerick, October 1984]

On the Isle of Man we used to make little crosses of mountain ash to put up above the door for protection. [Milton Keynes, Buckinghamshire, September 1985]

They plant rowan outside their houses for protection in Scotland. When my parents moved into their house in Harrow, where I still live, in 1938, my father planted a rowan sapling in the garden—it was a new house. He brought the sapling from Scotland; he didn't really believe, but he did it to keep up the custom. [Harrow, Middlesex, January 1991]

My mother, who is 86, remembers from her childhood in Higham Ferrers, Northants, that . . . a rowan tree kept witches away. [Waltham Abbey, Essex, March 1991]

The planting of rowan trees near houses has been continued by the descendants of Scottish settlers in New Zealand:

In the face of different work, climate and seasonal pattern of the Southern Hemisphere . . . rowan trees [are] still being planted at the entrance to most modest suburban [Dunedin] villas to avert the evil eye, witches, or any other potency of ill fortune . . . A (related?) custom of Otago children was to soak red rowan berries in water and then to sprinkle the fluid around doors and the like as some sort of preventative of evil. [Ryan, 1993: 8]

Three supple young rowan twigs, each tied into a simple and single knot, are displayed in the Pitt Rivers Museum, Oxford. These were acquired by the Museum in 1893, and bear the label:

Rowan tree loops, protective against witches. Two were placed on the railing of Dr Alexander's house, Castleton, Yorks, the third on a gateway before the church porch. They were placed by a horseman who turned his horse thrice before setting each loop.

Homes, crops, and cattle were particularly at risk on May Eve.

[Driney, Co. Leitrim:] The first smoke from a chimney on May morning is apt to be used by witches for bringing bad luck on a house. This may be

guarded against in the following way:—On May eve, get a bunch of
rowan leaves, and tie it up the chimney to dry, then on may morn, light
this, and let that be the first smoke to go out of the chimney; for the
witches can do nothing with it. [Duncan, 1896: 182]

May Eve they stick a piece of mountain ash in their crops, that way the
fairies would not take the luck of the crops. [IFCSS MSS 50: 323, Co.
Galway]

On May Eve the farmer cuts rowan berry in the shape of a ring and ties it
to the cow's tail with a red string. It is an old belief that butter would be
taken off the milk if rowan berry was not tied to cows' tails. [IFCSS MSS
1000: 156, Co. Cavan]

[Co. Wexford:] cows going out on May morning are struck with a quick-
erberry switch, which prevents any person putting any evil on them or
taking their profit or butter. [Clark, 1882: 81]

Rowan was also useful to protect people who attempted to rescue
others from the fairy realms. Thus in his *Celtic Folklore* (1901: 85), John
Rhys described a method for rescuing a captive dancing in a fairy ring.
Two or more strong men should hold a long rowan pole so that one
of its ends rested in the middle of the circle. When the invisible captive is felt to grasp the pole the men should pull with all their strength;
the fairies will not be able to intervene because of their aversion to
rowan wood. Similarly, in a Highland folk tale, recorded in 1823, a
man succesfully rescued his brother from a *shian*, or fairy hill, after
being advised: 'Return to the *shian* in a year and a day from the time
you lost him, fasten a rowan cross to your clothing and enter boldly,
and in the name of the Highest claim your brother' [Stewart, 1823: 91].

It is usually stated the protective qualities of rowan are due to its 'red
berries—there is no better colour against evil' [Grigson, 1987: 172].
However, rowan flowers, which are white, scented and messy, have
all the characteristics of such flowers as those of HAWTHORN and
MEADOWSWEET, which are considered to be inauspicious.

[During my childhood, *c.*40 years ago in Accrington, Lancashire] 'Some
people won't have rowan in the garden; I knew one woman who refused
to buy a house which she liked in every other way, because it had two
rowans.'
'Couldn't she have them cut down?'
'That would be as bad as transplanting them.'
[Worthing, West Sussex, March 1982]

70 Accrington schoolchildren (11–14 years old) were asked about
'unlucky' plants; according to one child it is 'unlucky to transplant mountain ash, or bring cuttings into the house.' [Nelson, Lancashire, August
1983]

[Hartland, Devon:] Never hit an animal with a mountain ash stick, as it is unlucky and brings wales up on the body. [Chope, 1927: 154]

Rowan appears to have been little used in folk medicine.

[Ireland:] an infusion of the leaves is a popular remedy for RHEUMATISM (an oz. to one pint); dose, one wineglassful. The leaves, when burned and inhaled are said to be useful in ASTHMA. [Moloney, 1919: 22]

My late parents came from Poland after the Second World War, and my mother occasionally used . . . herbal remedies . . . Frost-nipped rowan berries (the frost removes the sourness) were infused in vodka and after six months or so this was used as a medicine for stomach ache. [Bromley, Kent, April 1991]

Some gypsies I stayed with for a while used ground up [mountain] ash berries, dried first of course, as a flour for small cakes for unwell children. [Barnstaple, Devon, October 1993]

Royal fern (*Osmunda regalis*), occasionally known as bog onion.

In the Lake district, where the plant is known by the name of bog onion, the caudex is still used as an outward application for SPRAINS and BRUISES: it is beaten and covered with cold water, and allowed to remain thus during the night; in the morning a thick starchy fluid is the result, which is used to bathe the parts affected. [Britten, 1881: 178]

The bog onion resembles a fern in appearance but its root is somewhat the same as an onion bulb. The root is converted into a juicy substance and used as a rub for RHEUMATISM or sciatica; it is often found to be a complete cure. First the root is cut into slices and then pounded into a mash. It is then put into a bottle or corked vessel and water supplied in proportion to the size of the root. It is then left to set for about two days until it forms a thick juicy substance.

The bog-onion flowers at night in the month of June, but there is some mystery attached to it, because at the approach of daylight the flower disappears. It is known to be there by leaving seeds after it. [IFCSS MSS 50: 458, Co. Galway]

A poultice of bog-onion is a cure for a sprained limb. The onion is pounded and pressed to the sprain, and then is covered with a bandage. [IFCSS MSS 593: 43, Co. Clare]

Rue (*Ruta graveolens*). As a symbol of repentance and sorrow rue could be used to bless or curse, help or harm.

[In Herefordshire:] Nosegays of rue, enclosing a piece of half-eaten bread and butter, were dropt in the church porch by a deserted female, to denote an unhappy wedding. [Fosbroke, 1821: 74]

It is only a few years since a young girl went to Cusop [Herefordshire], to the wedding of a young man who had jilted her; waiting in the church porch till the bridegroom came out, she threw a handful of rue at him, saying 'May you rue this day as long as you live!' . . . the curse would come true, because the rue was taken direct from the plant to the church-yard, and thrown 'between holy and unholy ground' . . . if there was any difficulty in obtaining it [rue] for this spiteful purpose, rue-fern [i.e. wall rue], the leaves of which resemble it, might be used; it must be found growing on the churchyard wall, and be gathered directly from thence. [Leather, 1912: 115].

Infusions of rue were used to treat a variety of minor ailments.

[Horseheath, Cambridgeshire:] rue tea was prescribed for improving one's appetite. [Parsons MSS, 1952]

A former resident of Tulke, Staffordshire remembers having been given a tea made from rue as a child for the relief of COUGHS and colds. [Steele MSS, 1978: 88]

Runner or **kidney bean** (*Phaseolus vulgaris*). Local festivities in late April or May provided guidance for the planting of runner beans. The earliest dates were those associated with the feast day of St George (23 April).

[In north Devon] it is unwise to plant kidney beans until after George Nympton Revel. [Laycock, 1940: 115; the revel, last held in *c*.1939, was held on the Wednesday after the last Sunday in April]

They always used to say that kidney beans should be planted on the day of Hinton St George Fair. That used to be held on the third Thursday in April. [Thorncombe, Dorset, March 1975].

May 6 was known in the south of Somerset as Kidney Bean Day, and it was believed that, if you did not plant your beans then, they would not flourish. [K. Palmer, 1976: 102]

Alternatively, other plants could provide guidance.

Never plant kidney beans until the buds of the HAWTHORN bush have op-ened. [SLF MSS, Havercroft, West Yorkshire, January 1969]

[Weston, Warwickshire:] Do not plant your kidney beans until ELM leaves are as big as sixpences, or they will be killed by frost. [Wharton MSS, 1974: 35]

Rush (*Juncus* spp.). A legend recorded in 1937 in County Galway explained why tips of rushes become brown and withered.

One night as St Patrick went to bed he warned his servant lad that if he talked in his sleep he might be impolite. The servant was warned to listen to all that the Saint said. After sleeping for a while the Saint shouted: 'Bad luck to Ireland!' The listening boy responded: 'If so, let it be on the tips of the rushes!' After sleeping a little longer the Saint shouted again: 'Bad luck to Ireland!' The boy answered: 'If so, let it be on the highest part of the

white cows!' After another short sleep the Saint shouted: 'I'll say again
what I've said twice already: "Bad luck to Ireland!"' The boy answered:
'If so let it be on the bottom of the furze!' On waking the Saint asked his
servant if he had said anything during his sleep, and, if so, what. The boy
replied that he had said 'Bad luck to Ireland!' three times. 'And what did
you say?' asked the Saint. The boy explained what he had said. Ever since
the tips of the rushes have been withered, the tips of the horns of white
cows have been black, and the lower parts of GORSE bushes have been
withered, and every priest should have a boy serving him at Mass. [O'Sullivan, 1977: 113]

Alternatively:

St Patrick got a piece of a dog to eat in a house one day. When he found
out what it was he cursed the place. When he had it cursed he was sorry,
but he couldn't take back the curse . . . without putting it on some other
thing, so he put it on the tops of the rushes. [IFCSS MSS 770: 143, Co.
Longford]

In Ireland crosses are made for St Brigid's Day, 1 February. Although
these crosses were made from a variety of materials: straw, rushes,
sedge or bent grass, hay, wood, goose quills, tin, wire, cardboard . . .
cloth [O'Sullivan, 1973: 71], it appears that rushes were the original
material, and crosses sold in Irish craft shops are invariably made of
these [personal observation, Dublin, May 1993]. St Brigid is said to
have been an abbess, who lived from c.450 to 523 [Attwater, 1970: 75],
but facts about her life are few, and she appears to have absorbed many
of the attributes of a pre-Christian deity. According to tradition:

One day St Brigid was passing by an old shed and she heard a moaning
cry. She entered the shed and beheld a dying man. She went over to him
and spoke to him about God. He would not listen to her. She tried in vain
to bring him to Our Lord, but he would not listen. Finally St Brigid went
out and formed a cross of rushes. She returned to the man, and when he
saw the cross he was moved to sorrow. He made his confession and received the last sacrament. Such was the origin of St Brigid's cross. [IFCSS
MSS 975: 148, Co. Cavan]

Although rushes are now considered to be pests which should be
eradicated by draining and soil improvement, they were formerly
widely used in making candles.

Until about 60 years ago the people of Ireland had to provide their own
light. They had no oil lamps or no light of any kind except the rush candles
made by themselves. Each household made bundles of rush candles at a
time and used them as required. The man or woman of the house brought
in a bundle of rushes. He then peeled each rush to a small strip from one
end to the other. He treated each of the rushes in the same way. When he
had this done he prepared a vessel of fat. This vessel was boat-shaped

and he poured the heated grease into it. Then he dipped the rushes into the grease and drew them through it until every bit of the rush was covered with fat. Then he would allow the rushes to dry and afterwards they were again dipped, and so on until they were thick enough for use. They were taken and stored up for the winter months. [IFCSS MSS 175: 250, Co. Sligo]

In impoverished upland areas rushes provided some of the few available comforts.

[North Wales:] The church is a humble gothic structure, the floor covered with rushes . . . This practice is almost universal through Wales. The floors are without pavement, and as straw is scarce, quantities of dried rushes are laid thick over the floor, for sake of warmth and cleanliness. The houses, few in number, are principally mud cottages with rush-clad roofs; and, not being white washed, wear an aspect little inviting to the passing traveller . . . The hut consisted of one room . . . the floor was of native soil . . . a few bundles of rushes thrown down for a bed. [Evans, 1800: 55, 75, and 115]

The strewing of rushes on church floors was formerly widespread, and is frequently mentioned in the churchwardens' accounts:

S. Mary-at-Hill, London:
1493. — For three burdens of rushes for new pews, 3d.
1504. — Paid for 2 berdens rysshes for strewyng newe pewes, 3d.
S. Margaret's, Westminster:
1544. — Paid for rushes against the Dedication Day, 1s 5d.
Kirkham, Lancashire:
1604—Rushes to strew the Church cost this year 9s 6d. [Simpson, 1931: 6]

In a few churches rush-strewing continues to the present time, although it is the carrying of the rushes to the church—the rush-bearing—which is usually more important. In Cumbria rush-bearings are held at Ambleside, Grasmere, Musgrave, and Warcop. The Grasmere rush-bearing, which is said to be the oldest, is held each year on the Saturday nearest St Oswald's Day (5 August).

Preparations, supervised by Miss Rachel McAlpine, take several days. Apart from sorting out the children who will take part, the 'bearings' have to be made. These are devices which look as if they were made entirely of rushes but are in fact created by winding the rushes around strong and practical materials like wood, wire netting and string. They symbolize various biblical and historical themes, as well as things to do with St Oswald. There are nine big bearings each about five feet high and several smaller ones, all of traditional design and used year after year. Many of them have been carried in the procession by generations of the same family; the frames are kept in their houses and women carry out the decoration. Miss McAlpine claims the right to make the beautiful cross of golden helenium which is carried at the head of the procession. The work takes the best part of two days as the ladies diligently and lovingly shape the rushes into intricate forms.

Most of their preparations are complete by Saturday lunchtime. Meanwhile the church floor has, mysteriously, acquired a layer of rushes. Long before 4 o'clock, the children in their Sunday best begin to arrive in the vicarage garden to be instructed in their duties and to be given a new 5p piece for their trouble. Families appear in the streets at the same time, the children carrying home-made bearings, even the tiny ones come in push-chairs decorated with rushes and flowers. The bearings are handed over to their bearers, the larger ones for the choirboys, the smaller ones for the girls.

The most important people in the whole procession are the Rush Maidens. Originally, when the whole business really was to take rushes to the church, in Grasmere they used to carry them on cloth, or sacking, holding the corners. These girls do the same thing, only there are six of them, their load is symbolic, and they use a fine sheet woven very many years ago in the village . . .

By the time everyone was organized the procession consisted of about 200 people. The choirboys led with their special rush-bearings, the golden cross in front. Then came the band, then the adult choir and the clergy all carrying sprays of rushes. Next came the Rush Maidens, followed by the bigger girls. There were few dads to be seen. They started from the church, marched right round the village and returned for a special service. The official bearings were placed round the altar, except 'the serpent' which is traditionally cast out to a special place outside the Sanctuary. All the other bearings, baskets, posies and rush crosses were left on the window ledges where they remained over the weekend.

On Monday they all return, collect their bearings and go off on a shorter tour of the village after which they have sports and tea. [Shuel, 1985: 86]

Ambleside's rush-bearing is held on a Saturday in July, while Warcop holds its festival on St Peter's Day, 29 June, unless this falls on a Sunday, when the event is held on the preceding Saturday. A painting of the Grasmere rush-bearing, painted by Frank Bramley in 1905, hangs in Grasmere Hall, and a mural depicting the Ambleside festival in 1944 can be found in St Mary's Church, Ambleside.

Further south:

Under a bequest dated 1493 the floor of St Mary Redcliffe church [Bristol] is strewn with rushes on Whit Sunday, and a memorial sermon is preached at a special service attended by the Lord Mayor who goes in procession to the church accompanied by other civic officials; this commemorates a wealthy merchant of the city who restored the church in the fifteenth century and later became a priest. [Gascoigne, 1969: 12]

The flexible stems of rushes were widely used in children's pastimes.

[Dorset, over 60 years ago:] making little green baskets (only girls did this) from soft rush (*Juncus effusus*). [Sidmouth, Devon, October 1991]

[1920s] both boys and girls made articles using fresh green rushes—one was called a butterfly cage, another was like a long narrow box, I have forgotten the rest. [Larne, Co. Antrim, November 1991]

Rushes we picked, wound around and made [into] a boat. [Plymstock, Devon, January 1993]

In my young days [1940s] I used to make little 'braided' chains from the young pliant stems of *Juncus effusus*, a very common species in our islands. Two stems were tied at one end and by repeatedly laying one strand over the other a very simple chain could be produced. [Scalloway, Shetland, February 1994]

On the Shetland Islands it was observed that heath rush (*Juncus squarrosus*), known locally as burra or burri-stikkels, preferred drier ground than such species as the compact rush (*Juncus conglomeratus*) and round-fruited rush (*Juncus compressus*), known as floss. Thus people who wanted to remain dry-footed were advised:

> Stramp fair on da burra;
> Keep wide o' da floss.

[Tait, 1947: 80]

See also HEATH RUSH.

Rye grass (*Lolium perenne*)

[In Herefordshire] rye grass is often used for divination. Girls count the ears of rye, saying:

> Rich man, poor man, beggar man, farmer;
> Tinker, tailor, plough-boy, thief.

The word spoken to the last ear on the rye-stalk is to indicate her fate. [Leather, 1912: 63]

[In Sussex] children still play with the flowers and grasses as they did in days of yore, and every year they sit on the grass and pull off the seeds of Whats-your-sweetheart grass (rye grass) to find out the profession of their future husbands: 'Tinker, tailor, soldier, sailor, potboy, ploughboy, gentleman, thief.' [Candlin, 1947: 131]

[Retford district, Lincolnshire:] We used to count the rye grasses—we'd say 'He loves me, he doesn't, he would, if he could, but he can't' to the top. Then we'd say 'What house? little house? big house? pig stye? barn?' We'll get married: 'coach, carriage, wheelbarrow, muck cart.' What'll you marry in? 'silk, satin, muslin, rags.' How many children will you have?—then you'd count up the stalk. Oh, I've missed one. 'What sort of man will he be—rich man, poor man, beggar man, thief.' [Cottam MSS, 1989: 27]

Other plants used in love DIVINATION include ASH and OX-EYE DAISY.

S

Saffron (*Crocus sativus*)

The fishermen of both north and south Cornwall believe that saffron brings bad luck, and that saffron cake carried in a boat spoils the chance of a catch. [Townshend, 1908: 108]

In some parts of England JUNIPER was known as saffron.

Sage (*Salvia officinalis*). In common with other herbs, such as PARSLEY, sage is said to grow best either for the dominant partner of a marriage or where the wife is dominant.

[At Bishops Nympton, Devon] after a wedding the bride and bridegroom must each plant a small sage bush brandise-wise. The size to which the sage bushes grow will show which will be the ruler in the house; it will of course be the planter of the larger of the two bushes. [Knight, 1945: 94]

[In Plymouth it is said that when sage] flourishes well, it denotes that the mistress is head of the household. [Chope, 1935: 132]

In Bucks it is not only maintained that the wife rules where sage grows vigorously—a notion elsewhere attached to the ROSEMARY—but a farmer recently informed me that the same plant would thrive or decline as the master's business prospered or failed. He asserted that it was perfectly true, for at one time when he was doing badly, the sage began to wither; but as soon as the tide turned the plant began to thrive again. [Friend, 1884: 8]

As the sage bush flourishes so does the family. [Plymouth, Devon, January 1993]

In addition to its culinary uses sage was also used for cleaning teeth and treating ARTHRITIS and sore gums.

Teeth: clean with fresh sage leaves. [Stockport, Greater Manchester, April 1991]

A gypsy 'toothpaste' in the 1940s and 50s was chopped sage and salt in an equal parts mix, rubbed on the teeth with Irish linen. [Barnstaple, Devon, May 1991]

Boil sage leaves, drink water for arthritis. [Llanuwchyllyn, Gwynedd, April 1991]

A sage leaf with its thick vein removed will relieve sore gum if put between the dentures and the gum. [Whitchurch, Hampshire, October 1993]

St Alban – commemorated by holding a ROSE service on the Sunday nearest his feast day.

St Brigid's Day – RUSH crosses made.

St Candida's eyes – a west Dorset name for PERIWINKLE.

St Cedd – associated with the Gospel OAK át Polstead, Suffolk.

St Congar – asociated with a YEW tree at Congresbury, Avon.

St David's Day – DAFFODILS and LEEKS worn.

St Fintan – associated with a SYCAMORE tree which grows at Clonenagh, Co. Laois.

St Frankin's Days. In August 1894 Sabine Baring-Gould collected the following tradition at Chawleigh and at Burrington in north Devon:

> In the Taw valley, at Eggesford, Burrington, etc., there exists a saying that the 19th, 20th, or 21st May, or three days near that time, are 'Francismass' or 'St Frankin's days', and that then comes a frost that does much injury to the blossom of APPLES. The story relative to this frost varies slightly. According to one version, there was a brewer, name of Frankan, who found that cider ran his ale so hard that he vowed his soul to the Devil on the condition that he would send three frosty nights in May to cut off the apple-blossom annually.
>
> The other version of the story is that the brewers in North Devon entered into compact with the Evil One, and promised to put deleterious matter into their ale on condition that the Devil should help them by killing the blossom of the apple-trees. Accordingly, whenever these May frosts come, we know that his Majesty is fulfilling his part of the contract, because the brewers have fulfilled theirs by adulterating their beer. According to this version, St Frankin is an euphemism for Satan. [Amery, 1895: 120]

Thirteen years later, in the south of the county, at Newton St Cyres:

> My gardener, on being told to put some bedding plants from the greenhouse into the open to harden, said it would not be well to do so 'until Franklin nights were on.' To my inquiry, he answered that he did not know who St Franklin was, but people thereabouts never thought the cherries or mazzards were safe from frosts until St Franklin nights were over, and these nights were the 19th, 20th and 21st May. On these nights we had severe frost at St Cyres, and the potatoes were much cut. [Amery, 1907: 108]

St George's Day – red ROSES worn; DANDELIONS gathered; RUNNER BEANS planted on or about.

St John of Beverley – associated with PRIMROSES in Humberside.

St John's Eve – the best day to acquire MOTHERWORT; DIVINATION using RIBWORT PLANTAIN attempted.

St John's Wort (*Hypericum* spp.). Species of St John's wort were formerly much valued for their protective properties. The name *Hypericum* was originally given by the Greeks to a plant which was placed above religious figures with the purpose of warding off evil spirits [Robson, 1977: 293]. It is not known whether or not the plant used by the Greeks was, in fact, a species of what is known today as *Hypericum*, but *Hypericum* species have been much used throughout the British Isles for similar purposes.

In an early thirteenth-century work on the life of St Hugh of Lincoln, an account is given of a woman who was tormented by a 'licentious demon' in the shape of a young man. After much suffering she was approached by another spirit, also in the shape of a young man, who told her to take a certain plant, hide it in her bosom, and scatter it around her house. The demon lover found the plant 'disgusting and stinking,' and was unable to enter the house while the plant remained in place. The woman considered the plant, which was known as 'Ypericon in Greek, and in Latin either the perforated plant or St John's wort,' to be her sole defence against the demon, but later she found simple piety provided adequate protection. A monk to whom she showed the plant in turn displayed it to a young couple in Essex, who were subsequently cured and protected from attacks by the demons with whom they had been seen to speak.

The recorder of these traditions noted that physicians regarded St John's wort to be 'a sovereign remedy against poison—even if this is due to the bite of a poisonous animal'. Thus it was not 'ridiculous to suppose that a bodily remedy for snakebite should not by God's mercy have been effective against the assaults of the ancient Serpent' [Douie and Farmer, 1962: 121].

A more recent writer states that St John's wort is 'one of the most beneficent of magical herbs, protecting equally against fairies and the devil', and gives a couplet spoken by a demon lover who was unable to approach a girl carrying the plant:

> If you would be true love of mine
> Throw away John's Wort and Verbein.

> [Briggs, 1976: 346]

In the eighteenth century:

> The superstitious in Scotland carry this plant [perforate St John's wort, *Hypericum perforatum*] about with them as a charm against the dire effects of witchcraft and enchantment. They also cure, or fancy they cure, their ropy milk, which they suppose to be under some malignant influence by putting this herb into it and milking afresh upon it. [Lightfoot, 1777: 417]

The English translation of a Gaelic incantation collected from a Hebridean cottar in the nineteenth century runs:

> St John's wort, St John's wort,
> My envy whosoever has thee,
> I will pluck thee with my right hand,
> I will preserve thee with my left hand,
> Whoso findeth thee in the cattlefold,
> Shall never be without kine.
>
> [Carmichael, 1900: 103]

Similarly, also in the Hebrides:

> St John's wort is one of the few plants still cherished by the people to ward away second-sight, enchantment, witchcraft, evil eye and death, and to ensure peace and plenty in the house, increase and prosperity in the fold, and growth and fruition in the field. The plant is secretly secured in the bodices of the women, and in the vests of the men, under the left armpit. St John's wort, however, is effective only when the plant is accidentally found. When this occurs the joy of the finder is great. [Carmichael, 1900: 96]

In the Forest of Dean:

> [According to my grandparents, b. 1856 and 1858] St John's wort was brought into the house and tied into bunches, hung in the windows—I believe it was supposed to prevent LIGHTNING striking the house. [Cinderford, Gloucestershire, November 1993]

St John's wort's protective qualities were particularly valued at midsummer. According to one folklorist writing of the Feast of St John the Baptist or Midsummer's Day:

> the saint's own golden flower, St John's wort—which is quite clearly a sun-symbol—was brought indoors to promote good fortune and protect the house from fire. [Hole, 1977: 123]

Whether St John's wort is 'clearly a sun-symbol' or not, it has certainly been widely used to decorate and protect homes on MIDSUMMER'S EVE. According to John Stow [1987: 193] writing of London in 1603, but possibly describing practices of three and a half centuries earlier:

> On the vigil of St John the Baptist, and on St Peter and Paul the apostles, every man's door being shadowed with green BIRCH, long FENNEL, St John's wort, ORPIN[E], white lilies and such like, garnished upon with garlands of beautiful flowers, had also lamps of glass with oil burning in them all night . . . which made a goodly show, namely in New Fish street, Thames street, etc.

In Cornwall:

> [Midsummer was] the time for lighting Midsummer Bonfires, an ancient custom rescued from extinction by the Old Cornwall Movement in 1929 and still flourishing . . . At St Cleer the fire is crowned with a witch's

broom and hat, a sickle with a handle of newly cut OAK is thrown into
the flames and wreaths of St John's wort are hung around the village—
all this was traditionally said to banish witches. [Deane and Shaw, 1975:
177]

At the Cornish Midsummer Fire celebrations the *Arlodhes an Blejyow*
[Lady of the Flowers] casts a bunch of plants tied with coloured ribbons into the flames. These plants are chosen to represent both 'good'
and 'bad' herbs, and a booklet produced by the Federation of Old
Cornwall Societies lists thirty-six suitable species. First in the list is the
'good' St John's wort, known in Cornish as *losow sen Jowan* [Noall,
1977: 10].

In Wales:

[On St John's Eve] it was the custom in many parts of the country to place
over the doors of houses sprigs of St John's wort or, if this were not available, the common MUGWORT: the intention was to purify the house from
evil spirits. St John's wort gathered at noon on St John's Day was thought
to be good for several complaints and if dug at midnight on the Eve of St
John the roots were good for driving the devil and witches away. [Owen,
1978: 111]

In Ulster:

[On St John's Eve] the flower of St John's wort was brought into the
house as protection against the evil eye. [St Clair, 1971: 41]

Also on Midsummer's Eve, St John's wort could be used to foretell
the future.

In Hertfordshire and elsewhere in England, girls would use St John's wort
to test their chances of matrimony. On Midsummer's Eve they would
pluck a piece of the plant, if it appeared fresh the following morning the
prospects were good. [Wright, 1940: 16]

In the middle of the nineteenth century St John's wort was employed
in Wales to predict life expectancy. A piece of the plant was gathered
for each person in the house, cleaned 'free from dust and fly', and each
piece named after a member of the household before being hung on a
rafter. In the morning the pieces were examined; those whose pieces
had withered most were expected to die soonest [Trevelyan, 1909:
252].

In Aberdeenshire it was believed that if one slept with a plant of St
John's wort under one's pillow on St John's Eve, the saint would appear in a dream, give his blessing, and prevent one from dying during
the following year [Banks, 1941: 25].

Several writers mention St John's wort as being a valuable medicinal herb, but they are extremely unspecific about what illnesses it
can be used to treat.

There are a few herbs which are almost universal specifics. St John's Wort is one; an infusion of the leaves will cure CATARRH, grow hair, heal CUTS and make a poultice for SPRAINS. An ointment made from it is good for BURNS. [Tongue, 1965: 35]

See also TUTSAN.

St John the Baptist – associated with YELLOW RATTLE.

St Mary the Virgin – associated with COW PARSLEY, LUNGWORT, MADONNA LILY, and REDSHANK. Collections of plants associated with St Mary are grown in the cloister gardens of Lincoln Cathedral, and at the Knock Shrine in County Mayo. For extensive lists of plants associated with the Virgin see MacNamara, 1987.

St Moalrudha – associated with BUTTERWORT in the Hebrides.

St Nectan – associated with FOXGLOVE.

St Newlina – associated with a FIG tree at St Newlyn East, Cornwall.

St Patrick – explained the concept of the Trinity using SHAMROCK; cursed RUSHES.

St Patrick's cabbage – a name given to WATERCRESS in Co. Longford.

St Patrick's Day – POTATOES planted; SALLOW and SHAMROCK associated.

Early potatoes must be set before St Patrick's Day. You give your lawn its first cut before Patrick's Day. [Clonmel, Co. Tipperary, February 1993]

St Patrick's staff, **St Patrick's spit** – names given to BUTTERWORT in Northern Ireland.

St Valentine's Day or **Eve** – BROAD BEANS sown; plants used for love DIVINATION include BAY and HEMP.

St Vitus' dance – cured using WOOD SAGE.

St William of Rochester – associated with SWEET WILLIAM.

St Wite or St Candida – associated with PERIWINKLE.

St Withburga – associated with LORDS AND LADIES.

Salad burnet (*Sanguisorba minor*)

The chewed leaves have a cucumber-like flavour, and in some places, as about Ripon, have been in repute (infused in water) as a cure for, or an alleviant of, drunkard's thirst. [Lees, 1888: 208]

Sallow or pussy willow(*Salix caprea*)

[In Shropshire] the strongest condemnation of all lights on willow catkins. The soft round yellowish blossoms are considered to resemble
young goslings, and are accordingly called in various localities 'goosy gos-
lins,' 'gis an' gullies' or 'geese and gullies'. Whatever the name, however,
the ban on the blossom is the same. No vegetable goslings may be brought
into the house, for if they be, no feathered goslings will be hatched.
[Burne, 1883: 250]

Cf. PRIMROSE.

Great sallow and related species of willow were much used as 'palm'
on PALM SUNDAY in many parts of Europe. Throughout England great
sallow was widely known as 'palm' [Britten and Holland, 1886: 366;
Grigson, 1987: 258]. In its issue of Friday 11 April 1924 the *Daily Mail*
published a photograph of 'church helpers returning after gathering
palm at Ingatestone, Essex.' The photograph showed two young
women with their arms full of flowering sallow twigs.

In the Macclesfield area of Cheshire in the 1940s . . . we usually referred
to the Great Sallow or Pussy Willow as 'palm', and on Palm Sunday our
Methodist chapel always had a bunch of it on the Communion Table.
[Skipton, North Yorkshire, November 1991]

In some areas it was considered unlucky to bring flowering sallow indoors before Palm Sunday.

About 70 years ago, in Hampshire, it was thought unlucky to bring
palm—flowering willow—indoors before Palm Sunday. [Great
Bookham, Surrey, October 1979]

On Palm Sunday 1991 the sanctuary of Southwark Cathedral in London was decorated with LAUREL, YEW, dried palm leaves, and sallow
[personal observation], but it appears that sallow is rarely used on Palm
Sunday in English churches, most of which prefer to use imported
dried palm. However, sallow continues to be utilized in churches
used by Christians from some other parts of Europe. At the Polish
Catholic Church of Christ the King, in Balham, south London, bunches of BOX, sallow, and DAFFODILS are used on Palm Sunday [personal
observation, 27 March 1983]. On 14 April 1984—for Orthodox christians the Eve of Palm Sunday—at a service held at the Russian Orthodox Cathedral of the Dormition of the Mother of God, in South
Kensington, London, a large pile of flowering sallow twigs and two
jars of the same were blessed by the presiding bishop before each
member of the congregation was given a bunch, together with a
lighted wax taper. After the service the 'palm' was taken home and
placed near an icon [personal observation].

In Ireland, on ST PATRICK'S DAY:

> The children brought in a couple of bits of sally rod and the mother or grandmother stuck it into the fire and drew it out when charred. Then the sign of the Cross was made on everybody's arm with the charred end. [IFCSS MSS 325: 11, Co. Cork]

Around Brentwood in Essex:

> Willow and ROWAN were definitely 'good' trees and kept away witches if planted near the door. Willow twigs hung on a door kept away marsh witches, as did HAZEL twigs. [Yafforth, North Yorkshire, January 1990]

More enigmatically:

> Willow is, in my native East Yorkshire, the witches' tree. I stopped a puzzled Transylvanian Saxon prisoner of war from destroying one. [South Stainley, North Yorkshire, March 1992]

In Herefordshire:

> The willow brings luck if brought into the house on MAY DAY, and is potent against the EVIL EYE, especially if given by a friend. It is also believed that any young animal or child struck by a willow rod, usually called a 'withy stick' or 'sally twig', will cease to grow afterwards. A woman at Pembridge said, 'I've never hit nothing with a sally twig, nor shouldn't like to either.' [Leather, 1912: 19]

One of England's most beautiful folk carols associates the willow tree with Mary and her Son. In *The Bitter Withy* it is explained why the willow tree should rot and become hollow comparatively quickly. Jesus asks his Mother for permission to go and play at ball. Mary gives her permission, but entreats him to keep out of mischief. He meets three high-born children, greets them, and asks them to play with him. They reply that as 'lords' and ladies' sons, born in bower and hall', they cannot play with 'a poor maid's child, born in an ox's stall'. Christ makes a bridge of sunbeams and walks over it, the other children chase after him, but the bridge provides no support for them, so they fall and are drowned. Their distressed mothers protest to Mary, who punishes her son:

> So Mary mild fetched home her child,
> And laid him across her knee,
> And with a handful of willow twigs
> She gave him slashes three.

Whereupon Christ curses the willow:

> Ah bitter withy, ah bitter withy,
> You have caused me to smart,
> The willow must be the very first tree
> To perish at the heart.

[Lloyd, 1967: 124]

See also WILLOW.

Sally-my-handsome (*Carpobrotus acinaciformis*) – see under HOTTEN-
TOT FIG.

Samfer or **samper** – local names for MARSH SAMPHIRE.

Samphire – a name given to two unrelated plants: ROCK SAMPHIRE
(*Crithmum maritimum*) and MARSH SAMPHIRE (*Salicornia* spp.), both of
which are gathered for food.

Sampion – a Cheshire name for MARSH SAMPHIRE.

Sand crocus (*Romulea columnae*), known as *genotte* on Guernsey:

> Etymologically, this word signifies earth nut, and I have known children
> dig up the bulbs on the cliffs and eat them. [Marquand, 1906: 40]

Scalds – treated using HART'S TONGUE FERN.

Scarlet fever – prevented using ONION; cured using FOXGLOVE.

Scarlet pimpernel (*Anagallis arvensis*). The flowers of scarlet pimpernel are said to close when rain is on its way, consequently the plant has
such names as change-of-the-weather, Grandfather's weatherglass,
poor man's weatherglass, shepherd's warning, and weather-teller
[Grigson, 1987: 268].

> The shepherd's weatherglass is the little scarlet pimpernel, for when it is
> fully open it is said to be a sign of fine weather. [Parsons MSS, 1952]

In north Devon:

> In the early 1950s a lady used to walk the roadsides and lanes, always with
> a bicycle with a basket on the front into which she would put hedgerow
> and field wild flowers. Scarlet pimpernel, she told me, was better than cold
> tea for sore eyes, and also against STINGS. [Barnstaple, Devon, May 1991]

Sarvers, **sarves**, **sarvies** – Essex names for the fruit of the WILD SER-
VICE TREE.

Scented lily – a Shetland name for white NARCISSUS.

Sciatica – treated using HORSERADISH and HOP.

Scotch thistle – a County Antrim name for SPEAR THISTLE; other
species which have been claimed to be the Scottish THISTLE include
cardoon (*Cynara cardunculus*), COTTON THISTLE, dwarf thistle (*Cirsium acaule*), globe thistle (*Echinops ritro*), melancholy thistle (*Cirsium
heterophyllum*), milk thistle (*Silybum marianum*), musk thistle (*Carduus
natans*), *Onopordum arabicum*, stemless carline thistle (*Carlina
acaulis*), and woolly thistle (*Cirsium eriophorum*) [Dickson and Walker,
1981: 5].

Scots lovage (*Ligusticum scoticum*)
> Frequent in the Western islands of Jura, Isla, Iona and Skie, in which last it is call'd by the name of *shunis*, and is sometimes eaten raw as a sallad or boil'd as greens. [Lightfoot, 1777: 160]

Scots pine (*Pinus sylvestris*). Being a conspicuous evergreen tree, the Scots pine was formerly planted as landmarks, notably for marking drovers' routes, and farms which were willing to offer accommodation for them and their cattle [Watts, 1989]. In the Cotswolds Scots pines are said to have been planted as an expression of Jacobite sympathies, and indicated places where fugitive Jacobites could expect to find safe harbour [Briggs, 1974: 123]. See also PINE.

Scour (diarrhoea in cattle) – most prevalent when LILAC in bloom; caused by YELLOW BARTSIA; cured using SHEPHERD'S PURSE.

Scrofula – see KING'S EVIL.

Scurvy – cured by eating SCURVY GRASS and WATERCRESS.

Scurvy grass (*Cochlearia* spp.)
> [Shetland islanders] have much scurvey-Grass; God so ordering it in his wise Providence that *Juxta venenum nascitur Antidotum*, that seeing the SCURVY is a common Disease of the Countrey, they should have the Remedy at hand. [Brand, 1701: 80]

Sea beans, also known as Molucca beans. The seeds of about ten tropical plants are regularly carried by the Gulf Stream from the Caribbean islands or north-east South America onto the shores of western Europe [Guppy, 1917: 26]. The transatlantic origin of such seeds was known to European scientists as early as 1670 [Guppy, 1917: 33], but for the inhabitants of remote areas on the western coasts of the British Isles, the origins of the seeds remained obscure. The seeds which attracted most attention were those of two members of the pea family: *Caesalpinia* spp. and *Entada* spp., and a member of the convolvulus family: *Merremia discoidesperma*.

The largest and the most frequently found of these is the heart- or kidney-shaped seed of *Entada*, with which 'superstitions are asociated' in western Ireland [Nelson, 1978: 107], and which 'are washed ashore on the Isles of Scilly, where the children call them lucky beans' [St Mary's, Isles of Scilly, September 1992].

Carew [1602: 27] recorded:
> The [Cornish] sea strond is strowed with . . . certain Nuts, somewhat resembling a sheepes kidney . . . the outside consisteth of a hard darke coloured rinde: the inner part, of a kernell voyd of any taste, but not so of

337

vertue, especially for women trauayling in childbirth, if at least, old wiues tales may deserue any credit.

The Cuming Museum in the London Borough of Southwark houses a collection of objects assembled by Edward Lovett, who served on the Folk-lore Society's council from 1903 to 1920. These objects relate to London superstitions, and many of them were used to prevent illness and misfortune. Among the items of vegetable origin is an *Entada* seed—a 'Lucky Bean'—which was valued in north-west London, where it was supposed to ensure good fortune. The fresh, shiny appearance of the seed suggests that it has not undergone lengthy immersion in water, so it is probable that it was brought home by a traveller who acquired it in the tropics.

At about the same time as Lovett was assembling his collection, imported beans, possibly *Entada* beans, were being sold by quack doctors in some towns. A South Shields, County Durham, lodging-house keeper, who had several quacks (or 'crocuses' as they were commonly known) among her lodgers, remembered:

> Another would buy a pound of foreign beans from the chemist for a shillin'—like little hard pebbles they were—and sell them as lucky beans or magic beans at one and six each. If they put a thread through to wear round your neck, then it cost ye two bob. Proper bloody frauds they were. [Robinson, 1975: 58]

In the 1940s *Entada* seeds were searched for along the Pembrokeshire coast, and it was believed that the seeds would bestow good luck on their finder if they were worn on his (or, more usually, her) person. Many people had their seeds made into brooches, lockets or similar trinkets for this purpose [Lloyd, 1945: 307]. More recently *Entada* seeds have been offered for sale as 'Lucky Sea Beans' at seaside resorts, where they form part of the stock of shops selling sea ornaments, exotic seashells, and similar items. One assumes that these seeds have been imported from tropical regions. In Weymouth, Dorset, Lucky Sea Beans were offered for sale at 12p each in July 1984. Elsewhere the name given to the seeds sometimes varies according to the expected interests of potential buyers. Thus in October 1986 'Lucky Bingo Sea Beans' were on sale in the Promenade Shell Shop, Blackpool, Lancashire, while in September 1988 'Lucky Folklore Sea Beans' were obtainable, at 10p each, from the Waterhead Shell Shop at Ambleside, Cumbria.

It appears that *Caesalpinia* and *Merremia* seeds were valued only in the Highlands and Islands of Scotland. *Merremia* seeds, which have a characteristic cross-marking, were used as amulets to ease childbirth. In 1891 Lieutenant-Colonal Feilden sent such a seed, which he had acquired about twenty years earlier, to the Royal Botanic Gardens, Kew. This seed's Gaelic name meant Mary's Bean, and, in Roman Catholic communities in the Outer Hebrides, it was believed that if the seed was clenched in the hand of a woman in labour it would ensure an easy delivery. Such seeds might become treasured heirlooms, and Feilden's example had come from a North Uist woman who stated that it had formerly belonged to her grandmother [Hemsley, 1892: 371].

According to Alexander Carmichael, the great collector of Hebridean folklore:

> *Arna Moire*, kidney of Mary; *tearna Moire*, saving of Mary: This is a square thick Atlantic nut, sometimes found indented along and across, the indentations forming a natural cross on the nut. It is occasionally mounted in silver and hung round the neck as a talisman. Every nurse has one which she places in the hand of the woman to increase her faith and distract her attention. It was consecrated on the altar and much venerated. [Carmichael, 1928: 225]

In January 1893 a *Merremia* seed was sent by the Revd Alexander Stewart to a meeting of the Society of Antiquaries of Scotland.

> I send you a specimen of a kind of amulet very highly prized by the people of the three Uists—North Uist, Benbecula, and South Uist—which is known locally as *Airne Moire*—(Virgin) Mary's kidney. It is really a kind of bean occasionally picked up on the shores of the Outer Hebrides . . .
>
> It is considered all the more valuable and sacred if, as in this specimen, there is something like a cross on one side of it. Midwives use it as a charm to alleviate the pains of parturition. Very often also a small hole is drilled through either end and through these holes a string is passed and looped, so that it may be hung round the neck of children when they are TEETH-ING, or suffering under any infantile ailments. It is most in request amongst Catholics, as its local name implies; but Protestants also sometimes use it. It is oftenest met with in South Uist and the Island of Barra, where at least three-fourths of the people are Roman Catholics. Canary-coloured specimens are sometimes got, almost white, and these are very highly prized. These amulets are greatly valued, and it is not easy for outsiders to get specimens. [*Proceedings of the Society of Antiquaries of Scotland*, 27: 47, 1893]

Although the seeds of *Merremia* are characteristically brownish-black, Stewart stated that yellow or almost white seeds were occasionally found, and were more highly valued than the usual black seeds. It is probable that these light-coloured seeds were, in fact, of *Caesalpinia* rather than *Merremia*. *Caesalpinia* seeds are small, round, and light grey in colour, their external texture being acorn-like with hair-like cracks.

In his *Description of the Western Islands of Scotland* [1703: 38], Martin Martin gave information on the then current uses of *Caesalpinia* seeds. They were worn around children's necks to protect their wearers from witchcraft and the evil eye, and were believed to change from yellow to black if any evil was intended. Martin claimed to have observed this colour change, but was unable to provide any explanation for it.

Caesalpinia seeds were also used to protect cattle. Martin was told by Malcolm Campbell, Steward of Harris,

> that some weeks before my arrival there, all his cows gave blood instead of milk for several days together; one of the neighbours told his wife that this must be witchcraft, and it would be easy to remove it, if she would put the white nut, called the Virgin Mary's Nut, and lay it in the pail into which she was to milk the cows. This advice she presently followed, and having milked one cow into the pail with the nut in it, the milk was all blood, and the nut changed its colour to dark brown; she used the nut again, and all the cows gave pure good milk, which they ascribe to the virtue of the nut.

Sea beet (*Beta vulgaris* ssp. *maritima*)

[On the Isle of Wight] boiled, instead of greens, the sea beet is much relished by the poorer classes. [Bromfield, 1856: 421]

[On the Isles of Scilly] young leaves of sea beet are collected and boiled as spinach. [Woodnewton, Northamptonshire, June 1992]

Sea beet is still collected when young by some people for use as spinach. [St Saviour, Jersey, May 1993]

The sea beet is one subspecies of beet (*Beta vulgaris*); other subspecies include the foliage beet (varieties of which include spinach beet and Swiss chard) and the BEETROOT.

Sea bindweed (*Calystegia soldanella*)

A plant associated with the Stuarts is the sea bindweed . . . In 1745 Prince Charles Edward landed on the Island of Eriskay, and from his pocket he scattered seeds of this white striped pink convolvulus which he had gathered while waiting to embark from France. These seeds grew and seeded themselves in turn and are still to be found growing at this spot and nowhere else in the Outer Hebrides. [Fairweather, n.d.: 3]

Sea campion (*Silene uniflora*)

From an elderly friend in Porthnockie, about 30 miles from Burghead: Deadman's Bells = sea campion . . . it was untouchable, never picked and never brought into the house; she thinks the reason for this ban was that in that area of steep cliffs it grew on rocky ledges, highly dangerous for children.

A friend who used to live in Buckie knew sea campion as Devil's Hatties; it grew in a dangerous area called 'The Back o' the Head,' i.e. the headland of Burghead. [Edinburgh, December 1991]

Sea campion has five different Jersey-French-Norman names, three of which indicate its use in a children's game. The calyx is turned inside out and the petals removed together with all but two of the stamens, these being retained to represent the arms of a washerwoman hanging the washing on the line. This is sometimes called a crinolined lady, and heated exchanges have taken place over this point. [St Saviour, Jersey, May 1993]

Seaweed. In many coastal districts seaweeds were valued as manure and were also gathered and slowly burned in kilns to produce a hard lumpy residue known as kelp. When the kelp industry was at its peak between 1780 and 1830, an estimated 3000 people were employed in Orkney, their produce being exported to England for use in the production of glass, soap, and dyes. A second period of activity developed with the demand for iodine in the 1840s and lingered on until the late 1930s [Thomson, 1983]. In the nineteenth century kelp was also produced in Ireland, much of it being shipped to Glasgow for the extraction of iodine [Chapman, 1950: 54]. The Irish seaweed industry was revived in the early 1940s. According to the *Irish Times* of 27 December 1963:

[The] seaweed industry . . . [is] worth only £300,000 p.a. But this money gets into areas where it is probably needed most, the poorer parts of the poor western seaboard. For many families, this industry has been the godsend of their dreams; a sure weekly income to tide them through the difficult summer and actumn months.

This revival, like that on the Orkneys, was initiated to produce algal products, such as agar–agar, which had been imported from Japan but were unavailable during the war. Later it supplied the alginate industry, the products of which are used 'for purposes as diverse as stabilising ice-cream, keeping solids in suspension in fruit drinks, forming emulsions in salad dressings, and preserving a good "head" on a pint of beer . . . they are used in the paper-making and pharmaceutical industries, and precise casts for dental work may be made using their firm gel' [Thomson, 1983: 106]. However, the most widespread use of seaweed was as manure on coastal arable ground.

Along the [Pitsligo, Aberdeenshire] sea-board where seaweed—'waar'— is used as manure the farmers showed much anxiety on New Year's morning to have the first load of weed that was taken from the shore. When the first load was carted home, a small quantity was laid down at each door of the farm-steading, and the remainder was cast into the fields—a portion into each field. This was supposed to bring good-fortune. [Gregor, 1884a: 331]

Long ago when I was young I remember [I used] to see nine canoes cutting seaweed out in the strand outside Acnascaul. They used to cut the seaweed in the month of May and April, and sell it at 10 shillings a canoe load to people who wanted it for second manuring POTATOES.

There used to be a lot of horse cars waiting in the strand to buy the seaweed. It was said that a horse rail of seaweed was as good as a cart of guano. The guano was better manure for potatoes because the potatoes that was manured with guano was a lot drier for eating than those manured with seaweed.

The men . . . used to be cutting it in canoes out in the tide, they used to have a scythe made for the purpose. This scythe had a short blade and a very long handle, the handle used to be about 12 or 13 feet long. A man would stand up in the canoe, and put out the scythe under the water where the 'ribbons' (that [was] the name that kind of seaweed is called) and he would cut them. There was another man who had a long bent rack, called a seaweed rack. He would gather the seaweed out of the water with the rack, and put it into the boat.

Other people used to cut 'rock seaweed', i.e. seaweed that is growing on the rocks on the seashore. This seaweed is short black seaweed and have blisters on it. It is called 'blistered seaweed'.

This sort of seaweed wasn't so plenty because there used [to] be too many people cutting it. The people used to cut this with reaping hooks when the tide was out. [IFC MSS 782: 428, 1941]

In some Kerry coves weed drifting in the water was collected in a long purse net mounted on two poles and operated by two men who waded into the sea, holding the mouth of the net open and trailing the bag part behind them. They commonly walked in as far as their shoulders and when they had sufficient weed in the net they crossed one wing of the net over the other to close it and proceeded to haul it in. As a good haul could enclose about a ton of weed in the bag, four or five men often had to come to help haul it up on to the beach where it was emptied into a cart. [O'Neill, 1970: 13]

Early in the twentieth century Irish farmers valued seaweed to such an extent that they created artificial conditions to encourage its growth. At Darby's Point in Co Mayo:

Where rocks are present Fucus grows naturally, but where, as is usually the case, the shore is composed of sand, the farmers set to work to obtain a growth of Wrack by artificial means. Stones about a foot square are disposed in rows a yard apart, with paths left between for carting. Sporelings speedily appear on the stones and during the course of a year, develop into good-sized plants. The following season the Wrack is cut. [Cotton 1912: 153]

In Scotland the use of seaweed as manure continued along the Ayrshire coast until the 1960s.

> The early 1960s saw the virtual end of 'wrecking' [i.e. seaweed-gathering] in West Kilbride parish. Two main reasons are proffered by the local farmers. Firstly, the weed is no longer coming ashore in amounts which match earlier years, and, secondly, that which is cast up is so heavily polluted with polythene, plastics and other packaging materials that it is unusable as manure. [Noble, 1975: 81]

Many people used seaweed as a means of detecting changes in the WEATHER.

> Some of the old people kept a piece of dried seaweed hanging near the fire, when it got damp it was said to be a sign of rain. [IFC MSS 782: 271, Co. Kerry, 1941].

> Living by the sea we must mention seaweed, a long 'streamer' hung by the back door will tell you the weather better than those blokes on TV. [Ryde, Isle of Wight, November 1988]

> [Leicester, 1940:] Seaweed hung by the back door: dry = fine; soggy = wet weather. [Leamington Spa, Warwickshire, January 1993]

See also DULSE, LAVER, and OAR WEED.

Seg, seggie flooer – Shetland names for YELLOW IRIS.

Self-heal (*Prunella vulgaris*)

> [Around Selborne, Hampshire] Nursemaids will warn their little charges 'not to pick black-man flowers' (*Prunella vulgaris*) telling that the plant belongs to the devil, who is exceedingly annoyed when it is gathered, and will certainly appear in the night to carry off the child who has so angered him. [Fowler, 1891: 193]

Despite its name, there appear to be very few recent records of self-heal being used in folk medicine.

> [On Colonsay] a popular remedy for chest ailments, it [self-heal] was collected in summer, tied in bundles, and hung up to the kitchen roof to dry for winter use. The plants were boiled in milk and strained before using; butter was added. [McNeill, 1910: 158]

> If you are anxious to get rid of a COUGH, go out to the field and gather some little purple plants called self-heal. Put them in water and boil them. Then drink the juice which has boiled out. [IFCSS MSS 925: 7, Co. Wicklow]

> The minerac herb [self-heal] cures the minerac [a mysterious wasting] disease . . . Nine pieces are got (saying the name of the person you require it for) washed clean and rubbed until a froth is produced from it. The froth is mixed with water and turns it green. The person that needs it drinks it three mornings in succession and blesses himself each time. He is

not allowed meat, eggs or much butter when taking it. [IFCSS MSS 800: 53, Co. Offaly]

Semper – a County Donegal variant of samphire; see ROCK SAMPHIRE.

Serpent's meat – a Welsh name for BLACK BRYONY.

Service tree (*Sorbus domestica*). In August 1853 the Worcestershire Naturalists' Field Club paid a visit to the service tree that grew in Wyre Forest, and which at that time was the only representative of its species to have been recorded growing wild in the British Isles:

> There was an undoubted feeling of superstitious protection attached to the tree, whose fruit was commonly said, by foresters living in the vicinity, 'to keep out the witch from their habitations', and for this reason they hung up the hard fruit, which would remain a long time without decaying. The tree is commonly called by the foresters the Whitty, or Witten, pear; perhaps from the old English word *witten*, to know, meaning the *wise tree*. They distinguish it from the mountain ash [ROWAN], which they commonly call Witchen and though a protective power is attributed to a stick of that tree, yet the 'Whitty Pear,' they say is 'stronger'. [*Phytologist*, os 4: 1102, 1853]

See also WILD SERVICE TREE.

Seven sisters – an Irish name for SUN SPURGE.

Shakespeare, William – commemorated by wearing ROSEMARY on the anniversary of his birth.

Shallot (*Allium ascalonicum*). One of the most widely known sayings concerning the planting of crops is that shallots should be planted on the shortest day (21 December) and harvested on the longest (21 June).

> My late father worked on the land . . . [He was] a keen gardener, everything had to be done at the proper times. His shallots were planted upon the shortest day to be harvested on the longest day. [St Osyth, Essex, February 1989]

However, it seems that in recent years this has been merely a remembered saying rather than a regular practice.

> You should plant your shallots on the shortest day, and harvest them on the longest one. We did this once, and they kept really well. [Thorncombe, Dorset, March 1975]

> In the Ashford area of Kent . . . shallots planted shortest day, harvested longest day (though we usually planted ours in February). [Bexhill-on-Sea, East Sussex, February 1991]

Shamrock. Although the Irish government has adopted the harp as its official emblem, the shamrock leaf remains an important symbol for the Irish and their descendants overseas. The shamrock motif is also used to promote a large number of Irish products and organizations, ranging from garden peat to the national airline, Aer Lingus. During the struggles for Irish independence the shamrock motif was used by both those who wanted an independent state and those who sought to maintain Ireland within the United Kingdom, and the crest of the Royal Ulster Constabulary continues to depict a shamrock wreath [Nelson, 1991: 117 and 138].

The name shamrock which is believed to have been derived from the Irish *seamroge*—'little clover'—seems to have first appeared in print, as shamrote, in 1571. However, it was not until over a century later, in 1681, that the wearing of shamrocks on ST PATRICK's Day was first recorded, and the legend which associates shamrock with St Patrick's preaching about the Holy Trinity first appeared in print in 1726.

The earliest published references to shamrock describe its use as a food. In 1571 Edmond Campion described the diet of the Irish:

Shamrotes, watercresses, and other herbs they feed upon: oate mele and butter they cramme together. [Colgan, 1896: 216]

Later writers, including Richard Stanihurst [quoted in Colgan, 1896: 217] and Edmund Spenser, equated shamrock with WATERCRESS. Spenser, who was probably describing Ireland as he had observed it in about 1582, wrote:

Ere one yeare and a halfe they were broughte to such wretchedness as that anye stonye harte would have rued the same. Out of every corner of the woods and glinnes they came creeping foorthe upon theyr handes, for theyr legges could not beare them; they looked like anatomyes of death; they spake like ghostes crying out of theyr graves; they did eate of dead carrions . . . and yf they founde a plotte of watercresses or sham-rotes there they flocked as to feast for the time. [Colgan, 1896: 218]

However, in 1597 the herbalist John Gerard stated that shamrock was a species of clover.

There be divers sortes of three-leafed grasses, some greater, others lesser . . . and the first, of the common Medow Trefoiles, which are called in Irish Shamrockes. [Gerand 1597: 1017]

From the illustrations given by Gerard and his description of the 'common meadow trefoil' it is apparent that he was referring to the two agriculturally important species RED and WHITE CLOVER (*Trifolium repens* and *T. pratense*), and it is improbable that either of these is the plant to which Campion referred. However, as early as 1570, Matthias del L'Obel had recorded that a form of cake made from meadow trefoil was eaten by the Irish.

The Meadow Trefoil . . . with a purple flower called Purple Trefoil, and with a whitish flower White Trefoil . . . and there is nothing better known, or more frequent than either or more useful for the fattening whether of kine, or of beasts of burden. Nor is it from any other than this that the mere Irish, scorning all delights and spurs of the palate, grind the meal for their cakes and loaves which they knead with butter, and thrust into their groaning bellies, when, as sometimes happens, they are vexed and high maddened with three days' hunger. [L'Obel, 1570: 380; translation from Colgan, 1896: 214]

Later writers who mentioned the use of clover as food include Henry Mundy, who in his *Commentarii de aere vitali, Esculentis ac Potulentis*, claimed that:

[The Irish] nourish themselves with their shamrock (which is purple clover) are swift of foot and of nimble strength. [Nelson, 1991: 34]

Mundy's work, in which he strongly advocated a vegetarian diet, was published in Oxford in 1680, and enjoyed such popularity that six editions were produced before the end of the century. Later writers who made similar statements, presumably derived from the *Commentarii*, included John Ray in his *Historia Plantarum* (1686), and Linnaeus, who in his *Flora Lapponica* (1737) stated:

The swift and agile Irish nourish themselves with their shamrock which is Purple Trefoil: for they make from the flowers of this plant, breathing honey odour, a bread which is more pleasant than that made from the Spurrey. [Colgan, 1896: 355]

Although Linnaeus's comparison of bread made from clover flowers with that made from spurrey (*Spergula arvensis*) implies that he had at least sampled both breads, the similarity of his words to those of Mundy suggests that he was merely repeating what he had read.

It has been claimed that the first record of shamrock being associated with St Patrick occurs on a copper coin minted in Kilkenny 'for the use of the Confederate Irish in the wars of Charles I'. This coin was said to depict 'St Patrick, with mitre and crozier . . . displaying a trefoil to the assembled people' [Frazer, 1894: 135]. Although no such coins appear to have been produced during the reign of Charles I (1625–49), an attractive halfpenny piece minted during the 1670s accurately fits this description [see Seaby, 1970 for illustrations].

By 1681 or thereabouts shamrock was being worn, at least by the 'vulgar', on St Patrick's Day, for the English traveller Thomas Dinely recorded:

The 17th day of March yeerly is St Patrick's, an immoveable feast when ye Irish of all stations and condicions wear crosses in their hats, some of pins, some of green ribbons, and the vulgar superstitiously wear shamroges, 3-leaved grass, which they likewise eat (they say) to cause sweet breath. [Colgan, 1896: 349]

Since that time the wearing of St Patrick's crosses has declined, while the popularity of the shamrock has grown. What was once a practice of the 'vulgar' has now become widespread both among the Irish and their descendants overseas, whereas St Patrick's crosses were made only by girls and children at the opening of the twentieth century, and have now been completely abandoned [Danaher, 1972: 62].

The establishment of shamrock as an emblem of Ireland and the Irish seems to have been complete by the end of the seventeenth century. Thus, in 1689, when James Farewell published his *Irish Hudibras*, 'a coarse satire on everything Irish, religion, manners and customs, history and modes of speech,' he referred to Ireland as 'Shamroghshire'. Furthermore the *Irish Hudibras* is stated by its author to be 'taken from the Sixth Book of Virgil's Aeneid and adapted to present times,' and the shamrock is used in place of the golden bough which eased Aeneas' passage through the Underworld [Colgan, 1896: 351].

Almost thirty years later Caleb Threlkeld first recorded the association of shamrock with the Trinity. Writing of white clover, he noted:

This plant is worn by the people in their Hats upon the 17 Day of March yearly, (which is called St Patrick's Day.) It being Current Tradition, that by this Three Leafed Grass, he emblematically set forth to them the Mystery of the Holy Trinity. However that be, when they wet their Seamaroge, they often commit Excess in Liquor, which is not a right keeping of a Day to the Lord; Error generally leading to Debauchery. [Threlkeld, 1726: 160]

The actual identity of shamrock, the plant which St Patrick used to demonstrate the nature of the Trinity, has long been a matter of controversy. Different writers have suggested that it was a species of clover, a species of medick (*Medicago*), WOOD SORREL, or watercress. Irish tradition is unhelpfully vague.

First of all the mystic plant is not a clover, in the next place it never flowers, and finally it refuses to grow on alien soil. [Colgan, 1892: 96]

Similarly:

A half-Irish friend, in her late 50s, last night solemnly (and quite sincerely) made the statement that 'Shamrock will not grow in England.' Her mother, living in London, repeatedly brought back plants—they inevitably died, even when planted at the site of origin in pots with native soil and transported while apparently growing healthily. When pressed to say what the 'clover' was, she said it was never seen to flower and looked just like 'ordinary' clover. [Girton, Cambridge, March 1993]

Or, as a woman who described herself as 'a Northern Irish colleen', wrote:

> There are no spots on shamrock, it is pure green. The leaf is small, and it grows in bunches between grass on Irish soil. Shamrock must not be picked before St Patrick's Day, otherwise it dies off until the same time next year . . . Most Christian Irish people wear shamrock in their lapels with pride on St Patrick's Day. [Ashfield, New South Wales, Australia, April 1979]

In the 1950s schoolchildren who were unable to select true shamrock for St Patrick's Day and appeared wearing 'clover' were liable to be castigated by their companions and accused of not being truly Irish [Synnott, 1979: 39].

Although watercress is widely eaten, it would seem to be an unsuitable candidate to be shamrock as most of its leaves have more than three leaflets. It seems as if the equating of shamrock with watercress resulted from a misreading of Edmond Campion's *Historie of Ireland*, written in 1571. However, it is worth noting that a well on the Commons of Duleek in County Meath is known as Shamrock Well, and until the late 1940s watercress, which is still remembered as being the finest in the district, was gathered from it [Synnott, 1979: 39].

The suggestion that wood sorrel might be the true shamrock was promoted by the English botanist James Bicheno, who seems to have had his attention drawn to the subject in 1829 during an extended tour of Ireland. Bicheno admitted that the white clover was the plant then known as shamrock, but argued that wood sorrel was the plant originally known by this name [Bicheno, 1831].

Although this suggestion has not gained wide acceptance, it is worthy of examination. First there is the similarity of the names: *seamsoge*, the Irish name for wood sorrel, and *seamroge* the Irish name for clover. Second, wood sorrel can be readily equated with the edible shamrock of the earliest writers who mention the plant. BREAD AND CHEESE PLANT and similar country names demonstrate how wood sorrel was valued as a delicacy by children in rural areas [Britten and Holland, 1886: 597]. Moreover, the plant's sour taste would certainly freshen the mouth, even if it did not, as Dinely's informants claim, 'cause sweet breath'. Another early passage which probably refers to wood sorrel or watercress rather than a species of clover is found in Fynes Moryson's *Itinerary* (1617), based on observations made in 1599:

> They willingly eat the herbe Schamrocke being of a sharp taste which as they run and are chased to and fro they snatch like beasts out of the ditches. [Colgan, 1896: 219]

Clovers do not have a sharp taste, and the ditch habitat seems to suggest either watercress or wood sorrel.

However, Bicheno's arguments became less credible when he tried to explain why clover should have replaced wood sorrel as the plant worn on St Patrick's Day. According to him the reclamation of Irish woodland, and the subsequent cultivation of clover on the reclaimed land, led to wood sorrel becoming so scarce that it was eventually replaced by clover as the emblem used on St Patrick's Day. Perhaps there is a simpler explanation: wood sorrel has a major disadvantage as a plant for wearing in a buttonhole or pinned to a hat in that its leaves rapidly wilt, so the more robust leaves of clover would be better suited to this purpose.

Flowering shamrock is rarely depicted on St Patrick's Day greetings cards, but when it is wood sorrel is invariably the plant shown [personal observation, Dublin, February 1992]. In the United States, where potted 'shamrock' plants appear in supermarkets before St Patrick's Day, species of *Oxalis*, plants of the same genus as wood sorrel, are most frequently offered [Prof. W.T. Gillis, Michigan State University, March 1978]. However, in the British Isles the bunches of shamrock sold throughout the last century have nearly always been a species of clover or medick.

Apart from the instances given already, there seems to be little record, and certainly no recent records, of clover being used as a food by man in the British Isles on the same wide scale as wood sorrel leaves and flowers are nibbled by country children. However, the Irish traveller Dervla Murphy [1965, chapter 11] writes of eating stewed clover—'the very same as clover at home'—in Afghanistan and in Pakistan. It seems probable that Miss Murphy, exhausted after her day's hard journey, confused clover with a related pot-herb such as fenugreek (*Trigonella foenum-graecum*). Other references to clover being eaten are unconvincing. In 1777 John Lightfoot wrote that when corn was scarce poor people in Ireland would make bread, considered to be very wholesome and nutritious, from the powdered flowers of red and white clovers [Lightfoot, 1777: 405]. Unfortunately no recipe was given for this bread, and no recipe for its preparation has since been discovered. It appears that Lightfoot, usually a reliable recorder of plant-lore, was in this instance relying rather unwisely on Linnaeus's *Flora Lapponica* instead of oral informants.

In 1893 Nathaniel Colgan, a clerk with the Dublin constabulary, published his findings on the identity of shamrock. He had requested people to send him rooted bits of shamrock which he planted in his garden. When the plants were mature enough for accurate identification, it was found that four species were represented. White clover and lesser yellow trefoil were the plants most often considered to be shamrock, while red clover and black medick were less frequently favoured as such [Colgan, 1893].

In Dublin Colgan purchased shamrock from three hawkers, each of whom assured him that she sold the authentic plant. He planted his purchases, and when they were identifiable found that each was a different species: white clover, lesser yellow trefoil, and red clover [Colgan, 1893]. Eventually he concluded that the lesser yellow trefoil was probably the true shamrock. This was the plant which commonly decorated greeting cards said to contain genuine Irish shamrock. Several years before Colgan's investigations, James Britten had examined bunches of shamrock sold in London and concluded that they most often consisted of lesser yellow trefoil [Britten and Holland, 1886: 425]. The harp-shaped wreath placed at the base of the Guards Division Memorial in London on St Patrick's Day 1977 was composed of this species [personal observation].

In 1988 Colgan's survey was repeated on a much larger scale. As the result of appeals in local newspapers, and on radio and television, a botanist at the National Botanic Gardens, Glasnevin, received 221 plants which grew to maturity, and on examination proved to be much the same mixture of species as that sent to Colgan. In 1893 Colgan found that lesser yellow trefoil was the plant most commonly believed to be shamrock, being contributed by 51 per cent of his correspondents; in 1988 this was still the plant most commonly considered to be shamrock, being submitted by 46 per cent of correspondents. The second most popular candidate was white clover, which was sent in by 34 per cent of the 1893 correspondents and by 35 per cent of correspondents in 1988. As the instigator of the 1988 survey concluded, 'little significant change evidently has taken place during almost one century in the folk concept of shamrock' [Nelson, 1990].

A custom which took place towards the close of St Patrick's Day was drowning the shamrock. The wearer would remove his shamrock and place it in his final drink of the evening; when toasts had been drunk the shamrock would be removed from the bottom of the glass and thrown over the left shoulder [Danaher, 1972: 64].

Although many Irish people try to gather their own wild shamrock to wear on St Patrick's Day, at least in towns most of the shamrock worn is commercially produced [Synnott, 1979: 39]. Increasingly stringent legislation in the United States, whereby the importation of any living plant with intact roots is carefully restricted, has ensured that the amount of shamrock grown for export as living bunches is now negligible. Most of the commercial growers plant small areas, the size of their plantings apparently being limited by the amount of labour available to harvest and pack the plants.

A grower in the Kanturk area [of County Cork] has been growing the crop for the past eight years on about ½₀ acre. Seed is collected from selected plants in their plots. Selection is based on appearance, vigour and freedom from purpling. Seed is sown in early July in beds outdoors. The plants are planted in September at 6 in × 6 in into ground from which a crop of early potatoes has been taken. No fertiliser is added. Plants are lifted in early March and the roots washed. They are sold to an agent in Mallow who collects himself.

The gross value of the crop is about £200. About 70 per cent of the plants reach the required size. The main drawbacks are heavy labour requirements at harvesting, variable weather during the growing season, and diseases. Downy mildew (*Peronospora trifoliorum*) can be troublesome in damp seasons. [Daniel McCarthy, Instructor in Horticulture, Kanturk, February 1980]

Nowadays the President of the Irish Republic presents shamrock to members of the diplomatic corps and army on St Patrick's Day, and the Irish Government arranges for neat bunches of shamrock to be flown to all parts of the world so that they can be presented to heads of state and other dignitaries. Embassy receptions are held, and guests are given bunches of shamrock. A tale current in the late 1970s relates how a distinguished African diplomat was presented with a bunch of shamrock and a glass of whiskey when he arrived at a St Patrick's Day gathering. Not knowing any better, but determined to cause no offence, he politely sipped the whiskey and ate the shamrock. Since 1901 it has been customary for a member of the British Royal Family—since 1966 Queen Elizabeth the Queen Mother—to present shamrock to the Irish Guards on St Patrick's Day [*The Times*, 18 March 1994].

She-elder – a County Louth name for DWARF ELDER.

Sheep – bones weakened by BOG ASPHODEL; liverfluke treated using MALE FERN.

Sheep-rot – a name for BUTTERWORT.

Sheep's bit (*Jasione montana*)
The picking of flowers of sheep's bit is supposed to give one WARTS. [Truro, Cornwall, December 1993]

Sheep-shearing rose – a name for PEONY.

Shepherd's knot – a Berwickshire name for TORMENTIL.

Shepherd's purse (*Capsella bursa-pastoris*).

[In Yorkshire] on finding a root of shepherd's purse (*Capsella bursa-pastoris*) open a seed-vessel. If the seed is yellow you will be rich, but if green you will be poor. [Fowler, 1909: 302]

[In north-east England] children have a sort of game with the seed-pouch. They hold it out to their companions, inviting them 'to take a haud o' that.' It immediately cracks, and then follows a triumphant shout—'You've broken your mother's back.' [Johnston, 1853: 37]

In Middlesex, schoolboys offer to their uninitiated companions a plant of the shepherd's purse, and request them to pluck off one of the heart-shaped seed-pods, which done, they exclaim, 'You've picked your mother's heart out!' This was practised in Chelsea in my own school-days, and, as a Lancashire name for the plant is 'Mother's-heart', it seems likely that the custom is widely extended. [Britten, 1878: 159]

In the Invergowrie area of Perthshire in the 1950s: if you pick shepherd's purse your mother will die—associated with the plucking of the heart-shaped capsules. [Stevenage, Hertfordshire, May 1982]

Cf. COW PARSLEY, GREATER STITCHWORT, and HAWTHORN.

A cure for SCOUR in cattle and DIARRHOEA in human beings. When a young calf was bought at the mart she always gave it some of the tea made from shepherd's purse, and it would be better in an hour. They were nearly always affected by scour because of a change in their diet when they were newly bought. She used the root sometimes, but mostly the leaves, or as she called them the 'leafs'. [Andreas, Isle of Man, May 1963; Manx Folklife Survey]

Shepherd's warning – a name given to SCARLET PIMPERNEL in Lincolnshire and Somerset.

Shiners – a Fenland name for LORDS AND LADIES.

Shit-parsley – a Fenland name for COW PARSLEY.

Shoes and stockings – a Gwent name for BIRD'S-FOOT TREFOIL.

Shrove Tuesday – Cornish children threw TUBBENS at each other; CHRISTMAS GREENERY saved to provide fuel for cooking pancakes.

Silverweed (*Potentilla anserina*). In 1670 John Ray noted in his *Catalogus Plantarum Angliae* that children around Settle in the West Riding of Yorkshire dug up silverweed roots and ate them. Such practices are hinted at in Somerset, where the names bread-and-butter and bread-and-cheese have been recorded for the plant [Grigson, 1987: 147]. According to a writer born in Strood, Kent, in 1806:

Children in rural districts of England sometimes lay them [silverweed roots] over a brisk fire and then eat them. They are very small, but to some of us in childhood they seemed quite as pleasant as the fruit of the chestnut. [Pratt, 1857, 1: 31]

Particularly during times of scarcity, silverweed roots were valued as a food throughout the Highlands and Islands of Scotland. On Colonsay:

The roots were gathered and eaten raw and also boiled like potatoes. The local value, in former times, attached to this as an article of food may be realised from the fact that it was termed *an seachdamh aran* (the seventh bread). [McNeill, 1910: 119]

Alexander Carmichael [1941: 119], who was not always a reliable writer on plant-lore, noted:

The root [of silverweed, *brisgein*] was much used throughout the Highlands and Islands before the POTATO was introduced. It was cultivated, and so grew to a considerable size. As certain places are noted for the cultivation of potato, so certain places are noted for the cultivation of silverweed. One of these was Lag nan Tanchasg in Paible, North Uist, where a man could sustain himself on a square of ground of his own length. In dividing *morfhearann*, common ground, the people lotted their land for *brisgein* much as they lotted their fishing-banks at sea and their fish on shore. The poorer people exchanged *brisgein* with the richer for corn and meal, quantity for quantity and quality for quality. The *brisgein* was sometimes boiled in pots, sometimes roasted on stoves, and sometimes dried and ground into meal for bread and porridge. It was considered palatable and nutritious.

Silverweed was also valued as a cosmetic.

A friend, whose early home was a Highland manse has described . . . how eagerly the plant was gathered in summertime by the female part of the household, and steeped in buttermilk to remove the FRECKLES and brownness which the sun had brought to the fair cheek. [Pratt, 1857, 1: 32]

Sin, everlasting sin – Shropshire names for SLENDER SPEEDWELL.

Skeet plant – a Cornish name for HOGWEED.

Skullcap (*Scutellaria galericulata*)

Bunches of skull-cap used to be placed alongside the tea urn at Pilkingtons Glassworks [? Liverpool], as many men added it to their drink. [*Plants, People, Places*, 2, June 1993]

Slender speedwell (*Veronica filiformis*). Shropshire names for slender speedwell include 'everlasting sin' and 'sin'.

The local name 'sin' was reported . . . in the early 1950s. Said to be so called because 'it is so attractive and so prevalent'. [Sinker et al., 1985: 256]

Smallpox – treated using APPLE and COMMON VETCH.

Snake bite – treated using ASH, BEETROOT, and MALLOW.

Snake comb – a Devon name for STINKHORN.

Snakefood – a Devon name for LORDS AND LADIES.

Snakes – associated plants include BLACK BRYONY, LORDS AND LADIES, and STINKHORN; flowers which if taken indoors will bring snakes into the house include COW PARSLEY, HERB ROBERT, and RED CAMPION; see also ADDER.

Snakes flower – a Gloucestershire name for HERB ROBERT.

Snakes food – a Dorset name for HERB ROBERT.

Snakes' meat – a Devon name for LORDS AND LADIES.

Snapdragon – see ANTIRRHINUM.

Snapjack – a Dorset name for GREATER STITCHWORT.

Snompers – a Gloucestershire name for FOXGLOVE.

Snot-gobbles – a Bedfordshire name for YEW fruits.

Snowberry (*Symphoricarpos albus*)

In Kent in the 1930s it was believed that the juice of the fruit of the snowberry on the skin caused warts. I tried this on a thigh and sometime later three warts appeared. Fortunately they rubbed off easily. [Farnham, Surrey, December 1985]

Snowdrop (*Galanthus nivalis*). In common with some other white flowers, such as COW PARSLEY and HAWTHORN, snowdrops are often considered to be inauspicious.

In a London flowershop today—January 29, 1931—I asked for some snowdrops. The assistant replied: 'No, sir, we are not allowed to sell them.' I expressed surprise, and was told that Mr — (presumably the proprietor of the shop) thinks them unlucky. [*N & Q*, 160: 100, 1913]

I am a District Nursing Sister working in Lancashire, and the following story was related to me by an elderly patient at a farmhouse.

For many years her mother had refused to have snowdrops in the house, even though they grew profusely in the orchard. Girls from east Lancashire towns were often employed to help in the large house and would ask permission to pick the flowers to take home on their day off. This they were allowed to do so long as they left them in water on the doorstep.

After the old lady's death there was an occasion when a wedding party announced their intention, at short notice, of arriving to pay respects to an ailing relative. Snowdrops were brought in to decorate the tables, it being early in the year and no other flowers available so easily. Within three months the bridegroom was dead, and needless to say, snowdrops have never since been brought into the house. [Wiswell, Lancashire, April 1982]

My mother's family (Flintshire, north Wales, now Clwyd, and Montgomeryshire connections) firmly hold that snowdrops brought into the house mean a death in the immediate family. This does not mean snowdrops grown indoors in bowls, but cut snowdrops brought inside. [Aberystwyth, Dyfed, January 1983]

I must . . . tell you how I feel about snowdrops. I hate and detest them, and hasten to add, I adore all other flowers, and am a member of a Flower Club.

My mother started it all by saying never pick them and take them indoors, they are bad luck.

A few years ago my brother-in-law died of a brain tumour at the age of 35. When we were following the coffin to church both sides of the road were white with snowdrops.

Last January my father-in-law went into a private nursing home to die; he suffered until March. We visited him daily, the drive was dotted with snowdrops and outside his window there were thousands of the horrid things. As he lay suffering, we could only see them from the windows. It was awful. They are my unlucky flower. [Norwich, Norfolk, March 1984]

Snowdrops will bring a parting if brought indoors as a cut flower, but will bring happiness if outside under the windows in their beds.

When a former husband brought me some indoors—although I never voiced my unease—we split up within days and were divorced (with no regrets). This was in south Lincolnshire. [Paston, Cambridgeshire, November 1993]

Snowper – a Gloucestershire name for FOXGLOVE.

Snuff – scented using SPIGNEL.

Soap – made from BRACKEN.

Soapwort (*Saponaria officinalis*)
The chief use to which the herb was put in Ireland was the treatment of inflammation of the lungs. [Moloney, 1919: 16]

[Gypsy remedy:] a decoction of the root applied to a BRUISE, or to a black eye, will quickly get rid of the discoloration: slices of the freshly dug root laid on the place have the same effect but are slower in action. [Vesey-FitzGerald, 1944: 28]

The Jersey-French-Norman name of *des mains jointes* comes from the plant's jointed rhizomes, which were used to heal wounds in cattle. [St Saviour, Jersey, May 1993]

Both the scientific name *Saponaria* (from Latin *sapo*, soap) and the English name refer to the former use of the roots as a substitute for soap.

Soldiers – a Warwickshire name for CREEPING THISTLE.

Soldiers and sailors – a Dorset name for LUNGWORT.

Solomon's seal (*Polygonatum multiflorum*)
[Gypsy remedy:] an ointment made from the leaves and applied to a bruised or black eye will quickly get rid of the discoloration. [Vesey-Fitz-Gerald, 1944: 28]

Sookies – a Shetland name for LOUSEWORT.

Sookie sooricks – a Morayshire name for WOOD SORREL.

Sooricks, soorik – a Scottish name for SORREL.

Sorbus berries – an Isle of Wight name for the fruit of WILD SERVICE TREE.

Sores – treated using BUTTERBUR, BUTTERCUP, DOCK, HOUSELEEK, MALLOW, and ORANGE LILY.

Sorrel (*Rumex acetosa*). The refreshingly sour-tasting leaves and stems of common sorrel, also known as sour dock, are widely eaten by children.

[During my childhood in Dorset over 60 years ago:] common sorrel was, of course, eaten—'but it'll make 'ee bad if 'ee eats too much.' [Sidmouth, Devon, October 1991]

Sour sabs—like dock with red stems—we pulled and sucked the stems. [Plymstock, Devon, January 1993]

As children in wartime we used to search spring meadows for the first leaves of sorrel—called sour-docks in Berwickshire—to cure our spots. We sucked the sour juice and spat out the chewed leaves. [Old Cleeve, Somerset, October 1993]

This usage results in the plant being given a variety of local names, including: sooricks [Whitfield, Dundee, November 1988], sour grabs [Christchurch, Dorset, June 1991], and sour leeks [Lisburn, Co. Antrim, March 1986]

More rarely the plant is gathered by adults for culinary use. Thus common sorrel is a frequent ingredient of the BISTORT puddings made in north-west England.

My late parents came from Poland after the Second World War and my mother occasionally used certain plants . . . Sorrel (*Rumex acetosa*) leaves were collected for soup. [Bromley, Kent, April 1991]

Sorrel grass – a Hampshire name for SORREL.

Sour-dock – a widespread name for SORREL.

Sour dockling – a Cumberland name for SORREL.

Sour grass – a Dorset name for SORREL.

Sour leeks – a Co. Antrim name for SORREL.

Sour sabs – a Devon name for SORREL.

Sour-saps – an Isles of Scilly name for BERMUDA BUTTERCUP.

Southernwood (*Artemisia abrotanum*)

A form of proposal of marriage by an inarticulate young Fenman was provided by the plant Southernwood . . . known in the Fens as Old Man or Lad's Love. The youth . . . would cut some sprigs of the plant and put them in his buttonhole before setting out with the village lads on a spring or early summer evening stroll. Presently, leaving his companions, he would wander along the lanes, where he would find little groups of giggling girls, and would pass by them ostentatiously sniffing at his buttonhole to show that his thoughts were turned towards matrimony. If the girls went by unheeding, he knew that he was unlucky, but if they turned and came slowly back towards him he knew that his herbal decoration had not gone unnoticed. After a show of hesitation he then removed the buttonhole and handed it to the girl of his choice. If she spurned him, she probably threw his offering to the ground and might even smack the bold suitor on his face. If he was acceptable, however, she would inhale the pungent scent of the Lad's Love and, after some teasing from her companions, would put her arm through his and the pair would set off on their first courting stroll. [Porter, 1969: 2]

[According to my 86-year-old aunt] before the First World War the lads used to wear Lad's Love (Southernwood) as a buttonhole to attract females, or sprigs of WHEAT were used for the same purpose. [Histon, Cambridgeshire, January 1989]

Sow thistle (*Sonchus oleraceus*)

[The sow thistle] is a great cure for warts . . . cut the thistle and get the milk out of it and put it on the wart. [IFCSS MSS 717: 217, Co. Meath]
Cf. DANDELION.

Spear thistle (*Cirsium vulgare*). Also known as SCOTCH THISTLE in Ulster, where children would 'pull off the florets and their young pappuses and peel off the spiny bractlets, so that you would find a nice little nutty core' [Ballycastle, Co. Antrim, January 1991]. Similarly:

> My maternal uncles, when the thistle—*Cirsium vulgare*—was flowering, used to split and cut through the flowerheads, pull all the flowers out, and eat the succulent bases. [West Ealing, London, November 1991]

The authors of a 1981 article on the identity of the Scottish THISTLE concluded that the spear thistle is 'the species we choose as the Scottish Thistle' [Dickson and Walker, 1981: 18].

Speedwell (*Veronica* spp.)

> [In Cheshire] speedwells are known as Thunder-bolts, because picking them sometimes brings on thunder. [Hole, 1937: 47]

> As a small child I believed that if I picked the small blue flower—speedwell?—birds would come and peck my eyes out—this I'm sure came from other children's tales of horror; we used to call the flower Bird's Eye. [Wigston Magna, Leicestershire, July 1983]

> Blue speedwell is known as Bird's-eyes—it must not be picked at all, or the birds will pluck out one's eyes. [Driffield, Humberside, March 1985]

> Bird's-eye or speedwell—if you pick one your mother's eyes will drop out. [South Stainley, North Yorkshire, March 1992]

See also GERMANDER SPEEDWELL and SLENDER SPEEDWELL.

Speed-well-blue – a County Kerry name for GERMANDER SPEEDWELL.

Sphagnum moss (*Sphagnum* spp.). During the First World War sphagnum moss was widely gathered for use as a wound dressing. Thus at Langholme, in Dumfriesshire, the Duke of Buccleuch's head keeper would

> take us out on the hill to pick sphagnum moss as part of the war effort. We would collect it in sacks, and then lay it across the lawn on dust sheets to dry. Afterwards all the bits of heather and peat, dead frogs and other foreign bodies had to be picked out before it could be sent to the hospital. There it was used instead of cottonwool for swabbing out wounds—being full of iodine it was a a good disinfectant. [Gloucester, 1983: 49]

Similarly, in Northern Ireland:

> In 1916 we were asked to collect sphagnum moss for wound dressings. [Ballycastle, Co. Antrim, January 1991]

Spignel (*Meum athamanticum*). A specimen of spignel in the herbarium of Roberts Leyland, now in the Liverpool Museum, bears the label:

[Collected] in the 2nd lane after you pass the Booth Wood Inn on the road from Ripponden to Oldham, July 1837 . . . the plant is however nearly destroyed, not by the rapacity of Botanists but by Snuff takers in the neighbourhood of the place where it grows who dig up the roots for the purpose of scenting their snuff. [Edmondson, 1994: 46]

Spiked star of Bethlehem (*Ornithogalum pyrenaicum*)

Bath is famous for all sorts of things . . . Bath Asparagus, however, is not so well known. Passing through the streets at dusk one evening lately we saw what we took, at a glance, to be bunches of young Wheatears tied up. The morning's reflection convinced us that this could not be, and, moreover, revealed that they were the young flower-scapes of *Ornithogalum pyrenaicum*, and on visiting the market we saw a quantity of them, of which we purchased a sample, under the name 'Wild Asparagus' . . . all who partook declared it to be the best substitute for Asparagus yet tried . . . The abundance of the supply in Bath market was such that we can hardly imagine that it was all wild, some must surely have come from the cottage gardens. [*Gardeners' Chronicle*, 26 June 1873: 843]

See also STAR OF BETHLEHEM.

Spindle (*Euonymus europaeus*). According to John Aubrey (1626–97):

Prick-timber (*Euonymus*). This tree is common, especially in North Wilts. The butchers doe make skewers of it, because it doth not taint the meate as other wood doe: from whence it hath the name of prick-timber. [Aubrey, 1847: 56]

Spotted Mary – a Herefordshire name for LUNGWORT.

Sprains – cured using COMFREY, DOCK, ELDER, HORSE CHESTNUT, MALLOW, and ROYAL FERN.

Spring beauty (*Claytonia perfoliata*)

Some twenty years ago, children on the Isles of Scilly ate leaves of *Claytonia perfoliata*, and called them water weed. [Woodnewton, Northamptonshire, June 1992]

Spurge (*Euphorbia* spp.). The white sap of spurges, like that of DANDELION, is valued for the treatment of WARTS.

Wild spurge was used as a cure for warts—the milky substance from the stem was rubbed on them. [Islip, Oxfordshire, November 1976]

My grandmother cured warts with the juice of an annual spurge. [Tidmarsh, Berkshire, March 1986]

See also CAPER SPURGE, IRISH SPURGE, PETTY SPURGE, and SUN SPURGE.

Spurge laurel (*Daphne laureola*)

The Rev. G.E Smith tells me that the spurge laurel is collected in large quantity from the woods of Sussex, by persons who go at stated periods round the country for that purpose, and supply the markets at Portsmouth and Chichester, where it is sold as horse medicine, but he was unable to ascertain in what manner or for what diseases it was employed. [Bromfield, 1856: 437]

The acrid bark is in some counties used as a blister, and the still more acrimonious roots are employed to alleviate the TOOTHACHE; but they should be applied with caution. [Pratt, 1857, 1: 46]

Squatmore – a name for YELLOW HORNED POPPY.

Squeakers – a name given to WILD GLADIOLUS on St Martin's, Isles of Scilly.

Staff – plants said to have grown from saints' staffs include BUTTERWORT, the HOLY THORN, and St Newlina's FIG tree.

Stag's horn sumach (*Rhus hirta*)

In Worcestershire, in the Bromsgrove area, there is a belief that the stag's horn sumach, if growing in the garden of a house is sure to bring marital strife to the family living in the house. This was related to me by an old gardener, who died in 1973 full of years. He lived until he was about 90 years of age . . .

Notwithstanding more than fifty years of collecting such information, I have not encountered this belief elsewhere, but it was firmly held by other gardeners of my informant's generation. [Great Barr, West Midlands, October 1982]

Stammer – caused by biting YELLOW IRIS.

Starch – prepared from LORDS AND LADIES and POTATO.

Starch-root – a nineteenth-century Portland name for LORDS AND LADIES.

Star of Bethlehem (*Ornithogalum angustifolium*)

Tiny children used to search for star of Bethlehem flowers. As children in Sunday School we were told that the lilies alluded to by Jesus when warning his disciples against worrying about material provision: 'Consider the lilies of the field, how they grow; they toil not, neither do they spin; and yet I say unto you that even Solomon in all his glory was not arrayed like one of these.' Apparently stars of Bethlehem grew wild on the slopes and plains of Palestine . . . and were called lilies. This description captured the imagination and interest of small, young children, and when returning home they would walk and play in the nearby meadows seeking this flower—a treasure and a prize in their view if they were lucky enough to find one. To my knowledge there were only half a dozen or so of these plants in one meadow. [Felmersham, Bedfordshire, April 1993]

See also SPIKED STAR OF BETHLHEM.

Star of the earth – an East Anglian name for BUCK'S HORN PLANTAIN.

Stepmother's blessing – a Yorkshire name for COW PARSLEY.

Stinging nettle – see NETTLE.

Stings – treated using BETONY, CHICKWEED, DANDELION, ONION, and SCARLET PIMPERNEL.

Stinkhorn (*Phallus impudicus*)

A labourer's wife, age 35, at Hartland [Devon], tells me that the fungus *Phallus impudicus*, generally known as stink horn, is locally called 'snake-comb', in the belief that snakes emerge from it, as bees from honey-comb. It is thought that its disgusting odour is due to this fact, and children are warned against the plant for fear of their being 'stung' by snakes. [Chope, 1933: 122]

Stinking Billy – a Scottish name for RAGWORT.

Stinking iris (*Iris foetidissima*)

Having a purging qualitie . . . the country people of Sommersetshire have good experience, who use to drink the decoction of this roote. Others do take the infusion thereof in ale and such like, wherewith they purge themselves, and that unto very good purpose and effect. [Gerard, 1597: 54]

Stock (*Matthiola incana*). Double-flowered forms of the old-fashioned and powerfully scented stock were particularly valued.

In Alderney it was believed that if two single stock flowers were tied together exactly at noon on June 24th, (the festival of St Jean [John]), plants grown from their seed would be double-flowered. [Bonnard, 1993: 19]

Stonewort (Charophyta)

Stonewort—gaa-girse; the plant was boiled and given to cattle with liver complaint. [Lerwick, Shetland, March 1994]

Strawberry (*Fragaria* cv.).

At dinner my neighbour at table . . . mentioned that her father had been told by Bromsgrove people that 'strawberries are always best on St John the Baptist Day.' In fact he used to go to Bromsgrove on 24 June and return home laden with strawberries which were grown in the Bromsgrove area. [Stowbridge, West Midlands, June 1990]

BLACKBERRY and strawberry leaves were fed to constipated or off colour rabbits and guinea pigs. [Histon, Cambridgeshire, January 1989]

Strokes – prevented or cured using MILKWORT and TORMENTIL.

Styes – treated using BUTTERCUP, GOOSEBERRY, GREATER CELANDINE, and TREE MALLOW.

Sunburn – treated using BLACK BRYONY, DOCK, HOTTENTOT FIG, SUNDEW, and TORMENTIL.

Sundew (*Drosera* spp.). In common with other plants, such as BOG ASPHODEL and BUTTERWORT, which grow on wet, acidic, peaty places, the sundew was believed to make cattle and sheep ill.

> The name of red-rot, by which it is distinguished in some of our rural districts, on account of its supposed share in the injurious effects experienced by sheep which feed on pastures such as it loves, but of which it is most probably quite innocent. [Wilkinson, 1858: 33]

> [In Scotland] sundew (*Drosera rotundifolia*) has, according to one interpretation of the Gaelic, a somewhat uncomplimentary name—*Lus na Feàrnaich*, said to be 'the plant of *earnach*', a disease in cattle, sometimes identified as murrain, and reputed to be caused by eating this poisonous plant. [Bennett, 1991: 58]

On the Isle of Man:

> The sticky-leaved common sundew—*Lus ny Greih, Lus yn eiyrts* or *Lus y ghruiaghtys*—was used as a love charm. Traditionally it was surreptitiously slipped into the clothing of the person who was to be attracted. When the plant was on display in the Manx Museum (1964–1983) it usually vanished to become a signal between teenagers rather than a charm of power. [Garrad, 1984: 79]

On Colonsay:

> Some ladies mix the juice [of sundew] with milk so as to make it an innocent and safe application to remove FRECKLES and SUN BURNS. [McNeill, 1910: 123]

Sun spurge (*Euphorbia helioscopia*), known as seven sisters in Ireland.

> A new resident on the Isle of Man approached me recently with a request for the botanical name which he had been told Port St Mary fishermen used (as he delicately phrased it) 'to rub on themselves to get themselves a bit excited' . . . [the plant was recognized] as Sun Spurge, in Manx *Lus y Bwoid Mooar*, which Manx speakers had interpreted to me as 'the plant of the big knobs'. This I had accepted as a reference either to its well-known use as a WART cure, or to the flower's structure. The name properly means

... 'the plant of the big penis'. ... the milky juice of Sun Spurge was applied to the human penis, and promptly produced considerable swelling. If this caused excessive discomfort the organ could be dipped in milk (soured milk was usually recommended). [Douglas, Isle of Man, November 1988]

[In the Orkneys] the white, milky-like fluid in the hollow stem was applied to WARTS to remove them, hence the local name Warty-girse. [Spence, 1914: 103]

The seven sisters is a green branchy plant with seven stems on each stalk. It grows in tillage ground. When a stem is broken away a white milky fluid appears on the stalk. This if rubbed on warts is a cure. [IFCSS MSS 750: 293, Co. Longford]

[According to my 78-year-old cousin:] sun spurge ... was boiled up, the resultant yellow-green liquid was drained off and was drunk with an equal quantity of water, night and morning, to relieve aches and pains of a rheumatic nature. [Corbridge, Northumberland, February 1993]

See also SPURGE.

Swede (*Brassica napa* ssp. *rapifera*)

[Tiverton, Devon:] Swedes—for a COUGH—grate as finely as possible. Boil with dark brown sugar. Strain. [Knight, 1947: 47]

Cure for WHOOPING COUGH—slice a swede, cover each slice with brown sugar, leave until it is a syrup, then give a spoonful. [SLF MSS, Aldbrough, Humberside, April 1972]

For kidney stones, drink water from boiled swedes. [Llanuwchylln, Gwynedd, April 1991]

Sweet amber – a Sussex name for TUTSAN.

Sweet cicely (*Myrrhis odorata*). On the Isle of Man:

On Old Christmas Eve ... a watch was, and sometimes still is, kept for the flowering of the myrrh (sweet cicely). According to tradition this blooming lasts but an hour. In many years the first leaf buds can be found, and sometimes indeed there are flowers, but both are very soon cut by frost. [Garrad, 1984: 75]

Sweet flag (*Acorus calamus*)

Local anglers (Merseyside) used to pull up and chew the roots of sweet flag, a plant of the water's edge. [*Plants, People, Places*, 2, June 1993]

Sweethearts – a Yorkshire name for GOOSEGRASS.

Sweet rocket – a name for DAME'S VIOLET.

Sweet William (*Dianthus barbatus*). According to Prior [1863: 221] the name 'sweet william is so called from Fr[ench] *oeillet*, L[atin]

ocellus, a little eye, corrupted to Willy, and thence to William.' However, according to others the name associates the plant with William
the Conqueror, St William of Rochester, King William III, or William, Duke of Cumberland.

On 21 September 1984 a correspondent from Upholland, Lancashire, wrote to the *Daily Mirror*:

> You say that the flowers called sweet william were probably named after
> William the Conqueror, I was led to believe they were named after Wil-
> liam, Duke of Cumberland, who defeated the Scots at the battle of Cul-
> loden in 1746.
>
> Due to the atrocities committed by the English after the battle, he be-
> came known to the Scots as 'The Butcher of Culloden'. And when the
> English renamed a pretty flower sweet william in his honour, the
> Scots renamed their most obnoxious, smelly weed [RAGWORT] stinking
> billy.

A few years later, on 20 May 1991, a correspondent from Rochester,
Kent, wrote to the same paper:

> I wonder whether I have solved the old mystery of where the name sweet
> william originates. I have been told it comes from St William of Roches-
> ter (1154–1226).

This got the response:

> No one knows [the origin of the name], but all the Old Adams we know
> say it was found originally by William the Conqueror.

In the mythology of the Orange Lodges of Ulster, sweet William is
associated with King William III. When the Belfast lodges march on
12 July each year to commemorate William's victory at the Battle of
the Boyne in 1690, their banner-poles are decorated with 'ORANGE
LILIES and sweet william' [Belfast, May 1994].

Sycamore (*Acer pseudoplatanus*). An ancient sycamore tree at Clonenagh in County Laois is associated with the abbot St Fintan (d. 603).

> The tree is outside a graveyard on the main Dublin–Limerick road. The
> place is Clonenagh, the site of St Fintan's Monastery, which was one of the
> most famous monastic schools in Eire. Tradition says the tree grew on the
> site of St Fintan's Well, which was desecrated by allowing farm animals to
> drink in it, and the well was miraculously transferred to Cromogue about
> three miles away, and the site of another church or abbey of St Fintan.
>
> Water is always in [a cavity in] the tree, even during the driest summer
> weather, or prolonged drought, and is thought to come from a spring be-
> neath the tree through pores in the tree. In recent times con-celebrated
> Mass at the site has been offered to honour St Fintan, patron of this parish,
> and in memory of the dead interred in the seven graveyards in the vicinity
> of the tree.

The water was considered to give relief to people afflicted with weak eyes, and cure other bodily ills, as was also the water in the well at Cromogue. [Mountrath, Co. Laois, September 1977]

In Scotland the feudal lairds used sycamore trees, known as dool or JOUG trees, as their gallows.

The most remarkable Sycamores in Scotland are those which are called 'Dool trees'. They were used by the most powerful barons in the west of Scotland, for hanging their enemies and refractory vassals on, and were for these reasons called dool or grief trees. Of these there are three yet standing, the most memorable being one near the fine old castle of Cassilis, one of the seats of the Marquis of Ailsa, on the bank of the River Doon. It is not so remarkable for its girth of stem, as for its wide spreading branches and luxuriant foliage, among which twenty or thirty men could be easily concealed. It was used by the family of Kennedy, who were the most powerful barons of the west of Scotland, for the purpose abovementioned. The last occasion was about two hundred years ago, when Sir John Fau, of Dunbar, was hanged on it, for having made an attempt, in the disguise of a gypsy, to carry off the then Countess of Cassilis, who was the daughter of the Earl of Haddington, and to whom he had been betrothed prior to his going abroad to travel. Having been detained for some years a prisoner in Spain, he was supposed to be dead, and in his absence the lady married John, Earl of Cassilis. It is said that the lady witnessed the execution of her former lover from her bed-room window. [Johns, 1847: 118]

This tree was blown down on 28 January 1938 [Cooper, 1957: 170].

Further south, in Wiltshire:

Sycamores had slightly unlucky associations, perhaps because they were also sometimes known as 'hanging trees'. [Whitlock, 1976: 163]

At Aldenham in Hertfordshire. three sycamore trees grow from the grave of William Hutchinson (d.1697) and his wife Margaret (d.1706). It is said that William declared his disbelief in the Resurrection, and ordered a heavy stone tomb enclosed within iron railings; if a tree grew from the tomb future generations would know that there was a life after death. At Trewin, in the same county, is a tomb of Lady Anne Grimston (d.1713) which has an ASH tree which is said to have seven distinct stems, and a sycamore tree with a similar number of stems emerging from it. The dying Lady Grimston is said to have gathered her friends around her and told them: 'Bear witness, my friends, what I say. If there is any truth in the Word of God, may seven trees grow from my grave' [N & Q, 11 ser. 8: 425, 1913]. It is, perhaps, noteworthy that both of these graves are enclosed within substantial iron railings; they have been protected from any mowing of the churchyards, or grazing animals, thus encouraging the growth of trees upon them. A third ATHEIST'S TOMB, with a FIG tree growing from it, was at Watford.

In many parts of the British Isles children made WHISTLES from sycamore twigs. In the north Pembrokeshire village of St Nicholas in the late 1920s:

> Spring arrived to the music of hedgerow whistles. First efforts began at the end of March when buds of hedge sycamore were pushing out pale green spikes, tinged with pink, covered with pale silky hairs, though best results came later when the tinted veined leaves as well as flowers were fully formed. Then the shoots, thick as walking sticks, were cut off and trimmed into six-inch lengths, scored round with a penknife an inch from the end. The sugary wand was soaked with spittle, and then, holding it rigid in a handkerchief, first attempts were made to loosen the bark. It had to come off—snickingly—in one piece or one had to begin again. Then with a little channel to let in air, and the bark replaced and pulled over the tapering mouthpiece, the whistle was ready to join the birds—though unlike those music-makers, sycamore whistles became gurgley with spit. [Jones, 1980: 100]

T

Tamarisk (*Tamarix gallica*). In Guernsey tamarisk (known in Guernésiais as *chipre* or *saunier*) was formerly used to make the bottoms of crab pots as its wood 'long resists the action of sea water' [Marquand, 1906: 39]. Guernsey water diviners made their divining rods from tamarisk or HAZEL [De Garis, 1975: 41].

Tangerine (*Citrus reticulata*). Varieties of tangerine are associated with Chinese New Year celebrations in Hong Kong and elsewhere, including the British Isles. At England's best-known celebrations, at Soho in London, tangerines are frequently offered to the lions which go around the area, performing outside shops and restaurants. It is said that the tangerine is of particular value for the New Year celebrations because of the similarity of its name with the word for 'blessing' or 'fortune' [Goody, 1993: 388].

Tansy (*Tanacetum vulgare*)

Tansy: good for WORMS in children. [IFCSS MSS 313: 213, Co. Cork]

A cure for thread worms: boil the flowers or foliage of tansy weed and drink the infusion. Dose: a wineglass full each morning. [Taylor MSS, East Harling, Norfolk]

Occasionally known as yellow buttons—used as a MOTH repellent, and placed round the home it can discourage FLIES and other insects. It can be used as a vermifuge. [Lerwick, Shetland, March 1994]

[Gypsy remedies:] infusion of the flowers will expel worms. Hot fomentations of the herb good for GOUT. If you wear a sprig of tansy inside your boots you will never get AGUE (this is also an old Hampshire farm labourer's superstition). [Vesey-FitzGerald, 1944: 28]

Young chickens are subject to a disease known as 'the pip'. The chickens pick up a worm especially in wet weather. The worm lodges in the windpipe and will eat it away. The disease can be prevented by cutting finely the tansy leaf and giving it in their ordinary food. The 'pip' is the most prevalent and fatal disease of young chickens and turkeys also. [IFCSS MSS 350: 75, Co. Cork]

Married couples anxious to start a family would eat salads containing tansy. The plant grew on banks and in meadows on the upland fringes of the Littleport Fens [Cambridgeshire] and . . . children were sent long distances to gather the leaves. It was said that where there were wild rabbits there was sure to be tansy and, since these animals are noted for the large families they produce, the plant must have the same effect on human beings. On the other hand, many unmarried Fen girls who became pregnant chewed tansy leaves to procure a miscarriage. [Porter, 1969: 10]

Tares. The 'tares' sown by an enemy in a field of wheat in the New Testament (Matthew 13: 24–30) parable are interpreted as being darnel in the *New English Bible*. In the basic Biblical texts the plant is named *zizania*, which is generally agreed to be darnel, although since the 1880s the weed *Cephalaria syriaca* has also been considered to be a possible candidate. Darnel—a grass—is a common weed in the Middle East, which is difficult to remove from wheat crops, to which it bears a close resemblance when young. Furthermore, its seeds are difficult to separate from grain using primitive equipment and can be toxic, causing dizziness when eaten, if infested by a fungus.

Other writers have equated tares with a species of vetch—possibly the hairy vetch [Grigson 1987: 139]. Irish Bibles give tares as either *cogal*, probably meaning CORN COCKLE, or *fiaile*, meaning weeds in general [van der Zweep, 1984].

Teaplant (*Lycium* spp.)

The half wood (*Lycium chinense*) was used . . . [to cure CONVULSIONS] at Charlecot and Whitechurch [Warwickshire]. The stems were cut into half inch lengths, threaded through one end so that each section hung suspended. The plant was also used to cure lameness in swine. [Bloom, 1930: 245]

Teasel (*Dipsacus fullonum*)

[In West Sussex] for weakness in my EYES, I have been assured that the best application would be the water that is found in the hollow cup of the teasel. [Latham, 1878: 45]

[West Somerset, 1914–39:] the rain water held at the base of teasel leaves (basin of Venus) was thought to be a good remedy for sore eyes. [Breage, Cornwall, October 1993]

[Cambridgeshire, 1660:] rain water lying stagnant in the bases of the leaves of this plant is recommended for removing WARTS if the hands are washed in it several times. And from this it has perhaps acquired the name of Bath of Venus. [Ewen and Prime, 1975: 59]

The fuller's teasel (*Dipsacus sativus*) continues to be grown for raising the nap on cloth in the Taunton area of Somerset [Ryder, 1969: 117; Stace, 1991: 788].

[I was born in 1922] during my childhood they used to grow teasels near Ilton. Some schoolboys were employed to harvest these during the summer holidays. They were paid five shillings a week for five weeks. [Thorncombe, Dorset, November 1982]

Teething – eased used BITTERSWEET, OPIUM POPPY, PEONY, and SEA BEANS.

Thatch – plants used include BRACKEN, EELGRASS, GREATER TUSSOCK SEDGE, and HEATHER.

Thirst – prevented by BROAD BEAN, relieved by chewing SORREL.

Thistle (usually *Cirsium* spp.) In central Ireland thistles were considered to indicate fertile land.

It is good land where thistles grow. Old people tell a story of a blind man who went to buy a farm. 'Tie that horse to a thistle' he said to the son. 'I don't see any thistles' said the son. 'Oh' said the old man 'we'll go home so, I won't buy this land it's too poor and bad.' [IFCSS MSS 750: 296, Co. Longford]

However, thistles can be a major weed of cultivated ground, and difficult to eradicate. In Devon it was recommended:

Speed them in May
They are up the next day.
Speed them in June
They will come again soon.
Speed them in July
Then they soon will die.

[Moore, 1968: 369]

In Cornwall:

Cut dashels (thistles) in June
—it's a month too soon.
Cut in July
they are sure to die.

[St Ervan, Cornwall, January 1994]

The thistle has long been an emblem of Scotland, although the history of the emblem and the identity of the species of thistle are confused. In an article 'What is the Scottish Thistle?' published in the *Glasgow Naturalist* in 1981, it was concluded that

the more obvious candidate, in its strong prickliness, is C[irsium] *vulgare* [SPEAR THISTLE], the species we choose as the Scottish Thistle. [Dickson and Walker, 1981: 18]

Similarly in Northern Ireland, spear thistle was commonly known as 'Scotch thistle' [Ballycastle, Co. Antrim, January 1991].

The thistle as an emblem of Scotland has early but spurious associations. Achaius, an unrecognisable, if not non-existent, king of the Picts did not found the Order of the Thistle, the early history of which is unclear . . . In the 11th century did an invading Dane step bare-footed on a thistle and howl to alarm the Scots? This is a good tale, often told from at least as early as 1829 . . . without any stated original source. Can it be anything but pure myth? [Dickson and Walker, 1981: 1]

The first artefacts which might represent thistle decorations are the 'thistle-headed pins' and Norse thistle brooches of the eighth to tenth centuries in Scotland.

However, the heads of the pins are not decorated in detail as thistles, while brooches lodged in both the Hunterian and Kelvingrove Museums [in Glasgow] bear only the slightest superficial resemblance to thistle heads. [Dickson and Walker, 1981: 1]

It appears that the association between Scotland and thistles cannot be traced back beyond the late fifteenth century.

In a poem written by William of Dunbar, 'The Thrissil and the Rose', in honour of the marriage of Margaret Tudor and James IV in 1503, shows that the thistle was a Scottish emblem by the early 16th century at the latest. Queen Margaret (of Denmark, died 1486) possessed a bed or table covering embroidered with thistles and her husband James III issued this-tled coins. According to Innes (1959) the Earl of Orkney and Caithness is known to have been a Knight of the Order of the Thistle by 1470. [Dickson and Walker, 1981: 2]

Many recent authors [e.g. Martin, 1976: pl. 49, and Webster, 1978: 365] have given the name Scottish or Scotch thistle to the decorative thistle *Onopordum acanthium*, which has the recommended English name of cotton thistle [Dony et al., 1986: 110]. This species is considered by Stace [1991: 810] to be an introduction to the British Isles, although it might be native to East Anglia. Thus it is unlikely to have been found in Scotland as early as the fifteenth century, although, of course, if it was present it may well have been cultivated in royal gardens and hence become associated with the monarchy and the state. The first association of the cotton thistle with Scotland appears to date from King George IV's visit to the country in 1822.

Soon after the King's visit to Edinburgh, Scotland, some seeds were presented to the botanic garden at Bury St Edmunds by a relation of the Bishop of London, who received them as seeds of the identical thistle, or kind of thistle, carried in the processions that attended His Majesty in Scotland; these developed into *Onopordum acanthium*. [Denson, 1832: 356]

King George's visit to Scotland stimulated a great amount of some-what spurious Scottish pagentry, so it is probable that the handsome cotton thistle replaced the spear thistle—a common weed—as the national emblem at that time. For a list of other species which have been claimed to be the thistle of Scotland, see SCOTCH THISTLE. See also CREEPING THISTLE.

Thompson's curse – a name for HOARY CRESS.

Thorn-apple (*Datura stramonium*)

> This poisonous plant, very infrequently found 'in the wild' in the [Channel] Islands, was grown, and the leaves and stems dried and smoked like tobacco as a well-used remedy for ASTHMA. [Bonnard, 1993: 28]

Thunder – caused by picking RED CAMPION, ROSEBAY WILLOWHERB, SPEEDWELL, and WOOD ANEMONE; BAY protects against; see also LIGHTNING.

Thunder bolts – a Cheshire name for SPEEDWELL; a Staffordshire name for WOOD ANEMONE.

Thunderflower – a Cheshire name for ROSEBAY WILLOWHERB; a Northumbrian name for POPPY.

Thyme (*Thymus* spp.)

> To bring a sprig of Shepherd's Thyme, as wild Thyme is called, into the house is thought very unlucky, as by so doing you bring death or severe illness to some member of your family. My informant tells me that she was charged with hastening the death of her own sister in this way, and as the neighbours and family more than once accused her of this great crime, it preyed upon her mind till it made her almost ill herself. [Friend, 1884: 15]

> Gypsies regard this plant [wild thyme] as very unlucky, and will not bring it into their waggons or tents. But it may be used out of doors as a cure for WHOOPING COUGH, boiled in water with a little vinegar added and drunk cold. [Vesey-FitzGerald, 1944: 28]

> As a boy [in the 1940s and 50s] I was shown ways of helping and healing via herbs by a woman wise in the methods . . . She used wild thyme a great deal to help people with bronchial and stomach problems. [Barnstaple, Devon, August 1992]

> Some 30 years ago I was told by a South Country traveller that an infusion of wild thyme rubbed into the hair would preserve the natural colour. Well, I'm 74 today and I haven't got a grey hair on my thatch, which has remained thick and brown. [Colwyn Bay, Clwyd, June 1993]

Ti (*Cordyline fruticosa*). The tropical shrub ti is unusual in that small, apparently lifeless, bits of its stem will grow and produce leaves if placed in water or damp soil. Consequently small 'logs' of the plant are sold as curiosities. The notes on the packaging of a log, purchased in Covent Garden Market, London, in December 1989, read:

> Hawaiian Good Luck Ti Plant.
> Just plant a log and watch it grow! . . .
> In Hawaii, the Ti Plant is said to bring good luck to its owner and to keep evil spirits at bay. The large leaves are used for wrapping and serving food and even for the traditional Hula skirts.

For further information on the ethnobotany of ti in Polynesia, see Merlin, 1989.

Tide

> Never try to pull or dig up weeds when the tide is ebbing, as the weeds will be much harder to get out of the ground. [Lerwick, Shetland, March 1994]

Tissty-tossties – balls of COWSLIP flowers used in love DIVINATION.

Toadflax (*Linaria vulgaris*). According to John Ray in his *Catalogus Plantarum circa Cantabrigiam nascentium* (1660):

> Many people place this herb under the bare soles of their feet, and between the toes and heels to drive off quartan FEVER. [Ewen and Prime, 1975: 80]

Tobacco (*Nicotiana tabacum*)—substitutes include wild ANGELICA, BLACKTHORN, COLTSFOOT, ELDER, ELM, EYEBRIGHT, HOGWEED, HORSE CHESTNUT, MEADOWSWEET, MUGWORT, ROSEBAY WILLOWHERB, and TRAVELLER'S JOY.

In Ireland tobacco was used to alleviate TOOTHACHE.

> The cure the old people had for toothache was a leaf of tobacco [which] was put into the person's tooth and it was left there until the pain was gone. [IFCSS MSS 275: 450, Co. Cork]

Toilet paper – TREE MALLOW leaves used.

Tomato (*Lycopersicum esculentum*)

> We were never allowed to eat a tomato because birds would never peck them and worms would never eat them. [Barking, Essex, November 1985]

> The flesh of tomato helped to heal wounds. [St Osyth, Essex, February 1989]

Tom-bacca – a Sussex name for TRAVELLER'S JOY.

Tom thumb – a Gloucestershire name for EARLY PURPLE ORCHID; a Dorset name for BIRD'S-FOOT TREFOIL.

Toothache – alleviated using CHAMOMILE, DOG ROSE moss galls, HEN-BANE, SPURGE LAUREL, TOBACCO, and WILLOW.

Tormentil (*Potentilla erecta*; syn. *P. tormentilla* and *Tormentilla erecta*)

Tormentil root. – This is the root of *Potentilla tormentilla*, and is an ordinary medicine. Two girls inquired of one of my friends at Stratford-by-Bow [east London] for a 'pennorth of tormentel'. The next week they came for more, and were asked what they wanted it for. After much hesitation and nervousness, one of the girls said that the other, her sister, had been jilted by her young man. She had consulted an old woman who was 'wise', and this old woman told her to get a bunch of 'tormentel' root and to burn it at midnight on a Friday. This would so worry and discomfort the 'young man' that he would return to his sweetheart. My druggist friend told me that they came for three successive weeks, and then stopped. He does not know if they succeeded, or gave it up as a bad job, but he thinks they won! [Lovett, 1913: 121]

[Glen Gyle, Perthshire:] at this time of year, when over-exposure to the hot sun can catch the unwary, painful SUNBURN can be treated with a cooled lotion of tormentil steeped in boiling water. [Barrington, 1984: 103]

In the Lammermuirs the root is called Shepherd's-Knot, and is used, boiled in milk, for the cure of DIARRHOEA. [Johnston, 1853: 72]

[A cure for diarrhoea in Co. Cavan:] Boil 'tormenting root' and drink the juice and eat the root. It is a small miserable-looking plant which grows on barren soil or ditches. [Maloney, 1972: 74]

In the 1860s Duncan Deyell, a 17-year-old from the Westside of Shetland, became very ill while at sea and had to be put ashore in Southern Ireland. He saw a doctor there who told him he had rheumatic fever, and by the time the lad got back to Shetland he was unable to walk. He couldn't even sit on a horse, and his sister brought him home lying across a pony's back. A doctor was called in again, but he said there was nothing he could do for the young man, and gave him only six months to live. However a relative called Mary Fraser wouldn't accept this, and sent some members of the family to dig up aert-bark [tormentil root], which she boiled, then gave the stock to the patient. I don't know how long the treatment lasted, but the lad was well and back at sea again in a few months, and continued to work on board ship for ten years. He then retired from the sea and . . . lived until he was 74 . . . I heard this story from his grandson.

My mother, who was born in 1889 and lived to the grand age of 93, said that as a child she was given aert-bark boiled in milk quite regularly, as a tonic or for any stomach upset. [Lerwick, Shetland, March 1994]

On Guernsey tormentil was known as *esquinancée*, and 'valued as a remedy for quinsy'. It also shared with milkwort the name *herbe de paralysie*:

The Rev. R.H. Tourtel tells me that the country people recognise two different plants as effective in warding off or curing paralysis—(1) the milkwort, which is used in the case of men, and (2) the tormentil in the case of women. An old woman, who had lost the faculty of speech through an attack of paralysis, recovered it again after drinking a decoction of tormentil. I have reason to believe, however, that this distinction is not universal; because some years ago an old man at St Martin's showed me some tormentil which he had gathered, and which he said he was taking regularly as a 'tea,' to avert the danger of a paralytic stroke. [Marquand, 1906: 40]

In areas where trees were scarce or absent, tormentil roots were used for tanning leather.

[The island shoes] were altogether the production of Eigg, from the skin out of which they had been cut, with the lime that had prepared it for the tan, and the root by which the tan had been furnished, down to the last on which they had been moulded . . . There are few trees, and, of course, no bark to spare in the islands; but the islanders find a substitute in the astringent lobiferous root of the *Tomentilla erecta*, which they dig out for the purpose among the heath at no inconsiderable expense of time and trouble . . . it took a man nearly a day to gather roots enough for a single infusion. [Miller, 1858: 17]

[Tormentil] is generally used for tanning their nets by fishermen in the Western Isle, who call it *Cairt-Lair*. [McNeill, 1910: 118]

Ireland was particularly lacking in trees, and in 1727 the Irish Parliament awarded £200 to William Maple for discovering that leather could be tanned using tormentil roots. Maple published his findings in a pamphlet entitled *A Method of Tanning without Bark* in 1729. This contained an illustration of a tormentil plant, and thus has the distinction of being the first illustrated botanical work to be published in Ireland [Nelson and McCracken, 1987: 11].

Later in the eighteenth century tree bark was so scarce in Ireland that 'some tanners resorted to a more humble source of tannin, the roots of tormentil, to encourage which The Royal Dublin Society offered premiums in 1750' [Evans and Laughlin, 1971: 85].

Tormenting root – a Co. Cavan name for TORMENTIL.

Tramman or **trammon** – Manx names for ELDER.

Traveller's joy (*Clematis vitalba*)

[In Sussex traveller's joy is called Tom-bacca and] also called boys'-bacca, because the boys cut the small wood in pieces to smoke like cigars. [Britten and Holland, 1886; 471]

[As a boy in Bedfordshire in the late 1930s] I well remember . . . smoking Old Man's Beard, white flaxen weed the real name of which escapes me.

(it is however worth mentioning that it has no hallucinatory properties whatever, indeed all it does is make you cough a lot). [Norman, 1969: 34]

As children (I was born in 1943) . . . the young boys of about 8–13 years old used to smoke what we called whiffy cane. This was the woody stalk of old man's beard. [Clevedon, Avon, March 1993]

Jew guts = wild clematis, used in Beer [Devon] to make the bottoms of crab pots, being both flexible and hard wearing. [Laver, 1990: 236]

[Stratford-upon-Avon, Warwickshire:] Rings made by twisting into a loop the twining stems of traveller's joy . . . were placed round a child's neck as a cure for CONVULSIONS. [Bloom, 1920: 245]

Tree mallow (*Lavatera arborea*)

[In Cornwall tree mallow] is sometimes called 'ku-tree', because a fomentation of the leaves is used to cure a 'ku', or 'kennal', or 'STYE' or ulcer in the eye. It is generally believed that there are male and female plants, the leaves of which must be used on those of the opposite human sex. [Davey, 1909: 91]

MALLOW seeds are called 'cheeses'. We have common, tree, Cretan and dwarf mallows—preference is given to the tree, probably because of size rather than any other reason, The cheeses are eaten green after the remains of the sepals are removed. They taste rather like English cob nuts. They are used in salads, but I found I needed to chop them—otherwise they were suspected of being curled up caterpillars!

The leaves of mallow (preferably *Lavatera arborea*) are boiled until the resultant mush looks like well boiled spinach. It is used as hot as the patient can stand on swellings of joints—the poultice to be renewed as required, a number of times over a couple of days. This actually works. I carried out instructions on a swollen ankle—not from any act of faith, but I did it not to hurt the feelings of a dear friend, so that I could say truthfully, 'Oh, I tried it, but it didn't work'—but it did! [St Mary's, Isles of Scilly, September 1992]

On Jersey tree-mallow leaves were used in place of toilet paper.

[The tree-mallow] was much cultivated in cottage gardens on the coast. This . . . seemed strange until an elderly Jersey gentleman delicately pointed out that, in the past, the privy tended to be at the bottom of the garden and the tree mallows were strategically placed because of their leaves. Children used to eat the fruits, *des p'tits pains*. [Le Sueur, 1984: 96]

Tree of happiness – a name for MONEY TREE.

Tree of heaven – a name for MONEY TREE, also given to the tree *Ailanthus altissima*, a native of China which is planted as an ornamental and is now becoming naturalized in south-east England.

Trimmling jockies – a Yorkshire name for QUAKING GRASS.

Tubbens – clods of earth and grass.

> I was brought up in a mining village . . . half way between Land's End and St Ives—1920 onwards . . . On SHROVE TUESDAY, just like snowballing, people threw 'tubbens' (clods of earth and grass) at each other. Boys versus girls in the school playgrounds. [Pendeen, Cornwall, May 1990]

Tuberculosis – treated using DANDELION, FOXGLOVE, MULLEIN, and YARROW; caused by LORDS AND LADIES; reputedly prevalent near ELDER trees.

Tuberose (*Polianthes tuberosa*). Early in the twentieth century the sweetly scented flowers of tuberose were believed to act as an APHRODISIAC:

> He [Lord Wimborne] was incurably romantic, to him love must always be '*une grande passion*', otherwise it was not interesting. He always sent bunches of tuberoses (believed by the Edwardians to incite desire) to any woman he fancied. [Cartland, 1971, chapter 5]

Tufted hair grass (*Deschampsia cespitosa*). Known in the north of England as bull-fronts, bull-toppings or bull-faces, tufted hair grass was formerly used to make church hassocks.

> The Church hassocks were easy to make, though tough to dig up and they were never, as far as I know, covered with anything. Only the very largest tussock will make a good hassock . . . The late Rev. R. Kettlewell in 1938, writing his history of the Parish of Great Ayton, found an early eighteenth century Church charge of 2d each for 'Bull-front kneelers'. Within the last decade an old man of Lealholm Roman Catholic Church said: 'You owt ti hev a hassock: there's nowt mait comfortabler to kneel on than olf bull-front. Before we had a chetch here, there was two or three of t'owd hands at Ugthorpe had bull-front i' their pews. I haven't seen one used for forty years or mair.' [Teulon-Porter, 1956: 90]

Tulip (*Tulipa gesneriana*) – used to decorate floats in the Spalding FLOWER PARADE.

Tun-hoof – a name for GROUND IVY.

Turnip (*Brassica rapa*). Turnip lanterns are made in parts of Ireland and northern England for HALLOWE'EN.

> Lamps out of turnips are made now only at Hallowe'en. The lamps were made by scooping the centre out of the turnip, and by cutting holes in the front for windows. Then a candle or wick is put inside which shows the light. [IFCSS MSS 950: 248, Co. Monaghan]

Turnip lanterns are still made in this area. Indeed, I assumed it was fairly common throughout the country. Certainly our children always made them until they grew too old for that sort of thing, but, as far as I know, it was only on Hallowe'en, and I have not seen them around on Guy Fawkes' Night. [Corbridge, Northumberland, January 1980]

Cf. MANGOLD and PUMPKIN.

Alternatively, on the Shetland Islands:

Ducking for APPLES was not a common practice . . . However an excellent substitute was found in slices of turnip cut into letters of the alphabet, which were put into a tub of water to be retrieved in the mouth by lads and lasses. It was great fun trying to get the initials of your heart's desire, and should you end up with strange letters, it was always exciting trying to work out who the Fates had in store for you. [Lerwick, Shetland, March 1994]

In common with other crops, local festivities provided guidance as to when the various stages in the cultivation of turnips should take place.

Turnips, as far as I can remember should be sowed before the 15th June (locally the Feast of St Columcille). [Daingean, Co. Offaly, January 1985]

Turnips should be singled by Crewkerne Fair (4 and 5 September). [Thorncombe, Dorset, September 1977]

In folk medicine turnips were used to cure COLDS.

[This cure was used by my father-in-law's grandmother, around Melton Constable, Norfolk, about 60 years ago.] Take a large white turnip, wash it and slice it about ⅛ to 3/16″ thick. Lay the slices around the sides of a dish . . . Sprinkle each slice with brown sugar (demerara). A liquid will in time . . . run into the centre of the dish. Drink this to cure the cold. [West Stow, Suffolk, January 1991]

Tutsan (*Hypericum androsaemum*), occasionally known as touch and heal leaf.

The tutsan, a shrubby herb common . . . in Hampshire is known as 'touchen' or 'touched' leaves, and its glossy berries which turn from green to red are said to be stained with the BLOOD of the Danes. [Boase, 1976: 114]

To prevent a mark: Touch and heal leaf. This grows in fields; you will find an odd one at river's edge. There is a berry on it, first it's red, then turns black. The ointment is made with lard and the leaves mixed together, the leaves being pounded first. [IFCSS MSS 200: 75, Co. Leitrim]

In England, and also on the Channel coast of France, the dry leaves, for their scent (likened to ambergris, so the names 'Amber' and 'Sweet Amber') for good luck, were put between the pages of prayer books and the Bible. [Grigson, 1987: 75]

U

Ulcers – created using CELERY-LEAVED BUTTERCUP; cured using CAB-
BAGE, COMFREY, DWARF ELDER, ELDER, MARSH WOUNDWORT, PELLI-
TORY OF THE WALL, POTATO, and WATER FIGWORT.

Umbellifers (i.e. members of the carrot family, Umbelliferae). Several members of the Umbelliferae, such as COW PARSLEY, are widely
perceived as being inauspicious, and in some areas it appears that most,
if not all, white-flowered members of the family were considered to
be 'unlucky'.

> Here in Northumberland the local name for all members of the Umbel-
> liferae is bad-man's oatmeal. [Whitley Bay, Tyne and Wear, March 1984]

> Umbellifers in general—known as mother die on Merseyside and must
> not be picked at all. [Bromborough, Merseyside, November 1990]

> We never touched or picked umbellifers. They were all termed poison-
> ous. I suppose it was to stop us picking HEMLOCK. [Plymouth, Devon,
> February 1993]

V

Valerian (*Valeriana officinalis* and *V. phu*)

[Valerian] was always called cut-leaf and I well remember being told to rub the leaf into CUTS and scratches. [Birdham, West Sussex, July 1993]

[He told me that valerian (*Valeriana phu*) is] called God's hand leaf . . . He explained that the leaves were wrapped round such things as an infected sore on a finger and kept in place overnight. [Greenway, Gloucestershire, September 1993]

Vegetable lamb. The legend of a vegetable lamb—a lamb-like organism which shared both plant and animal characteristics—was first brought to England by Sir John Mandeville, who was reputedly born in St Albans, Hertfordshire, and left in 1322 for travels lasting thirty-two years 'through many diverse lands'.

[Beyond the Land of Cathay] there groweth a manner of fruit, as though it were gourds. And when they be ripe, men cut them atwo, and men find within a little beast, in flesh, in bone, and blood, as though it were a little lamb without wool. And men eat both the fruit and the beast. And that is a great marvel. Of that fruit I have eaten. [Mandeville, 1964: 174]

It is generally assumed that Mandeville's plant was, in fact, the cotton. However, it is noteworthy that he states that the lamb was without wool. Surely if the seed-pod was that of the cotton, then its characteristic fibres would have ensured that the lamb was described as woolly, rather than wool-less. The fact that there are no records of cotton seed-pods being eaten also suggests that Mandeville's plant is something other than cotton.

Another description of a vegetable lamb can be found in the *Talmud Ierosolimitanum*, written in 436.

It was in form like a lamb, and from its navel grew a stem or root by which this zoophyte or plant-animal was fixed, attached, like a gourd to the soil below the surface of the ground, and according to the length of its stem or root, it devoured all the herbage which it was able to reach within the circle of its tether. [Lee 1887: 6]

During the sixteenth and seventeenth centuries this creature—the 'Scythian Lamb'—excited considerable curiosity, with several respected European scholars believing in its existence, and several supposed lambs being exhibited. The title-page of John Parkinson's *Paradisi in Sole Paradisus Terrestris* (1629) depicts Adam and Eve surrounded by the plants of the Garden of Eden, which include what is usually interpreted as being a vegetable lamb, although it looks rather more like a dead wolf slumped over a tree trunk.

In 1698 Sir Hans Sloane exhibited at a meeting of the Royal Society an object which

> is commonly, but falsely, in India, called 'the Tartarian Lamb'. This was more than a foot long, as big as one's wrist, having seven protuberances, and towards the end some foot-stalks about three or four inches long, exactly like the foot-stalks of ferns, both without and within. [Sloane, 1698: 461]

Thus Sloane correctly identified the origin of the vegetable lambs then reaching Europe. In September 1725 the Royal Society again turned its attention to the lamb, when Dr John Philip Breyn endorsed Sloane's conclusions:

> A certain learned and observant man, passing through our city [Dantzic] on his return from a journey through Muscovy, enriched my museum with . . . one of these 'Scythian Lambs' . . . It was about six inches in length, and had a head, ears, and four legs. Its colour was that of iron-rust, and it was covered all over with a kind of down, like the fibres of silk-plush, except upon the ears and legs, which were bare, and were of a somewhat darker tawny hue. On careful examination of it, I discovered that it was not an animal production, nor yet a fruit, but either the creeping root, or the climbing stem, of some plant, which by obstetric art had acquired the form of a quadruped animal. [Lee, 1887: 33]

A specimen of the vegetable lamb can be found in Sloane's 'Collection of Vegetables and Vegetable Substances', now housed in the Botany Department of the Natural History Museum, London. It is part of a rhizome of the fern *Cibotium barometz* and in its twentieth-century state is unconvincing.

> By skillful treatment the inhabitants of Southern China occasionally converted the thick root-stock of one of these tree-ferns, *Dicksonia barometz*, into a rough semblance of a quadruped, which quadruped, by a foregone conclusion, was supposed to be a lamb. They removed entirely the fronds that grew upward from the rhizome, excepting four, and these four they trimmed down until only about four inches of each stalk was left. The object thus shaped being turned upside down, the root-stock represented the body of the animal, and was supported by the four inverted stalks of the fronds, as upon four legs. [Lee, 1887: 41]

It seems that these objects were originally made by the Chinese as toy dogs, but in Europe they were perceived as being lambs, even though they had no direct link with the vegetable lamb described by Mandeville and various continental travellers. It appears that none of these travellers actually claimed to have seen a living vegetable lamb. Thus the vegetable lamb was derived from several sources: Mandeville's account of an as yet unidentified fruit, the description in the *Talmud Ierosolimitanum*, toys made from the rhizomes of *Cibotium barometz*, and vague descriptions of cotton plants, of which it was written as early as 445 BC:

> Certain trees bear for their fruit fleeces surpassing those of sheep in beauty and excellence, and the natives [of India] clothe themselves in cloths made therefrom. [Lee, 1887: 46]

Vermicides – plants used include BISTORT, BOG MYRTLE, BOX, BRACKEN, FUMITORY, GORSE, HELLEBORE, HOP, HORSERADISH, TANSY, and WORMWOOD.

Vervain (*Verbena officinalis*)

Many persons now living can remember how general a practice it was, some years since, to hang a piece of vervain around the neck of a child to avert infection; some believing it to be an amulet or charm, others thinking it a herb of powerful properties. Besides this, it was taken medicinally, or worn to cure existing disease, and was deemed efficacious in 30 different complaints, in some of which it was particularly recommended that it should be tied round the neck with a white ribbon. [Pratt, 1857, 2: 184]

[In West Sussex] vervain dried leaves 'worn in a black silk bag', are recommended as a cure for weakly children. [Latham, 1878: 38]

On the Isle of Man MOTHERWORT was often considered to be vervain.

Vervine – a Manx name for MOTHERWORT and VERVAIN.

Vetch (*Vicia* spp. especially *V. sativa*)

About 40 years ago I attended a country school . . . on the way to and from school we ate everything . . . vetches—little black peas in a green pod, the fruit of a purple wild flower. [Clonmel, Co. Tipperary, February 1993]

In England a decoction of them [vetch seeds] in water is sometimes given by nurses to expel the SMALL POX and MEASLES. [Lightfoot, 1777: 396]

Violet (*Viola* spp., especially *V. odorata*)

I was born in 1914. This area was then pure farming. Occasionally we would eat violet seeds—not the green pod—when they were white. [Plymouth, Devon, January 1993]

Boil wild violets and drink the juice and it would cure a pain in the head. [IFCSS MSS 500: 74, Co. Limerick]

Violet leaves cure CANCER. [IFCSS MSS 560: 378, Co. Tipperary]

[Gypsy remedy:] a poultice of the leaves steeped in boiling water is good for cancerous growths: an infusion of the leaves will aid in internal cancers, and, I have been told, will even cure them. [Vesey-FitzGerald, 1944: 28]

Recipe for infusion of violet leaves for use in cases of cancer: Take a handful of fresh green violet leaves, and pour about a pint of boiling water on them. Cover them, and let them stand for about 12 hours (until water is green), then strain off the liquid and dip into it a piece of lint. Warm a sufficient quantity of the liquid. Put on the wet lint hot wherever the malady is. Cover the lint with oil-skin or thin mackintosh. Change the lint when dry or cold. An infusion should be made fresh about every alternate day . . . Originated, I think, in Maidstone, it has been in the family many years. [UCL EFS MSS M9, Bromley, Kent, September 1963]

Virgin Mary's milk-drops – a Monmouthshire name for LUNG-WORT.

W

Wake robin – a seventeenth-century name for LORDS AND LADIES.

Wall barley (*Hordeum murinum*)

As children in north London in the late fifties/early sixties we would pick a flower-spike of Barley Grass (*Hordeum murinum*) and break it into quite effective darts which could easily get lodged in the hair or clothing of whoever we threw them at—dislodging them was, of course, another matter! [Exeter, Devon, March 1991]

[As children about 40 years ago] we used to bombard each other with grass darts which we said were FLEA-ridden. They stuck very well to woollen clothes when thrown, and as children we used to get very ratty if we got one on our jumper without realising it for sometime, as everyone said they were full of fleas! [Totton, Hampshire, August 1993]

Wall rabbits – a Dorset name for IVY-LEAVED TOADFLAX.

Wall rue (*Asplenium ruta-muraria*)—could be used as a substitute for RUE by a jilted girl on the marriage of her former young man.

Walnut (*Juglans regia*)

A falling walnut tree is the herald of calamity. A great walnut tree on the lawn at my old [Berwickshire] home keeled over one teatime in 1939. [Old Cleeve, Somerset, October 1993]

Boiled walnut shells make a very successful DYE for wool, popular because it does not require a mordant (to fix the colour). [Corbridge, Northumberland, March 1993]

War – foretold by an abundance of FOXGLOVES.

Wart flower – a Cornish name for POPPY.

Warts – caused by POPPY, SHEEP'S BIT, and SNOWBERRY; cured using ASH, BROAD BEAN, CORN, ELDER, GREATER CELANDINE, HOUSELEEK, PETTY SPURGE, SOW THISTLE, SPURGE, SUN SPURGE, and TEASEL.

Wartweed – a Cornish name for PETTY SPURGE.

Warty-girse – an Orkney name for SUN SPURGE.

Watercress (*Rorippa nasturtium-aquaticum*). The earliest mentions of SHAMROCK refer to an edible plant which both Stanihurst (1577) and

Spenser (1633) equate with watercress. Probably these authors had misread a passage in Edmond Campion's 1571 unpublished *First Boke of the Histories of Ireland*, where he described the diet of the Irish:

> Shamrotes, watercresses, and other herbs they feed upon: oatmele and butter they cramme together. [Colgan, 1896: 216]

However, possible evidence to support the indentification of shamrock with watercress can be found in County Meath, where a well on the Commons of Duleek is known as Shamrock Well, and in the 1940s watercress, 'which is still remembered as being the finest in the district', was gathered from it [Synnott, 1979: 41].

A more direct association between watercress and ST PATRICK is provided by one of the names given to the plant.

> Watercress, or watergrass, could be gathered from a clean, running stream, cooked and used instead of cabbage. It could also be eaten raw with bread and butter . . . Some people called it St Patrick's Cabbage as it needed no dressing. [Lenamore, Co. Longford, April 1991]

There was a widespread belief that watercress should not be gathered for eating when there is no letter R in the name of the month. Two explanations have been given for this: wild watercress is usually in flower and therefore unsuitable for eating during the summer months [Thorncombe, Dorset, *c*.1962], or, as water levels are likely to be low and streams sluggish during the summer, the watercress might be unclean then [Shepherdswell, Kent, November 1979].

In north Devon:

> A 'simple' person down here was said to have 'never ate his watercress', and thus it was thought that the plant, which is common enough even today in the wild, was one which gave intelligence, rather like fish. [Barnstaple, Devon, May 1991]

There are occasional records of watercress being used in folk medicine.

> Watercress rubbed on the skin takes away rash and other skin blemishes. [IFCSS MSS 98: 347, Co. Mayo]

> Watercress eaten raw is good for heart disease. [IFCSS MSS 770: 63, Co. Longford]

> RHEUMATISM: it is said to eat watercress was used as a cure. [IFCSS MSS 975: 27, Co. Cavan]

> [On the Isle of Mull:] watercress was eaten as a cure for SCURVY. It was a common disease after the '45, when many people lived on shellfish and salt meat. They came from miles away for the cress. [SSS MSS SA1963.32.A9]

Water figwort (*Scrophularia auriculata*; syn. *S. aquatica* auct.). In Devon water figwort was known as crowdy-kit:

An interesting word, coming from the Welsh for Fiddle . . . this plant is known as 'Fiddles', and 'Fiddle-wood' in some places, 'so called because the stems are by children stripped of their leaves and scraped across each other fiddle-fashion, when they produce a squeaking noise.' [Friend, 1882: 18]

Fiddle-wood: (*Scrophularia aquatica*)—E. Yorks. So called because the stems are by children stripped of their leaves, and scraped across each other fiddler fashion, when they produce a squeaking sound. [Britten and Holland, 1886: 181]

For crowdy-kit-o'-the-wall see BITING STONECROP.

[In Cornwall] the leaves of this plant were formerly held in high repute as an application for ULCERS. [Davey, 1909: 325]

I was recently told that the old people in Ipplepen, near Newton Abbot, use 'Water Betony' or water figwort for curing ULCERS and CUTS externally. Several people still living had it applied by their parents and say it was very effective. [Little Waltham, Essex, January 1978]

Watergrass – a Co. Longford name for WATERCRESS.

Water starwort (*Callitriche stagnalis*)

[On Colonsay] formerly used as an ingredient in plasters for promoting suppuration. [McNeill, 1910: 124]

Water weed – a name given to SPRING BEAUTY on the Isles of Scilly.

Wavverin leaf – a Shetland name for GREATER PLAINTAIN.

Waxplant – a name given to HOUSELEEK in Offaly and Westmeath.

Weather forecasting – plants used include LILAC, PENNYWORT, SCARLET PIMPERNEL, SEAWEED, WEEDS, WHITEBEAM, and WHITE POPLAR; see also THUNDER.

Weather-teller – a Somerset name for SCARLET PIMPERNEL.

Weather tree – a name for WHITE POPLAR.

Wedding flowers. As at other times of celebration, plant materials are used extensively at marriage ceremonies, the use of flowers on such occasions being a major source of income for flower-growers and florists. The commitment of two people in marriage is demonstrated by a ceremony which should be both meaningful and memorable. Two things which can make such an occasions meaningful are its visual impact and the shared meal or 'reception'. For early man, and the poor, this visual excitement could be most easily achieved by the use of flowers and foliage, the one source of bright colours most readily available. Later, flowers became part of the wedding tradition and acquired symbolic roles.

At present the value of long-term commitment of a couple in lasting marriage is being increasingly questioned, many couples prefer simply to live together without any formal ceremony to mark their commitment, and many formal marriages fail to survive. Although this situation is condemned by the older generation brought up with Victorian or Edwardian attitudes to marriage, it appears that it is merely a reversion to a more usual state of affairs, with the Victorian and Edwardian attitude to marriage and the family being the exception rather than the rule. Matrimony was proclaimed a sacrament and a church ceremony was decreed as indispensable only as late as the Council of Trent in 1563 [Warner, 1978: 145]. Even in Victorian times men in the aristocratic classes seem to have been free to be sexually promiscuous both before and after marriage, while early sociological surveys have shown that among the poor marriage was often considered to be unimportant. In his *London Labour and the London Poor*, Charles Booth [1861, 1: 20] estimated that not more than one tenth of costermonger couples were married. There was 'no honour attached to the marriage state, and no shame to concubinage'. No doubt country squires and factory owners enforced greater respectability in villages and small industrial towns, but the marriage ceremony, if celebrated at all, was a restrained affair for the majority of the poor.

At country weddings, the path of the bride might be strewn with flowers and RUSHES. In Guernsey the wild YELLOW IRIS was a favourite plant for strewing at weddings and was much sought after for this purpose [MacCulloch, 1903: 101].

The bouquet, which is carried by most British brides, has a long history but does not appear to have been considered an essential bridal accessory until the eighteenth century. Over the years the flowers favoured by brides have undergone gradual change. It seems that originally a cheerful posy of seasonal flowers was considered appropriate. Later there was a vogue for white flowers, such as MADONNA LILIES, MYRTLE, ORANGE blossom, stimulated by Victorian ideas about the purity of the bride, and later, with the invention of photography, the fact that white flowers photographed well, whereas darker flowers could appear as a dark amorphous mass. More recently, when many if not most brides are no longer 'pure', and most, if not all, wedding photography is done in colour, a wider range of colours is used in bridal flowers. The choice of flowers now appears to be governed by the idea that the bouquet should complement the bride's dress, rather than the symbolism of, or the bride's sentimental attachment to, any particular flower.

After the wedding the bouquet is sometimes thrown into the air, so that whoever catches it will be the next to marry [South Kensington, London, October 1979].

If a North Oxfordshire bride throws her bouquet out of a window after the ceremony, the bridesmaid who catches it, or is first to reach it, will be the first to marry. [Briggs, 1974: 114]

Alternatively the bouquet may be placed on the grave of a dead grandparent or some other relative. If the grandparent has been cremated the bouquet may be placed in or tied to a rose bush planted in the grandparent's memory in the crematorium's garden of remembrance [personal observation, South London Crematorium, May 1981, and West London Crematorium, August 1981].

Not only the bride has flowers at weddings. It is customary for her attendants to carry bouquets, and for the groom, and at least the principal guests, to wear buttonholes, usually of CARNATIONS. The buttonhole on the left lapel of men's jackets was first introduced in the 1840s to hold such decorations [Cunnington and Lucas, 1972: 70]. At the weddings of fairground showpeople it is usual for bouquets to be presented to the mothers of the bride and groom, grandmothers, and any other important lady guests [see, for example, *World's Fair*, 1 January 1977].

Weeds

[USA:] in the course of a conversation with an old Welsh coal miner late in the fall, he remarked that we had a long hard winter before us, and that he was therefore sure of steady work at good wages until spring.

Struck by the absolute confidence of his tone, I inquired how he knew.

'Why,' he replied, 'look around you. See those weeds. Did you ever see taller? It is the same everywhere—in the fields, in gardens, along the roadside, the weeds are higher than I ever remember seeing them before. That means that we will have the deepest snows during the coming winter seen here for many years. The reason is this. The little snowbirds live on the seeds of weeds all winter. If the snow covered up the weeds the birds would starve; so the weeds always grow somewhat higher than the deepest snow will be. When the winter is to be soft and open with little snow, the weeds only grow a few inches tall. I am an old man and I have never known this sign to fail.' . . .

That winter, at least, the old coal miner's faith was justified. Since then I have proved that the same belief is prevalent among Welsh in all sections of the country. I have even heard it referred to in the pulpit by Welsh clergymen as an instance of God's watchful care over his creatures. [Cowan, 1902: 132]

Shetlanders advised that weeds should not be pulled when the TIDE was ebbing.

Well-dressing. In the Peak District of Derbyshire a thriving traditional custom is the annual creation of floral pictures on screens to decorate village wells throughout the summer months. The well-dressing season traditionally starts at Tissington on Ascension Day, and continues until the Late Summer Bank Holiday, at the end of August, when wells at Eyam and Wormhill are dressed.

As with many other traditional customs, little is known about the origins of well-dressing. According to one popular theory:

> Springs and wells have always been venerated, from exceedingly remote times onwards, because water is a basic necessity of life . . . Wells were honoured with religious ceremonies and dances, and decorated with flowers and green branches at the greater festivals. When Christianity came, water-worship, as such, was strictly forbidden, but most of the ancient and well-loved springs were purged of their pagan associations, purified, and rededicated to the Blessed Virgin Mary or to one of the Saints . . . well-dressing in Derbyshire is a relic of this ancient form of worship, though it is hardly necessary to say that in no part of that county has it continued uninterrupted since pagan times. [Hole, 1976: 212]

According to some writers, the dressings at Tissington began in 1350 as a thanksgiving for the fact that Tissington, apparently due to the pureness of its water, had not been ravaged by the Black Death. Alternatively, the Tissington dressings started in 1615, when Tissington's wells continued to produce water even though the surrounding countryside was drought-stricken [Porteous, 1973: 5].

It appears that well-dressing in its present form evolved sometime in the late eighteenth or early nineteenth century.

> A visitor to Tissington, writing in 1758 said: 'We saw the spring adorned with garlands; in one of these was a tablet inscribed with rhymes.' If there had been pictures, surely he would have said. But when Ebenezer Rhodes went there in 1818 he found 'newly gathered flowers disposed in various devices,' some arranged on boards 'cut to the figure intended to be represented, and covered with moist clay, into which the stems of flowers are inserted.' [Porteous, 1973: 1]

The method mentioned by Rhodes in 1818 is virtually the same as that employed in recent years.

> Wooden trays, c.2.5 cm deep and up to 3.7 m in length, are filled with moist clay onto which is pressed natural, mostly plant, materials to form vivid mosaic-like pictures usually depicting religious themes or ecclesiastical buildings. Materials commonly used include: petals, sepals of HYDRANGEA, fruits of ALDER (*Alnus glutinosa*), various seeds, PARSLEY leaves,

and LICHENS. When the picture is completed the tray is placed in an erect
position at a village well, the well remaining dressed for about a week
[Vickery, 1975: 178]

Obviously the plant materials used vary according to when the dressing takes place. Hydrangea flowers, which are a favourite material late ◄
in the summer, are obviously not available when Tissington dresses its
wells.

The hydrangea must surely be considered as the most important of all. Its
availability throughout a long season, together with a wide colour range,
provides dressers with petals for skies, robes, pattern and backgrounds.
Subtle colour changes in the petals also take place from day to day during
the life of a screen. [Womack, 1977: 26]

Lichens, which lose no colour and do not deteriorate, are also widely
used:

The present writer visited Wormhill and Eyam during their well-dressing
festivals in 1973 and 1974; some lichen material was used in dressing each
of the four wells seen on both occasions. The most frequently used lichens
are *Parmelia saxatilis* and *Xanthoria parietina*, both of which are common in
the area. *Parmelia saxatilis*, collected from gritstone walls, is used in two
ways: a velvety black effect is obtained by placing thalli upside down so
that their undersurfaces are exposed; whilst thalli arranged exposing the
upper cortex, give a dull grey effect frequently used to fill in between
lettering and to cover unimportant and little seen areas. *Xanthoria parietina*, gathered from limestone walls, is carefully sorted by the dressers so that
plants of various shades can be used for a whole range of colours ranging
from bright orange through yellow to green. Clarence Daniel, an Eyam
well-dresser and local historian, states in correspondence, that *Xanthoria* is
'sometimes used upside down because it has the appearance of limestone
itself and is used in simulating buildings.' At Wormhill, the 1974 design,
which depicted the parish church, utilized, in addition to the two species
previously mentioned, a large amount of *Parmelia caperata*, a species which
. . . is extinct in Derbyshire. Correspondence with Oliver Shimwell,
who has been involved in well-dressing for over fifty years, established
that the material of this species, together with material of a bright orange
maritime form of *Xanthoria parietina*, used at Wormhill, was collected by
Mr Shimwell's sister whilst on holiday in Cornwall. [Vickery, 1975: 178]

Local rules at different villages, or those followed by different dressers,
lay down what materials are or are not acceptable. In some villages
only natural plant materials are allowed. At the other extreme, at
Wirksworth, where competitions are held for the best screens:

Faces, hands and feet are permitted modelled in relief . . . a watch was
allowed as the 'face' of Big Ben, and there have been such things used
as actual leather belts, bowie knives, and knitted 'waves'. [Porteous,
1973: 10]

Usually flowers are stripped of their petals, and each petal is pressed individually into the damp clay as the screen is covered, but

> Barlow has 'gone it alone' with 'whole flower' dressing. Each bloom is cut to half-an-inch of stalk, which is pushed into a knife-slit in the clay. This has to be much thicker—three inches—than for petalling, the extra weight making it necessary to dress the screens in position . . . Although it would be foolish to say the screens are more effective than petalled ones, they are very attractive, with deeper colour saturation, though less precise in outline. [Porteous, 1973: 16]

Although religious themes are usually favoured, local or national anniversaries are also featured. At Tissington:

> At the well-dressing in 1900 one well had a medallion portrait of the Queen, whose birthday fell on Ascension Day that year, and another had a view of Windsor Castle. This last was worked out almost entirely with elder catkins [presumably alder fruits] and grey lichens, and was very effective. [Meade-Waldo, 1902: 1]

More recently:

> A topical screen for Conservation Year appeared at Bradwell—'Plant a Tree in 1973'. Queen Elizabeth's Silver Jubilee provided an obvious source of inspiration just as it did in 1935 for the jubilee of King George V and Queen Mary . . . One screen made at the youth well in Ashford-in-the-Water was entitled 'Progress?' Made at a time when both the excitement and controversy of lunar exploration ran high, it depicted the earth with a rocket going to the moon and a hungry hand with an empty bowl reaching out from the third world. [Womack, 1977: 30]

Despite the tremendous amount of painstaking work involved in well-dressing at Tissington a local population of about 200 people manage to dress five wells—the activity continues to expand with more and more villages and towns producing annual dressings. In 1974 the Peak National Park Office, in its leaflet *1974 Events in the Peak National Park*, listed dressings in eleven towns and villages. The 1993 Wirksworth well-dressings programme listed forty-eight dressings with the season being extended from 3 May until 18 September. Well-dressings have also spread far outside the custom's traditional boundaries.

> They have this pretty wishing-well at Upwey [Dorset], at the source of the River Wey, which they dress. They didn't use to dress wells in Dorset, well-dressing being a more northern thing, but they make these pictures using flowers and leaves and beans—they use beans for the shoes—and the children do a maypole dance. [New Southgate, London, May 1989]

Even further afield, Tom Shaw, who was born in Derby in 1916 and migrated to Australia in 1956, produced three well-dressings at Perth, Western Australia in 1985 [Hults, 1987].

Wet-the-bed – a Cheshire name for DANDELION.

What's-your-sweetheart-grass – a Sussex name for RYE GRASS.

Wheat (*Triticum aestivum*). In Nottinghamshire a good wheat year was said to coincide with a good PLUM year; in Dorset the price of wheat could be foretold by counting the number of flowers on MADONNA LILIES.

According to a hand-written history of the church of St Margaret of Antioch, Sea Palling, Norfolk, on display in the church in 1989:

> In years gone by, corn from one of the sheaves with which Palling Church was decorated for Harvest Thanksgiving was germinated in a bowl and placed on the communion table at Easter. How and when this originated is not known, but for many years it was in abeyance until it was last revived at Easter 1952, when wheat from the Harvest Thanksgiving of 1951 was used.

Similarly a visitor attending an Easter service at the Ukrainian Catholic Cathedral of the Holy Family in Exile, in London's Mayfair, records:

> The bishop, priests and acolytes are shining in pure white vestments; the church alive with lilies and pots of new green wheat—loveliest symbol of the Resurrection. [Tull, 1976: 22]

Today the wheat commonly cultivated in the British Isles is bread wheat (*T. aestivum*). Rivet wheat (*T. turgidum*) was formerly widely cultivated in Ireland and the north and west of the United Kingdom, but is now only rarely grown, usually for animal feed. Some forms of rivet wheat have a tendency to produce multi-headed ears, which have been the focus of legend.

In the late nineteenth and early twentieth centuries it was claimed that these multi-headed forms had grown from seeds found in ancient Egyptian tombs.

> It would appear that grains of wheat, usually blackened in some way to suggest age, have been sold to tourists by unscrupulous local guides as wheat from the tombs or mummy wheat. Such wheat, being relatively fresh, often germinated if sown.

However, wheat seeds are not long-lived and do not remain viable for much over twenty-five years [Youngman, 1951: 423]. Several specimens labelled as 'Egyptian wheat', 'Mummy wheat', or 'Pharaoh's wheat' found their way into the collections of the Natural History Museum, London, during the late nineteenth century.

A field of rivet wheat formerly existed in the parish of Llanllwchaearn in Powys.

This was told to me about 30 years ago by an Anglican clergyman in Tunbridge Wells, the husband of a descendant of the family involved. Both he and his wife came from old families on the Welsh borders.

This was at the time when preachers had to be licenced by Church and State. There was this unlicenced preacher who had been out to a local centre—presumably a secret meeting—where he had preached on the text 'I will bless the Lord at all times'—it's the first verse of one of the psalms, I forget which one. Even when things go wrong you should praise the Lord.

During the following week he walked to the local market. When he returned home he found his house on fire, his father dead in the kitchen, killed by soldiers, and his wife and son missing. He stood in the kitchen and said 'I will bless the Lord at all times,' reaffirming his belief.

This had three results. The wind reversed direction; the soldiers had only fired the house at one end, leaving the wind to do the rest, but the wind changing direction put the fire out. He discovered his wife and son were safe. They had crossed a river, which was flooded, using stepping stones which were just covered by the water, which they knew of but the soldiers did not. The soldiers actually burnt and destroyed the wheat crop, but when the BARLEY crop came up it had five heads on each stalk. They interpreted this as the barley with the wheat returned four-fold. [Hornby, Lancashire, November 1992]

Another version of this legend is given by Robin Gwyndaf in his *Welsh Folk Tales* [1989: 63], where the preacher is identified as Henry Williams (1624–84).

Following the Restoration of the Monarchy in 1660 he spent a total of nine years in prison. During those years his furniture and farm stock were either stolen or destroyed and his house was burnt to the ground.

When everything seemed to have been lost and his family were on the verge of starvation, fate intervened. Wheat sowed in a field near the house grew prolifically and astonished the whole country. From that time Henry Williams and his family suffered no more poverty . . . The field where the marvellous wheat had grown is called *Cae'r Fendith* ('the field of blessing') to this day.

Two multi-branched ears of wheat, not barley as the first version of the legend suggests, which are said to have come from the field and been preserved by Williams' descendants, are on display at the Welsh Folk Museum, St Fagans.

The gathering of stray ears of wheat left in fields after they had been harvested was an important activitity for many cottagers until the early years of the twentieth century, and was briefly revived during the Second World War.

Every harvest time after the cutting of the corn and the stacking of the sheaves, women and children would don aprons with large pockets almost the size of the apron, and glean the ears of corn left on the stubble. Sacks were then filled and taken home to feed hens throughout the winter. I gleaned the corn fields many times with my grandmother, stuffing my apron and chewing the grains of corn as we worked. [Felmersham, Bedfordshire, April 1993]

Whiffy cane – an Avon name for woody stalks of TRAVELLER'S JOY.

Whin – see GORSE.

Whisky – flavoured using BITTER VETCH.

Whistles – made from LIME, SYCAMORE, WHITE DEAD-NETTLE, WILD GLADIOLUS, and WILLOW.

Whistling jacks – a name given to WILD GLADIOLUS on the Isles of Scilly.

Whitebeam (*Sorbus aria*, agg.)
The leaves of the whitebeam trees slightly turned and giving glimpses of their silvery underside predict rain. [Letter from Drumshanbo, Co. Leitrim, in *Ireland's Own*, 19 March 1993]
Cf. WHITE POPLAR.

White bryony (*Bryonia dioica*). In parts of rural Britain the roots of white bryony were known and used as MANDRAKE.
Out of this Root knavish Impostures form Shapes which they style Mandrakes to deceive the Vulgar. [Threlkeld, 1726: 29]
Sometimes such 'mandrakes' would be partially hollowed out and have grass seeds or grains of corn planted in the cavity, so that on germination they gave the appearance of hair. Thus Sir Hans Sloane (1660–1753) had in his 'Collection of Vegetable and Vegetables Substances': 'A mandrakes beard . . . Corn putt into the root of white bryony and thence sprouting'.
In December 1908, a man employed in digging a neglected garden half a mile from Stratford upon Avon, cut a large root of white bryony through with his spade. He called it mandrake, and ceased to work at once, saying it was 'awful bad luck'. Before the weeek was out, he fell down some steps and broke his neck. [*Folk-lore*, 24: 240, 1913]
A 60-year-old gardener in Cambridge, asked to dig up some bryony roots, said 'That's mandrake, that is; my old dad would never touch it; said it might scream horribly if you did' . . . Farmers whose barns and outhouses were overrun by rats would send one of their men on the task of digging up 'mandrake' roots, which were then crushed and put into the rat holes to drive the vermin away . . .

White clover

A bryony root, as does one of mandrake, often resembles the trunk, legs and thighs of a human being. W.H. Barrett [b.1891] remembers old Fenmen digging up roots, selecting those most human in shape, washing them carefully and putting on their marks—few of the older generations could read or write. On their visits to the local inn the men took their roots to join others arranged on the taproom mantelshelf ready to be judged in a competition for which each entrant paid a small fee. On Saturday night the landlord's wife would be called in to judge the exhibits, a prize being awarded for the root which most resembled the female figure. The 'Venus Nights' were popular with both landlord and customers, because the entrance fees were spent on beer and tobacco.

After the prize had been awarded the winning root stayed on the shelf until it was ousted by a finer specimen. Even then it was not discarded, for if it was suspended by a string from the rafters of a sow's stye it was reckoned that more piglets would be produced. When the root was dry and shrivelled it was placed among the savings kept in an old stocking hidden under the mattress as a guarantee that the hoard would increase. [Porter, 1969: 46]

White bryony roots were also widely used as a conditioner for horses.

My father-in-law, now around 70 years of age, says that the powdered root of white bryony was added to the food ration of working horses on a farm where he worked in north Norfolk. The roots were placed in the household oven, at cool heat just enough to dry them, not bake them. Just a pinch was used once a day, and he still maintains 'it put a shine into their coats.' [West Stow, Suffolk, March 1989]

In the village of Ascott-under-Wychwood somewhere in the mid-1930s, I watched a groom preparing a mash for his hunter and adding shavings from something which looked like a dried-up parsnip hanging on the wall. On enquiring as to its identity, I received the reply 'Mandrake, the best physic there is for 'osses.' On smelling and tasting a shaving I realised that it was white bryony. [Charlbury, Oxfordshire, January 1991]

In the nineteenth century white bryony was used to treat RHEUMATISM.

[White bryony root] is very acrid in its properties, and is often scraped and applied to the limb affected with rheumatism, when it causes a stinging sensation in the skin, similar to that produced by the nettle. [Pratt, 1857, 2: 70]

Cf. DWARF ELDER.

White clover (*Trifolium repens*)

Shamrock on St Patrick's Day . . . before 1920 we (as children) gathered what we thought to be SHAMROCK to send to an aunt in England—believing (as most people did) that it only grew in Ireland. We looked for a clover with small neat trefoil leaves—certainly almost always *Trifolium repens*. [Ballycastle, Co. Antrim, January 1991]

Some years ago I lived in Cornwall: mutton rose = white clover. [Canford Heath, Dorset, August 1987]

[I asked a local farmer about mutton rose] he said he had heard it was clover good for ewes. [St Ervan, Cornwall, February 1992]

Names my friends and I used in our childhood days of the 20s and 30s . . . around Burghead, Moray . . . white clover = milkies (we sucked them). [Edinburgh, October 1991]

White dead-nettle (*Lamium album*)

[In north-east England] the leaves 'shorn into bits', are sometimes given to young turkeys. [Johnston, 1853: 163]

[In Horseheath, Cambridgeshire] the girls made WHISTLES too, but they used the stems of white nettles which were soft to cut. It was easy to make the mouthpiece by cutting off a stem slantwise and shaving a flat on top and it was not hard to make the vent. Never the less, many attempts had to be made before an instrument was produced that would whistle. [Parsons MSS, 1952]

As a child I remember sucking the flowers of the white dead-nettle to extract the nectar. [Little Barford, Bedfordshire, March 1993]

We sucked the nectar from the flowers of the white nettle. [Maulden, Bedfordshire, April 1993]

White flowers. Many white flowers, such as COW PARSLEY, HAW-THORN, LILY, and SNOWDROPS are considered to be inauspicious when taken indoors. Some people extend this belief to include all white flowers.

People dislike having white flowers in the house. In Long Compton [Warwickshire] some people would not enter a church which had been decorated with white flowers.

It is bad luck if the first flowers of the year to be brought into the house are white. Some say that white flowers portend death. [Wharton MSS, 1974: 34]

My 73-year-old mother from Rothes in Morayshire reports the following plants as strictly forbidden in the house: Any white flowers on their own, especially SNOWDROPS, BLACKTHORN, MAY blossoms, CHRYSANTHEMUMS— these were associated with funerals and therefore death.

Associated with this was the refusal ever to put RED AND WHITE FLOWERS on their own in a vase. They could only be associated in a mixed display. [Stanton-on-the-Wolds, Nottinghamshire, January 1983]

When I was a child (in rural Norfolk) any white flowers were known as 'funeral flowers', and we were not allowed to bring them indoors. [Islington, London, May 1984]

My mother would never allow any white flowers into the the house. I gathered a bunch of white blossoms once; she was very apologetic, but very firm, she wouldn't let me bring it into the house. [Radnage, Buckinghamshire, July 1990]

White heather. The idea that white heather is 'lucky' appears to be a Highland belief which was more widely popularized by Queen Victoria. On 29 September 1855 the Queen recorded:

> Our dear Victoria was this day engaged to Prince Frederick William of Prussia . . . during our ride up Craig-na-Ban this afternoon he picked a piece of white heather, (the emblem of 'good luck'), which he gave to her; this enabled him to make an allusion to his hopes and wishes. [Victoria, 1868: 154]

In 1862, when Queen Victoria met Princess Alexandra of Denmark, the future wife of the Prince of Wales:

> The Queen's heart warmed towards the exquisite creature . . . She spoke kindly to her and presented her with a sprig of white heather picked by the Prince at Balmoral, saying she hoped it would bring her luck. [Battiscombe, 1969: 36]

When out for a drive on 9 September 1872, her servant Brown:

> espied a piece of white heather, and jumped off to pick it. No Highlander would pass by it without picking it, for it was considered to bring good luck. [Victoria, 1884: 197]

Other Victorian references to white heather include those 'in connection with the weddings of Princess Helena on April 28, 1882, Princess Beatrice on July 22, 1885 and Princess Mary on July 8, 1893, when white heather was included in the bouquets of the bride or bridesmaids' [McClintock, 1970: 159].

The reasons why white heather should be considered lucky are vague and varied. It has been suggested that it is lucky because, unlike plants which produce normal coloured flowers, it escaped from being stained by blood which was spilt on ancient battlefields [Waring, 1978: 118].

> I have been told that the belief [that white heather is lucky] dates back to Mary, Queen of Scots or, inevitably, to Prince Charles, the Young Pretender. But not a shred of evidence have I been able to find in support. White heather is the badge of certain clans, but hardly a convenient one to produce for a posse of men at any time of the year. One of them is the Clan Macpherson, because of a story in post-Culloden times of Cluny, who attributed his escape on one occasion from searchers to the fact that he had been sleeping on a clump of white heather . . . There is a similar story of the Clan Ranald, which dates back to 1544, when a battle was said to have been won because the MacDonalds stuck white heather in their bonnets. [McClintock, 1970: 159]

There are occasional records of white heather being considered unlucky.

My grandfather (a Scottish Royalist) always said that white heather was unlucky because of its connection with the banishment of Bonny Prince Charles. [Towcester, Northamptonshire, August 1982]

However, such beliefs are rare, for white heather, and objects depicting it, are widely sold in Scottish gift shops, and, in London, by gypsy hawkers, who often use dried white statice as a substitute. The gypsy women who sell heather tend to be vague and unimaginative when asked what sort of good luck it is supposed to convey: 'makes your hair grow' [Balham, London, February 1982].

Nowadays, white heather is an industry. There are white heather farms north and south. The heathers they grow differ: white heather is in demand on Burns' Night in January, when you will find none in flower on the moors. A tree heath, which originally came from Portugal, is grown commercially in the south-west because there it starts to flower before Christmas, and the trade is supplied from there. I have seen the same heather being hawked in London early in the year. Why people choose to grow this and not one of the superb hardy winter ones, I cannot say, but there it is. The normal white heather—the one that flowers in late summer—is commercially always ling—that is the one that gypsies sell. [McClintock, 1970: 159]

White lily – a Shetland name for white NARCISSUS.

White poplar (*Populus alba*)

I was told the reason why the poplar is always trembling [is] that the cross on which Our Lord was crucified was made of poplar, therefore it is always trembling with fear. [IFCSS MSS 750: 104, Co. Longford]

The [white poplar] tree may frequently be noticed turning up the white surface of its leaves during the huffling winds which we often experience in summer, and this is a pretty sure indication of approaching rain:
'I think there will be rain' a little girl was overheard to say 'for the WEATHER tree is showing its white lining.' [Johns, 1849: 357]

Cf. WHITEBEAM.

Whitethorn – see HAWTHORN.

White waterlily (*Nymphaea alba*). On the Inner Hebrides:

A black dye, for dyeing wool and yarn, is obtained from the large roots [of white waterlily] which are cut up and boiled. [McNeill, 1910: 97]

A native of Islay . . . referring to dyeing black with ruamalach [roots of white waterlily] says that when she had a little logwood at hand, she used it along with the ruamalach, and it improved the colour, but when she had no logwood, she just used ruamalach. [*Tocher* 36/37: 433, 1982]

Whitlow grass (*Erophila verna*)
Farmers used to use the flowering of whitlow grass as a sign to sow spring BARLEY. I found it growing in the steps to the lychgate of Woolhope Church, Herefordshire—how useful for checking every Sunday! [Mordiford, Hereford, December 1991]

Whitsun – churches decorated with BIRCH, RED AND WHITE FLOWERS.

Whitty pear – a Worcestershire name for SERVICE TREE.

Whitty-tree – a name for ROWAN.

Whooping cough – cured using shrew ASH, BRAMBLE, BROAD BEAN, CHIVES, CROW GARLIC, DOG ROSE moss galls, GARLIC, ONION, SWEDE, and wild THYME.

Whortleberry – see BILBERRY.

Widow's willow – a Sussex name for CRACK WILLOW.

Wiggle woggles – a Dorset name for QUAKING GRASS.

Wild asparagus – see STAR OF BETHLEHEM.

Wild cherry (*Prunus avium*)
[In the North Country] CHERRY blossom, in particular wild cherry—the gean flower—is an unlucky decoration for a wedding. The only time I heard this—dark mutterings behind handbags—the bridegroom turned out to be impotent. [Old Cleeve, Somerset, October 1993]

Wild garlic – see RAMSONS.

Wild gladiolus (*Gladiolus communis*). Originally planted by farmers on the Isles of Scilly to supply the cut-flower market, *Gladiolus communis* has been replaced as a commercial crop by more showy varieties of gladiolus, but it persists as a troublesome weed.
I have heard farmers refer to it as 'Jacks' and 'Rogues'. On St Martin's Geoffrey Grigson was told in 1940 that they call it 'Squeakers'. This no doubt has the same origin as 'Whistling Jacks' which Mr P.Z. MacKenzie tells me is the usual local name because the children use the leaves as reeds to WHISTLE. [Lousley, 1971: 276]

Wild liquorice – a north of England name for RESTHARROW.

Wild onion – see CROW GARLIC.

Wild pansy (*Viola* spp., especially *V. tricolor*)

[Fillongley, Warwickshire, for HEART TROUBLE:] Collect the heads of the wild pansy (called heart-ease), boil them, and drink a wine glass full of the infusion every morning. [Wharton MSS, 1974: 185]

Wild rhubarb – a name for JAPANESE KNOTWEED.

Wild service tree (*Sorbus torminalis*)

The fruit is well known in Sussex by the name of chequers. from its speckled appearance, and sold both there and in this island [of Wight], in the shops and public markets, tied up in bunches, principally to children. At Ryde they go under the name of sorbus berries, but are not much in request. [Bromfield, 1856: 166]

Some people squeeze or sieve the pulp out and eat only that, but the fruit is best consumed in its entirety . . . the taste is something like dried apricots or tamarinds and has been described as sharpish, softly mealy and agreeably acid, of an exceedingly pleasant acid flavour . . . English botanists writing in the late eighteenth and early nineteenth centuries, seem on the whole familiar with wild services as a dessert fruit and speak of it being widely on sale . . . The principal demand, especially in the nineteenth century, for the raw fruit appears to have come from children . . . My own father who lived as a boy on a farm on the edge of Epping Forest in Essex in the early years of this century has often recounted how all the rural children knew where wild services grew, although they were very scarce trees, and great enthusiasm and energy was displayed every autumn in obtaining the fruit which were known as sarves, sarvers, or sarvies. [Roper MSS]

It has been suggested the name Chequers which is sometimes given to inns in southern England derives from the wild service or chequer tree.

At the Chequers [Inn] in Smarden [in the Weald of Kent] there is a wild service growing in the rear courtyard and evidence to show that the inn was named after the tree is given in D.C. Maynard's *Old Inns of Kent* (1925): 'Mr Mills, a local archaeologist, who has lived in Smarden for over 84 years . . . informed me that the origin of the Chequers sign is not that generally accepted—the early form of ready reckoner—for he could well remember when he was a boy seeing the sign of the inn garlanded in the autumn of the year with the fruit of the chequer tree. [Roper MSS]

See also SERVICE TREE.

William III, King – associated with ORANGE LILY and SWEET WILLIAM.

Willow (*Salix* spp.). The use of willow as an emblem of grief probably originated in Psalm 137:

> By the rivers of Babylon we sat down and wept
> when we remembered Zion.
> There on the willow-trees
> we hung up our harps,
> for there those who carried us off
> demanded music and singing,
> and our captors called on us to be merry:
> 'Sing us one of the songs of Zion.'
> How could we sing the Lord's song
> in a foreign land?

Recent writers on Biblical plants have stressed that the trees mentioned by the psalmist were poplars rather than willows, but willow
continues to be associated with grief.

> The 'willows' on which the exiled Israelites hung their musical instru-
> ments grew beside the rivers of Babylon. These were the Euphrates pop-
> lar [*Populus euphratica*] and not the weeping willow (*Salix babylonica*), in
> spite of its epithet, since it is usually considered to have originated in
> China. [Hepper, 1980: 15]

In the sixteenth and seventeenth centuries willow became particularly
associated with the grief of forsaken lovers. In the folksong 'The Seeds
of Love', which is thought to have been written in the seventeenth
century [Grigson, 1987: 256], the forsaken lover laments

> For in June there's the red ROSE bud,
> And that is the flower for me;
> But I oftentimes have snatched at the red rose-bud
> And gained but the willow-tree.
>
> Oh the willow-tree will twist,
> And the willow-tree will twine,
> And I wish I were in that young man's arms,
> Where he once had the heart of mine.
>
> [Lloyd, 1967: 184]

The idea that a rejected lover should wear a wreath or hat of willow
persisted for several centuries.

> Willow caps were presented to all people who were disappointed in love.
> It is customary in the present day for villagers in Wales to ask a rejected
> suitor on the morning of his sweet-heart's marriage to another man,
> 'Where is your willow cap?' or 'We must make you a willow cap.' The
> same applies to a spinster whose lover discards her for another girl.
> [Trevelyan, 1909: 105]

In the nineteenth century weeping willow was commonly depicted
on gravestones and mourning cards.

Dioscorides, in his *De Materia Medica* written in AD 77, stated that a
decoction of leaves of the white willow was 'an excellent fomentation

for ye GOUT' [Gunther 1934: 75]. This decoction was also applied externally to ease such painful conditions as HEADACHE, TOOTHACHE, and EARACHE, and there are occasional records of willow twigs being chewed to alleviate pain.

> I am nearly 70 years of age and was born and bred in Norfolk . . . my father, if he had a 'skullache' as he called it, would often chew a new growth willow twig, like a cigarette in the mouth. [Two Locks, Gwent, March 1993]

In 1827 a French chemist isolated from MEADOWSWEET a chemical which was later found in the sap and bark of willows and given the name salicin. From this was derived salicylic acid, and eventually, at the end of the nineteenth century, acetylsalicylicacid, which is more commonly known as the analgesic aspirin [Stockwell, 1989: 67].

Children made young willow twigs into WHISTLES.

> After the small branches are cut to the proper form the bark is notched round with a knife, it is then beat on the knee with the knife haft, and the following lines are repeated:
>
> > Sip sap, sip sap,
> > Willie, Willie, Whitecap.
>
> [Morris, 1869: 79]

See also CRACK WILLOW and SALLOW.

Winter aconite (*Eranthis hyemalis*). When the six-year-old Dorothy L. Sayers moved to her new home at Bluntisham Rectory in the Fens, in January 1897:

> As the fly turned into the drive she cried out with astonishment, 'Look auntie, look! The ground is all yellow, like the sun.'
> This sudden splash of gold remained in her memory all her life. The ground was carpeted with early flowering aconites. Later her father told her the legend that these flowers grew in England only where ROMAN soldiers have shed their blood, and Bluntisham contains the outworks of a Roman camp. So as early as this and as young as she was, her imagination was caught by ancient Rome. [Hitchman, 1975: 22]

Witchen – a Worcestershire name for ROWAN (see under SERVICE TREE).

Witches – associated plants include BIRD CHERRY and FOXGLOVE; plants which deter them include BAY, BITING STONECROP, BUTTERWORT, CAPER SPURGE, ROSEMARY, ROWAN, SALLOW, and SERVICE TREE. ELDER is considered to be both a 'witch tree' and a tree which deters witches.

Witches' butter (*Exidia truncata*, syn. *E. glandulosa*). The jelly fungus witches' butter appears on dead branches of deciduous trees and is dark brown when young but soon turns black. In Wales:

> A pin thrust into Witch's Butter could cause the witch to undo her work. Witch's Butter is the name given to a kind of fungus . . . [which] resembles little lumps of butter, hence its name. Should anyone think himself witched, all that he has got to do is procure Witch's Butter, and then thrust a pin into it. It was thought that this pin penetrated the wicked witch, and every pin thrust into the fungus went into her body, and thus she was forced to appear, and undo her mischief, and be herself relieved from bodily pain by relieving others. [Owen, 1896: 249]

> Some 40 years ago, a resident of Llanafan [Dyfed] one morning discovered the shafts of a new waggon he had just bought besmeared with what a workman declared to be 'witch's butter'. He scraped off the substance with an axe and burnt it. The belief was that when the substance was being burnt, the witch would appear. An old man, of inoffensive character, happened to call, and the family believed him to have tried to bewitch the new waggon. [Jones, 1930: 128]

> Another witch to suffer because witches' butter had been tampered with . . . was Gwenllian David of Llangadog, Dyfed. At the Court of Great Sessions held on 16 June 1656 in Carmarthen she was accused of witchcraft. In her testimony one Margaret Rogers swore that 'there was a kind of matter or substance pitched upon the door post of the house of Thomas John her husband' which she later referred to as witches' butter. Subsequently, one of her neighbours took a knife, placed it in the fire until red hot, and then forced it through the fungus and into the wood. The knife remained there for a fortnight during which time Gwenllian David 'lay sicke and cryed to take the knife out of her backe'. Once this request was complied with Gwenllian was immediately relieved of her pain. [Gruffydd, 1985: 64]

Witches' thimbles – a North Country name for FOXGLOVE.

Witten pear – a Worcestershire name for SERVICE TREE.

Wood

> BEECHWOOD fires are bright and clear,
> If the logs are kept a year;
> CHESTNUT only good they say,
> If for long it's laid away;
> Make a fire of ELDER tree,
> Death within your house shall be;
> But ASH new or ash old
> Is fit for Queen with crown of gold.
> BIRCH and FIR logs burn too fast,

Blaze up bright and do not last;
ELMWood burns like churchyard mould—
E'en the very flames are cold;
    But Ash green or Ash brown
    Is fit for Queen with golden crown.
POPLAR gives a bitter smoke,
Fills your eyes and makes you choke;
APPLE wood will scent your room
With an incense-like perfume.
OAKen logs, if dry and old,
Keep away the winter's cold;
    But Ash wet or Ash dry
    A King shall warm his slippers by.

[Letter from Five Ashes, Sussex, in *The Times*, 1 March 1929]

When something is said which tempts misfortune it is customary to touch wood.

'Touching wood' is too persistent to warrant localizing. I remember during the last war when Mr Asquith was speaking on the then insignificant loss of life, the First Lord of the Admiralty, then A.J. Balfour, leant forward and gravely touched the clerk's table, to the amusement of his colleagues who noticed the mystic rite. We see it performed daily. [Heather, 1943: 344]

R: 'How's your husband now?'
A: 'Oh, he's getting along; the trouble is getting him to eat anything . . . I don't know if it's the pills they're giving him or what, but he's a lot better than he was, touch wood and whistle.'
A reached out and touched the wooden edge of her work bench, but made no attempt to whistle. [South Kensington, London, July 1987]

I remember how superstitious people were during the last war; you were for ever touching wood, hoping things would turn out. [Northampton, January 1991]

Sussex children rub BRUISES, etc. on wood to speed healing:
    Rub it on wood
    Sure to come good.
        [Worcester Park, Surrey, February 1978]

In Yorkshire:
If the palm of either hand itches—'rub it on wood it's sure to be good.'
    If it's the right hand, it means that you'll be paying money, but the left hand is for receiving. [SLF MSS, Sheffield, September 1972]

Wood anemone (*Anemone nemorosa*)

One of my earliest recollections of Staffordshire is the wood anemone, which grows in very great profusion round Stanton. The natives gave it the name of thunderbolt, and explained to me very carefully that I must on no account pluck it, if I did, it would certainly bring on a THUNDERSTORM, and without a doubt I would be struck . . . By chance one day I went to an outlying farm, where unkown to me a wedding feast was in progress. The door was opened by someone with a very smiling face, which suddenly changed to a face with alarm written on it, because I had a wood anemone in my buttonhole! I was the bringer of bad luck to the wedding. [Deacon, 1930: 26]

Wood avens (*Geum urbanum*)

The crushed root is used [by gypsies] as a cure for DIARRHOEA, and a little in boiling water relieves sore throats. [Vesey-FitzGerald, 1944: 22]

Wood rush (*Luzula campestris*), known as chimney-sweeps or chimney-sweepers in Cheshire and Lancashire in the nineteenth century.

When Cheshire children first see this plant in spring they repeat the following rhyme, possibly to bring them good luck:

Chimney-sweeper, all in black,
Go to the brook and wash your back;
Wash it clean, or wash it none;
Chimney-sweeper, have you done.

[Britten and Holland, 1886: 102]

Wood sage (*Teucrium scorodonia*)

In the island of Jersey the inhabitants use it in brewing instead of hops. [Lightfoot, 1777: 303]

Around Dursley neighbourhoood [Gloucestershire] the leaves are gathered in spring by country folk, dried and stored to make an infusion which is drunk like tea as a cure for RHEUMATISM. [Riddelsdell et al., 1948: 398]

An old lady recently deceased cured two cases of St Vitus' dance with a brew of wood sage, after doctors had given them up. About 1930ish. [Gronant, Clwyd, April 1994]

Wood sorrel (*Oxalis acetosella*)

In the Basingstoke area of Hampshire children used to eat buds of HAWTHORN, known as BREAD AND CHEESE, also leaves of wood sorrel. [Maida Hill, London, March 1978]

In west Dorset during the 1950s wood sorrel was known as BREAD AND CHEESE PLANT, and its flowers were eaten by children. [Streatham, London, March 1986]

Other names which relate to the use of wood sorrel as a food include cuckoo's bread and cheese in Radnorshire, egg and cheese in Sussex, and sookie sooricks in Morayshire.

In the island of Arran I was informed that a whey or tea of it was used in putrid and other fevers, with good success. [Lightfoot, 1777: 238]

James Bicheno (1831) identified wood sorrel as the true SHAMROCK, while Lady Wilkinson [1858: 54] claimed:

[The name alleluja was given to wood sorrel because of] the veneration formerly paid to the plant for even among the Druids, it was an emblem of the mysterious Three in One, which they claimed as their own peculiar secret, and endeavoured to illustrate in every possible particular of their worship. And their reverence for the plant was doubtless increased by the fact that each leaflet of the trifid leaf, is marked by a pale crescent, the emblem of the moon, and another of their sacred symbols.

Worms – see VERMICIDES.

Wormwood (*Artemisia absinthium*)

I was brought up in Anglesey . . . wormwood grew in abundance . . . boiling water poured on and then drunk as a tonic and to give one an appetite after illness. [Bangor, Gwynedd, March 1993]

Wormwood was used for an infusion to deal with threadWORMS, or where this was suspected, i.e. if the patient was scratching the rear end or squirming about instead of sitting good and quiet, as was expected of my generation. [Gronant, Clwyd, April 1994]

According to John Ray (1627–1705):

Those who go through the countryside . . . and by chance come upon a nasty tasting beer can improve and render it more pleasant to the palate and digestion by adding an infusion of wormwood. For the bitterness removes acidity even better than sugar. [Ewen and Prime, 1975: 37]

Y

Yallowin' girse – a Shetland name for AMPHIBIOUS BISTORT.

Yarrow (*Achillea millefolium*). In common with other white flowers, such as COW PARSLEY and HAWTHORN, yarrow flowers were sometimes considered to be inauspicious when picked and taken indoors.

> Yarrow—known as MOTHER-DIE or Fever-plant: unlucky to pick or bring into house, it is thought to cause sickness. [Driffield, Humberside, March 1985]

Yarrow was widely used in love DIVINATION.

> [Co. Donegal:] On May Eve the boys and girls cut a square sod in which grows yarrow . . . and put it under their pillow, if they have not spoken between the time of cutting the sod and going to sleep they will dream of their sweetheart. The sod ought to be of a certain size, but what the size should be seems uncertain. This custom is said to have been introduced into the country by the Scotch settlers. [Kinahan, 1884: 90]

> [South Devon:] If a maiden wants to know who her be going to marry, her must go to the churchyard at midnight, and pluck a bit o' yarra off the grave of a young man. I knawed a woman what did it, and her told us all about it, when us was maidens. Her went up to the churchyard and her found a bit o' yarra on a young man's grave, and as the church clock struck twelve her picked 'un and as her picked 'un her saith:

> > Yarra, yarra, I seeks thee yarra,
> > And now I have thee found.
> > I prays to the gude Lord Jesus
> > As I plucked 'ee from the ground.

> Then, her said, her took 'un home, and when her got to bed her put the yarra in her right stocking, and tied 'un to her left leg, and her got into bed backwards, and as her got he saith:

> > Good night to thee yarra
> > Good night to thee yarra
> > Good night to thee yarra.

> And again three times:

> > Gude night, purty yarra,
> > I pray thee sweet yarra,
> > Tell me by the marra
> > Who shall me true love be.

> Then my old friend said to me in rather awed tones: 'He come to her in the night, and he saith, 'I be thee own true love Jan.' And first her

married Jan Scoble, and then her married Jan Wakeham. [Morris, 1925: 306]

According to my 86-year-old aunt, girls used to go out on moonlit nights into a field of yarrow and, with their eyes closed, pick some yarrow. If this remained wet in the morning it meant that their boyfriends would soon start taking an interest in them. [Histon, Cambridgeshire, January 1989]

On May Eve a girl should look for the yarrow plant. Nine leaves were taken off and the following verse was to be said:

> Yarrow for yarrow, if yarrow you be
> By this time tomorrow
> My true love to see
> The colour of his hair
> The clothes he does wear
> The first words he will speak
> When he comes to court me.

The leaves should then be put under a pillow and the girl was supposed to dream of a future husband. [Belfast, February 1991]

A girl who had a lover could use yarrow to find out if he was faithful.

In Suffolk . . . a leaf is placed in the nose, with the intention of making it bleed, while the following lines are recited:

> Green 'arrow, green 'arrow, you wears a white blow,
> If my love love me, my nose will bleed now;
> If my love don't love me, it on't bleed a drop;
> If my love do love me, 'twill bleed every drop.
>
> [Britten, 1878: 156]

Yarrow was used to stop BLEEDING, and particularly NOSE-BLEEDS, or to provoke nose-bleeds.

[In south Lincolnshire]—Nosebleeding, to stop this smell the flower of the yarrow; called locally 'Nosebleed'. [Rudkin, 1936: 26]

I have learned, living in south Scotland, that yarrow was used for nose-bleed, but in the north a handkerchief dipped in cold water and placed over the bridge of the nose was the usual cure. [Edinburgh, October 1991]

The common people in order to cure the HEADACHE, do sometimes thrust a leaf of it up their nostrils, to make their nose bleed; an old practice which gave rise to one of its English names [nosebleed]. [Lightfoot, 1777: 497]

The local [Jersey] name [*d'la tcherpentchiethe*] means carpenter's herb and . . . a well known chemist for many years said that if a carpenter cut himself he would apply this plant to the wound to staunch bleeding. [Le Sueur, 1984: 157]

[My grandparents, b. 1856 and 1858] put yarrow in boiling water and then over the nose for nosebleed. [Cinderford, Gloucestershire, November 1993].

Infusions of yarrow were used to treat a wide range of ailments.

> They found a great cure in yarrow for consumptive people. First of all they pulled it and cut it into small little bits Then they boiled it in a saucepan and then they used to drink the juice and it cured that severe ailment. [IFCSS MSS 112: 48, Co. Mayo]

> For BRONCHITIS: take the flowers of the yarrow, stew and drink when strained. [Taylor MSS, Great Yarmouth, Norfolk]

> In the late summer mother would send us out into the local pastures to gather stalks and flower heads of yarrow. These would be wrapped in newspaper, tied with string, and put outside (under cover) to dry throughly. Then in the winter days when colds, flu and COUGHS were threatening, the yarrow would be broken down, put into a jug and infused with boiling water and left on the hob to keep warm. It would be served up as a medicine to all the family as required—a noxious brew, but it put paid to all colds, etc. Mum said it was the quinine in the yarrow which effected the cure, but I have my doubts. [Halesowen, West Midlands, October 1990]

> I can remember quite distinctly looking for a yarrow plant which my grandmother infused on the hob of our old fashioned range, back in the 1930s—her cure for aches and pains. [Bettws, Gwent, February 1991]

> I was told my an old Scillonian that yarrow was picked and hung in the kitchen to dry . . . During the winter it would be used—the dried leaves boiled up and the resultant liquid used as a cow drench for cattle with stomach problems. [St Mary's, Isles of Scilly, September 1992]

Yellow bartsia (*Parentucellia viscosa*)

> In 1958 when on holiday in Cornwall, I did some botanical recording. I got a farmer's permission to examine his paddock, and he came and asked if I knew what made his cows SCOUR when in this field. He pointed to *Parentucellia viscosa* and said 'I thought it might be this; I don't know what you call 'e, but us call 'e arse-smart.' [Syston, Leicester, January 1991]

Yellow buttons – a name for TANSY.

Yellow corydalis (*Pseudofumaria lutea*).
In the Craven and Wharfedale areas of Yorkshire yellow corydalis was called Italian Weed, because it was 'said to follow the ROMANS' [Britten and Holland MSS].

Yellow horned poppy (*Glaucium flavum*)

> Horned poppy with a yellow flower, vulgarly called in Hampshire and Dorsetshire, Squatmore, or Bruseroot (as I was there informed) where they use it against BRUISES external and internal. [Newton, 1698: 263]

Yellow iris (*Iris pseudacorus*).

Another amusement of mine, long ago [1940s], was to make 'sailing boats' from, the leaves of *Iris pseudacorus*. A long leaf was selected and a small lengthwise slit made in the leaf perhaps about half-way along its length. The tip of the leaf was then bent up and over until its apex would be pushed a little way through the slit, thus forming a 'sail' and a 'keel' at the same time. The little boats were either sailed down a burn or released into the sea during an offshore wind. In the lightest of winds they covered small distances until they were lost from sight. We called them seggie boats. [Scalloway, Shetland, February 1994]

Yellow iris = seg, seggie floooer, dug's lug—it produces blue-grey and dark green DYE, and children use the leaves of the plant to make little sailing boats. It's also believed that anyone who bites a seg will develop an impediment of speech, such as a stammer. [Lerwick, Shetland, March 1994]

In Guernsey the wild yellow iris was formerly a favourite plant for strewing in front of a bride on her way to her wedding ceremony [MacCulloch, 1903: 101].

During the German Occupation of Jersey (1940–5) well-roasted seeds of yellow iris were used as a substitute for coffee [Le Sueur, 1984: 184].

In Arran, and some other of the Western isles, the roots are used to dye black; and in Jura they are boil'd with copperas to make ink. [Lightfoot, 1777: 86]

Yellow loosestrife (*Lysimachia vulgaris*)

[Gypsy remedy:] infusion of leaves cures DIARRHOEA. [Thompson, 1925: 162]

Yellow rattle (*Rhinanthus minor*)

[In Buckinghamshire called] locusts (pronounced locus) . . . locally supposed to have been the food of St John the Baptist. [Britten and Holland, 1886: 312]

When the yellow rattle is in flower hay is said to be ready for cutting. [Davey, 1909: 339]

Yellow root plant – a Co. Kerry name for IRISH SPURGE.

Yew (*Taxus baccata*). In Ireland yew is frequently used as palm on PALM SUNDAY, which to many Irish-speakers is known as *Domhnach an Iuir* (Yew Sunday) [Danaher, 1972: 68].

Yew tree branches are used in Catholic church ceremonies on Palm Sunday and afterwards distributed to the congregation. It may be worn and afterwards some is placed in the dwelling house and byres to bring good luck.

Yew tree is usually burned to make the ash for Ash Wednesday ceremonies. [Daingean, Co. Offaly, January 1985]

For Palm branches on Palm Sunday, pieces of the yew tree were used; it
grew near churchyards or where there was a landlord's estate. It used to
be collected, taken to church and distributed at Mass. It was always the
yew and people called it Palm. Some people liked to get a good branch as
they put some in the cow byre. We didn't put it in the out-buildings; we
put it at the side of a picture in the kitchen. Now people bring it to the
church and it is blessed there, this year it was outside in the grounds.
While I and some others still bring yew, others bring whatever tree or
shrub is handy, sometimes CYPRESS. [Lenamore, Co. Longford, May
1991]

After Mass on Palm Sunday palm is distributed around the rails. It is
brought home and a piece of it put up in each room of the dwelling house
and also the outhouses. This was done to bring a blessing on the inhabitants. [IFCSS MSS 1020: 290, Co. Cavan]

Although most parts of the yew tree are poisonous, there are occasional records of children eating the fleshy red aril which surrounds
the poisonous seed.

When I was yoong and went to schoole, divers of my schoole fellowes
and likewise myselfe did eate our fils of the berries of this tree . . . without
any hurt at all, and that not one time, but many times. [Gerard, 1597:
1188]

Some kids ate the red flesh of the yew berries despite the actual seeds
being noxious. [Dorchester, Dorset, February 1992]

[I am 88] as far as plant names are concerned the one that stands out is
snot-gobbles referring to the berries of the yew tree. Not a very elegant
name but truly descriptive of the berries I well remember tasting as a
child. [Maulden, Bedfordshire, April 1993]

[Wye, Kent, 1940s:] we knew that yew seeds were poisonous, but we
would eat, for its sweetness, the sticky red covering, which was known as
red snot. [Alton, Hampshire, June 1993]

The reason for yew trees being found in churchyards has long been a
matter of debate.

It was the custom to plant yew trees in churchyards, not only to provide
shade, but to provide wood for the bows. Every Sunday the bowmen
practised their shooting, and many church walls have deep indentations,
evidence that the 'yewmen' or yeomen, sharpened their arrows on the
sandstone walls. [Jeacock, 1982]

Yew trees were planted in graveyards as they thrived on corpses and were
then readily available to make excellent bows. [Chandler, 1992: 5].

Yew trees were planted in churchyards to prevent archers from procuring suitable branches for making bows and thus having good weapons to oppose the 'King's Men'. To cut a tree in a churchyard was a punishable offence! [Chandler, 1992: 5]

Yew-wood is used for making bows, and it was therefore necessary for each town to have a supply of yew trees. Before enclosure, a village's livestock would wander around unchecked . . . As yew trees are poisonous they had to be planted out of reach of the grazing animals, and so they were planted in the churchyard, which was the only area in the village which was fenced off. [Chandler, 1992: 5]

I was always given to believe that yews were planted round churches to discourage farmers from letting their cattle stray from common land to consecrated. [Chandler, 1992: 6]

In the country churches are usually surrounded by fields . . . yew berries are poisonous if eaten by cattle. Local farmers round the church and churchyard are therefore willing to keep church hedges and/or fences surrounding them in good repair . . . A cow broke into our churchyard on Christmas Day 20 years ago and died of eating berries from our ancient tree . . . the farmer concerned has kept our boundaries beautifully ever since! [Chandler, 1992: 6]

The Druids regarded the yew as sacred and planted it close to their temples. As the early Christians often built their churches on these consecrated sites, the association of yew trees in churchyards was perpetuated. [Label at the Royal Botanic Gardens, Kew, Surrey, October 1993]

A yew tree in the village churchyard at Coldwaltham, near Pulborough, West Sussex, has been confirmed to be one of the oldest trees in England . . . probably planted around 1,000 B.C. by Druids. [*The Times*, 19 August 1993]

Yew [was] planted in graveyards to ward off evil spirits. [Stoke, Devon, April 1993]. Yew wood is distinctly red and white, especially when the trunk is freshly cut. The heartwood is red, the sapwood is . . . white. The colours were used to symbolize the blood and body of Christ. [Chandler, 1992: 6]

At Fortingall, in Perthshire, stands an extremely ancient yew, which is stated to be 'incontestably the most ancient specimen of vegetation in Europe'. It is also claimed that as a baby 'Pontius Pilate had been suckled beneath the tree when his father was a legionary during an early Roman expedition' [Wilks, 1972: 101].

Local tradition has it that funeral processions passed through the arch made by the ancient tree. Today only a little of the shell of this ancient hulk remains, but some parts have regrown, and several newer trunks are standing in a circle with a vast hollow centre. [Milner, 1992: 82]

Young man's death

A yew tree at Congresbury, Avon, is associated with St Congar, who is believed to have been an eighth-century hermit.

> It is said that St Congar wished for a yew tree to provide shade; he planted his staff in the earth and on the following day it put forth leaves and grew into a wide-spreading tree. A portion of ancient yew in the churchyard is still known locally as St Congar's walking stick. [Church guide book, January 1992]

At Ambergate, Derbyshire:

> A gang of 18th century charcoal burners anticipated the current clamour for workplace creches by hollowing out the bough of a yew tree to make a cradle. Their tree . . . which inspired the nursery rhyme 'Rock-a-Bye-Baby,' is to be preserved. [*The Times*, 3 January 1991]

At Stoke Gabriel, Devon:

> The churchyard . . . has an imposing old yew, in good condition, with some fertility legends invested in it. For instance, if you are male, and walk backwards around it, or female and walk forwards, fertility is assured. Another superstition promises that wishes come true if you walk around the yew seven times. Certainly the area beneath the tree is weed free, possibly indicating the large numbers of the credulous regularly performing these rites. The tree is female, 45ft in height, 17ft in girth. [Wilks, 1972: 131].

Recently taxol, a chemical which occurs in yew, has been found to be effective against some types of CANCER.

> The autumnal pruning of yew trees in the grounds of a Hampshire church could aid cancer victims.
>
> Strange as it may sound, the clippings taken from 102 trees at St Mary's Church, in the village of Hook with Warsash, will be the basis for a new anti-cancer drug. [*Southern Evening Echo*, 15 October 1993].

> At Crathes Castle near Banchory, in Grampian, the great yew hedges, which date from 1702, have been given their annual trim . . . This year the clippings are being collected and sent to Germany to be used in cancer research. [*Daily Telegraph*, 23 October 1993]

Young man's death – a Perthshire name for BINDWEED.

Yucca (*Yucca* spp.) In the 1980s the yucca became a popular houseplant, and also became part of an urban legend of the 'dreadful contamination' type.

> This was told to us in good faith by one of our employees. A friend of a cousin had bought a yucca from Marks and Spencer. The plant, despite care, died.
>
> She returned it to Marks and Spencer in exchange for tokens. Marks and Spencer analysed the plant and found a dead male tarantula in the pot.

Two experts arrived at her house stating that where there was a dead male, there will be a female with offspring.

The search duly revealed the female and eight babies inside the duvet. Marks and Spencer replaced free of charge all the bed linen and also the bed, but insisted on a secrecy agreement, agreeing to no disclosure. [Poole, Dorset, April 1992]

BIBLIOGRAPHY

Published Sources

Addison, J. 1985. *The Illustrated Plant Lore*, London.
Aitken, J. 1944. *English Diaries of the XIX Century, 1800–1850*, Harmondsworth.
Akeroyd, J. 1990. Further comments on conkers, *BSBI News* 56: 20–1.
Albertus Magnus *see* Best, M.R. and Brightman, F.H.
Allen, D.E. 1980. A possible scent difference between *Crataegus* species, *Watsonia* 13: 119–20.
Amery, P.F.S. 1895. Thirteenth report of the Committee on Devonshire folk-lore, *Report and Transactions of the Devonshire Association for the Advancement of Science* 27: 61–74.
—— 1905. Twenty-second report of the Committee on Devonshire folk-lore, *Report and Transactions of the Devonshire Association for the Advancement of Science* 37: 111–21.
——1907. Twenty-fourth report of the Committee on folklore, *Report and Transactions of the Devonshire Association for the Advancement of Science* 39: 105–9.
Anon., 1520. *Here begynneth the Lyfe of Joseph of Armathia*, London.
Anon., 1916. Notes on Irish folklore, *Folk-lore* 27: 419–26.
—— 1967. *Royal Pageantry: Customs and Festivals of Great Britain and Northern Ireland*, Paulton.
—— [1977] *The Glastonbury Thorn* [pamphlet produced and sold in aid of the restoration of the church of St John the Baptist, Glastonbury].
—— [n.d.] *The Cathedral of Our Lady and St Philip Howard Arundel*, St Ives.
—— [n.d.] *A Guide to Glastonbury and its Abbey*, Glastonbury.
Arber, A. 1938. *Herbals*, 2nd ed., Cambridge [first published 1912; 3rd ed. with an introduction and annotations by W. T. Stearn, 1986]
Archer, F. 1990. *Country Sayings*, Stroud.
Armstrong, S. 1976. *A Croft in Clachan*, London.
Asberg, M. and Stearn, W.T. 1973. Linnaeus's Öland and Gotland journey 1741, *Biological Journal of the Linnean Society* 5: 1–107.
Asch, J. 1968. Botanical emblems of the nations, *Garden Journal* [New York Botanical Garden] 18: 55–7.
Atkins, E.A. 1986. *Tales from our Cornish Island*, London.
Attwater, D. 1970. *The Penguin Dictionary of Saints*, Harmondsworth.
Aubrey, J. 1847. *The Natural History of Wiltshire*, ed. J. Britton, London.
—— 1881. *Remaines of Gentilisme and Judaisme*, ed. J. Britten, London.

Bacon, F. 1631. *Sylva Sylvarum*, 3rd ed., London.
Baker, A.E. 1854. *Glossary of Northamptonshire Words and Phrases*, vol. 1, London.
Baker, M. 1974. *Discovering the Folklore Customs of Love and Marriage*, Princes Risborough.
—— 1975. *Discovering the Folklore of Plants*, Princes Risborough.
—— 1977. *Wedding Customs and Folklore*, Newton Abbot.
Banks, M.M. 1941. *British Calendar Customs: Scotland*, vol. 3, London.
Barrett, H. 1967. *Early to Rise*, London.
Barrington, J. 1984. *Red Sky at Night*, London.
Basford, K. 1978. *The Green Man*, Ipswich.
Batten, E.C. 1881. The holy thorn of Glastonbury, *Proceedings of the Somerset Archaeological and Natural History Society* 26(2): 118–25.

Battiscombe, G. 1969. *Queen Alexandra*, London.

Bean, J.W. 1914. *Trees and Shrubs hardy in the British Isles*, vol. 1, London.

Bennett, M. 1991. Plant lore in Gaelic Scotland, in R. J. Pankhurst and J. M. Mullin, *Flora of the Outer Hebrides*, London, pp. 56–60.

Bergamar, K. n.d. *Discovering Hill Figures*, Tring.

Best, M.R. and Brightman, F.H. (eds) 1973. *The Book of Secrets of Albertus Magnus*, Oxford.

Bett, H. 1952. *English Myths and Traditions*, London.

Bicheno, J.E. 1831. On the plant intended by the shamrock of Ireland, *Journal of the Royal Institution of Great Britain* 1: 453–8.

Biden, W.D. 1852. *The History and Antiquities of Kingston-upon-Thames*, Kingston.

Blamey, M. and Grey-Wilson, C. 1989. *The Illustrated Flora of Britain and Northern Europe*, London.

Bloom, J.H. 1920. Modern folklore of Warwickshire: cures, *Notes and Queries* 12 ser. 7: 245–6.

—— 1930, *Folk Lore, Old Customs and Superstitions in Shakespeare Land*, London.

Bloxham, C. and Picken, M. 1990. *Love and Marriage*, Exeter.

Boardman, J. and Scarisbrick, D. 1977. *The Ralph Harari Collection of Finger Rings*, London.

Boase, W. 1976. *The Folklore of Hampshire and the Isle of Wight*, London.

Bonnard, B. 1993. *Channel Island Plant Lore*, Guernsey.

Booth, C. 1861. *London Labour and the London Poor*, vol. 1, London.

Booth, E.M. 1980. *The Flora of County Carlow*, Dublin.

Boyes, G. 1991. Not quite blue: colour in the mock–obscene riddle, in J. Hutchings and J. Wood (eds), *Colour and Appearance in Folklore*, London. pp. 40–5.

Boys, W. 1792. *Collections for an History of Sandwich in Kent*, Canterbury.

Brand, J. 1701. *A Brief Description of Orkney, Zetland, Pightland-Firth and Caithness*, Edinburgh.

—— 1853. *Observations on the Antiquities of Great Britain*, revised by Sir H. Ellis, London.

Brentnall, M. 1975. *Old Customs and Ceremonies of London*, London.

Briggs, K.M. 1971. *A Dictionary of British folk-tales*, part B, vol. 2, London.

—— 1974. *The Folklore of the Cotswolds*, London.

—— 1976. *A Dictionary of Fairies*, London.

Briggs, K.M. and Tongue, R.L. (eds). 1965. *Folktales of England*, London.

Brightman, F.H. and Nicholson, B.E. 1966. *The Oxford Book of Flowerless Plants*, London.

Britten, J. 1869. Spring flowers, *Hardwicke's Science Gossip*: 122.

—— 1878. Plant-lore notes to Mrs Latham's West Sussex Superstitions, *Folk-lore Record* 1: 155–9.

—— 1881. *European Ferns*, London.

Britten, J. and Holland, R. [1878–]1886. *A Dictionary of English Plant-names*, London.

Bromfield, W.A. 1856. *Flora Vectensis*, London.

[Brontë, E.] 1847. *Wuthering Heights*, London.

Brown, T. 1951. Forty-eighth report on folk-lore, *Report and Transactions of the Devonshire Association for the Advancement of Science* 83: 73–8.

—— 1952. Forty-ninth report on folk-lore, *Report and Transactions of the Devonshire Association for the Advancement of Science* 84: 296–301.

—— 1953. Fiftieth report on folk-lore, *Report and Transactions of the Devonshire Association for the Advancement of Science* 85: 217–25.

—— 1955. Fifty-second report on folklore, *Report and Transactions of the Devonshire Association for the Advancement of Science* 87: 353–9.

—— 1959. Fifty-sixth report on folklore, *Report and Transactions of the Devonshire Association for the Advancement of Science* 91: 198–203.

—— 1971. 68th report on folklore, *Report and Transactions of the Devonshire Association for the Advancement of Science* 103: 265–71.

—— 1972. 69th report on folklore, *Report and Transactions of the Devonshire Association for the Advancement of Science* 104: 263–8.

Burdy, S. 1792. *Life of the Late Rev. Philip Skelton*, Dublin.

Burne, C.S. 1883. *Shropshire Folk-lore*, London.

C., E. 1951. Fragments of Oxfordshire plant-lore, *Oxford and District Folklore Society Annual Record* 3: 11–13.

Calderbank, D.A. 1984. *Canny Leek Growing*, Wimborne.

Cameron, J. 1883. *Gaelic Names of Plants*, Edinburgh.

Candlin, L.N. 1947. Plant lore of Sussex, *Sussex County Magazine* 21: 130–1.

Carew, R. 1602. *The Survey of Cornwall*, London.

Carmichael, A. 1900. *Carmina Gadelica*, vol. 1, Edinburgh.

—— 1928. *Carmina Gadelica*, vol. 2, Edinburgh.

—— 1941. *Carmina Gadelica*, vol. 4, Edinburgh.

Carre, F. 1975. *Folklore of Lytchett Matravers Dorset*, St Peter Port.

Cartland, B. 1971. *We Danced all Night*, London.

Challenger, F. 1955. Chemistry—the grand master key, *University of Leeds Review* 4(3): 264–72.

Chamberlain, E. 1990. *29 Inman Road*, London.

Chandler, J. 1992. Old men's fancies: the case of the churchyard yew. *FLS News* 15: 3–6.

—— 1993. The days of May, *FLS News* 17: 11–12.

Chapman, V.J. *Seaweeds and their Uses*, London.

Child, F.J. (ed.) 1889. *The English and Scottish Popular Ballads* vol. 3, Boston, Massachusetts.

Chope, P.R. 1926. Twenty-seventh report on Devonshire folk-lore, *Report and Transactions of the Devonshire Association for the Advancement of Science* 57: 107–31.

—— 1927. Twenty-eighth report on Devonshire folk- lore, *Report and Transactions of the Devonshire Association for the Advancement of Science* 59: 145–72.

—— 1929. Thirtieth report on Devonshire folk-lore, *Report and Transactions of the Devonshire Association for the Advancement of Science* 61: 125–31.

—— 1931. Thirty-first report on Devonshire folk-lore, *Report and Transactions of the Devonshire Association for the Advancement of Science* 63: 123–35.

—— 1932. Thirty-second report on Devonshire folk-lore, *Report and Transactions of the Devonshire Association for the Advancement of Science* 64: 153–68.

—— 1933. Thirty-third report on Devonshire folk- lore, *Report and Transactions of the Devonshire Association for the Advancement of Science* 65: 121–7.

—— 1934. Thirty-fourth report on Devonshire folk-lore, *Report and Transactions of the Devonshire Association for the Advancement of Science* 66: 73–91.

—— 1935. Thirty-fifth report on Devonshire folk-lore, *Report and Transactions of the Devonshire Association for the Advancement of Science* 67: 131–44.

—— 1938. Devonshire calendar customs. Part II. Fixed festivals. *Report and Transactions of the Devonshire Association for the Advancement of Science* 70: 341–404.

Christensen. K.I. 1992. Revision of *Crataegus* sect. *Crataegus* and Nothosection *Crataeguineae* (Rosaceae—Maloideae) in the Old World, *Systematic Botany Monographs* 35.

Christy, M. 1928. On the variability and instability of coloration in the flowers of the primrose (*Primula vulgaris*) and the cowslip (*P. veris*), *Vasculum* 14: 89–94.

Clapham, A.R., Tutin, T.G., and Warburg, E.F. 1962. *Flora of the British Isles*, 2nd ed., Cambridge.

Clark, R. 1882. Folk-lore collected in Co. Wexford. *Folk-lore Record* 5: 81–3.

Coles, W. 1656. *The Art of Simpling*, London.

—— 1657. *Adam in Eden*, London.

Colgan, N. 1892. The shamrock: an attempt to fix its species. *Irish Naturalist* 1: 95–7.

—— 1893. The shamrock: a further attempt to fix its species, *Irish Naturalist* 2: 207–11.

—— 1896. The shamrock in literature: a critical chronology, *Journal of the Royal Society of Antiquaries of Ireland* 26: 211–26 and 349–61.

Collinson, J. 1791. *History and Antiquities of the County of Somerset*, Bath.

Combermere, Mary, Viscountess, and Knollys, W.W. 1866. *Memoirs and Correspondence of Field Marshal Viscount Combermere*, vol. 2, London.

Conquer, L. 1970. Corn-dollies and 'trees', *Folklore* 81: 145–7.

Cooper, R.E. 1957. The sycamore tree, *Scottish Forestry* 11(4): 169–76.

Copper, B. 1971. *A Song for Every Season*, London.

Cornish, V. [1941]. *Historic Thorn Trees in the British Isles*, London.

Cotton, A.D. 1912. Clare Island Survey, no. 15: Marine algae, *Proceedings of the Royal Irish Academy*, sect. B, vol. 31.

Court, T. 1967. 'Urt' picking on Exmoor, *Exmoor Review* 1967: 42–3.

Cowan, J.L. 1902. Welsh superstitions, *Journal of American Folklore* 15: 131–2.

Culpeper, N. 1649. *The Physicall Directory*, London.

—— 1652. *The English Physician*, London.

Cunnington, P. and Lucas, C. 1972. *Costume for Births, Marriages and Deaths*, London.

Curwen, J.F. 1898. *Historical Description of Levens Hall*, Kendal.

Dacombe, M.R. (ed.). 1951. *Dorset Up Along and Down Along*, 3rd ed., Dorchester.

Dallas, D. 1971. *The Travelling People*, London.

Danaher, K. 1972. *The Year in Ireland*, Cork.

Darlington, A. and Hirons, M.J.D. 1975. *The Pocket Encyclopaedia of Plant Galls in Colour*, Poole.

Dartnell, G.E. and Goddard, E.H. 1894. *Wiltshire Words*, London.

Davey, F.H. 1909. *Flora of Cornwall*, Penryn.

Davies, A.S. 1949. *The 'Mheillea' and its Meaning*, Iver Heath.

Deacon, E. 1930. Some quaint customs and superstitions in north Staffordshire and elsewhere, *North Staffordshire Field Club Transactions and Annual Report* 64: 18–32.

Deane, T. and Shaw, T. 1975. *The Folklore of Cornwall*, London.

De Garis, M. 1975. *Folklore of Guernsey*, St Pierre du Bois.

Delgado, P. 1992. *Crop Circles: Conclusive Evidence?* London.

Delgado, P. and Andrews, C. 1989. *Circular Evidence*, London.

Denson, J. 1832. The thistle of Scotland, *Gardener's Magazine* 8: 335–6.

Dickson, J.H. and Walker A. 1981. What is the Scottish thistle? *Glasgow Naturalist* 20(2): 1–21.

Dinneen, P. 1927. *Irish-English Dictionary*, Dublin.

Dixon, D.D. 1890. Northumbrian plant names, *Nature Notes* 1: 110–11.

Donald, J. 1973. *Long Crendon: a Short History, part II, 1800–1914*, Long Crendon.

Dony, J.G. 1953. *Flora of Bedfordshire*, Luton.

Dony, J.G., Jury, S.L., and Perring, F. 1986, *English Names of Wild Flowers*, London.

Douglas, S. 1989. The hoodoo of the Hanging Tree, in G. Bennett and P. Smith (eds), *The Questing Beast* [Perspectives on Contemporary Legend, vol. 4], Sheffield, pp. 133–43.

Douie, D.L. and Farmer, H. 1962. *Magna Vita Sancti Hugonis*, London.

Drury, S.M. 1984. The use of wild plants as famine foods in eighteenth century Scotland and Ireland, in R. Vickery, (ed.) *Plant-lore Studies*, London, pp. 43–60.

Duncan, L.L. 1893. Folk-lore gleanings from County Leitrim, *Folk-lore* 4: 176–94.

—— 1896. Fairy beliefs and other folklore notes from County Leith, *Folk-lore* 7: 161–83.

Dunsford, M.E. 1978. 79th report on dialect, *Report and Transactions of the Devonshire Association for the Advancement of Science* 110: 208–09.

—— 1981. 23rd report of the Folklore Section, *Report and Transactions of the Devonshire Association for the Advancement of Science* 113: 173–6.

Dyer, T.F.Thiselton 1889. *The Folk-lore of Plants*, New York.

E. 1884. Oak and Nettle Day in Northamptonshire, *Folk-lore Journal* 2: 381–2.

Eachard, J. 1645. *Good Newes for all Christian Souldiers*, London.

Eastwood, J. [n.d.] *The Mole Race*, Burton Bradstock.

Eberley, S.S. 1989. A thorn among the lilies: the hawthorn in medieval love allegory, *Folklore* 100: 41–52.

Edmondson, J.R. 1994. Snuffed out for snuff: *Meum athamanticum* in the Roberts Leyland herbarium, *Naturalist* 119: 45–6.

Elliott, B. 1984. The Victorian Language of Flowers, in R. Vickery (ed.), *Plant-lore Studies*, London, pp. 61–5.

Emecheta, B. 1986. *Head above Water*, London.

[Emslie, J.P.] 1915. Scraps of folklore collected by John Philipps Emslie, *Folk-lore* 25: 153–70.

Evans, A.J. 1895. The Rollright Stones and their folklore, *Folk-lore* 6: 5–50.

Evans, E.E. and Laughlin, S.J. 1971. A County Tyrone tan yard, *Ulster Folklife*, 17: 85–7.

Evans, G.E. 1969. Aspects of oral tradition, *Folk Life* 7: 5–14.

—— 1971. *The Pattern under the Plough*, London.

Evans, J. 1800. *A Tour through Part of North Wales in the year 1798, and at other times*, London.

Evershed, H. 1877. The Cedars of Lebanon, *Gardeners' Chronicle* ns 7: 39–40.

Ewen, A.H. and De Carteret, A.R. 1974. The Guernsey Lily. *Reports and Transactions, La Société Guernésiaise* 19: 269–86.

Ewen, A.H. and Prime, C.T. 1975. *Ray's Flora of Cambridgeshire*, Hitchin.

Fairweather, B. [n.d.] *Highland Plant Lore*, Glencoe.

Ffennell, M.C. 1898. The shrew ash in Richmond Park, *Folk-lore* 9: 330–6.

Foley, W. 1974. *A Child in the Forest*, London.

Folkard, R. 1884. *Plant Lore, Legends and Lyrics*, London.

Forby, R. 1830. *The Vocabulary of East Anglia*, London.

Fosbroke, T.D. 1821. *Ariconesia, or Archaeological Sketches of Ross and Archenfield*, Ross.

Fowler, W.M.E. 1891. Superstitions regarding wild flowers in the Selborne country, *Nature Notes* 2: 193–4.

—— 1909. Yorkshire folklore, in T.M. Fallow (ed.), *Memorials of Old Yorkshire*, London, pp. 286–305.

Francis, A.A. 1988. In a strange land, in Anon., *More Bristol Voices*, Bristol, pp. 91–6.

Fraser, A.S. 1973. *The Hills of Home*, London.

Frazer, J.G. 1922. *The Golden Bough*, abridged edition, London.

Frazer, W. 1894. The Shamrock: its history, *Journal of the Royal Society of Antiquaries of Ireland* 24: 132–5.

Fried, A. and Elman, R.M. 1969. *Charles Booth's London*, London.

Friend, H. 1882. *A Glossary of Devonshire Plant-names*, London.

—— 1884. *Flowers and Flower Lore*, London.

Gailey, A. 1972. The last sheaf in Ireland, *Ulster Folklife* 18: 1–33.

Gamble, R. 1979. *Chelsea Child*, London.

Garrad, L.S. 1984. Some Manx plant-lore, in R. Vickery (ed.), *Plant-lore Studies*, London, pp. 75–83.

Gascoigne, M. 1969. *Discovering English Customs and Traditions*, Tring.

Gaskell, Elizabeth. 1848. *Mary Barton*, London.

Gerard, J. 1597. *The Herball, or Generall Historie of Plants*, London.

Gibbs, R. 1885. *A History of Aylesbury, with its Borough and Hundreds*, Aylesbury.

Gilmore, L. and Oalcz, C. 1993. *The History and Meaning of the Blackthorn in Ireland*, Belfast.

[Gloucester, Duchess of] 1983. *The Memoirs of Princess Alice, Duchess of Gloucester*, London.

Gmelch, G. and Kroup, B. 1978. *To Shorten the Road*, Dublin.

Gomme, A.B. 1894–8. *The Traditional Games of England, Scotland and Ireland*, 2 vols, London.

Gomme, G.L. (ed.). 1884. *The Gentleman's Magazine Library: Popular Superstitions*, London.

Goodrich-Freer, A. 1902. More folklore from the Hebrides, *Folk-lore* 13: 29–62.

Goody, J. 1993. *The Culture of Flowers*, Cambridge.

Gospelles of Dystaues, The, 1507, London.

Graves, R. 1948. *The White Goddess*, London.

Green, M. 1990. The rings of time: the symbolism of crop circles, in R. Noyes (ed.), *The Crop Circle Enigma*, Bath, pp. 137–71.

Gregor, W. 1874. *An Echo of the Olden Time*, London.

—— 1881. *Notes on the Folk-lore of the North-east of Scotland*, London.

—— 1884a. Some old farming customs and notions in Aberdeenshire, *Folk-lore Journal* 2: 329–32.

—— 1884b. Unspoken nettles, *Folk-lore Journal* 2: 377–8.

—— 1889. Some folk-lore on trees, animals and river-fishing from the north-east of Scotland, *Folk-lore Journal* 7: 41–4.

Grierson, S. 1986. *The Colour Caldron: the history and use of natural dyes in Scotland*, Tibbermore.

Grigson, G. 1975, 1987. *The Englishman's Flora*, London. [The history of this work, first published in 1955, is confusing; two editions have been used in the preparation of this dictionary: the Paladin edition of 1975 and the Phoenix House edition of 1987; the former includes material not in the latter.]

Gruffydd, E. 1985. Witches Butter in Wales. *Bulletin of the British Mycological Society* 19: 63–5.

Gunther, R.W.T. 1934. *The Greek Herbal of Dioscorides*, Oxford.

Guppy, H.P. 1917. *Plants, Seeds and Currents in the West Indies and the Azores*, London.

Gupta, S.M. 1971. *Plant Myths and Traditions in India*, Leiden.

Gutch, Eliza. 1901. *County Folk-lore*, vol. 2. *Printed extracts concerning the North Riding of Yorkshire, York and the Ainsty*, London.
—— 1912. *County Folk-lore*, vol. 6. *Printed extracts concerning the East Riding of Yorkshire*, London.
Guzmán, G. 1983. *The Genus Psilocybe*, Vaduz.
Gwyndaf, R. 1989. *Welsh Folk Tales*, Cardiff.

Hadfield, M. 1957. *British Trees: A Guide for Everyman*, London.
Halsband, R. (ed.) 1965. *The Complete Letters of Lady Mary Wortley Montagu*, vol. 1, Oxford.
Hardy, J. (ed.) 1892–5. *The Denham Tracts*, 2 vols, London.
Hardy, T. 1887. *The Woodlanders*, London.
Harley, L.S. 1988. *Polstead Church and Parish*, Hadleigh.
Harris, A. 1992. Gorse in the East Riding of Yorkshire, *Folk Life* 30: 17–29.
Hart, H.C. 1873. *Euphorbia hyberna, Equisetum trachypodon* &c. in Co. Galway, *Journal of Botany* 11: 338–9.
—— 1879. On the flora of north-western Donegal, *Journal of Botany* 17: 77–83, 106–14, 143–50.
Heanley, R.M. 1901. The Vikings: traces of their folk-lore in Marshland, *Saga book of the Viking Club* 3: 35–62.
Heather, P.J. 1940. Folk-lore Section, *Papers and Proceedings of the Hampshire Field Club and Archaeological Society* 14: 402–9.
—— 1941. Folk-lore Section, *Papers and Proceedings of the Hampshire Field Club and Archaeological Society* 15: 115–22.
—— 1943. Folk-lore Section, *Papers and Proceedings of the Hampshire Field Club and Archaeological Society* 15: 344–9.
Helm, A. 1981. *The English Mummers' Play*, Woodbridge.
Hemsley, W.B. 1892. A drift-seed (*Ipomoea tuberosa* L.), *Annals of Botany* 6: 369–72.
Henderson, G. 1856. *The Popular Rhymes, Sayings and Proverbs of the County of Berwick*, Newcastle-on-Tyne.
Hepper, F.N. 1980. *Bible Plants at Kew*, London.
Hersom, K. 1973. Games with flora, *Countryman* 78(3): 79–85.
Hewins, A. 1981. *The Dillen: Memories of a Man of Stratford upon Avon*, Oxford.
—— 1985. *Mary, after the Queen: Memories of a Working Girl*, Oxford.
Hillaby, J. 1983. *Journey through Britain*, London.
Hitchman, J. 1975. *Such a Strange Lady*, London.
Hodson, R. 1917. Notes on Staffordshire folklore, *Folk-lore* 28: 452.
Hoeg, O.A. 1941. Jonsokgras, *Plantago lanceolata, Kongelige Norske Videnskabernes Selskabs Forhandlinger* 13: 157–60.
Hole, C. 1937. *Traditions and Customs of Cheshire*, London.
—— 1950. *English Custom and Usage*, 3rd ed., London.
—— 1965. *Saints in Folklore*, London.
—— 1975. *English Traditional Customs*, London.
—— 1976. *British Folk Customs*, London.
—— 1977. Protective symbols in the home, in H.R.E. Davidson (ed.), *Symbols of Power*, Cambridge, pp. 121–30.
Holt, J.C. 1983. *Robin Hood*, London.
Hone, W. [n.d.] *The Everyday Book*, vol. 2, London.
Horwood, A.R. 1921. *A New British Flora*, London.
Howell, J. 1640. *Dodona's Grove*, London.
Howse, W.H. 1949. *Radnorshire*, London.

Hults, D.S. 1987. A Derbyshire custom in transition? Well dressing in Perth, Western Australia, *Australian Folklore* 1: 25–43.
Hunt, R. 1881. *Popular Romances of the West of England*, London.

Jackson, T. 1873. *Recollections of my own Life and Times*, London.
James, E.O. 1961. *Seasonal Feasts and Festivals*, London.
Jeacock, R. 1982. *Plants and Trees in Legend, Fact and Fiction*, Chester.
Jewell, C.H. [n.d.] *The Crying of the Neck*, place of publication not stated.
Johns, C.A. [1847], 1849. *Forest Trees of Britain*, London.
Johnston, G. 1853. *The Botany of the Eastern Borders*, London.
Jones, A.E. 1980. Folk medicine in living memory in Wales, *Folk Life* 18: 58–68.
Jones, B.H. 1908. Irish folklore from Cavan, Meath, Kerry and Limerick. *Folk-lore* 19: 315–23.
Jones, L. 1980. *Schoolin's Log*, London.
Jones, T.G. 1930. *Welsh Folklore and Folk-custom* London.
Jones-Baker, D. 1977. *The Folklore of Hertfordshire*, London.
Judge, R. 1978. *The Jack in the Green*, Cambridge.

Karpeles, M. 1987. *The Crystal Spring*, Oxford.
K'Eogh, J. 1735. *Botanalogia Universalis Hibernica*, Cork.
Keyte, H. and Parrott, A. 1992. *The New Oxford Book of Carols*, Oxford.
Killip, M. 1975. *The Folklore of the Isle of Man*, London.
Kilvert, F. *Diary see* Plomer, W. (ed.).
Kinahan, G.H. 1881. Notes on Irish folk-lore, *Folk-lore Record* 4: 96–125.
―― 1884. Co. Donegal, May Eve, *Folk-lore Journal* 2: 90–1.
―― 1888. Irish plant-lore notes, *Folk-lore Journal* 6: 265–7.
King, R.J. 1877. Second report of the Committee on Devonshire folklore, *Report and Transactions of the Devonshire Association for the Advancement of Science* 9: 88–102.
Kitchen, P. 1990. *For Home and Country*, London.
Knight, W.F.G. 1945. Forty-second report on Devonshire folk-lore, *Report and Transactions of the Devonshire Association for the Advancement of Science* 77: 93–7.
―― 1947. Forty-fourth report on folk-lore, *Report and Transactions of the Devonshire Association for the Advancement of Science* 79: 47–9.

Lafonte, A.M. 1984. *Herbal Folklore*, Bideford.
Lake, C. [n.d.] *The Battle of Flowers Story*, St John.
Lambeth, M. 1969. *A Golden Dolly: The Art, Mystery and History of Corn Dollies*, London.
―― 1977. *Discovering Corn Dollies*, Princes Risborough.
Latham, C. 1878. Some west Sussex superstitions lingering in 1868, *Folk-lore Record* 1: 1–67.
Laver, F.J. 1990. 91st report on dialect, *Report and Transactions of the Devonshire Association for the Advancement of Science* 122: 233–8.
Laycock, C.H. 1940. Thirty-ninth report on Devonshire folk-lore, *Report and Transactions of the Devonshire Association for the Advancement of Science* 72: 115–16.
Leather, E.M. 1912. *The Folk-lore of Herefordshire*, Hereford.
Lee, H. 1887. *The Vegetable Lamb of Tartary*, London.
Lees, E. 1856. *Pictures of Nature around the Malvern Hills*, Malvern.
Lees, F.A. 1888. *The Flora of West Yorkshire*, London.
Legg, P. 1986. *So Merry let us be—the Living Tradition of Somerset Cider*, Taunton.
Lester, G. 1972. *Castleton Garland*, Sheffield.

Le Sueur, F. 1984. *Flora of Jersey*, Jersey.

Lightfoot, J. 1777. *Flora Scotica*, London.

Lindegaard, P. 1978. The colliers' tale—a Bristol incident of 1753, *Journal of the Bath and Avon Family History Society* Spring 1978: 8.

Linnard, W., trans. and ed. 1985. *An Autumn in Wales (1856)*, Cowbridge.

Linton, E.F. 1908. Notes on the Dorset flora, *Proceedings of the Dorset Natural History and Antiquarian Field Club* 29: 14–29.

Lloyd, A.L. 1967. *Folk Song in England*, London.

Lloyd, B. 1945. Notes on Pembrokeshire folklore, superstitions, dialect words, etc. *Folk-lore* 56: 307–20.

[Lloyd George, D.] 1938. *War Memoirs of David Lloyd George*, London.

L'Obel, M. de. 1570. *Stirpium adversaria nova*, London.

Loftus, B. 1994. *Mirrors: Orange and Green*, Dundrum.

Logan, P. 1965. Folk medicine in the Cavan-Leitrim area, II, *Ulster Folklife* 11: 51–3.

Lomax, A. and Kennedy, P. 1961. Notes to accompany the record *Songs of Ceremony* (Folk Songs of Britain, 8), London.

Lousley, J.E. 1971. *Flora of the Isles of Scilly*, Newton Abbot.

Lovett, E. 1913. Folk-medicine in London, *Folk-lore* 24: 120–1.

Lownes, A.E. 1940. The strange case of Coles vs. Culpeper, *Journal of the New York Botanical Garden*, 41: 158–66.

Lucas, A.T. 1960. *Furze: A Survey and History of its Uses in Ireland*, Dublin.

—— 1963. The sacred trees of Ireland, *Journal of the Cork Historical and Archaeological Society* 68: 16–54.

—— 1979. Furze: a survey and history of its uses in Ireland, *Bealoideas* 45–47: 30–45.

Mabberley, D. 1987. *The Plant-Book*, Cambridge.

Mabey, R. 1972. *Food for Free*, London.

McBride, D. 1991. *What they did with Plants*, Banbridge.

McClintock, D. 1970. Why is white heather lucky?, *Country Life*, 15 January: 159.

—— 1975. *The Wild Flowers of Guernsey*, London.

—— 1987. *Supplement to 'The Wild Flowers of Guernsey' (Collins 1975)*, St Peter Port.

MacCulloch, E. 1903. *Guernsey Folk Lore*, London.

Mac Manus, D. 1973. *The Middle Kingdom: The Faery World of Ireland*, Gerrards Cross.

Macmillan, A.S. 1922. *Popular Names of Flowers, Fruits, etc.*, Yeovil.

MacNamara, S. 1987. *The Knock Mary Garden*, Knock.

MacNeil, M. 1962. *The Festival of Lughnasa*, Oxford.

McNeill, M. 1910. *Colonsay*, Edinburgh.

McNicholas, E. 1992. The four-leafed shamrock and the cock, *ARV* 47: 209–16.

MacNicholas, E., O Dulaing, D., and Ross, M. 1990. The legend of the four-leaved shamrock and the cock, *Sinsear* 6: 83–90.

Malone, F.E., Kennedy, S., Reilly, G.A.C., and Woods, F.M. 1992. Bog asphodel (*Narthecium ossifragum*) poisoning in cattle, *Veterinary Record*, 1 August 1992: 100–3.

Maloney, B. 1972. Traditional herbal cures in County Cavan: part 1, *Ulster Folklife*, 18: 66–79.

Mandeville, J. 1964. *The Travels of Sir John Mandeville*, New York.

Maple, E. 1971. *Superstition and the Superstitious*, London.

Marquand, E.D. 1906. The Guernsey dialect and its plant names, *Transactions of the Guernsey Society of Natural Science and Local Studies* 5: 31–47.

Marson, C. 1904. Preface to A.A. Hilton, *In the Garden of God*, London.

Martin, M. 1703. *Description of the Western Islands of Scotland*, London.

Martin, W.K. 1976. *The Concise British Flora in Colour*, 3rd ed., London.
Marwick, E. 1975. *The Folklore of Orkney and Shetland*, London.
Mayhew, H. 1861. *London Labour and the London Poor*, vol. 1, London.
Meade-Waldo, Mrs. 1902. Tissington well-dressing, *Journal of the Derbyshire Archaeological and Natural History Society* 24: 1–4.
Melton, J. 1620. *Astrologaster, or the Figure-Caster*, London.
Merlin, M. 1989. The traditional geographical range and ethnobotanical diversity of *Cordyline fruticosa* (L.) Chevalier, *Ethnobotany* 1: 25–39.
Miles, C.A. 1912. *Christmas in Ritual and Tradition, Christian and Pagan*, London.
Miller, H. 1858. *The Cruise of the Betsey*, London.
Milner, J.E. 1992. *The Tree Book*, London.
Mitchell, M.E. and Guiry, M.D. 1983. Carrageen: a local habitation or a name? *Journal of Ethnopharmacology* 9: 347–51
Mitchison, N. 1973. A harvest experience, *Folklore* 84: 252–3.
Moloney, M.F. 1919. *Irish Ethnobotany*, Dublin.
Montagu, Lady Mary Wortley. *Letters see* Halsband, R. (ed.).
Moore, G.F. 1968. 71st report on dialect. *Report and Transactions of the Devonshire Association for the Advancement of Science* 100: 367–71.
Morris, J.P. 1869. *A Glossary of Words and Phrases of Furness (North Lancashire)*, London.
Morris, R.E. 1925. Some old-time superstitions of Devon, *Report and Transactions of the Devonshire Association for the Advancement of Science*, 56: 305–8.
Murphy, D. 1965. *Full Tilt—from Ireland to India by Bicycle*, London.

Naylor, P. 1991. *Discovering Dowsing and Divining*, Princes Risborough.
Nelson, E.C. 1978. Tropical drift fruits and seeds on the coasts of the British Isles and Western Europe, I. Irish beaches. *Watsonia* 12: 103–12.
—— 1990. Shamrock 1988, *Ulster Folklife* 36: 32–42.
—— 1991. *Shamrock: Botany and History of an Irish Myth*, Aberystwyth.
Nelson, E.C. and McCracken, E.M. 1987. *The Brightest Jewell: A History of the National Botanic Gardens, Glasnevin, Dublin*, Kilkenny.
Newall, V. 1971. *An Egg at Easter*, London.
Newton, J. 1698. An account of some effects of *Papaver Corniculatum luteum*, etc., *Philosophical Transactions of the Royal Society* 20: 263–4.
Newton, L. 1951. *Seaweed Utilisation*, London.
Nicholson, C. 1861. *The Annals of Kendal*, 2nd ed., London.
Nixon, D.B. 1977. *Walk Soft in the Fold*, London.
Noall, C. 1977. *The Cornish Midsummer Eve Bonfire Celebrations*, Penzance.
Noble, R.R. 1975. An end to 'wrecking': the decline of the use of seaweed as a manure on Ayrshire coastal farms, *Folk Life* 13: 80–3.
Norman, F. 1969. *Banana Boy*, London.
Noyes, R. (ed.). 1990. *The Crop Circle Enigma*, Bath.

Ó'Ceirin, C. and K. 1980. *Wild and Free*, London.
Ó Danachair, C. 1970. The luck of the house, *Ulster Folklife* 15/16: 20–7.
Ogden, J. 1978. Marbles and conkers, *Lore and Language* 2(9): 71–2.
O'Neill, T.P. 1970. Some Irish techniques of collecting seaweed, *Folk Life* 8: 13–19.
Opie, I. and P. 1959. *The Lore and Language of Schoolchildren*, London.
—— 1969. *Children's Games in Street and Playground*, London.
—— 1985. *The Singing Game*, Oxford.
Opie, I. and Tatem, M. 1989. *A Dictionary of Superstitions*, Oxford.

Ó'Suilleabhain, S. 1967. *Irish Folk Custom and Belief*, Dublin.
O'Sullivan, J.C. 1973. St Brigid's crosses, *Folk Life* 11: 60–81.
O'Sullivan, S. 1966. *Folktales of Ireland*, Chicago.
—— 1977. *Legends from Ireland*, London.
Owen, E. 1986. *Welsh Folklore*, Oswestry.
Owen, T.M. 1978. *Welsh Folk Customs*, Cardiff.

Palmer, G. and Lloyd, N. 1972. *A Year of Festivals*, London.
Palmer, K. 1973. *Oral Folk-tales of Wessex*, Newton Abbot.
—— 1976. *The Folklore of Somerset*, London.
Palmer, R. 1976. *The Folklore of Warwickshire*, London.
—— 1979. *Everyman's Book of English Country Songs*, London.
—— 1985. *The Folklore of Leicestershire and Rutland*, Wymondham.
Parker, A. 1923. Oxfordshire village folklore, II, *Folk-lore* 34: 323–33.
Parker, S. and Stevens Cox, G. 1974. *The Giant Cabbage of the Channel Islands*, 2nd ed., St Peter Port.
Parkinson, J. 1629. *Paradisi in Sole Paradisus Terrestris*, London.
—— 1640. *Theatrum botanicum*, London.
Partridge, J.B. 1917. Notes on English folklore, *Folk-lore* 28: 311–15.
Patten, R.W. 1974. *Exmoor Custom and Song*, Dulverton.
Peate, I.C. 1971. Corn ornaments, *Folklore* 82: 177–84.
Peter T. (ed.). 1915. Cornish folklore notes, *Journal of the Royal Cornwall Institution* 20: 117–33.
Phelps, H. 1977. *Just over Yonder*, London.
Philbrick, H. and Gregg, R.B. 1991. *Companion Plants*, Shaftesbury.
Philip, N. 1989. *The Cinderella Story*, London.
Phillips, H. 1825. *Floral Emblems*, London.
Plants, People, Places, 1993- [newsletter produced by the Natural History Centre, Liverpool Museum].
Pliny the Elder, *Natural History see* Rackham, H. (trans.)
Plomer, W. (ed.) 1977. *Kilvert's Diary: A Selection*, Harmondsworth.
Pollock, A.J. 1960. Hallowe'en customs in Lecale, Co. Down, *Ulster Folklife* 6: 62–4.
Poole, C.H. 1877. *The Customs, Superstitions and Legends of the County of Somerset*, London.
Porteous, C. 1973. *The Well-dressing Guide*, Derby.
Porter, E.M. 1958. Some folk beliefs of the Fens, *Folklore* 69: 112–22.
—— 1969. *Cambridgeshire Customs and Folklore*, London.
—— 1974. *The Folklore of East Anglia*, London.
Pratt, A. 1857. *Wild Flowers*, London.
Prime, C.T. 1960. *Lords and Ladies*, London.
Prior, R.C.A. 1863. *On the Popular Names of British Plants*, London.
Purslow, F. 1972. *The Constant Lovers: More English Folk Songs from the Hammond and Gardiner Manuscripts*, London.

Quelch, M.T. 1941. *Herbs for Daily Use*, London.
Quennell, P. (ed.) 1984. *Mayhew's London*, London.

Rackham, H. (trans.) 1968. *Pliny the Elder, Natural History, IV, Books XII-XVI*, London.
Radford, E. and M.A. 1961. *Encyclopaedia of Superstitions*, ed. and rev. by C. Hole, London.
Raglan, Lady. 1939. The Green Man in church architecture, *Folk-lore* 50: 45–57.

Ramsbottom, J. 1953. *Mushrooms and Toadstools*, London.

Ransom, F. 1949. *British Herbs*, Harmondsworth.

Raphael, S. 1990. *An Oak Spring Pomona*, Upperville, Virginia.

Raven, J. 1978. *The Folklore of Staffordshire*, London.

Rawlence, E.A. 1914. Folk-lore and superstitions still obtaining in Dorset, *Proceedings of the Dorset Natural History and Antiquarian Field Club* 35: 81–7

Rawlinson, R. 1722. *The History and Antiquities of Glastonbury*, Oxford.

Rhys, J. 1901. *Celtic Folklore*, Oxford.

Richards, D. 1979. Folklore and medicine, *WHEN* (World Health and Ecology News) 1(3): 13.

Rickard, R.J.M. 1990. 'Clutching at straws' in R. Noyes (ed.), *The Crop Circle Enigma*, Bath, pp. 62–71.

Riddelsdell, H.J., Hedley, G.W., and Price, W.R. 1948. *Flora of Gloucestershire*, Cheltenham.

Roberts, R. 1971. *The Classic Slum*, Manchester.

Robinson, J. 1975. *The Life and Times of Francie Nichol of South Shields*, London.

Robson, N.K.B. 1977. Studies in the genus *Hypericum* L. I. Infrageneric classification, *Bulletin of the British Museum (Natural History), Botany* 5: 293–355.

Rolph, C.H. 1980. *London Particulars*, Oxford.

Ross, A. 1976. *The Folklore of the Scottish Highlands*, London.

Rowling, M. 1976. *The Folklore of the Lake District*, London.

Rudkin, E. 1936. *Lincolnshire Folklore*, Gainsborough.

Ryan, J.S. 1993. Halloween and other traditional customs in Scottish New Zealand, *FLS News* 18: 8–10.

Ryder, M.L. 1969. Teasel growing for cloth raising, *Folk Life* 7: 117–19.

Rymer, L. 1976. The history and ethnobotany of bracken, *Botanical Journal of the Linnean Society* 73: 151–76.

St Clair, S. 1971. *Folklore of the Ulster People*, Cork.

Salaman, R.N. 1949. *The History and Social Influence of the Potato*, Cambridge.

Salmon, W. 1710. *The English Herbal*, London.

Sanderson, S.F. 1969. Gypsy funeral customs, *Folklore* 80: 181–7.

Sandford, L. and Davis, P. 1964. *Decorative Straw Work*, London.

Schnabel, J. 1993. *Round in Circles*, London.

Scott, W. and Palmer, R. 1987. *The Flowering Plants and Ferns of the Shetland Islands*, Lerwick.

Seaby, P. 1970. *Coins and Tokens of Ireland*, London.

Seed, P. 1988. Quakers and the white poppy, *Quaker Monthly* 67: 218–20.

Sharman, N. 1977. *Nothing to Steal*, London.

Short, E. 1983. *I knew my Place*, London.

Shuel, B. 1985. *The National Trust Guide to Traditional Customs of Britain*, Exeter.

Simpson, B. 1987. *Spalding in Flower*, Norwich.

Simpson, G.M. 1931. *The Rushbearing in Grasmere and Ambleside*, Manchester.

Simpson, Jacqueline. 1973. *The Folklore of Sussex*, London.

—— 1976. *The Folklore of the Welsh Border*, London.

Simpson, John (ed.). 1982. *The Concise Oxford Dictionary of Proverbs*, Oxford.

Sinker, C.A., et al. 1985. *Ecological Flora of the Shropshire Region*, Shrewsbury.

Skipwith, G.H. 1894. Popular explanation of tree-decay, *Folk-lore* 5: 169.

Sloane, Sir Hans. 1698. A further account of the contents of the China cabinet mentioned in the last Transaction, p. 390, *Philosophical Transactions of the Royal Society* 20: 461–2.

Smith, A. [W.]. 1958. Notes on the folk-life of the East London child, *Folklore* 69: 39–43.

—— 1959. Some local lore collected in Essex, *Folklore* 70: 414–15.

Smith, J. 1989. *Fairs Feasts and Frolics: Customs and Traditions in Yorkshire*, Otley.

Spence, M. 1914. *Flora Orcadensis*, Kirkwall.

Spenser, E. 1633. *View of the Present State of Ireland*, London.

Stabursvik, A. 1959. A phytochemical study of *Narthecium ossifragum* (L.) Huds., *Norges Tekniske Vitenskapsakademi*, ser. 2, 6.

Stace, C. 1991. *New Flora of the British Isles*, Cambridge.

Stanihurst, R. 1577. *A Treatise contayning a Playne and Perfect Description of Irelande*, London.

Stearn, W.T. 1976. From Theophrastus and Dioscorides to Sibthorp and Smith: the background and origin of the *Flora Graeca*, *Biological Journal of the Linnean Society* 8: 285–98.

Stevens Cox, J. 1970. *Mumming and the Mummers Play of St George* [Monographs on the Life, Times and Works of Thomas Hardy, 67], St Peter Port.

—— 1971. *Guernsey Folklore recorded in the Summer of 1882*, St Peter Port.

Stewart, S. 1987, *Lifting the Latch*, Oxford.

Stewart, W.G. 1823. *The Popular Superstitions and Festive Amusements of the Highlanders of Scotland*, London.

Stockwell, C. 1989. *Nature's Pharmacy*, London.

Stow, J. 1987. *The Survey of London*, ed. E.B. Wheatley, London.

Sykes, H. 1977. *Once a Year: Some Traditional British Customs*, London.

Synnott, D.M. 1979. Folk-lore, legend and Irish plants, in C. Nelson and A. Brady (eds), *Irish Gardening and Horticulture*, Dublin, pp. 37–43.

Tait, R.W. 1947. Some Shetland plant names, *Shetland Folk Book* 1: 74–88.

Taylor, J. 1649. *John Taylor's Wanderings to see the Wonders of the West*, London.

Teulon-Porter, N. 1956. Bull-fronts as church hassocks, up to the mid-nineteenth century, *Gwerin* 1: 90–1.

Thomas, K. 1971. *Religion and the Decline of Magic*, London.

Thompson, F. 1939. *Lark Rise*, London.

Thompson, T.W. 1925. English gypsy folk-medicine, *Journal of the Gypsy Lore Society*, ser. 3, 4: 159–72.

Thompson, W.P.L. 1983. *Kelp-making in Orkney*, Stromness.

Threlkeld, C. 1726. *Synopsis stirpium Hibernicarum*, Dublin. [In the original edition the pages are unnumbered; the page numbers cited are those given in the Boethius Press, 1988, facsimile.]

Thurston, E. 1930. *British and Foreign Trees in Cornwall*, London.

Tighe, W. 1802. *Statistical Observations relating to the County of Kilkenny*, Dublin.

Tongue, R.L. 1965. *Somerset Folklore*, London.

—— 1967. *The Chime Child*, London.

Townshend, D. 1908. Fishers' folklore, *Folk-lore* 19: 108.

Trevelyan, M. 1909. *Folk-lore and Folk-stories of Wales*, London.

Tull, G.F. 1976. *The Heritage of Centuries*, Ashford, Middlesex.

Udal, J.S. 1922. *Dorsetshire Folk-lore*, Hertford.

van der Zweep, W. 1984. Linguistic, artistic and folklore aspects of tares in the biblical parable, in R. Vickery (ed.), *Plantlore Studies*, London, pp. 162–79.

Vaughan Williams, R. and Lloyd, A.L. 1968. *The Penguin Book of English Folk Songs*, Harmondsworth.

Venables, U. 1956. *Life in Shetland: A World Apart*, Edinburgh.

Verrall, P. 1991. Queen Victoria's wedding bouquet—1, *BSBI News* 58: 28.

Vesey-FitzGerald, B. 1944. Gypsy medicine, *Journal of the Gypsy Lore Society* 23: 21–33.

Vickery, [A.] R. 1975. The use of lichens in well-dressing, *Lichenologist* 7: 178–9.

—— 1978. West Dorset folklore notes, *Folklore* 89: 154–9.

—— 1979. *Holy Thorn of Glastonbury*, St Peter Port.

—— 1983. *Lemna minor* and Jenny Greenteeth, *Folklore* 94: 247–50.

—— 1985. *Unlucky Plants*, London.

—— 1991. Early collections of the Holy Thorn (*Crataegus monogyna* cv. Biflora), *Bulletin of the British Musuem (Natural History) Botany* 21: 81–3.

Victoria, Queen. 1868. *Leaves from the Journal of a Life in the Highlands*, London.

—— 1884. *More Leaves from the Journal of a Life in the Highlands*, London.

Viney, E. 1979. A brief guide to St Mary's, Aylesbury, in Anon., *Souvenir Guide to St Mary's Aylesbury*, Aylesbury.

Waring, E. 1977. *Ghosts and Legends of the Dorset Countryside*, Tisbury.

Waring. P. 1978. *A Dictionary of Omens and Superstitions*, London.

Warner, M. 1978. *Alone of all her Sex*, London.

Waters, C. 1987. *Who was St Wite?* Broadoak.

Watson, W.G.W. 1920. *Calendar of Customs, Superstitions, Weather-lore, Popular Sayings and Important Events connected with the County of Somerset*, Taunton.

Watts, K. 1989. Scots pine and droveways, *Wiltshire Folklife* 19: 3–6.

Weaver, O.J. 1987. *Boscobel House and White Ladies Priory*, London.

Webster, M.M. 1978. *Flora of Moray, Nairn and East Inverness*, Aberdeen.

Wenis, E. and H. 1990. Multi-leaved clovers—again, *BSBI News* 56: 24.

Wentersdorf, K.P. 1978. Hamlet: Ophelia's long purples, *Shakespeare Quarterly* 29: 413–17.

Westwood, J. 1985. *Albion: A Guide to Legendary Britain*, London.

Wherry, B.A. 1905. Miscellaneous notes from Monmouthshire, *Folk-lore* 16: 63–7.

Whistler, C.W. 1908. Sundry notes from west Somerset and Devon, *Folk-lore* 19: 88–91.

White, G. 1822. *The Natural History of Selborne*, London [first published in 1789].

Whitlock, R. 1976. *The Folklore of Wiltshire*, London.

—— 1977. *The Folklore of Devon*, London.

—— 1978. *A Calendar of Country Customs*, London.

Wiliam, E. 1991. *The Welsh Folk Museum Visitor Guide*, Cardiff.

Wilkinson, Lady. 1858. *Weeds and Wild Flowers: Their Uses, Legends, and Literature*, London.

Wilks, J.H. 1972. *Trees of the British Isles in History and Legend*, London.

Willey, G.R. 1983. Burning the ashen faggot: a surviving Somerset custom, *Folklore* 94: 40–3.

Williams, A. 1922. *Round about the Upper Thames*, London.

Williams, D. 1987. *Festivals of Cornwall*, Bodmin.

Williams, F.R. 1944. Some Sussex customs and superstitions, *Sussex Notes and Queries* 10: 58–62.

Williams-Davies, J. 1983. A time to sow and a time to reap: The Welsh farmer's calendar, *Folklore* 94: 229–34.

Wilson, E.M. 1940. A Westmorland initiation ceremony, *Folk-lore* 51: 74–6.

Wiltshire, K. 1975. *Wiltshire Folklore*, Salisbury.

Withering, W. 1776. *A Botanical Arrangement of the Vegetables naturally growing in Great Britain*, Birmingham.
—— 1792. *Systematic Arrangement of British plants*, 2nd ed., London.
—— 1822. An account of the foxglove and some of its medical uses, in *The Miscellaneous Tracts of the late William Withering*, London, vol. 2, pp. 103–306.
Womack, J. 1977. *Well-dressing in Derbyshire*, Clapham.
Wright, A.R. 1936. *British Calendar Customs: England*, 1, London.
—— 1938. *British Calendar Customs: England*, 2, London.
—— 1940. *British Calendar Customs: England*, 3, London.
Wright, J. [1898–]1905. *The English Dialect Dictionary*, London.

Yallop, H.J. 1984. An example of 17th century Honiton lace, *Devon Historian* 28: 27–31.
Yarham, E.R. 1944. Seashore harvest. *Country Life* 95: 814–15.
Youngman, B.J. 1951. Germination of old seeds, *Kew Bulletin* 6: 423–6.

Unpublished sources

Britten and Holland MSS – slips accumulated by James Britten (1846–1924) and, especially, Robert Holland (1829–93) intended for a supplement to their *Dictionary of English Plant-names* (1878–86), now in the Botany Library, the Natural History Museum, London.
Cottam MSS, 1989 – 'A survey of the farming traditions and the role of animals in Retford and the surrounding district', student project by T. Cottam, the Centre for English Cultural Tradition and Language, University of Sheffield, 1989.
Dickinson MSS, 1974 – 'Ayton past and present', thesis for the examination of English Special Studies BA supervised by Mr Sanderson of the Folk Life Studies Department [University of Leeds], by M.E. Dickinson.
Hammond MSS, 1970 – 'The folklore of wild flowers in the parish of Leckhampton, Cheltenham, in Gloucestershire, collected in the summer of 1970', thesis by Penelope Ruth Hammond, University of Leeds, towards the degree of BA (Hons.).
Hole MSS – notes accumulated by Christina Hole (1896–1986), now in the archives of the Folklore Society, University College London.
IFC MSS – material collected by professional collectors working for the Irish Folklore Commission (since 1971, the Department of Irish Folklore, University College, Dublin), 1935–; now in the Department of Irish Folklore, University College, Dublin.
IFCSS MSS – material contributed to the Irish Folklore Commission's Schools' Scheme, 1937–8, during which children in 5000 Irish primary schools collected and recorded folklore; now in the Department of Irish Folklore, University College, Dublin.
Macpherson MSS – card-index 'Collection of Folk Medicines' compiled by J. Harvey Macpherson; now in the archives of the Folklore Society, University College London.
McKelvie MSS, 1963 – 'Some aspects of oral, social and material tradition in an industrial urban area', a thesis presented for the degree of PhD, University of Leeds, by D. McKelvie.

Milner MSS, 1991–2 – transcripts of interviews made by J. Edward Milner in connection with his television series 'The Spirit of Trees', shown on Channel Four TV, October–December 1992; copy in the author's collection.

Newton MSS, 'Mr Newton's Mss Notes as set down in his Catalogus Plant. Angl.' copied by an unknown hand in an interleaved copy of John Ray's *Catalogus Plantarum Angliae*, London, 1677; now in the Botany Library of the Natural History Museum, London. James Newton (*c.* 1639–1718) is believed to have compiled these notes in *c.* 1683; the original notes appear to be missing.

NHM MSS, herbarium . . . – information extracted from notes on herbarium specimens in the Department of Botany, the Natural History Museum, London.

Parsons MSS, 1952 – 'Horseheath: some recollections of a Cambridgeshire village', by Catherine E. Parsons (1952), copy in the Cambridge Record Office.

Robson MSS, 1988 – 'Calendar customs in nineteenth and twentieth century Dorset: Form, function and patterns of change', thesis submitted for the degree of Master of Philosophy, Department of English Language, University of Sheffield, by P. Robson.

Roper MSS – 'Report on the wild service tree, *Sorbus torminalis*: economics and sociology', by Patrick Roper, F.L.S.; copy in the author's collection.

SLF MSS – items contributed to the Survey of Folklore and Language (now the Centre for English Cultural Tradition and Language), University of Sheffield.

SSS MSS – transcriptions or summaries of tape recordings in the School of Scottish Studies, University of Edinburgh.

Steele MSS, 1978 – 'The medicinal value and usage of plants', by Margaret Ann Steele, student project, the Centre for English Cultural Tradition and Language, University of Sheffield, 1978.

Taylor MSS – notes compiled in the 1920s by Dr Mark Taylor on East Anglian herbal remedies and folklore; in the Norfolk Record Office, Norwich.

UCL EFS MSS – material accumulated in the 1960s as a result of a Survey of English Folklore conducted by staff of the Department of English, University College London.

Wharton MSS 1974 – 'The folklore of south Warwickshire: a field collection with comparative annotations and commentary', thesis presented for the degree of PhD in the Institute of Dialect and Folk Life Studies, School of English, University of Leeds, 1974, by C. Wharton.

INDEX OF SCIENTIFIC NAMES

INDEX OF SCIENTIFIC NAMES

Caltha palustris L. – see MARSH
  MARIGOLD.
Calystegia sepium (L.) R.Br. – see HEDGE
  BINDWEED (entry under LARGE
  BINDWEED).
C. silvatica (Kit. ex Schrader) Griseb. –
  see LARGE BINDWEED.
C. soldanella (L.) R. Br. – see SEA
  BINDWEED.
Campanula rotundifolia L. – see
  HAREBELL.
Cannabis sativa L. – see HEMP.
Capsella bursa-pastoris (L.) Medikus –
  see SHEPHERD'S PURSE.
Cardamine pratense L. – see CUCKOO
  FLOWER.
Carex paniculata L. – see GREATER
  TUSSOCK SEDGE.
Carpobrotus acinaciformis (L.) L. Bolus –
  see SALLY-MY-HANDSOME (entry
  under HOTTENTOT FIG).
C. edulis (L.) N.E. Br. – see HOTTENTOT
  FIG.
Castanea sativa L. – see CHESTNUT.
Cedrus libani A. Rich – see CEDAR.
Centaurea cyanus L. – see CORNFLOWER.
C. nigra L. – see KNAPWEED.
Centaurium spp. – see CENTAURY.
Centranthus ruber (L.) DC. – see RED
  VALERIAN.
Chamaecyparis spp., especially
  C. lawsoniana (A. Murray) Parl. –
  see CYPRESS.
Chamaemelum nobile (L.) All. – see
  CHAMOMILE.
Chamaenerion angustifolium (L.) Holub –
  see ROSEBAY WILLOWHERB.
Charophyta – see STONEWORT.
Chelidonium majus L. – see GREATER
  CELANDINE.
Chenopodium album L. – see FAT HEN.
C. bonus-henricus L. – see GOOD KING
  HENRY.
Chondrus crispus Stackh. – see
  CARRAGEEN.
Chrysanthemum segetum L. – see CORN
  MARIGOLD.
Cibotium barometz (L.) J. Sm. – see
  under VEGETABLE LAMB.
Cichorium intybus L. – see CHICORY.
Cirsium spp. – see THISTLE.

C. arvense (L.) Scop. – see CREEPING
  THISTLE.
C. vulgare (Savi) Ten. – see SPEAR
  THISTLE.
Citrus limon (L.) Burm.f. – see LEMON.
C. reticulata Blanco – see TANGERINE.
C. sinensis (L.) Osbeck – see ORANGE.
Claytonia perfoliata Donn ex Willd. –
  see SPRING BEAUTY.
Clematis vitalba L. – see TRAVELLER'S JOY.
Cochlearia spp. – see SCURVY GRASS.
Cocos nucifera L. – see COCONUT.
Cola sp. – see KOLANUT.
Conium maculatum L. – see HEMLOCK.
Conopodium majus (Gouan) Loret – see
  PIGNUT.
Convallaria majalis L. – see LILY OF THE
  VALLEY.
Convolvulus arvensis L. – see BINDWEED.
Coriandrum sativum L. – see CORIANDER.
Cordyline fruticosa (L.) Chevalier – see TI.
Cornus suecica L. – see DWARF CORNEL.
Corylus avellana L. – see HAZEL.
Crassula ovata (L.) Druce – see MONEY
  TREE.
Crataegus spp. – see HAWTHORN.
C. monogyna Jacq. cv. 'Biflora' – see
  HOLY THORN.
Crithmum maritimum L. – see ROCK
  SAMPHIRE.
Crocosmia spp. – see MONTBRETIA.
Crocus sativus L. – see SAFFRON.
Cucumis sativus L. – see CUCUMBER.
Cucurbita maxima Duchesne ex Lam. –
  see PUMPKIN.
× *Cupressocyparis leylandii* (A.B. Jackson &
  Dallimore) Dallimore – see CYPRESS.
Cuscuta epithymum (L.) L. – see DODDER.
Cyclamen spp. – see CYCLAMEN.
Cymbalaria muralis P. Gaertner, Meyer,
  & Schreber. – see IVY-LEAVED
  TOADFLAX.
Cynosurus cristatus L. – see CRESTED
  DOG'S-TAIL.
Cyperus longus L. – see GALINGALE.
Cytisus scoparius (L.) Link – see BROOM.

Daphne laureola L. – see SPURGE LAUREL.
D. mezereum L. – see MEZEREON.
Datura stramonium L. – see
  THORN-APPLE.

Daucus carota L. – see CARROT.
Dendranthema cv. – see CHRYSANTHEMUM.
Deschampsia cespitosa (L.) P. Beauv. – see TUFTED HAIR GRASS.
Dianthus barbatus L. – see SWEET WILLIAM.
D. caryophyllus L. – see CARNATION.
Digitalis purpurea L. – see FOXGLOVE.
Dipsacus fullonum L. – see TEASEL.
D. sativus (L.) Honck. – see TEASEL.
Drosera rotundifolia L. – see SUNDEW.
Dryopteris filix-mas (L.) Schott, agg. – see MALE FERN.

Elytrigia repens (L.) Desv. ex Nevski – see COUCH GRASS.
Empetrum nigrum L. – see CROWBERRY.
Entada spp., especially *E. gigas* (L.) Fawcett & Rendle – see under SEA BEANS.
Equisetum telmateia Ehrh. – see GREAT HORSETAIL.
Eranthis hymenalis (L.) Salisb. – see WINTER ACONITE.
Erinus alpinus L. – see FAIRY FOXGLOVE.
Eriophorum spp. – see COTTON GRASS.
Erophila verna (L.) DC. – see WHITLOW GRASS.
Euonymus europaeus L. – see SPINDLE.
Euphorbia spp. – see SPURGE.
E. helioscopia L. – see SUN SPURGE.
E. hyberna L. – see IRISH SPURGE.
E. lathyris L. – see CAPER SPURGE.
E. peplus L. – see PETTY SPURGE.
Euphrasia spp. – see EYEBRIGHT.
Exidia truncata Fr. – see WITCHES' BUTTER.

Fagus sylvatica L. – see BEECH.
Fallopia japonica (Houtt.) Ronse Decraene – see JAPANESE KNOTWEED.
Ficus carica L. – see FIG.
Filipendula ulmaria (L.) Maxim. – see MEADOWSWEET.
Foeniculum vulgare Miller – see FENNEL.
Forsythia spp. – see FORSYTHIA.
Fragaria cv. – see STRAWBERRY.
Frangula alnus Miller – see ALDER BUCKTHORN.
Fraxinus excelsior L. – see ASH.

Fritillaria imperialis L. – see CROWN IMPERIAL.
F. meleagris L. – see FRITILLARY.
Fuchsia spp., especially *F. magellanica* L. – see FUCHSIA.
Fucus vesiculosus L. – see BLADDER WRACK.
Fumaria spp. – see FUMITORY.

Galanthus nivalis L. – see SNOWDROP.
Galium aparine L. – see GOOSEGRASS.
G. tricornutum Dandy – see CORN CLEAVERS.
G. verum L. – see LADY'S BEDSTRAW.
Genista tinctoria L. – see DYER'S GREENWEED.
Gentianella amarella (Willd.) Boerner – see AUTUMN GENTIAN.
G. campestris (L.) Boerner – see FIELD GENTIAN.
Geranium robertianum L. – see HERB ROBERT.
Geum urbanum L. – see WOOD AVENS.
Gladiolus communis L. – see WILD GLADIOLUS.
Glaucium flavum Crantz – see YELLOW HORNED POPPY.
Glechoma hederacea L. – see GROUND IVY.
Gypsophila paniculata L. – see GYPSOPHILA.

Hebe spp. – see HEDGE VERONICA.
Hedera helix L. – see IVY.
Helleborus spp. – see HELLEBORE.
Heracleum sphondylium L. – see HOGWEED.
Hesperis matronalis L. – see DAME'S VIOLET.
Hordeum murinum L. – see WALL BARLEY.
H. vulgare L. – see BARLEY.
Humulus lupulus L. – see HOP.
Hyacinthoides non-scripta (L.) Chouard ex Roth. – see BLUEBELL.
Hydrangea macrophylla Ser. – see HYDRANGEA.
Hyoscyamus niger L. – see HENBANE.
Hypericum spp. – see ST JOHN'S WORT.
H. androsaemum L. – see TUTSAN.

Ilex aquifolium L. – see HOLLY.
Inula helenium L. – see ELECAMPANE.

Nardus stricta L. – see MAT GRASS.
Narthecium ossifragum (L.) Huds. – see
 BOG ASPHODEL.
Nerine sarniensis (L.) Herbert – see
 GUERNSEY LILY.
Nicotiana tabacum L. – see TOBACCO.
Nymphaea alba L. – see WHITE WATERLILY

Ochrolechia tartarea (L.) Massal. – see
 under LICHENS.
Ononis repens L. – see RESTHARROW.
Onopordum acanthium L. – see COTTON
 THISTLE.
Ophioglossum vulgatum L. – see ADDER'S
 TONGUE FERN.
Orchis mascula (L.) L. – see EARLY
 PURPLE ORCHID.
Ornithogalum angustifolium Boreau – see
 STAR OF BETHLEHEM.
O. pyrenaicum L. – see SPIKED STAR OF
 BETHLEHEM.
Osmunda regalis L. – see ROYAL FERN.
Oxalis acetosella L. – see WOOD SORREL.
O. pes-caprae L. – see BERMUDA
 BUTTERCUP.

Paeonia spp. – see PEONY.
Papaver rhoeas L. – see POPPY.
P. somniferum L. – see OPIUM POPPY.
Parentucellia viscosa (L.) Caruel – see
 YELLOW BARTSIA.
Parietaria judaica L. – see PELLITORY OF
 THE WALL.
Parmelia spp. – see under LICHENS.
Passiflora caerulea L. – see PASSION
 FLOWER.
Pastinaca sativa L. – see PARSNIP.
Pedicularis sylvatica L. – see LOUSEWORT.
Pelargonium spp. – see GERANIUM.
Pericallis hybrida R. Nordenstam – see
 CINERARIA.
Persicaria amphibia (L.) Gray – see
 AMPHIBIOUS BISTORT.
P. bistorta (L.) Samp. – see BISTORT.
P. maculosa Gray – see REDSHANK.
Petasites hybridus (L.) P. Gaertner,
 Meyer & Schreber – see BUTTERBUR.
Petroselinum crispum (Miller) Nyman ex
 A.W. Hill – see PARSLEY.
Phacelia tanacetifolia Benth. – see
 PHACELIA.

Phallus impudicus L. – see STINKHORN.
Phaseolus vulgaris L. – see RUNNER BEAN.
Philadelphus coronarius L. – see MOCK
 ORANGE.
Phyllitis scolopendrium (L.) Newman –
 see HART'S TONGUE FERN.
Picea abies (L.) Karsten – see NORWAY
 SPRUCE.
Pilosella officinarum F. Schultz &
 Schultz-Bip. – see MOUSE-EAR
 HAWKWEED.
Pinguicula vulgaris L. – see BUTTERWORT.
Pinus spp. – see PINE.
P. sylvestris L. – see SCOTS PINE.
Pisum sativum L. – see PEA.
Pittosporum crassifolium Sol. ex Putterl. –
 see KARO.
Plantago spp. – see PLANTAIN.
P. coronopus L. – see BUCK'S HORN
 PLANTAIN.
P. lanceolata L. – see RIBWORT PLANTAIN.
P. media L. – see HOARY PLANTAIN.
P. major L. – see GREATER PLANTAIN.
Polianthes tuberosa L. – see TUBEROSE.
Polygala vulgaris L. – see MILKWORT.
Polygonatum multiflorum (L.) All. – see
 SOLOMON'S SEAL.
Polypodium vulgare L. – see POLYPODY.
Polytrichum spp. – see under MOSS.
Populus spp. – see POPLAR.
P. alba – see WHITE POPLAR.
P. nigra L. – see BLACK POPLAR.
P. tremula L. – see ASPEN.
Porphyra umbilicalis (L.) J. Agardh – see
 LAVER.
Potentilla anserina L. – see SILVERWEED.
P. erecta (L.) Rauschel – see TORMENTIL.
P. reptans L. – see CREEPING CINQUEFOIL.
Primula elatior (L.) Hill – see OXLIP.
P. veris L. – see COWSLIP.
P. vulgaris Huds. – see PRIMROSE.
Prunella vulgaris L. – see SELF-HEAL.
Prunus spp. – see CHERRY.
P. avium (L.) L. – see WILD CHERRY.
P. domestica L. – see PLUM.
P. dulcis (Miller) D. Webb = ALMOND
 (see entry under NUT).
P. laurocerasus L. – see LAUREL.
P. padus L. – see BIRD CHERRY.
P. persica (L.) Batsch – see PEACH.
P. serrulata Lindley – see CHERRY.

P. spinosa L. – see BLACKTHORN.
Pseudofumaria lutea (L.) Borkh. – see YELLOW CORYDALIS.
Psilocybe semilanceata (Fr.) Kumm. – see LIBERTY CAP.
Pteridium aquilinum L. – see BRACKEN.
Pulmonaria spp. – see LUNGWORT.
Pulsatilla vulgaris Miller – see PASQUE FLOWER.
Pyrus communis L. – see PEAR.

Quercus petraea (Mattuschka) Liebl. – see OAK.
Q. robur L. – see OAK.
Q. suber L. – see CORK OAK.

Ramalina siliquosa (Hudson) A.L. Sm. – see under LICHENS.
Ranunculus ficaria L. – see CELANDINE.
R. flammula L. – see LESSER SPEARWORT.
R. hederaceus L. – see IVY-LEAVED CROWFOOT.
R. repens L. – see BUTTERCUP.
R. sceleratus L. – see CELERY-LEAVED BUTTERCUP.
Raphanus sativus L. – see RADISH.
Rheum × *hybridum* Murray – see RHUBARB.
Rhinanthus minor L. – see YELLOW RATTLE.
Rhodymenia palmata (L.) Grev. – see DULSE.
Rhus hirta (L.) Sudw. – see STAG'S HORN SUMACH.
Ribes nigrum L. – see BLACK CURRANT.
R. sanguineum Pursh – see FLOWERING CURRANT.
R. uva-crispa L. – see GOOSEBERRY.
Romulea columnae Sebast. & Mauri – see SAND CROCUS.
Rorippa nasturtium-aquaticum (L.) Hayek – see WATERCRESS.
Rosa cv. – see ROSE.
Rosa canina L. – see DOG ROSE.
R. pimpinellifolia L. – see BURNET ROSE.
Rosmarinus officinalis L. – see ROSEMARY.
Rubus fruticosus L., agg. – see BRAMBLE.
R. idaeus L. – see RASPBERRY.
Rumex spp. – see DOCK.
R. acetosa L. – see SORREL.

Ruscus aculeatus L. – see BUTCHER'S BROOM.
Ruta graveolens L. – see RUE.

Sagina procumbens L. – SEE PEARLWORT.
Salicornia spp., especially *S. europaea* L. – see MARSH SAMPHIRE.
Salix spp. – see WILLOW.
S. caprea L. – see SALLOW.
S. fragilis L. – see CRACK WILLOW.
Salvia officinalis L. – see SAGE.
S. verbenaca L. – see CLARY.
Sambucus ebulus L. – see DWARF ELDER.
S. nigra L. – see ELDER.
Sanguisorba minor Scop. – see SALAD BURNET.
S. officinalis L. – see GREAT BURNET.
Saponaria officinalis L. – see SOAPWORT.
Scleranthus annuus L. – see ANNUAL KNAWEL.
Scrophularia auriculata L. – see WATER FIGWORT.
Scutellaria galericulata L. – see SKULLCAP.
Sedum acre L. – see BITING STONECROP.
S. anglicum Hudson – see ENGLISH STONECROP.
S. praealtum A. DC. – see GREATER MEXICAN STONECROP.
S. rupestre L. – see REFLEXED STONECROP.
S. telephium L. – see ORPINE.
Sempervivum tectorum L. – see HOUSELEEK.
Senecio jacobaea L. – see RAGWORT.
S. vulgaris L. – see GROUNDSEL.
Silene spp. – see CAMPION.
S. dioica (L.) Clairv. – see RED CAMPION.
S. uniflora Roth. – see SEA CAMPION.
Sinapis arvensis L. – see CHARLOCK.
Smyrnium olusatrum L. – see ALEXANDERS.
Solanum dulcamara L. – see BITTERSWEET.
S. melongena L. – see AUBERGINE.
S. tuberosum L. – see POTATO.
Solidago spp. – see GOLDENROD.
Sonchus oleraceus L. – see SOW THISTLE.
Sorbus aria (L.) Crantz, agg. – see WHITEBEAM.
S. aucuparia L. – see ROWAN.
S. domestica L. – see SERVICE TREE.
S. torminalis (L.) Crantz – see WILD SERVICE TREE.

Spergula arvensis L. − see CORN SPURREY.

Sphagnum spp. − see SPHAGNUM MOSS.

Stachys officinalis (L.) Trev. − see BETONY.

S. palustris L. − see MARSH WOUNDWORT.

Stellaria holostea L. − see GREATER STITCHWORT.

S. media (L.) Villars − see CHICKWEED.

Succisa pratensis Moench − see DEVIL'S BIT SCABIOUS.

Symphoricarpus albus (L.) S.F. Blake − see SNOWBERRY.

Symphytum spp. − see COMFREY.

Syringa vulgaris L. − see LILAC.

Tagetes erecta L. − see AFRICAN MARIGOLD.

T. patula L. = FRENCH MARIGOLD (see entry under AFRICAN MARIGOLD).

Tamarix gallica L. − see TAMARISK.

Tamus communis L. − see BLACK BRYONY.

Tanacetum parthenium (L.) Schultz-Bip. − see FEVERFEW.

T. vulgare L. − see TANSY.

Taraxacum officinale Wigg., agg. − see DANDELION.

Taxus baccata L. − see YEW.

Teucrium scorodonia L. − see WOOD SAGE.

Thalictrum alpinum L. − see ALPINE MEADOW-RUE.

Thymus spp. − see THYME.

Tilia × *vulgaris* Hayne − see LIME.

Tragopogon pratensis L. − see GOAT'S BEARD.

Trifolium spp. − see CLOVER.

T. dubium Sibth. − see LESSER YELLOW TREFOIL.

T. pratense L. − see RED CLOVER.

T. repens L. − see WHITE CLOVER.

Triticum aestivum L. − see WHEAT.

T. turgidum L. − see WHEAT.

Tulipa gesneriana L. − see TULIP.

Tussilago farfara L. − see COLTSFOOT.

Typha latifolia L. − see BULRUSH.

Ulex europaeus L. − see GORSE.

Ulmus spp. − see ELM.

Umbilicus rupestris (Salisb.) Dandy − see PENNYWORT.

Urtica dioica L. − see NETTLE.

Usnea spp. − see under LICHENS.

Vaccinium myrtillus L. − see BILBERRY.

V. oxycoccos L. − see CRANBERRY.

Valeriana officinalis L. − see VALERIAN.

V. phu L. − see VALERIAN.

Verbascum thapsus L. − see MULLEIN.

Verbena officinalis L. − see VERVAIN.

Veronica spp. − see SPEEDWELL.

V. chamaedrys L. − see GERMANDER SPEEDWELL.

V. filiformis Smith − see SLENDER SPEEDWELL.

Vicia spp. − see VETCH.

V. faba L. − see BROAD BEAN.

V. hirsuta (L.) Gray − see HAIRY VETCH.

V. sativa L. − see COMMON VETCH.

Vinca spp. − see PERIWINKLE.

Viola spp., especially *V. odorata* L. − see VIOLET.

V. spp., especially *V. tricolor* L. − see WILD PANSY.

V. × *wittrockiana* Gams ex Kappert − see PANSY.

Viscum album L. − see MISTLETOE.

Vitis vinifera L. − see GRAPE.

Xanthoria parietina (L.) Th. Fr. − see under LICHENS.

Yucca spp. − see YUCCA.

Zantedeschia aethiopica (L.) Sprengel − see ARUM LILY.

Zostera marina L. − see EELGRASS.